# Continuous and Discrete Control Systems

## McGraw-Hill Series in Electrical and Computer Engineering

**Stephen W. Director, University of Michigan, Ann Arbor,** *Senior Consulting Editor*

Circuits and Systems
Communications and Signal Processing
Computer Engineering
Control Theory and Robotics
Electromagnetics
Electronics and VLSI Circuits
Introductory
Power
Antennas, Microwaves, and Radar

*Previous Consulting Editors*

**Ronald N. Bracewell, Colin Cherry, James F. Gibbons, Willis W. Harman, Hubert Heffner, Edward W. Herold, John G. Linvill, Simon Ramo, Ronald A. Rohrer, Anthony E. Siegman, Charles Susskind, Frederick E. Terman, John G. Truxal, Ernst Weber, and John R. Whinnery**

# Continuous and Discrete Control Systems

## Modeling, Identification, Design, and Implementation

John Dorsey
*Georgia Institute of Technology*
*Atlanta, Georgia*

Boston   Burr Ridge, IL   Dubuque, IA   Madison, WI   New York   San Francisco   St. Louis
Bangkok   Bogotá   Caracas   Kuala Lumpur   Lisbon   London   Madrid   Mexico City
Milan   Montreal   New Delhi   Santiago   Seoul   Singapore   Sydney   Taipei   Toronto

# McGraw-Hill Higher Education

*A Division of The* **McGraw-Hill** *Companies*

CONTINUOUS AND DISCRETE CONTROL SYSTEMS: MODELING, IDENTIFICATION, DESIGN, AND IMPLEMENTATION

Published by McGraw-Hill, a business unit of The McGraw-Hill Companies, Inc., 1221 Avenue of the Americas, New York, NY 10020. Copyright © 2002 by The McGraw-Hill Companies, Inc. All rights reserved. No part of this publication may be reproduced or distributed in any form or by any means, or stored in a database or retrieval system, without the prior written consent of The McGraw-Hill Companies, Inc., including, but not limited to, in any network or other electronic storage or transmission, or broadcast for distance learning.

Some ancillaries, including electronic and print components, may not be available to customers outside the United States.

This book is printed on acid-free paper.

International 1 2 3 4 5 6 7 8 9 0 QPF/QPF 0 9 8 7 6 5 4 3 2 1 0
Domestic    1 2 3 4 5 6 7 8 9 0 QPF/QPF 0 9 8 7 6 5 4 3 2 1 0

ISBN 0–07–248308–3
ISBN 0–07–112191–9 (ISE)

General manager: *Thomas E. Casson*
Publisher: *Elizabeth A. Jones*
Sponsoring editor: *Catherine Fields Shultz*
Developmental editor: *Michelle L. Flomenhoft*
Executive marketing manager: *John Wannemacher*
Lead project manager: *Peggy J. Selle*
Production supervisor: *Enboge Chong*
Designer: *K. Wayne Harms*
Cover design: *So Yon Kim*
Cover image: *Anne Sutherland*
Senior supplement producer: *Stacy A. Patch*
Media technology senior producer: *Phillip Meek*
Compositor: *Interactive Composition Corporation*
Typeface: *10/12 Times Roman*
Printer: *Quebecor World Fairfield, PA*

**Library of Congress Cataloging-in-Publication Data**

Dorsey, John.
    Continuous and discrete control systems: modeling, identification, design, and implementation / John Dorsey. — 1st ed.
       p. cm. — (McGraw-Hill series in electrical and computer engineering)
     ISBN 0–07–248308–3 — ISBN 0–07–112191–9 (ISE)
     1. Automatic control. 2. Control theory. I. Title. II. Series.

TJ213 .D673    2002
629.8—dc21                         2001034507
                                       CIP

www.mhhe.com

*For Andrew, James, John Gauw, Mary Ann, and Thelma*

# CONTENTS

When I first began teaching the senior elective in control systems at Georgia Tech twenty years ago, I had no interest in writing a textbook on the subject. There were plenty of good texts available, as there are today. Over time, though, I began to typeset my own notes and hand them out to the students. Eventually, those notes became complete enough that the students seem to prefer them to the official text. Even at that point my attitude was simply that the notes offered the students an alternative point of view to that of the official text, thereby enhancing their understanding.

Around 1984 Abe Haddad joined the faculty and within a year or so had managed to pry some money out of the dean of engineering to create a control system laboratory. He asked me to build that lab and I agreed. It took a long time to get that laboratory to function the way I wanted, mainly because I had the students design all the equipment for the laboratory. I had no interest in off-the-shelf experiments or off-the-shelf equipment. The students designed power supplies, power amplifiers, and any number of test fixtures.

Meanwhile, I was trying to design a sequence of laboratory sessions that would take the students through the whole design cycle, beginning with the modeling and identification of the plant transfer function, proceeding through the analysis and design stages, and ending with the implementation of the control on the actual physical system. Eventually, I ended up with three basic devices or "systems" and sixteen laboratory sessions. During those sixteen sessions the students who took the two quarter sequence in control went through the complete design cycle on each of the three systems. Those three basic systems, and a some of the content of those sixteen laboratory sessions appear in this book as three case studies that also take the reader through the entire design cycle.

So it was that when Catherine Fields showed up in my office a couple of years ago, asking if I wanted to write a book, I was somewhat less reluctant that I had been sixteen years previously. Catherine is a very good listener, and very patient, and she let me ramble on about control system education, laboratories, and cheetahs for a long time. In the end, her patience was rewarded because she convinced me to send her a manuscript.

When the initial reviews came back and were favorable, I began to overcome my natural pessimism and started thinking about how I was going to turn a set of class notes into a book in less than six months. Along the way I decided to add an introductory chapter on modern robust control, and after the second round of reviews I made some major revisions to answer the legitimate complaints of the reviewers. Like most writers I would have liked more time, but I kept remembering the character in Albert Camus' novel *The Plague* who spent twenty years trying to get the first sentence of his novel "just right."

I think the distinguishing feature of this book is that I have tried to lay out for the reader all the steps in what I call the design cycle: modeling, identification, analysis, design, simulation, and implementation. Chapters 8, 13, and 16 are case studies that take the reader through the entire design cycle for three different systems. My intent is to bring the reader as close to a real laboratory experience as I can within the confines of a textbook. In the end there is no substitute for getting in the laboratory and getting your hands dirty, but I have tried to come as close to that as I could.

The first two steps in the design cycle, modeling and identification, are to my mind the most crucial. Once the plant has been determined with sufficient accuracy, the design, simulation, and implementation normally follow without too much trouble. In this book modeling means finding the structure of the transfer function, by which I mean deciding how many poles and zeros the transfer function has. Once that decision is made, the more difficult problem of parameter identification, deciding on the exact locations of the poles and zeros, has to be addressed.

Most books do a good job with the first step, but I don't know of many, at least at the undergraduate level, that put much emphasis on parameter identification, which, to me, is the most crucial step in the whole design cycle. Beginning in Chapter 3, and again in Chapters 8, 9, 13, and 16, I provide the student with a variety of techniques for parameter identification, *and* some experience in implementing these techniques.

Parameter identification is not easy. In describing it to students in the laboratory I often paraphrase the great running back Jim Brown, who was once asked by a sportswriter, who had probably never carried a football in his life, to describe the techniques and the finesse he had used to gain all those yards. Brown snorted and replied something like, "it's not technique, it's not finesse, I just go out there and scuffle and claw for every yard I can get." That to me is the perfect description of parameter identification, and in Chapters 8, 13, and 16 I have endeavored to show the reader how to scuffle and claw his way to a viable model of a physical system. Once the parameters of the transfer function are identified, the control turns out to be very straightforward, almost anticlimactic.

Aside from Chapters 8, 13, and 16, the book contains the same material found in most undergraduate control books, although in a slightly different arrangement. My goal was to get the student designing control systems as quickly as possible. Thus, after discussing transfer functions and feedback in Chapters 3 and 4, I introduce root locus analysis in Chapter 5 and then follow it with a chapter on specifications. Most books go about it the other way around, which is fine, but my goal was to get the root locus technique in front of the student and then pose the question: now that we have a picture of all the possible *sets* of closed-loop poles, which set do we want to choose? Having answered that question in Chapter 6, the student begins designing systems in Chapter 7, using the root locus method. Thus, 164 pages into the book, the student is designing.

In Chapter 8, I build on Chapter 7 by taking the student through the whole design cycle. First two models, i.e., transfer functions, both based on the analysis of a dc motor from Chapter 3, are chosen. Then the parameters of these two transfer functions are identified using two identification techniques, one that was introduced in Chapter 3, and a second developed in Chapter 8. Then a control is designed, implemented, and compared with simulation results for both systems. In Chapter 8, I try to give the student something close to an actual laboratory experience. Of course it isn't a real laboratory experience, but I hope the student can at least see the basic steps that have to be followed to implement the control.

Chapters 9 through 13 might be called the heart of the book. Chapter 9 begins with frequency response analysis and ends with the design of compensators that provide disturbance rejection for disturbances at the output. Along the way I spend some time discussing some of the other positive benefits of feedback, a discussion originally begun in Chapter 4. Chapter 10 covers the Nyquist criterion, in preparation for Bode design in Chapter 11 and robust control in Chapter 12. Chapter 13 is again a case study, taking the student through the entire design cycle for a simple robotic system, namely, a positioning table.

Chapters 10, 11, and 12 cover a good deal of the history of control, starting with Nyquist's contributions in Chapter 10; continuing with the contributions of Bode, Nichols, Chestnut, Axleby, Truxal, and many others in Chapter 11; and finishing with the contributions of Doyle, Francis, Tannenbaum, and others in Chapter 12. I think these chapters fit together pretty well, and the student should come away with a sense of the importance of the ideas first introduced in the 1930s and 1940s. Chapter 12 is really only an introduction to robust control, as I try to point out at the beginning of the chapter. But I think it does give the student an idea of how robust control builds on previous work, and hence some sense of the evolution of control design.

Chapter 14 is a review of discrete systems and is followed by Chapter 15 on the design of sampled data systems. Chapter 16 is the third, and final, case study, and is based on an apparatus that captures the essential pitch dynamics of an airplane. This time the modeling and parameter identification are done using frequency domain methods, and the control design and implementation are for a sampled data system.

Chapter 17 is devoted to systems that have a transportation lag. Both continuous and sampled data systems are discussed. The pure delay, or transportation lag, and the the zero-order hold have similar effects on the stability of a system. Both introduce negative phase, which tends to destabilize the closed-loop system, and that was the motivation for having a separate chapter devoted to this subject. It is possible, however, to use only the portion of the chapter devoted to continuous systems, or that on sampled data systems.

Chapters 18, 19, and 20, cover continuous and discrete state models, and the controller/observer formulation of feedback control for the single input single output case. This is pretty standard fare. In Chapter 18 the continuous state model is derived from a transfer function. Second-order state models are then studied in depth using phase portraits to provide some intuition for stability. The extension to systems of higher dimension is quite easy. Chapter 19 begins with the discretization of the state model. This is followed by an informal discussion of pole placement. Controllability, observability, and the associated canonical forms are then introduced. Chapter 20 covers the controller/observer for both the regulator and tracking problems. Current as well as prediction estimators are discussed. At the end of Chapter 20 I tie the state model and transfer functions methods together by showing that the controller/observer and plant can be turned back into a closed-loop transfer function.

It is not realistic to try to cover the entire book in one semester. There are, however, several "one-semester books" within the book. Which one you choose depends on the background of the students. Some of the different courses that could be taught from the book are now discussed.

## INTRODUCTION TO DESIGN

For students with no background in control, the first thirteen chapters represent a thorough treatment of continuous systems, beginning with an introduction to the Laplace transform, ending with modern robust control, and offering the student two case studies that cover the entire design cycle. This is not likely to be an option for electrical engineers (EEs), but it might be a good one for mechanical or civil engineers.

## SENIOR ELECTIVE FOR EEs—OPTION A

Most electrical engineering students get a reasonably thorough treatment of transform theory and linear systems at the junior level. This means that a senior-level course could begin in Chapter 4, or even or Chapter 5. In that case it should be possible to cover the material up through Chapter 16 in one semester. By omitting some of the design methods in Chapter 15, Chapter 17 could also be included.

## SENIOR ELECTIVE FOR EEs—OPTION B

If the students have seen the $\mathcal{Z}$ transform, then Chapter 14 will be mostly a review and won't take up much time. Then by being selective in Chapters 15, 17, and 18 it should be possible to cover Chapters 5–20. Some places where the instructor can be selective are:

1. In Chapter 15 a variety of design techniques are presented. A couple of techniques can be omitted without much loss.
2. Chapter 17 is a very thorough study of transportation lags for both continuous and discrete systems. Some time could be saved by simply omitting transportation lags for discrete systems.
3. The material in Chapter 18 on the method of isoclines and generalized eigenvectors and the Jordan form does not impact the presentations in Chapters 19 and 20 and could be omitted.
4. Chapter 20 covers both prediction and current observers. Just covering the prediction observer provides the basics of controller/observer design. One could also omit the development on the tracking problem and concentrate on regulators.

## SENIOR ELECTIVE FOR EEs—OPTION C

It is also possible to teach a traditional senior level course by leaving out the case studies in Chapters 8, 13, and 16. In that case I think Chapters 5, 6, 7, 9, 10, 11, 12, 14, 15, 17, 18, 19, and 20 could be covered in one semester by omitting some topics in Chapters 15, 17, 18 and 20, as discussed under option B.

## DIGITAL CONTROL

Chapters 14–20 provide a thorough coverage of digital control and are suitable for a one *quarter* course on that subject. Chapter 18 covers state models for continuous systems, and can be included or omitted as the instructor sees fit. I would probably include it, but it is really a matter of taste.

I consider the book MATLAB-friendly but not MATLAB-crazy. I think the MATLAB control toolbox is of great use, *once* the students have done some hand calculations and know what they are doing. For me, the best thing about MATLAB is not the "canned" routines, but the fact that I can very quickly write a fifteen- or twenty-line m-file that lets me see the effect of varying a parameter, such as a pole or zero, over a range of values. This is something that would be hard to do with hand calculations, and is, I think, the most valuable feature of MATLAB. Many of the problems are designed to get the student to write this kind of program. The CD-ROM that comes with the book discusses the MATLAB commands relevant to each chapter and provides some examples of how to use these commands.

The CD-ROM also includes some actual test data for the three systems introduced in Chapters 8, 13, and 16. In the solution manual, I provide the results of the actual implementation of the control designs for the problems in these chapters.

In summary, I think the book offers some unique features, most notably attention to the parameter identification problem at a level that an undergraduate can understand, plus three complete trips through the design cycle. Not being much of a salesman I will stop short of saying your life will change if you adopt this book, and merely add that the students at Georgia Tech, who are about the same as the students at Nebraska, Penn State, Michigan State, or Kansas, or for that matter MIT, seem to like the notes on which this book is based.

# ACKNOWLEDGMENTS

When I got out of the Navy at the end of 1967, having survived eleven months in-country in Viet Nam with the Marine special landing force, I wanted to get an engineering degree. My time in the service had made it clear that to really understand the twentieth century you needed a technical education. The trouble was I had exited the electrical engineering program at Purdue after my sophomore year to pursue a degree in the arts. It wasn't grades that drove me out of engineering but rather sheer boredom. The electrical engineering curriculum of the early sixties was not very exciting.

However, when I applied to Purdue for graduate school they wouldn't even answer my letter. My application to the University of Michigan received the same gracious treatment. So I got in my MGA, drove to East Lansing, and started barging into offices and asking questions. No one threw me out; in fact, they were quite cordial and I ended up in the chairman's office, talking to Harry Hedges. Harry was an ex-marine, and when he found out where I had just come back from, he and Herman Koenig found me an assistantship. So it was that with a bachelor's degree in creative writing I managed to acquire a master's degree in systems science. It is only fitting that the system science degree is no longer offered *anywhere*.

Never one to take advantage of my good luck, I left with my master's degree, and worked in the aerospace and automobile industries for a few years before throwing my skis in my Mustang and heading for the Rockies. Over the next few years you could have found me anywhere between Montana and Peru, ruminating on life in general and the perils of undeclared wars in particular. Finally, in 1976, when I decided I was too young to retire, I reapplied to Michigan State, and, unbelievably, they let me back in.

It goes without saying that I am deeply indebted to Michigan State University and to the faculty of the Electrical Engineering Department. Herman Koenig, Gerald Park, Roland Zapp, Don Reinhard, Jim Resh, Bob Barr, and Bob Schlueter were not only great teachers but good friends.

I am especially indebted to Jim Resh and Gerald Park. They are two of the best engineers I have ever known. Jim Resh took me out for a beer midway through the PhD experience when I was ready to go skiing again and showed me how to finish. Without him I probably would be working in a ski resort somewhere. Gerald Park is one of the most intelligent and literate people I have ever met. Broadly educated, tremendously perceptive, and extremely articulate, he contributed to my education in ways he never knew.

When I threw my earthly possessions in the back of my Truck (it was a great truck and deserves a capital letter) in 1980 and drove out of East Lansing to take a job at Georgia Tech, I didn't expect to be there long. Twenty years later I am still at Tech, but truth be known probably eighty percent of the faculty wish I had never darkened the door of the place. Actually, I feel the same way, and it is only because of the efforts of a few individuals that I am still on the job. George "Pete" Rodrique, Bill Sayle, William "Russ" Callen, Cecil Alford, and Dan Fielder kept me going in the early years.

Then Abe Haddad showed up and became a lifelong friend. I owe him more than I can say. He pried the money loose from the dean of engineering in 1985 so I could build a controls laboratory. He patiently helped with the review of this book. And, most importantly, he went out of his way to help Zhihua Qu, one of the most gifted individuals I have ever met, who did me the great honor of letting me be his advisor. Abe was kind enough to help Zhihua in a number of ways that I could not, and for that I am forever in his debt.

After Abe left for Northwestern, Ed Kamen came back to Tech. He was a great supporter from the beginning. He helped me get promoted and underwrote the rejuvenation of the controls laboratory. I owe him a lot as well.

The days of asking a colleague to proof a book are long gone. I did the next best thing and got McGraw-Hill to pay Nathan "Scott" Clements, who will soon finish his PhD and become a colleague, a thousand bucks to go through the manuscript and check all the calculations. I think this worked out to a penny an hour, and I very much appreciate Scott's efforts. I have a tendency to jab the four inch brush in the can and start slinging paint around. Meticulous is not my middle name, and Scott's help was invaluable. Bruce McFarland made important contributions to Chapters 8, 13, and 16.

Of course, I would also like to thank the reviewers of this book, both those who have graciously allowed me to use their names, as well as those who didn't. The comments of Abraham Haddad, Naim A. Kheir of Oakland University, Augustus Morris of Central State University, and Gordon Parker of Michigan Technological University were extremely helpful. The enthusiasm of Augutus Morris for the book lifted my spirits at a time when I was realizing that the reviewers were on target and I had a lot of work yet to do. I took all the reviewer criticisms seriously and implemented about ninety percent of their suggestions.

Finally, Ann Sutherland did the cover. She and I share an admiration for the large cats, and especially for the endangered cheetah, one of nature's great control systems. If you ever visit the Atlanta Zoo you can admire her lifesize bronzes of lions and cheetahs. The little kids love them, and I have never visited the zoo when the kids were not climbing all over the cats. I am very grateful to Ann for her wonderful work. My feeling is that even if you don't like the book you can tear off the cover and frame it, and your money will still be well spent. On the other hand, if you like the book you can visit my Georgia Tech website and get Ann's address. She will send you a limited edition, quality print for a very fair price.

**j. dorsey**

# Chapter 1

# Preliminaries

## 1.1 | WHY CONTROL?

From an aisle seat just behind the wings of a modern jet airliner it is possible to watch the control surfaces of both wings. The smaller outboard control surfaces are the ailerons. When one aileron pitches down, the other pitches up. Together, along with the rudder and elevator on the tail, they control the direction of flight. The inner, large control surfaces are commonly referred to as "flaps." Passengers are more familiar with the action of these large control surfaces since they are active during take off and landing. Their purpose is to change the surface geometry of the wing, thereby giving the aircraft more, or less, lift.

The pilot moves the control surfaces via a linkage system consisting of electrical, mechanical, and hydraulic components. In the case of the ailerons, the pilot moves the "yoke." The yoke also controls the rudder and elevator on the tail, acting very much like an automobile steering wheel. The pilot usually controls the flaps by moving a mechanical lever fore or aft.

In any case, sitting aft of the wings, watching the control surfaces during a descent into a modern airport, it becomes perfectly clear how these linkage systems that connect the pilot to the control surfaces should work if the plane is to land safely: these systems should move the control surfaces quickly and accurately to the position requested by the pilot. This is the heart of control: precise, responsive performance of a physical system such as a jetliner.

One might ask why control is even necessary, that is, why the system wasn't designed to operate "better" in the first place. This is a valid question. In some cases, for instance in biological systems, the control schemes are quite minimal because the system has been superbly designed by the long process of evolution. The larger birds of prey, such as hawks and eagles, are a good example of this. These birds can hover nearly motionless in a head wind by making very slight adjustments in the feathers on the trailing edges of their wings.

In other cases, limitations to the basic design of a system require the addition of control. For instance, consider the cheetah whose prey are antelope and gazelle that can run about 45 mph for several minutes. The cheetah, on the other hand, can run in short bursts at speeds up to 70 mph. But speed is not enough. A Thompson's gazelle can change direction on a dime, and to catch the gazelle, the cheetah must be able to react to its prey's maneuvers. To do so it has a superb control system consisting of excellent eyesight, a brain, and exceptional reflexes. The cheetah can overtake the gazelle in less than 5 s, but without a good control system it would never catch the gazelle.

An industrial analog of the cheetah versus the gazelle is a large motor driving a load. If the load presented a constant torque to the motor shaft, then no control would be required. Such a constant torque load would be like a gazelle that never changed direction. But the load does change, and as a result control is required if the motor is to achieve its purpose.

As an example, a typical industrial application may require the motor to achieve and maintain a sequence of different speeds while working against a load of varying torque. It is usually desirable for these speed changes to be accomplished as rapidly as possible. Figure 1.1 shows what the speed change might look like with no control. The speed rises gradually, so that a considerable length of time elapses before the speed gets close to its final value.

**Figure 1.1 |** Response without control.

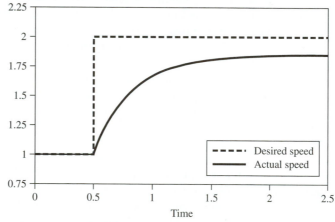

Thinking back to the descent of the airliner, we conclude that this type of response from the flaps might make the landing quite exciting. In the case of the airplane, however, there is an important additional control system present, namely the pilot. Skilled pilots have been able to land planes whose control systems are badly damaged. In one case, the plane could only fly in circles but the pilot managed to get the plane down onto a runway. Thus even if the control were inaccurate, the pilot would probably be able to land safely.

The figure also shows that the final speed is not exactly the requested speed. That is, there is an offset or steady state error. Thus, two improvements that could be expected from a control scheme are a faster rise in the speed, so that the motor speed reaches the new set point as quickly as possible, and a reduction or elimination of the steady state error.

Figure 1.2 shows some potential responses when control is added. Curve *a* would seem to be ideal, but it may be difficult to achieve and possibly undesirable if the load on the motor is large. Curve *b* might be a better choice, in the sense that tolerating a certain amount of overshoot enables the system to get near the final value as soon as possible without requiring the system to make the abrupt change in speed required by curve *a*. Indeed, if the system has a great deal of mass, it may be necessary to accept the overshoot to prevent damage to the system. This last consideration also makes curve *c* an undesirable choice, since large oscillations would be detrimental to many systems.

**Figure 1.2 |** Possible responses with control.

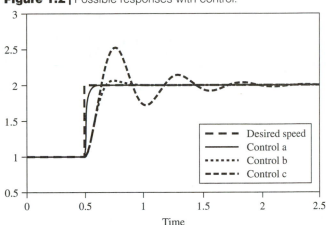

This short discussion of speed control has uncovered most of the essential features of a good control system:

1.  The graph of the system output versus time should show the system moving rapidly and smoothly toward the desired final value. This period is referred to as the transient period, and the idea is to have a "fast," smooth transient response. It is worth noting that fast is a relative measure. For an electromechanical system, fast might be a few tenths of a second, while for a chemical process, fast might be half an hour.
2.  The offset, or error, between the desired final system output and the actual final output should be small. This offset is referred to as the steady state error.
3.  The response of the system should be smooth and devoid of large fluctuations or oscillations. Large oscillations are indicative of an unstable response.

These three qualities—speed of response, steady state error, and stability—are central issues in designing any control system. It is worth noting that the performance has been defined in terms of a step change in the reference input signal. While a step is not the only input signal applied to control systems, it is certainly the most common, because in the majority of cases the goal is to drive the system from one steady state to another. The response of the system to other inputs such as sinusoids, ramps, and impulses will be considered, but the single most important input is the step, because it is far and away the most common in practice.

## 1.2 | FEEDBACK

To this point we have talked in very general terms about the purpose of control and listed some qualitative measures of the performance of a control system. But there is one central idea common to almost all control strategies that we have not considered, and that is feedback.

**Figure 1.3 |** The cheetah as a control system.

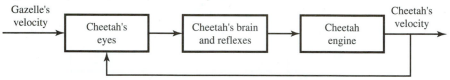

To better understand feedback consider Fig. 1.3, where the cheetah has been "rearranged" somewhat. By "cheetah engine" we mean the cheetah's skeletal, muscular, and cardiovascular systems, which propel it at very high speeds. The cheetah's eyes play a central role as it chases a gazelle. By watching the gazelle and listening to its own nervous system, the cheetah can adjust its own velocity to that of the gazelle. When the gazelle turns, the cheetah's brain and reflexes come into play and enable it to adjust its velocity to track the gazelle. This is feedback, the very heart of control.

Now consider Fig. 1.4. This block diagram looks a little different, but it accomplishes the control in essentially the same way as the cheetah. The speed of the motor is measured by a transducer. Later in the book, we often leave out the transducer and just show the speed being fed back. But the transducer is always there, required in most cases to make the signal fed back compatible with the desired speed being applied to the summer. In this particular case, the transducer could be something as simple as a "tach generator," a small dc motor operating as a generator and whose shaft speed is proportional to that of the large industrial load. The output of the tach generator is a voltage, proportional to its shaft speed, say 3 V per 1000 rpm. This means the desired speed could be input as a voltage, for instance, 3.2 V, signifying 1200 rpm.

**Figure 1.4 |** Feedback control of a motor.

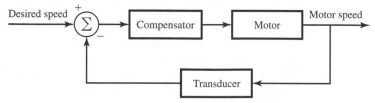

The difference of the desired speed and the actual speed, the so-called error signal, is then fed to the block labeled "compensator." The compensator is itself a system, designed by the control engineer to produce a signal that can, in turn, be applied to the large industrial motor to bring it to the proper speed. It is worth noting that the compensator "system" could be electrical, mechanical, hydraulic, or chemical in nature. In this book, the compensators will be electronic circuits, but that is not always the case.

**Figure 1.5 |** Feedback control of an antiaircraft gun.

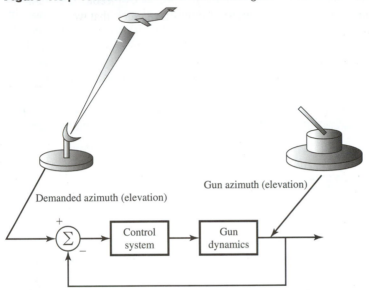

Figure 1.5 shows yet another system that uses feedback, namely, an antiaircraft gun. In this particular system, a radar system feeds a signal to the gun telling it where to point next. Actually, two feedback circuits are required, one to rotate the gun (azimuth) and a second to lift or lower the barrel (elevation). Both circuits have the same characteristics so only one is shown. The control strategy is identical to that in the previous two cases we have considered. The difference between the demanded and actual azimuth (elevation) of the gun is fed to a compensator, which, in turn, generates the command signal for the gun.

This last example is noteworthy because it comes from what we might call the "golden age" of control in the century just passed. Control theory began to come of age in the early 1930s when electric power systems and telephone systems had begun to proliferate and grow in complexity. In the case of power systems, the problem was generator "hunting." The power system in this country operates at 60 Hz, and the frequency has to be held as nearly as possible right at 60 Hz. However, the generators tended to oscillate in a small frequency range about 60 Hz. Better controls were needed to prevent the hunting. About this time, the problem of stabilizing the nonlinear repeater amplifiers used in the telephone systems arose.

But the real stimulus to control was World War II. With the war came control problems of every stripe. Radar-controlled antiaircraft systems had to be designed. The large guns on ships needed to be stabilized against the roll of the ship if they were to fire accurately. Tracking radars needed control systems to help them maintain a "lock" on the target. Surface radars needed to be designed and controlled so that ships could navigate and fight in fog.

The war effort definitely accelerated the rate of advancement in science and technology in general, and control theory was no exception. The advances in control theory made during the war and in the years immediately after are with us still. And there is no doubt that control technology played a significant role in winning the war. I had the great honor to talk at length with Nathaniel Nichols about some of these developments. Nichols worked on, among other things, several of the radar systems developed during the war. He recounted to me being aboard an aircraft carrier steaming up Chesapeake Bay in a pea soup fog at 18 knots. Every other ship in the bay was at anchor, but the carrier had one of the first surface radars ever put on a ship, and its captain could see every ship around him. It was a major breakthrough in naval warfare. At the heart of many of these advances was the concept of feedback control.

## 1.3 | THE SCOPE OF THE BOOK

If we reconsider the three examples of feedback control discussed in Section 1.2, we see that we can describe all three of them with the block diagram of Fig. 1.6.

The physical "plant" to be controlled—e.g., the cheetah, the motor, and the antiaircraft gun—is represented by $G_p$. The signal to be tracked, the gazelle's velocity, or the commanded azimuth for the antiaircraft gun, is represented by $R$. The actual output of the system, the cheetah's velocity or the speed of the motor, is represented by $C$. The control system is represented by $G_c$. In the feedback loop, $H$ represents another system. Potentially part of the control system, it could also represent a transducer, as already discussed.

At the moment Fig. 1.6 is simply an abstraction. The goal of this book is to give meaning to this abstraction by providing examples of what might be called the complete "design cycle."

The first stage of the design cycle is to find an appropriate mathematical model of the system to be controlled, e.g., the cheetah or the dc motor. This modeling process usually involves using both the known laws of the appropriate underlying science and an identification technique. From the underlying science, be it physics, chemistry,

**Figure 1.6 |** Block diagram of feedback.

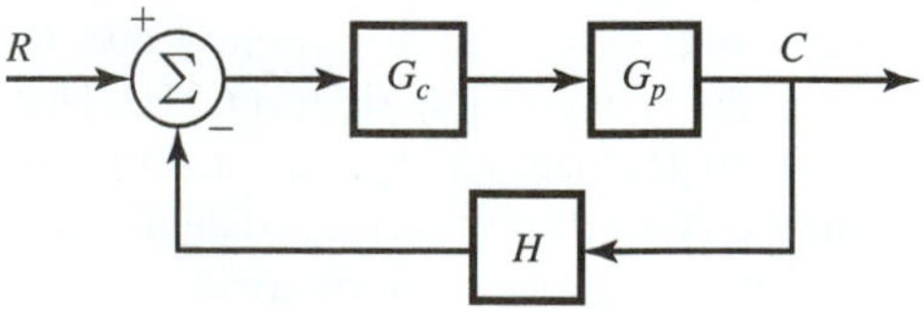

biology, or a combination thereof, we obtain a mathematical structure consisting of dependent and independent variables and parameters. From the identification process we obtain values for the parameters.

Once the model of the system to be controlled has been determined, we can analyze it and formulate a preliminary control strategy. We usually test this control strategy by doing a computer simulation. Normally, we may have to try several strategies or "designs" before we finally find one that seems to fit our needs or "specifications."

The final stage of the design cycle is to implement the controller on the actual system. If our modeling, identification, analysis, and design procedures have been successful, then the implementation will work as planned. If not, then we may have to return to one of the previous steps in the design cycle and try again.

In addition to the analysis and design techniques normally found in control textbooks, this book contains three case studies that cover every aspect of the design cycle. In each case study, we begin by finding an appropriate model for the system we wish to control and then identifying the parameters for this model. We next design a controller and then build the controller, using electronic circuits. Finally, we implement the control on the real system. In so doing we treat in detail every aspect of the design cycle: modeling, identification, design, and implementation. These case studies are presented as separate chapters so that the reader can see clearly each step of the design cycle.

Probably the salient difference between this book and others is the emphasis on system identification and implementation. It will become abundantly clear as we proceed that without an adequate model of the system to be controlled, it is hard to realize an effective control design. From the perspective of this book, modeling and identification is the most crucial phase of the whole design cycle.

The implementation phase is also an important part of the learning process. It is one thing to produce a mathematical control design, and quite another to turn this mathematical design into a piece of hardware or software that works on a real system. As we will see, the actual control system requires "tuning" or "tweaking," because our mathematical representation, while precise and convenient, is only an approximation to the actual physical system.

We assume throughout that the physical system to be controlled can be adequately modeled by ordinary differential equations with constant coefficients. Such a system is called linear time invariant (LTI). LTI systems have enormous importance because they can be analyzed using transform theory.

For continuous LTI systems, the unilateral (one-sided) Laplace transform is used. For discrete systems the unilateral $Z$ transform is employed. While familiarity with transform theory is assumed, reviews of the Laplace and $Z$ transforms are provided to help those readers whose transform skills are a bit rusty. The Laplace transform is covered in Chapter 2 and the $Z$ transform in Chapter 14. Those readers who are confident of their knowledge of transform theory can skip these chapters.

Chapter 3 is spent building up the necessary tools to understand the complete design cycle. The idea of a transfer function is introduced and then an example of how a transfer function can be derived from the underlying science is presented. The example chosen is a dc motor, partly because it is an excellent example of how science can be applied to engineering, but also because the dc motor is used in all three case studies. Indeed, electric motors are used in a very wide variety of control systems.

The modeling process leads naturally to the identification problem, also discussed in Chapter 3. Once we have the mathematical structure, we need to find numbers for the parameters in this model. Several identification strategies are provided throughout the book. The one discussed in Chapter 3 is representative of the other techniques discussed later. It is included in to give the reader some appreciation of the difference between identification and modeling.

Chapter 3 also contains a fairly lengthy discussion of how to implement a control strategy once it has been designed mathematically. The primary means of implementation is active electronic circuits, particularly circuits that use operational amplifiers (opamps). There are many different ways to implement a control strategy but electronic circuits using opamps are the most common.

By the end of Chapter 3 the reader is equipped to model, identify, and implement a control strategy, and our discussion of control can be initiated.

The journey begins with a more precise discussion of feedback, and then proceeds through the various analysis and design techniques. Root locus analysis and design are covered first because they are the most intuitive and are followed by Bode design. Continuous systems are considered first, again because they are more intuitive. The same techniques are then applied to discrete systems.

An elementary discussion of robust control is included along with a thorough discussion of transportation lags. The final portion of the book is devoted to state space analysis as applied to control. In the end, we are able to firmly connect state space design for single-input single-output state models to the transfer function approach introduced in the first part of the book.

Finally, it is worth a paragraph to discuss the generic nature of the control techniques presented in this book. If a physical system can be represented by an ordinary differential equation with constant coefficients, then the techniques in this book are applicable. Physical systems that can be so represented are very diverse. The most common are the electromechanical systems that we have discussed, but chemical processes, hydraulic systems, biological systems, and economic systems can often be represented in this way as we have seen. Thus the control techniques in this book have very broad application and are used in all the engineering disciplines.

## 1.4 | Problems

1. Make a block diagram with feedback of an osprey (fish eagle) swooping down to catch a fish just below the surface of the water.

2. Make a block diagram of a the flap control for a jetliner with the pilot in the feedback loop. Assume that the flap control is an open loop hydraulic system.

3. Suppose a cheetah can run at 70 mph and a Thompson's gazelle at 40 mph. Suppose the cheetah is 10 ft behind the gazelle when the gazelle abruptly turns 45° to the left. If it takes the cheetah 0.1 s to react to the gazelle's turn, find the

location of the cheetah and the gazelle 0.1 s later. Do you think the cheetah will catch the gazelle?

4. Figure 1.7 shows the essential one-degree-of-freedom robot arm. A plate is attached to one end of the shaft of a dc motor. The other shaft end of the dc motor is attached to a heliopot. A heliopot it simply a rheostat, or voltage divider, where the resistance coil is shaped like a circle. The ends of the resistance coil are attached to voltages of $\pm 15$ V, as show in part (b) of the figure. The "wiper" then gives the position of the table as a voltage between $+15$ V and $-15$ V. Draw a block diagram showing how feedback would be used to control the position of the table.

**Figure 1.7** | (a) Simple robot and (b) inner workings of a heliopot.

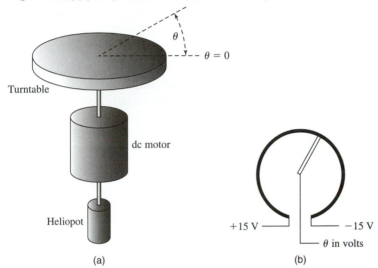

5. Build a block diagram model of a cruise control system for a car. Assume that the speedometer provides a voltage proportional to speed. The driver then indicates the desired speed by driving at that speed and simultaneously pushing a button for 2 s. To break the cruise control, the driver either brakes the car or changes the position of the accelerator rapidly.

# FURTHER READINGS

Black, H. S. 1934. Stabilized feedback amplifiers. *Bell Systems Technical Journal* 13:1–18.

Getting, Ivan A. 1989. *All in A Lifetime, Science in the Defense of Democracy.* New York: Vantage Press.

Nyquist, H. 1932. Reeneration theory. *Bell Systems Technical Journal* 11:126–147.

# 2 Chapter

# The Laplace Transform

## 2.1 | OVERVIEW

The unilateral, or "one-sided," Laplace transform has proven to be a natural and powerful means of analyzing linear systems, particularly control systems. It is assumed that the reader has previously studied this transform and its cousin the Fourier transform. This chapter is aimed at those readers whose transform theory skills are rusty. It is not intended to be a thorough study but rather a review of the important properties of the Laplace transform as they pertain to the analysis of control systems.

The Laplace and Fourier transforms are very powerful analysis tools for a certain class of systems, namely, linear time-invariant systems. Since most of the systems encountered in nature or built by man are nonlinear, linear analysis techniques would not seem to be of much use. However, many of these nonlinear systems have regions of operation in which their behavior is "reasonably" linear, making them amenable to analysis by techniques such as the Laplace transform. This is fortunate because the analysis techniques available for linear systems, particularly linear time-invariant systems, are much more powerful and general than those that apply to nonlinear systems. Thus, being able to make the assumption that a system is linear is crucial.

A good example of how a nonlinear system can be linearized is the ideal pendulum shown in Fig. 2.1. If the pivot point is frictionless, and the rod, of length $\ell$, is rigid but light enough that all the mass $m$ can be assumed to be concentrated in the bob, then the force acting to restore the pendulum to equilibrium is

$$F = -mg\sin\theta. \qquad \textbf{[2.1]}$$

We also know that

$$F = ma = m\ell\frac{d^2}{dt^2}\theta. \qquad \textbf{[2.2]}$$

**Figure 2.1 |** Ideal pendulum.

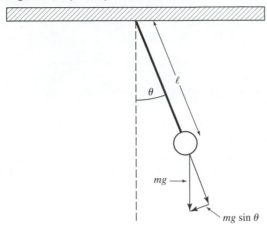

Letting

$$\ddot{\theta} \triangleq \frac{d^2}{dt^2}\theta,$$

we can combine Eqs. [2.1] and [2.2] to obtain

$$m\ell\ddot{\theta} = -mg\sin\theta,$$

or finally

$$\ell\ddot{\theta} + g\sin\theta = 0. \tag{2.3}$$

Equation [2.3] is nonlinear because $\theta$ appears as the argument of the sine function. If $\theta$ is a small angle of a few degrees, however, as it would be in the case of a grandfather clock, then $\sin\theta \approx \theta$, and Eq. [2.3] becomes

$$\ell\ddot{\theta} + g\theta = 0. \tag{2.4}$$

Equation [2.4] is linear. Thus, for the ideal pendulum, the linear region of operation merely means that $\theta$ must be small.

Equation [2.4] is not only linear but linear with constant coefficients. This is the subset of linear systems for which the Laplace transform is a powerful analysis tool. Application of the Laplace transform turns a differential equation into an algebraic equation that is much easier to manipulate and interpret. The remainder of the chapter is devoted to defining and understanding this important transform.

## 2.2 | LAPLACE TRANSFORM

The Laplace transform, a cousin of the Fourier transform, is defined next.

> **Definition 2.2.1**
>
> Let $g(t)$ be a piecewise continuous function. Then the unilateral Laplace transform, denoted by $\mathcal{L}\{g(t)\}$, or $G(s)$, is
>
> $$G(s) = \int_0^\infty g(t)e^{-st}\,dt, \qquad\qquad [2.5]$$
>
> provided the integral exists, and where $s = \sigma + j\omega$ is a complex number.

The existence of the transform does not turn out to be a matter of great concern because the class of functions that arise in the analysis of linear control systems are well behaved and the transform always exists. Indeed, from the definition it is apparent the integral will converge for any function that can be dominated by a decaying exponential function. Thus, functions like the step and the ramp will have simple transforms. The reader familiar with the Fourier transform will remember that the step function does not have a "simple" Fourier transform, but rather one that contains an impulse. Thus, the presence of the exponential weighting function $e^{-st}$, where the Laplace variable $s$ has a nonzero *real part,* makes the Laplace transform quite different from the Fourier transform.

The finite lower limit on the integral is worthy of a little discussion. The goal is to use the one-sided Laplace transform to solve systems that can be represented by ordinary differential equations with constant coefficients. The problem of most interest is the initial value problem where a set of initial conditions are given for a particular time. For linear time-invariant systems, the time at which the initial conditions are applied is inconsequential since the response will be the same. Thus, it is convenient to let this time be zero. We often also apply forcing functions to the differential equation. These are also normally applied at time zero for the same reason.

## 2.3 | FUNDAMENTAL TRANSFORMS

In this section the fundamental transforms needed for linear control theory are determined. In point of fact, only a handful of transforms (about eight) are needed. The fact that only a small number of transforms is required is what makes the Laplace transform so powerful. If we had to remember hundreds of transform pairs, Laplace transforms would be of far less value. But because, for the most part, only a few transform pairs are needed, the transform approach is very potent.

### 2.3.1   The Exponential Function

The first function whose Laplace transform we will find is, by far, the most important and most fundamental. That function is

$$g(t) = \begin{cases} e^{-at} & \text{for } t \geq 0 \\ 0 & \text{for } t < 0. \end{cases} \qquad\qquad [2.6]$$

Before finding the transform, it is worth noting that $g$ is assumed to be zero for $t < 0$. Since the lower limit on the integral that defines the transform is zero, it would not at first glance appear to matter what value $g$ has for negative time. The ultimate goal, however, is to establish a transform "pair," that is, a *unique* pairing of a time function with a transform. To achieve this the function, $g$ must be defined for both positive and negative time. The simplest way to accomplish this is to let the functions to be transformed be zero for negative time. That said, we can now find

$$
\begin{aligned}
G(s) &= \int_0^\infty e^{-at} e^{-st}\, dt \\
&= \int_0^\infty e^{-(s+a)t}\, dt \\
&= \frac{-1}{s+a} \left[ e^{-(s+a)t} \right]_{t=0}^{t=\infty} \\
&= \frac{1}{s+a} \left[ 1 - \lim_{t\to\infty} e^{-(s+a)t} \right].
\end{aligned}
$$

To complete the derivation, we assume for simplicity that $a$ is real and write

$$
\begin{aligned}
\lim_{t\to\infty} e^{-(s+a)t} &= \lim_{t\to\infty} e^{-(\sigma+j\omega+a)t} \\
&= \lim_{t\to\infty} e^{-(\sigma+a)t} e^{-j\omega t}.
\end{aligned}
$$

The term $e^{-j\omega t}$ in the last step on the right-hand side is a complex number with magnitude one and argument $-\omega t$, as is easily seen by writing

$$
e^{-j\omega t} = \cos(-\omega t) + j\sin(-\omega t) = \cos\omega t - j\sin\omega t.
$$

Thus, as $t \to \infty$, $e^{-j\omega t}$ will not approach a limit. As a consequence, if

$$
\lim_{t\to\infty} e^{-(s+a)t}
$$

is to exist, then that limit must be zero. Proving that the limit is zero rests with the term $e^{-(\sigma+a)t}$. That is, if

$$
\sigma + a > 0,
$$

or equivalently

$$
-a < \sigma,
$$

then

$$
\begin{aligned}
\lim_{t\to\infty} \left| e^{-(s+a)t} \right| &= \lim_{t\to\infty} \left| e^{-(\sigma+a)t} \right| \left| e^{-j\omega t} \right| \\
&= \lim_{t\to\infty} \left| e^{-(\sigma+a)t} \right| \\
&= 0,
\end{aligned}
$$

and the limit does not exist otherwise. Thus, for $-a < \sigma$,

$$
G(s) = \frac{1}{s+a}.
$$

This same result holds if $a$ is complex.

**Figure 2.2** | Region of convergence: (a) $a > 0$ and (b) $a < 0$.

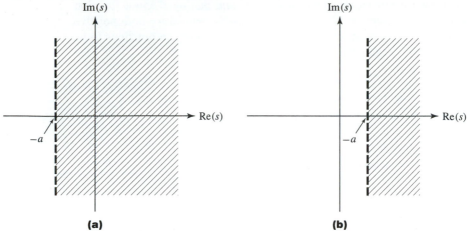

**(a)**                              **(b)**

The regions of convergence for both $a > 0$ and $a < 0$ are shown in Fig. 2.2. The region of convergence is an infinite half plane that lies strictly to the right of a vertical line through $s = -a$. For $a$ complex the vertical line passes through the negative of the real part of $a$.

The transform of the function defined by Eq. [2.6] is the core result in Laplace transform theory, at least for its application to linear time-invariant systems. In fact, it is not much of an exaggeration to say that this transform is the whole story. The justification of this statement is not far off.

### 2.3.2  The Step Function

A second transform of great importance is the unit step function, defined as follows.

$$\mathbf{1}(t) = \begin{cases} 1 & \text{for } t \geq 0 \\ 0 & \text{for } t < 0. \end{cases}$$

The notation $\mathbf{1}(t)$ releases $u(t)$ to be used for an arbitrary input to a linear system. This notation has one minor liability. The common practice is to use a lowercase letter for a time function and the corresponding uppercase letter for its Laplace transform. The use of $\mathbf{1}(t)$ makes it impossible to follow this convention. With only a minor inconsistency in notation, however, the Laplace transform of $\mathbf{1}(t)$ will be represented as $\mathbf{1}(s)$.

Applying the Laplace transform to the unit step yields

$$\mathbf{1}(s) = \int_0^\infty e^{-st}\, dt$$

$$= \frac{-1}{s}[e^{-st}]_{\lim t \to 0^+}^{t=\infty}$$

$$= \frac{1}{s}\left[1 - \lim_{t \to \infty} e^{-st}\right]$$

$$= \frac{1}{s},$$

where $\lim_{t \to \infty} e^{-st} = 0$ if $\text{Re}\{s\} > 0$. Thus, the region of convergence is the open half plane to the right of the $j\omega$ axis. Note that the correct result can be obtained by simply setting $a = 0$ in the expression for the Laplace transform of the exponential function $e^{-at}$.

### 2.3.3 The Impulse Function

The impulse, or delta, function is of great importance in science and engineering. In many cases, the intrinsic behavior of a system can be discovered by abruptly disturbing the system when it is at rest. Abruptly disturbing the system means injecting a finite amount of "energy" into the system in a very short period of time. An example would be a very sharp blow with a hammer to the bob of the ideal pendulum considered earlier. In this case, the blow from the hammer results in a nearly instantaneous change in the momentum of the pendulum.

The impulse function gives mathematical form to the physical impulse. As usual, the mathematical model requires somewhat more precision than the physical model from which it is drawn. In particular, the mathematical model requires that the transfer of "energy" be instantaneous rather than *nearly* instantaneous.

There are a number of ways to represent the impulse. The representation here is the one that most closely approximates the physical analogy from which it is drawn. That representation is shown in Fig. 2.3. The impulse can be thought of as the limiting case of a sequence of functions, indexed by integer subscripts, each with unit area. As $n \to \infty$ the width of the base shrinks to zero and the height becomes arbitrarily large. However, each member of the sequence still has unit area. This area can be thought of as one unit of "energy" imparted to the system.

The literature includes several alternative ways of defining a nested sequence of functions whose limit is the delta function. The particular choice presented here can be "justified" as discussed next. In the analysis of control systems, the system is

**Figure 2.3** | Sequence of approximations to the impulse function.

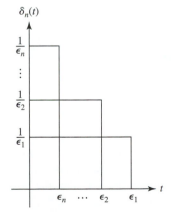

usually at rest at time $t = 0$, at which time some input function is applied, imparting "energy" to the system. In the case of the physical impulse function, the "energy" is imparted in a short period *after* $t = 0$, hence the choice of this particular sequence of functions.

The delta function is commonly written as $\delta(t)$. Applying the definition of the Laplace transform yields

$$\mathcal{L}\{\delta(t)\} = \int_0^\infty \delta(t)e^{-st}\, dt$$

$$= \lim_{\epsilon \to 0} \int_0^\epsilon \frac{e^{-st}}{\epsilon}\, dt$$

$$= \lim_{\epsilon \to 0} \frac{-1}{\epsilon s} \left[ e^{-st} \right]_0^\epsilon$$

$$= \lim_{\epsilon \to 0} \frac{1 - e^{-\epsilon s}}{\epsilon s}.$$

This last expression can be evaluated by treating numerator and denominator as functions of $\epsilon$ and applying L' Hospital's rule to obtain

$$\lim_{\epsilon \to 0} \frac{1 - e^{-\epsilon s}}{\epsilon s} = \lim_{\epsilon \to 0} \frac{(d/d\epsilon)(1 - e^{-\epsilon s})}{(d/d\epsilon)\epsilon s} = \lim_{\epsilon \to 0} \frac{e^{-\epsilon s}s}{s} = 1.$$

Thus, the Laplace transform of the delta function is simply one, the area or "energy" under each of the functions in the sequence that defines the delta function. It should be noted that this result depends on the way the impulse has been defined. Other definitions of the impulse are possible, but the definition chosen gives the result that is best suited to the analysis of control systems.

At this point we have developed the three most fundamental Laplace transforms. There are four or five more transforms that arise in the study of linear systems, but these can all be derived from the three transform pairs already developed by using some of the basic properties of the Laplace transform treated in Section 2.4. Thus, the derivation of the remaining transforms will follow the discussion of these fundamental properties.

## 2.4 | PROPERTIES OF THE LAPLACE TRANSFORM

As the properties of the Laplace transform are developed, it is important to keep in mind that the goal is to use the transforms to solve ordinary differential equations with constant, real coefficients, such as the *linearized* differential equation for the pendulum.

We will show that applying the Laplace transform to a differential equation yields a simple, algebraic equation in the variable $s$. In fact, the equation will be a polynomial equation in $s$. Further, the fact that the coefficients of this polynomial equation are *real* means that the roots of this polynomial equation will be either real or complex conjugate pairs. This, in turn, makes the inverse transforms easy to compute. The power of all these properties depends, however, on the linearity property of Theorem 2.4.1.

## 2.4.1 Linearity

**Theorem 2.4.1**

If *a* and *b* are real numbers and $f(t)$ and $g(t)$ functions whose Laplace transforms exist, then

$$\mathcal{L}\{af(t) + bg(t)\} = a\mathcal{L}\{f(t)\} + b\mathcal{L}\{g(t)\} \qquad [2.7]$$

***Proof*** Let $f(t)$ and $g(t)$ be functions whose Laplace transforms exist. Then

$$\mathcal{L}\{af(t) + bg(t)\} = \int_0^\infty [af(t) + bg(t)]e^{-st}\, dt$$

$$= \int_0^\infty af(t)e^{-st}\, dt + \int_0^\infty bg(t)e^{-st}\, dt$$

$$= a\int_0^\infty f(t)e^{-st}\, dt + b\int_0^\infty g(t)e^{-st}\, dt$$

$$= a\mathcal{L}\{f(t)\} + b\mathcal{L}\{g(t)\}.$$

∎

This proof goes through so easily simply because the operation of integration itself is linear and because the coefficients are constants that can be factored out of the integrals. But the simplicity of the proof belies the importance and power of this theorem. It is the *essential reason* that the Laplace transform or any of its cousins, such as the Fourier or $Z$ transform are so powerful.

## 2.4.2 Laplace Transforms of Derivatives of a Function

The application of the Laplace transform to the solution of differential equations requires that we know the initial conditions associated with the equation. Theorems 2.4.2 and 2.4.3 bear on this issue.

**Theorem 2.4.2**

If $f(t)$ is a function whose Laplace transform exists and is represented by $F(s)$, then

$$\mathcal{L}\left\{\frac{df(t)}{dt}\right\} = sF(s) - f(0).$$

***Proof*** Assume that the Laplace transform of $f(t)$ exists. Integrating the Laplace transform of $f(t)$ by parts yields

$$\int_0^\infty f(t)e^{-st}\,dt = \left[\frac{f(t)e^{-st}}{-s}\right]_0^\infty - \int_0^\infty \frac{df(t)}{dt}\frac{e^{-st}}{-s}\,dt$$

$$= \frac{f(0)}{s} + \frac{1}{s}\int_0^\infty \frac{df(t)}{dt}e^{-st}\,dt$$

$$= \frac{f(0)}{s} + \frac{1}{s}\mathcal{L}\left\{\frac{df(t)}{dt}\right\}.$$

It then follows that

$$\mathcal{L}\left\{\frac{df(t)}{dt}\right\} = sF(s) - f(0).$$

∎

The value of $f(0)$ is usually either given or easily determined from basic physical principles. Having found the Laplace transform for the first derivative of a function $f(t)$, it is an easy matter to extend this result to higher derivatives.

> **Theorem 2.4.3**
>
> Let $f(t)$ be a function whose Laplace transform exists and whose first $n$ derivatives exist, with the $i$th derivative being signified by $f^{[i]}$. Then,
>
> $$\mathcal{L}\left\{f^{[2]}(t)\right\} = s^2 F(s) - sf(0) - f^{[1]}(0),$$
>
> and more generally,
>
> $$\mathcal{L}\left\{f^{[n]}(t)\right\} = s^n F(s) - s^{n-1} f(0) - s^{n-2} f^{[1]}(0)\cdots - sf^{[n-2]}(0) - f^{[n-1]}(0).$$

***Proof*** Let $f(t)$ be a function whose Laplace transform exists, and whose first $n$ derivatives also exist. Defining

$$f^{[1]}(t) = g(t),$$

and applying the previous theorem yields

$$\mathcal{L}\left\{f^{[2]}(t)\right\} = \mathcal{L}\left\{g^{[1]}(t)\right\}$$

$$= s\mathcal{L}\{g(t)\} - g(0)$$

$$= s\mathcal{L}\left\{f^{[1]}(t)\right\} - g(0)$$

$$= s\{sF(s) - f(0)\} - f^{[1]}(0)$$

$$= s^2 F(s) - sf(0) - f^{[1]}(0).$$

∎

Having proved the theorem for $n = 2$, it should be clear that repeated application of this approach will yield the general formula, and the details are left to the reader as a useful and straightforward exercise.

### 2.4.3 Laplace Transform of the Integral of a Function

A companion theorem of some interest is the Laplace transform of the integral of a function.

---

**Theorem 2.4.4**

Let $f(t)$ be a function whose Laplace transform exists and is represented by $F(s)$, and further let

$$g(0) = \lim_{t \to 0^+} \int_0^t f(t)\, dt$$

$$= \int_0^{0^+} f(t)\, dt.$$

Then

$$\mathcal{L}\left\{\int_0^t f(\tau)\, d\tau\right\} = \frac{F(s)}{s} + \frac{g(0)}{s}.$$

---

Before giving the proof, it is worth noting that $g(0)$ is an integral that will evaluate to zero if $f(0^+)$ is finite. Thus, even if there is a step discontinuity in $f$ at zero, $g(0)$ will be zero. A nonzero value of $g(0)$ can only occur if $f$ contains, for instance, an impulse at the origin, a rarity.

***Proof***   Assume that the Laplace transform of $f$ exists and is represented by $F(s)$. Let

$$g(t) = \int_0^t f(\tau)\, d\tau \quad \text{and} \quad G(s) = \mathcal{L}\{g(t)\}.$$

Then

$$g(0) = \int_0^{0^+} f(t)\, dt,$$

and, by Leibniz's formula

$$\frac{dg(t)}{dt} = f(t).$$

Hence,

$$\mathcal{L}\left\{\frac{dg(t)}{dt}\right\} = \mathcal{L}\{f(t)\} = F(s). \qquad \textbf{[2.8]}$$

However, applying Theorem 2.4.2 yields

$$\mathcal{L}\left\{\frac{dg(t)}{dt}\right\} = sG(s) - g(0).$$ [2.9]

Equating the right-hand sides of Eqs. [2.8] and [2.9] then yields

$$G(s) = \frac{F(s)}{s} + \frac{g(0)}{s}.$$

■

If $g(0) = 0$, which is almost always the case, then

$$G(s) = \frac{F(s)}{s}.$$

This theorem will be of importance in interpreting block diagrams involving Laplace transforms, because it shows that division by $s$ in the Laplace domain corresponds to integration in the time domain.

### 2.4.4  Laplace Transform of *tf(t)*

Given that the Laplace transform of $f(t)$ is known, it is easy to find the transform of $g(t) = tf(t)$.

---

**Theorem 2.4.5**

Let $f(t)$ be a function whose Laplace transform exists and is represented by $F(s)$. Then, if $g(t) = tf(t)$,

$$\mathcal{L}\{g(t)\} = -\frac{d}{ds}F(s).$$

---

***Proof***   Let the Laplace transform of $f(t)$ exist and be represented by $F(s)$. Then

$$\frac{d}{ds}F(s) = \frac{d}{ds}\int_0^\infty f(t)e^{-st}\,dt$$

$$= \int_0^\infty \frac{d}{ds}\left[f(t)e^{-st}\right]dt$$

$$= -\int_0^\infty tf(t)e^{-st}\,dt$$

$$= -\mathcal{L}\{tf(t)\}.$$

■

In proving this theorem, differentiation with respect to the complex variable $s$ has been performed as if $s$ were a real variable. It so happens that in this case we get the correct result. For the most part, the properties of complex variables required in this book map over identically from the properties of functions of a real variable. There are, however, important differences between functions of real and complex variables, and one cannot, in general, apply the results for functions of a real variable in a cavalier fashion.

Having developed some of the basic properties of the Laplace transform, the next topic of discussion is the inverse transform and the use of the transform in solving differential equations.

## 2.5 | The **INVERSE LAPLACE TRANSFORM**

Formally, the definition of the inverse Laplace transform is similar to that for the inverse Fourier transform.

---

**Definition 2.5.1**

Let $f(t)$ be a function whose Laplace transform exists and is represented by $F(s)$. Then $f(t)$ can be expressed in terms of $F(s)$ as

$$f(t) = \mathcal{L}^{-1}\{F(s)\} = \frac{1}{2\pi j} \int_{\sigma - j\infty}^{\sigma + j\infty} F(s)e^{st}\,ds,$$

where the path from $\sigma - j\omega$ to $\sigma + j\omega$ lies within the region of convergence of $F(s)$.

---

The integration is along a straight-line path of infinite extent within the region of convergence, as shown in Fig. 2.4. The inverse transform can be found from this integral expression. If the degree of the numerator polynomial is less than that of the denominator, making the Laplace transform a "proper" ratio of polynomials, then contour integration can be used. That is, the integration path is turned into a closed path by adding a semicircle of infinite radius from $s = \sigma + j\infty$ to $s = \sigma - j\infty$. The residue theorem from complex variable theory can then be used to evaluate the integral. It is important to note that taking the inverse Laplace transform is a linear operation.

**Figure 2.4 |** Integration path for the inverse transform.

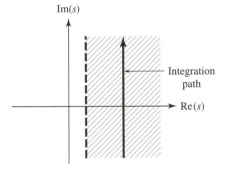

For proper Laplace transforms, a method equivalent to employing the residue theorem is the method of "partial fraction expansion." We now introduce the essentials of this method of inverting a Laplace transform. We will continue to develop our skills with this method in subsequent sections.

The idea of the partial fraction expansion method is to expand $F(s)$ as a sum of partial fractions, and then find $f(t)$ as the sum of the inverse transforms of the individual members of the partial fraction expansion. The reason this works so well is that the Laplace transforms that arise in the study of linear systems and linear control are ratios of polynomials in $s$ with real coefficients. These functions are readily factored and hence the partial fraction approach is easy to employ. Further, the partial fractions will always be simple enough that the inverse transform of each term in the expansion is known. As a consequence, with some practice, it is possible to do the inverse transformation by inspection. The ability to do this is at the heart of the analysis developed in subsequent chapters. The partial fraction expansion method is best illustrated by example.

**EXAMPLE 2.5.1**

Consider the ordinary differential equation

$$y^{[2]}(t) + 5y^{[1]}(t) + 6y(t) = 0, \qquad\qquad \text{[2.10]}$$

with initial conditions $y(0) = 1$, $y^{[1]}(0) = 0$, where, as before,

$$y^{[n]} \triangleq \frac{d^n}{dt^n} y(t).$$

Applying the Laplace transform to both sides of this equation and using Theorem 2.4.3, yields

$$s^2 Y(s) - sy(0) - y^{[1]}(0) + 5[sY(s) - y(0)] + 6Y(s) = 0.$$

This equation can be rearranged as

$$(s^2 + 5s + 6)Y(s) = sy(0) + 5y(0) + y^{[1]}(0).$$

Substituting the initial conditions gives

$$(s^2 + 5s + 6)Y(s) = s + 5.$$

Dividing both sides by $s^2 + 5s + 6$ then yields

$$Y(s) = \frac{s+5}{s^2 + 5s + 6} = \frac{s+5}{(s+2)(s+3)}.$$

The next step is to rewrite the right-hand side in partial fraction form. That is,

$$Y(s) = \frac{A}{s+2} + \frac{B}{s+3}. \qquad\qquad \text{[2.11]}$$

Applying the inverse Laplace transform to both sides of Eq. [2.11] yields

$$y(t) = \mathcal{L}^{-1}\{Y(s)\} = \mathcal{L}^{-1}\left\{ \frac{A}{s+2} + \frac{B}{s+3} \right\}$$

$$= \mathcal{L}^{-1}\left\{ \frac{A}{s+2} \right\} + \mathcal{L}^{-1}\left\{ \frac{B}{s+3} \right\}$$

$$= Ae^{-2t} + Be^{-3t}.$$

Note carefully how the linearity of the inverse Laplace transform enables the right-hand side to be broken into two simple, easily recognizable transforms. Note also that since the polynomial

$$c(s) = s^2 + 5s + 6$$

has real coefficients, the roots will be real or complex conjugate pairs. The roots of this polynomial determine the time functions that show up in the solution, namely, $e^{-2t}$ and $e^{-3t}$.

At this juncture, it should also be clear that once the expression for $Y(s)$ is factored, the time functions that will show up in the solution can be determined *by inspection*. All that is left is the evaluation of $A$ and $B$. There are a number of ways to find the constants $A$ and $B$. One method is presented here, and alternative methods will be discussed as we proceed.

Given

$$\frac{s+5}{(s+2)(s+3)} = \frac{A}{s+2} + \frac{B}{s+3},$$

the right-hand side can be put over a common denominator to give

$$\frac{s+5}{(s+2)(s+3)} = \frac{(A+B)s + (3A+2B)}{(s+2)(s+3)}.$$

Equating the coefficients of like powers of $s$ in the *numerators* of both sides of the equation yields

$$A + B = 1,$$

$$3A + 2B = 5.$$

These linear equations can be solved for $A$ and $B$. For instance, substituting $1 - B$ for $A$ in the second equation results in

$$3(1 - B) + 2B = 5,$$

or

$$B = -2.$$

Then

$$A = 1 - B = 3.$$

Thus, the final solution is

$$y(t) = [3e^{-2t} - 2e^{-3t}]1(t).$$

It is very important to note that the *form* of the solution, namely,

$$y(t) = [Ae^{-2t} + Be^{-3t}]1(t),$$

is known once the expression

$$Y(s) = \frac{s+5}{(s+2)(s+3)}$$

has been obtained. This importance of this will become clear when we subsequently are able to predict the output of a compensated control system by looking at the factors in the denominator of a ratio of polynomials in $s$. In the majority of cases, the denominator, or characteristic polynomial, will have unrepeated, real roots. In those cases, the analysis will be no more difficult than that just completed. It is therefore easy to see why the exponential function $e^{-at}$ is so central to the study of linear differential equations with constant coefficients.

A final note of importance is that the unfactored denominator of $Y(s)$ can be written down by inspection from the left-hand side of the original differential equation by writing

1. $s^2$ in place of $y^{[2]}(t)$,
2. $5s$ in place of $5y^{[1]}(t)$,
3. $6$ in place of $6y(t)$.

Reviewing the solution of the problem shows why. After applying the Laplace transform, the left-hand side of the resulting equation looked like

$$s^2 Y(s) - sy(0) - y^{[1]} + 5[sY(s) - y(0)] + 6Y(s).$$

However, the terms due to initial conditions did not involve $Y(s)$ and were moved to the right-hand side, leaving

$$s^2 Y(s) + 5Y(s) + 6Y(s),$$

which was then factored into

$$(s^2 + 5s + 6)Y(s).$$

Division of the right-hand side, which contained all the terms due to initial conditions, by $s^2 + 5s + 6$ then gave the expression for $Y(s)$. Thus, the denominator of $Y(s)$ can be found by inspecting the left-hand side of the original differential equation. This polynomial, referred to as the "characteristic" polynomial, is just that because its factors determine the time functions that show up in $y(t)$. In other words, it characterizes the time response of the system.

---

Example 2.5.1 is practically the whole story on solving ordinary differential equations with constant coefficients. This may seem like an oversimplification, but it really is not. The so-called characteristic polynomial encountered in this example is representative of all the characteristic polynomials encountered in this book. It is a polynomial in the complex Laplace variable $s$, with *real* coefficients. Because the coefficients are real, the roots of the equation obtained by setting this polynomial equal to zero will either be real or complex conjugate *pairs*. As a result, we will need to remember only a small number of transform pairs. This is very important. We would be far less inclined to use the Laplace approach if we had to remember a thousand transform pairs as opposed to the eight or ten that we actually use.

It is possible for the characteristic equation to have repeated real roots, or potentially even repeated complex roots. However, repeated roots are relative rare occurrences, and so, in principle, the characteristic polynomial of Example 2.5.1 is representative of any that will be encountered in the rest of the book. However, since repeated real roots and complex roots do occur in engineering problems, our next goal is to find the time functions that correspond to repeated real roots and complex roots.

## 2.6 | THE REMAINING TRANSFORMS

### 2.6.1 Transform of $te^{-at}$

The Laplace transform of

$$g(t) = \begin{cases} te^{-at} & \text{for } t \geq 0 \\ 0 & \text{for } t < 0, \end{cases}$$

can be obtained using Theorem 2.4.5. Letting $f(t) = e^{-at}$, with Laplace transform

$$\mathcal{L}\{f(t)\} = \frac{1}{s+a},$$

and applying Theorem 2.4.5 yields

$$\mathcal{L}\{te^{-at}\} = -\frac{d}{ds}\frac{1}{s+a}$$

$$= \frac{1}{(s+a)^2}.$$

This result gives us the transform needed when a factor $(s+a)^2$ is encountered. The transform of $g(t) = t^2 e^{-at}$ can be obtained by letting $f(t) = te^{-at}$ and reapplying the theorem. That is,

$$\mathcal{L}\{t^2 e^{-at}\} = -\frac{d}{ds}\frac{1}{(s+a)^2}$$

$$= \frac{2}{(s+a)^3}.$$

It is easy enough to see at this point that

$$\mathcal{L}\{t^n e^{-at}\} = \frac{n!}{(s+a)^{n+1}}.$$

In reality, a factor of the form $(s+a)^3$ is very rare in engineering applications.

It is also worth noting that this same approach yields the Laplace transforms for the time function

$$f(t) = t^n \mathbf{1}(t), \qquad n = 1, 2, \ldots.$$

The resulting Laplace transform is

$$\mathcal{L}\{t^n \mathbf{1}(t)\} = \frac{n!}{s^{n+1}}, \qquad n = 1, 2, \ldots.$$

### 2.6.2 Complex Roots

Complex roots appear frequently in engineering because they represent oscillations. As a consequence, the time function corresponding to a pair of complex roots is very important. Consider

$$G(s) = \frac{\alpha(s)}{(s + \sigma - j\omega)(s + \sigma + j\omega)} = \frac{M}{s + \sigma - j\omega} + \frac{M^*}{s + \sigma + j\omega},$$

where $M^*$ is the conjugate of $M$. As discussed earlier, complex roots occur in conjugate pairs. Finding the inverse transform for these complex roots affords us a chance to learn another technique for finding the constants (residues) in a partial fraction expansion.

Note in the earlier expression that multiplying both sides by $s + \sigma - j\omega$ gives

$$(s + \sigma - j\omega)G(s) = M + \frac{M^*(s + \sigma - j\omega)}{s + \sigma + j\omega}.$$

Then,

$$(s + \sigma - j\omega)G(s)\big|_{s=-\sigma+j\omega} = \left[\frac{\alpha(s)}{s + \sigma + j\omega}\right]_{s=-\sigma+j\omega} = \frac{\alpha(-\sigma + j\omega)}{2j\omega} = M.$$

In like fashion

$$(s + \sigma + j\omega)G(s)\big|_{s=-\sigma-j\omega} = \left[\frac{\alpha(s)}{s + \sigma - j\omega}\right]_{s=-\sigma-j\omega}$$

$$= \frac{\alpha(-\sigma - j\omega)}{-2j\omega}$$

$$= \frac{[\alpha(-\sigma + j\omega)]^*}{[2j\omega]^*}$$

$$= M^*.$$

Note that

$$\alpha(-\sigma - j\omega) = \alpha^*(-\sigma + j\omega).$$

This results from the fact that $\alpha(s)$ is assumed to be a polynomial in $s$ with *real* coefficients.

Since $M$ is usually complex, it is convenient to represent it in polar form as $M = |M|e^{j\phi}$. Thus,

$$\frac{M}{s + \sigma - j\omega} + \frac{M^*}{s + \sigma + j\omega} = \frac{|M|e^{j\phi}}{s + \sigma - j\omega} + \frac{|M|e^{-j\phi}}{s + \sigma + j\omega}.$$

Then,

$$g(t) = \mathcal{L}^{-1}\{G(s)\} = \mathcal{L}^{-1}\left\{\frac{|M|e^{j\phi}}{s + \sigma - j\omega} + \frac{|M|e^{-j\phi}}{s + \sigma + j\omega}\right\}$$

$$= \mathcal{L}^{-1}\left\{\frac{|M|e^{j\phi}}{s + \sigma - j\omega}\right\} + \mathcal{L}^{-1}\left\{\frac{|M|e^{-j\phi}}{s + \sigma + j\omega}\right\}$$

$$= |M|e^{j\phi}e^{(-\sigma+j\omega)t} + |M|e^{-j\phi}e^{(-\sigma-j\omega)t}$$

$$= 2|M|e^{-\sigma t}\left[\frac{e^{j(\omega t+\phi)} + e^{-j(\omega t+\phi)}}{2}\right].$$

Finally, recalling that

$$\cos \theta = \frac{e^{j\theta} + e^{-j\theta}}{2}$$

and letting $\omega t + \phi$ play the role of $\theta$ we have

$$g(t) = \begin{cases} 2|M|e^{-\sigma t} \cos(\omega t + \phi), & t \geq 0 \\ 0, & t < 0. \end{cases}$$

This is a very important transform pair, because when designing a control system we will often strive for a solution that has a pair of complex conjugate poles.

All of the transform pairs needed in the remainder of the book have now been derived and are collected in Table 2.1. Two additional transform pairs, those for $\sin \omega t$ and $\cos \omega t$ are also given.

**Table 2.1 |** Essential Laplace transform pairs.

| f(t) | F(s) |
|------|------|
| $\mathbf{1}(t)$ | $\dfrac{1}{s}$ |
| $t\mathbf{1}(t)$ | $\dfrac{1}{s^2}$ |
| $e^{-at}$ | $\dfrac{1}{s+a}$ |
| $te^{-at}$ | $\dfrac{1}{(s+a)^2}$ |
| $2|M|e^{-\sigma t} \cos(\omega t + \phi)$ | $\dfrac{|M|e^{j\phi}}{s+\sigma - j\omega} + \dfrac{|M|e^{-j\phi}}{s+\sigma + j\omega}$ |
| $\cos \omega t$ | $\dfrac{s}{s^2 + \omega^2}$ |
| $\sin \omega t$ | $\dfrac{\omega}{s^2 + \omega^2}$ |

Example 2.6.1, considered next, uses all the transform pairs previously derived, and contains a partial fraction expansion representative of those encountered later in the book.

**EXAMPLE 2.6.1**

The goal is to solve the differential equation

$$y^{[4]}(t) + 6y^{[3]}(t) + 22y^{[2]}(t) + 30y^{[1]}(t) + 13y(t) = 13\mathbf{1}(t),$$

with $y(0) = y^{[1]}(0) = y^{[2]}(0) = y^{[3]}(0) = 0$. The first step is to apply the Laplace transform to both sides of the equation to obtain

$$s^4 Y(s) + 6s^3 Y(s) + 22s^2 Y(s) + 30sY(s) + 13Y(s) = \frac{13}{s}.$$

Factoring out $Y(s)$ and dividing out the characteristic equation yields

$$Y(s) = \frac{13}{s(s^4 + 6s^3 + 22s^2 + 30s + 13)}$$

$$= \frac{13}{s(s+1)^2(s+2-j3)(s+2+j3)}.$$

Expanding the right-hand side of this equation into partial fractions yields

$$\frac{13}{s(s+1)^2(s+2-j3)(s+2+j3)} = \frac{A}{s} + \frac{B}{s+1} + \frac{C}{(s+1)^2}$$

$$+ \frac{M}{s+2-j3} + \frac{M^*}{s+2+j3}. \qquad \textbf{[2.12]}$$

Thus,

$$y(t) = [A + Be^{-t} + Cte^{-t} + 2|M|e^{-2t}\cos(3t + \phi)]\mathbf{1}(t).$$

All that remains is to find the constants $A$, $B$, $C$, and $M$.

The reader may wonder why both the terms

$$\frac{B}{s+1} \quad \text{and} \quad \frac{C}{(s+1)^2}$$

are present. In certain cases, $B = 0$, but in general it will not be zero. This simply means that to make the numerators on both sides of Eq. [2.12] agree, both terms may have to be present in the partial fraction expansion.

This example offers the chance to demonstrate some alternative methods of finding the constants in the partial fraction expansion. As a first step multiply both sides of Eq. [2.12] by $s$ to obtain

$$sY(s) = \frac{13}{(s^4 + 6s^3 + 22s^2 + 30s + 13)}$$

$$= A + \frac{sB}{s+1} + \frac{sC}{(s+1)^2} + \frac{sM}{s+2-j3} + \frac{sM^*}{s+2+j3}.$$

Setting $s = 0$ reduces the right-hand side to $A$. All the other terms go to zero. Thus,

$$A = sY(s)|_{s=0}$$

$$= \left[\frac{13}{(s^4 + 6s^3 + 22s^2 + 30s + 13)}\right]\Bigg|_{s=0}$$

$$= 1.$$

This same strategy will work in finding

$$C = (s+1)^2 Y(s)|_{s=-1}$$

$$= (s+1)^2\left[\frac{13}{s(s+1)^2(s+2-j3)(s+2+j3)}\right]\Bigg|_{s=-1}$$

$$= \frac{13}{(-1)(-1+2-j3)(-1+2+j3)}$$

$$= -1.3$$

and

$$M = (s + 2 - j3)Y(s)|_{s=-2+j3}$$

$$= \left[ \frac{13}{s(s+1)^2(s+2+j3)} \right] \Big|_{s=-2+j3}$$

$$= \frac{13}{(-2+j3)(-1+j3)^2(j6)}$$

$$= 0.0601\underline{/-1.2315}\ r.$$

Finding the constant $B$ is somewhat more difficult. It is possible to put all the terms over a common denominator and then equate coefficients in like powers of $s$ in the numerator. An alternative approach is the following. Multiplying both sides of Eq. [2.12] by $(s+1)^2$ yields

$$(s+1)^2 Y(s) = \frac{A(s+1)^2}{s} + B(s+1) + C + \frac{M(s+1)^2}{s+2-j3} + \frac{M^*(s+1)^2}{s+2+j3}.$$

Differentiating both sides then gives

$$\frac{d}{ds}(s+1)^2 Y(s) = \frac{2A(s+1)}{s} - \frac{A(s+1)^2}{s^2} + B$$

$$+ \frac{2M(s+1)}{s+2-j3} - \frac{M(s+1)^2}{(s+2-j3)^2}$$

$$+ \frac{2M^*(s+1)}{s+2+j3} - \frac{M^*(s+1)^2}{(s+2+j3)^2}.$$

Setting $s = -1$ reduces the right-hand side to $B$. Thus,

$$B = \frac{d}{ds}[(s+1)^2 Y(s)]|_{s=-1}$$

$$= \frac{d}{ds}\left[ \frac{13}{s(s+2-j3)(s+2+j3)} \right] \Big|_{s=-1}$$

$$= \frac{d}{ds}\left[ \frac{13}{s^3 + 4s^2 + 13s} \right] \Big|_{s=-1}$$

$$= \left[ \frac{-13(3s^2 + 8s + 13)}{(s^3 + 4s^2 + 13s)^2} \right] \Big|_{s=-1}$$

$$= -1.04.$$

The final solution is then

$$y(t) = [1 - 1.04e^{-t} - 1.3te^{-t} + 0.1202e^{-2t}\cos(3t - 1.2315)]\mathbf{1}(t).$$

Example 2.6.1 is representative of the use made of the Laplace transform in subsequent chapters. As mentioned before, the real power of Laplace transform theory is that only a handful of transforms are required. This chapter concludes with some additional theorems that will prove useful later.

## 2.7 | ADDITIONAL PROPERTIES

### 2.7.1   Final Value Theorem

The final value theorem proves very useful in quickly assessing the final, steady state value of the time response of a linear system.

---

**Theorem 2.7.1 (Final Value)**

If $f(t)$ and $df(t)/dt$ both have Laplace transforms and if the function $sF(s)$ has no poles in the right half of the $s$ plane or on the imaginary axis of the $s$ plane with the exception of poles at the origin. Then

$$\lim_{t \to \infty} f(t) = \lim_{s \to 0} sF(s).$$

---

***Proof***   Under the assumptions made in the statement of the theorem, application of Theorem 2.4.2 gives

$$\int_0^\infty \frac{df(t)}{dt} e^{-st}\, dt = sF(s) - f(0). \tag{2.13}$$

However,

$$\lim_{s \to 0} \int_0^\infty \frac{df(t)}{dt} e^{-st}\, dt = \int_0^\infty \frac{df(t)}{d}\, dt$$

$$= \lim_{t \to \infty} f(t) - f(0). \tag{2.14}$$

Equating the right-hand sides of Eqs. [2.13] and [2.14] then yields

$$\lim_{t \to \infty} f(t) - f(0) = \lim_{s \to 0}[sF(s)] - f(0),$$

or

$$\lim_{t \to \infty} f(t) = \lim_{s \to 0}[sF(s)]. \qquad \blacksquare$$

It should be clear that if $sF(s)$ has poles strictly in the right half of the $s$ plane then $\lim_{t \to \infty} f(t)$ is unbounded while $\lim_{s \to 0} sF(s)$ approaches a finite value. If $sF(s)$ has poles on the imaginary axis in the $s$ plane away from the origin, then $f(t)$ has a nondecaying oscillatory mode and will not approach a limit. However, the theorem will give the correct result for poles at the origin. For a single pole at the origin

$$\lim_{t \to \infty} f(t) = \lim_{s \to 0} sF(s) = \text{finite value},$$

so long as $F(s)$ is a ratio of polynomials in $s$ with real coefficients. If there are multiple poles at the origin, then

$$\lim_{t \to \infty} f(t) = \lim_{s \to 0} s F(s) = \infty.$$

Again this is correct, because if there are multiple poles at the origin, then $f(t)$ is unbounded.

## 2.7.2 Initial Value Theorem

An additional theorem, that gets much less use in the analysis of control systems is the initial value theorem. It is included here for completeness.

---

**Theorem 2.7.2 (Initial Value)**

If $f(t)$ and $df(t)/dt$ both have Laplace transforms, and if in addition $\lim_{s \to \infty} s F(s)$ exists, then

$$\lim_{s \to \infty} s F(s) = f(0).$$

---

***Proof*** Suppose both $f(t)$ and $df(t)/dt$ have Laplace transforms and that $\lim_{s \to \infty} s F(s)$ exists. Then

$$\lim_{s \to \infty} \int_0^\infty \frac{df(t)}{dt} e^{-st} \, dt = \int_0^\infty \lim_{s \to \infty} \frac{df(t)}{dt} e^{-st} \, dt = 0. \qquad \textbf{[2.15]}$$

The limit can be taken under the integral since the integration is with respect to $t$ not $s$.

Alternatively, applying Theorem 2.4.2 yields

$$\lim_{s \to \infty} \int_0^\infty \frac{df(t)}{dt} f(t) e^{-st} \, dt = \lim_{s \to \infty} s F(s) - f(0). \qquad \textbf{[2.16]}$$

Then equating the right-hand sides of Eqs. [2.15] and [2.16] yields

$$\lim_{s \to \infty} s F(s) - f(0) = 0.$$

∎

It is worth noting that if $f(t)$ has a finite discontinuity at $t = 0$, then $f(0^+)$ should be used in place of $f(0)$.

## 2.7.3 Time Delay

In the sequel, we will encounter systems with time delays called "transportation lags." For such systems, the following theorem is very useful.

---

**Theorem 2.7.3**

If $f(t)$ has Laplace transform $F(s)$, then

$$\mathcal{L}\{f(t - T)\mathbf{1}(t - T)\} = e^{-sT} F(s).$$

---

***Proof***   Suppose that the Laplace transform of $f(t)$ exists. Then, by definition,

$$F(s) = \int_0^\infty f(\tau)e^{-s\tau}\,d\tau$$

$$= \int_0^\infty [f(\tau)\mathbf{1}(\tau)]e^{-s\tau}\,d\tau.$$

Changing the variable of integration by letting $\tau = t - T$, then yields

$$F(s) = \int_T^\infty [f(t-T)\mathbf{1}(t-T)]e^{-s(t-T)}\,dt = e^{sT}\int_T^\infty [f(t-T)\mathbf{1}(t-T)]e^{-st}\,dt.$$

Next, by definition,

$$\mathcal{L}\{f(t-T)\mathbf{1}(t-T)\} = \int_0^\infty f(t-T)\mathbf{1}(t-T)e^{-st}\,dt.$$

However, since the function $\mathbf{1}(t - T)$ is zero on the interval $[0, T]$, we can write

$$\int_T^\infty [f(t-T)\mathbf{1}(t-T)]e^{-st}\,dt = \int_0^\infty f(t-T)\mathbf{1}(t-T)e^{-st}\,dt.$$

Thus, finally,

$$\mathcal{L}\{f(t-T)\mathbf{1}(t-T)\} = e^{-sT}F(s). \qquad\qquad [\mathbf{2.17}]$$

∎

It is worth noting that Eq. [2.17] results in a transfer function that is *not* a simple ratio of polynomials in $s$, because the Laplace variable $s$ occurs in the argument of the exponential function.

### 2.7.4  Convolution

We prove here a fundamental theorem relating the time domain to the Laplace domain that we will need at several points in the book. Suppose $f_1(t)$ and $f_2(t)$ are piecewise continuous, and further that $f_1(t) = f_2(t) \equiv 0$ for $t < 0$. Then the convolution of $f_1$ and $f_2$, often written $f_1 * f_2$, is

$$\int_0^t f_1(t-\tau)f_2(\tau)\,d\tau = \int_0^t f_1(\tau)f_2(t-\tau)\,d\tau.$$

This integral comes into play when we consider the output of a linear system to an input $u(t)$. If the impulse response of the linear system is $g(t)$, then the output $y(t)$ is given by

$$y(t) = \int_0^t g(t-\tau)u(\tau)\,d\tau.$$

Theorem 2.7.4 proves very useful later when we discuss the relationships between the time domain and the Laplace domain.

**Theorem 2.7.4 (Convolution)**

Suppose that $f_1(t)$ and $f_2(t)$ are both identically zero for $t < 0$ and that $F_1(s)$ and $F_2(s)$ exist. Then

$$\mathcal{L}\left\{\int_0^t f_1(t-\tau)\,f_2(\tau)\,d\tau\right\} = F_1(s)F_2(s).$$

***Proof*** Since we have assumed that both $f_1$ and $f_2$ are identically zero for $t < 0$, we can write

$$\int_0^t f_1(t-\tau)f_2(\tau)\,d\tau = \int_0^\infty f_1(t-\tau)f_2(\tau)\,d\tau,$$

because $f_1(t-\tau)$ will be zero for $\tau > t$. Then

$$\mathcal{L}\left\{\int_0^t f_1(t-\tau)f_2(\tau)\,d\tau\right\} = \mathcal{L}\left\{\int_0^\infty f_1(t-\tau)f_2(\tau)\,d\tau\right\}$$

$$= \int_0^\infty \left[\int_0^\infty f_1(t-\tau)f_2(\tau)\,d\tau\right]e^{-st}\,dt$$

$$= \int_0^\infty \int_0^\infty f_1(t-\tau)f_2(\tau)e^{-st}\,d\tau\,dt$$

Because $f_1$ and $f_2$ are assumed to be well-behaved functions, normally piecewise continuous, or at worst having a countably infinite number of finite "jumps," and because $F_1$ and $F_2$ exist, we can interchange the order of integration to obtain

$$\mathcal{L}\left\{\int_0^t f_1(t-\tau)f_2(\tau)\,d\tau\right\} = \int_0^\infty \int_0^\infty f_1(t-\tau)f_2(\tau)e^{-st}\,dt\,d\tau$$

$$= \int_0^\infty \left[\int_0^\infty f_1(t-\tau)e^{-st}\,dt\right]f_2(\tau)\,d\tau.$$

We next make the change of variables $\lambda = t - \tau$ on the inner integral to obtain

$$\mathcal{L}\left\{\int_0^t f_1(t-\tau)f_2(\tau)\,d\tau\right\} = \int_0^\infty \left[\int_{-\tau}^\infty f_1(\lambda)e^{-s(\lambda+\tau)}\,dt\right]f_2(\tau)\,d\tau.$$

Since we have assumed that $f_1$ and $f_2$ are identically zero for $t < 0$, we can change the lower limit of integration on the inner integral on the right-hand side to zero and we have

$$\mathcal{L}\left\{\int_0^t f_1(t-\tau)f_2(\tau)\,d\tau\right\} = \int_0^\infty \left[\int_0^\infty f_1(\lambda)e^{-s\lambda}e^{-st}\,dt\right]f_2(\tau)\,d\tau$$

$$= \int_0^\infty \left[\int_0^\infty f_1(\lambda)e^{-s\lambda}\,dt\right]f_2(\tau)e^{-s\tau}\,d\tau$$

$$= \left[\int_0^\infty f_1(\lambda)e^{-s\lambda}\,dt\right]\left[\int_0^\infty f_2(\tau)e^{-s\tau}\,d\tau\right]$$

$$= F_1(s)F_2(s).$$

■

We will have cause to refer to this theorem later in the book when we discuss the relationships between the time domain and the frequency domain.

## 2.8 | REPRISE

The purpose of this chapter was to provide a review of Laplace transform theory, emphasizing those elements of the theory most needed in subsequent chapters. There are some points worth summarizing at this point.

First, the physical systems considered in subsequent chapters can be represented by ordinary differential equations with constant coefficients. Systems of this type can be readily analyzed using the unilateral Laplace transform.

Second, the resulting Laplace transforms are ratios of polynomials in $s$ with *constant* coefficients. As a result, only a small number of transform pairs occur. These transforms are easy to commit to memory, and hence the process of inverting the Laplace transform can be done essentially by inspection if all that is needed is the *form* of the time function. Finding the constants in the partial fraction expansion takes some work, but a good deal of the analysis done in the $s$ plane does not require explicit computation of these constants. It is the *form* of the time function that is important.

Finally, using the Laplace transform, differential equations are transformed to algebraic equations, making the analysis much easier. Again the ease of analysis hinges on the fact that only a small number of transform pairs occur in the analysis of these algebraic equations.

The significance of these statements will become clearer in later chapters. The next goal is to show how a physical system described by ordinary differential equations with constant coefficients can be represented by a "transfer function."

## 2.9 | PROBLEMS

### 2.9.1 Laplace Transforms from Definition

For each of these functions, find the Laplace transform by applying the definition of the transform.

**1.** $f(t) = \begin{cases} 1 & 0 \le t \le T \\ 0 & \text{otherwise} \end{cases}$      **2.** $f(t) = \begin{cases} 1 & t \le T \le 2T \\ 0 & \text{otherwise} \end{cases}$

**3.** $f(t) = \begin{cases} 1 & 0 \le t \le T \\ 0 & T < t \le 2T \\ 1 & 2T < t \le 3T \\ 0 & \text{otherwise} \end{cases}$      **4.** $f(t) = \begin{cases} t & 0 \le t \le T \\ 0 & \text{otherwise} \end{cases}$

**5.** $f(t) = \begin{cases} t & 0 \le t \le T \\ T & t > T \\ 0 & \text{otherwise} \end{cases}$      **6.** $f(t) = \begin{cases} 0 & 0 \le t \le T \\ t - T & t > T \\ 0 & \text{otherwise} \end{cases}$

**7.** $f(t) = \begin{cases} t & 0 \le t \le T \\ 2T - t & T < t \le 2T \\ 0 & \text{otherwise} \end{cases}$

**8.** $f(t) = \begin{cases} A & 0 \le t \le T \\ e^{-2t} & T < t \le 2T \\ 0 & \text{otherwise} \end{cases}$

**9.** $f(t) = \begin{cases} A & 0 \le t \le T_1 \\ B & T_1 < t \le T_2 \\ C & T_2 < t \le T_3 \\ 0 & \text{otherwise} \end{cases}$

**10.** $f(t) = \begin{cases} e^{-3t} & 0 \le t \le T_1 \\ e^{-3T_1} & T_1 < t \le T_2 \\ C & T_2 \le t < T_3 \\ 0 & \text{otherwise} \end{cases}$

## 2.9.2 Laplace Transforms of Combinations of Simple Functions

Each of the functions described in Section 2.9.1 can be expressed as a combination of simple functions whose transforms are known. For instance the function described in 2.9.1, number 1, can be written

$$f(t) = \mathbf{1}(t) - \mathbf{1}(t - T).$$

Express each function as a linear combination of simple functions and then find its Laplace transform.

**1.** $f(t) = \begin{cases} e^{-at} & 0 \le t \le T \\ 0 & \text{otherwise} \end{cases}$

**2.** $f(t) = \begin{cases} 0 & 0 \le t \le T \\ e^{-at} & t \le T \le 2T \\ 0 & \text{otherwise} \end{cases}$

**3.** $f(t) = \begin{cases} A & 0 \le t \le T \\ B & T < t \le 2T \\ 0 & \text{otherwise} \end{cases}$

**4.** $f(t) = \begin{cases} t & 0 \le t \le T \\ T & T < t \le 2T \\ 0 & \text{otherwise} \end{cases}$

**5.** $f(t) = \begin{cases} te^{-at} & 0 \le t \le T \\ 1 & t > T \end{cases}$

**6.** $f(t) = \begin{cases} 0 & 0 \le t \le T \\ t^2 & T < t < 2T \\ 0 & \text{otherwise} \end{cases}$

**7.** $f(t) = \begin{cases} \cos t & 0 \le t \le \pi/2 \\ 0 & \text{otherwise} \end{cases}$

**8.** $f(t) = \begin{cases} t & 0 \le t \le T \\ e^{-2t} & T < t \le 2T \\ 0 & \text{otherwise} \end{cases}$

**9.** $f(t) = \begin{cases} A & 0 \le t \le T_1 \\ B & T_1 < t \le T_2 \\ C & T_2 < t \le T_3 \\ 0 & \text{otherwise} \end{cases}$

**10.** $f(t) = \begin{cases} e^{-3t} & 0 \le t \le T_1 \\ e^{-3T_1} & T_1 < t \le T_2 \\ C & T_2 \le t < T_3 \\ 0 & \text{otherwise} \end{cases}$

## 2.9.3 Laplace Transforms of Useful Functions

The functions listed here are useful to engineers. Find the Laplace transform of each of these functions. Assume the functions are zero for $t < 0$

1. $\cos \omega t$
3. $\cosh(t) = \frac{1}{2}(e^t + e^{-t})$

2. $\sin \omega t$
4. $\sinh(t) = \frac{1}{2}(e^t - e^{-t})$

### 2.9.4 Inverse Laplace Transforms

For each $F(s)$ find the corresponding time function.

1. $F(s) = \dfrac{10(s+5)}{s(s+10)}$

2. $F(s) = \dfrac{10(s+2)}{s^2(s+4)}$

3. $F(s) = \dfrac{25}{s(s^2+6s+25)}$

4. $F(s) = \dfrac{5(s+1)}{s(s+4)^2}$

5. $F(s) = \dfrac{5(s+1)}{(s+2)(s+3)}$

6. $F(s) = \dfrac{6}{(s+1)(s+5)}$

7. $F(s) = \dfrac{1}{s(s-2)}$

8. $F(s) = \dfrac{1}{s(s^2+9)}$

9. $F(s) = \dfrac{(s-1)}{s^2(s+1)}$

10. $F(s) = \dfrac{1}{s(s^2-1)}$

### 2.9.5 Solution of Differential Equations

Solve each differential equation for the specified initial conditions using Laplace transforms.

1. $y^{[2]}(t) + y^{[1]}(t) - 2y(t) = 0, \quad y(0) = 0, \quad y^{[1]} = 3$
2. $y^{[2]}(t) - 2y^{[1]}(t) - 3y(t) = 0, \quad y(0) = 1, \quad y^{[1]} = 7$
3. $y^{[2]}(t) + 2y^{[1]}(t) - 8y(t) = 0, \quad y(0) = 1, \quad y^{[1]} = 8$
4. $y^{[2]}(t) + 2y^{[1]}(t) - 3y(t) = 0, \quad y(0) = 0, \quad y^{[1]} = 4$
5. $y^{[2]}(t) + 4y^{[1]}(t) - 3y(t) = 0, \quad y(0) = 8, \quad y^{[1]} = 0$
6. $y^{[2]}(t) - 4y^{[1]}(t) + 5y(t) = 0, \quad y(0) = 1, \quad y^{[1]} = 3$
7. $y^{[2]}(t) + 2y^{[1]}(t) + 5y(t) = 0, \quad y(0) = 2, \quad y^{[1]} = -4$
8. $y^{[2]}(t) - 4y^{[1]}(t)y(t) = 0, \quad y(0) = 1, \quad y^{[1]} = -2$
9. $y^{[2]}(t) - 4y^{[1]}(t) + 4y(t) = 0, \quad y(0) = 0, \quad y^{[1]} = 2$
10. $y^{[2]}(t) + 2y^{[1]}(t) + 10y(t) = 0, \quad y(0) = 0, \quad y^{[1]} = 3$
11. $y^{[2]}(t) + 4y^{[1]}(t) + 4y(t) = 0, \quad y(0) = 2, \quad y^{[1]} = -3$

### 2.9.6 Solution of Circuit Problems Using Laplace Transforms

Use Laplace transforms to solve each circuit problem for the specified initial conditions and $e(t)$.

1. Figure 2.5(a). Let $e(t) = V$, a constant ideal voltage source. Find $i(t)$.
2. Figure 2.5(a). Let $e(t) = A \cos \omega t$. Find $i(t)$.
3. Figure 2.5(b). Let $e(t) = V$, a constant ideal voltage source.
4. Figure 2.5(b). Let $e(t) = A \sin \omega t$. Find $i(t)$.
5. Figure 2.5(c). Let $e(t) = V$, a constant ideal voltage source.
6. Figure 2.5(c). Let $e(t) = A \cos \omega t$. Find $i(t)$.
7. Figure 2.5(d). Let $e(t) = V$, a constant ideal voltage source.
8. Figure 2.5(d). Let $e(t) = A \cos \omega t$. Find $i(t)$.
9. Figure 2.5(e). Let $e(t) = V$, a constant ideal voltage source. Find $i(t)$.
10. Figure 2.5(f ). Let the initial charge on the capacitor be 10 V. Find $i(t)$.

**Figure 2.5 |**

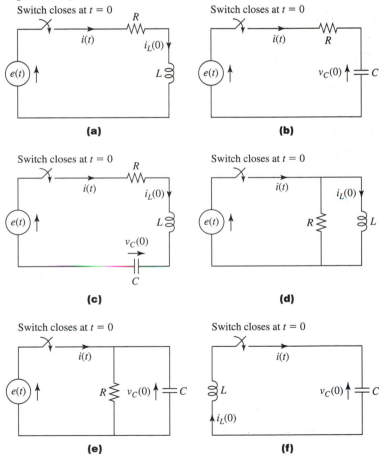

# FURTHER READINGS

Bartle, Robert G., 1976. *The Elements of Real Analysis*. New York: John Wiley and Sons.

Kreyzig, Erwin, 1967. *Advanced Engineering Mathematics*. New York: John Wiley and Sons.

Ogata, K., 1970. *Modern Control Engineering*. Englewood Cliffs, N.J.: Prentice-Hall.

Saucedo, R., and E. E. Schiring, 1968. *Introduction to continuous and Digital Control Systems*. New York: MacMillan.

# The Transfer Function

## 3.1 | OVERVIEW

In this chapter we introduce the concept of a transfer function and then build up some related tools required to model, identify, and implement transfer functions. These tools will all be needed in later chapters when we go through the entire design cycle, outlined in Chapter 1, for several real systems. A good deal of the rest of the book is devoted to the analysis and design of control strategies, on the assumption that we already have an adequate model of the system to be controlled. At three points in the chapter, however, we stop and go through the entired design cycle, and at those points we will need the tools developed in this chapter.

That said, there are two strategies for reading this chapter. One is to treat it as an "in line" appendix, by scanning the material in the chapter and then returning to it later for a more in-depth look when the material is actually needed. The other is to simply invest the time to thoroughly understand the material presented. Both strategies can be used successfully. In either case, there are a variety of problems at the end of the chapter that serve as a gauge of one's mastery of the material.

A transfer function is nothing more than the $s$ plane representation of a physical system that can be described by an ordinary differential equation with constant coefficients. In some cases, we can obtain the transfer function from "first principles"—that is, we can apply the appropriate laws of physics, chemistry, or electricity to the physical system being studied to obtain a differential equation that describes the system. The Laplace transform can then be used to derive the transfer function.

In other cases, it may be very difficult to find the underlying transfer function from first principles. This is often the case if the system is complex. For instance, suppose we want to find the moment of inertia $J$ of an irregularly shaped object, say the space shuttle with a payload on board ready for launch. Calculating the moment of inertia from first principles might prove challenging.

Instead, suppose we conduct a torsion pendulum experiment. First the irregularly shaped object, the shuttle in this example, is hung from a cable and set into oscillation, as shown in Fig. 3.1(a). The period of oscillation $T_{\text{shuttle}}$ is recorded. Then the shuttle

**Figure 3.1** | Determining the moment of inertia of an irregular object.

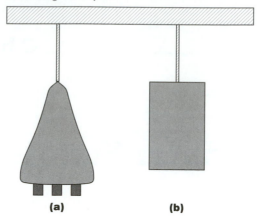

(a)                          (b)

is replaced by a symmetrically shaped weight, as shown in Fig. 3.1(b). Because of its symmetry and uniform density, it is an easy matter to calculate the moment of inertia of the weight. Again the period of oscillation $T_{weight}$ is recorded. The moment of inertia of the irregular object, such as the shuttle, can then be found from the formula

$$J_{shuttle} = J_{weight} \left( \frac{T_{shuttle}}{T_{weight}} \right)^2 .$$

Similar simple experiments can be conducted on a physical system to help determine its transfer function. One such experimental procedure will be discussed in this chapter and others will be introduced in chapters 8, 9, 13, and 16.

In this chapter we will also discuss the ideal operational amplifier (opamp) and show how simple transfer functions can be implemented using operational amplifiers. The goal is not to become an expert analog designer, but rather to achieve a level of skill that will enable us to build and test analog compensators (controllers) in later chapters. The art of analog design is indeed an art, and its more arcane features are outside the scope of this book. At the same time, we do need some competence in the design of opamp circuits if we are to build and implement simple compensators.

The concept of a transfer function developed in this chapter sets the stage for the introduction of feedback in Chapter 4. Once feedback and its effects are understood, we can begin to develop techniques for using feedback to improve the performance of physical systems.

## 3.2 | THE TRANSFER FUNCTION

Consider the simple network shown in Fig. 3.2. The output voltage is

$$v_o(t) = i(t)R_2 = \left[ C\frac{d}{dt}v_c(t) + \frac{v_c(t)}{R_1} \right] R_2.$$

**Figure 3.2 |** Simple *RC* circuit.

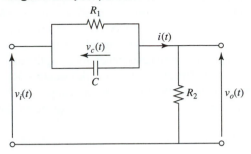

Rearranging terms yields

$$R_1 v_o(t) = R_1 R_2 C \frac{d}{dt} v_c(t) + R_2 v_c(t). \tag{3.1}$$

We next apply the Laplace transform to Eq. [3.1] to obtain

$$R_1 V_o(s) = R_1 R_2 C[s V_c(s) - v_c(0)] + R_2 V_c(s). \tag{3.2}$$

Assuming zero initial conditions, that is, $v_c(0) = 0$, and noting that

$$v_c(t) = v_i(t) - v_o(t),$$

we can substitute $V_i(s) - V_o(s)$ for $V_c(s)$ in Eq. [3.2] to obtain

$$R_1 V_o(s) = R_1 R_2 C[s V_i(s) - s V_o(s)] + R_2[V_i(s) - V_o(s)]. \tag{3.3}$$

The reason for assuming zero initial conditions is that we want to determine the behavior of the network itself, independent of any initial conditions. By so doing we arrive at a characterization intrinsic to the network.

Equation [3.3] can be rearranged as

$$\frac{V_o(s)}{V_i(s)} = \frac{R_1 R_2 C s + R_2}{R_1 R_2 C s + (R_1 + R_2)} = \frac{b_1 s + b_0}{a_1 s + a_0}, \tag{3.4}$$

where $a_0 = R_1 + R_2$, $b_0 = R_2$, and $a_1 = b_1 = C R_1 R_2$.

The right-hand side of Eq. [3.4] is called the transfer function between the input $V_i(s)$ and the output $V_o(s)$.

The simple example just discussed leads directly to a general form for the transfer function. Consider the differential equation

$$y^{[n]}(t) + a_{n-1} y^{[n-1]}(t) + \cdots + a_0 y(t) = b_0 u(t) + b_1 u^{[1]}(t) + \cdots + b_m u^{[m]}(t), \tag{3.5}$$

where, as previously defined, the notation $f^{[i]}$ means the $i$th derivative of the function $f$. The coefficient of the highest derivative of $y$ is assumed to be one. If it isn't, it can be made one by dividing both sides of the equation by the original value of the coefficient.

For real physical systems, $m < n$. At first glance, this statement seems to be at odds with the transfer function for the simple network we have just found. Actually it is not. The transfer function of the simple network was derived using *ideal* mathematical models of the resistors and capacitor. These models are more than adequate for use in control applications where the frequencies generally are quite low. At extremely high frequencies, the models fail. The electrical network just considered, like all physical systems, will eventually give no output as the frequency of the input becomes very high. However, if we use the network at much lower frequencies, then the ideal models are perfectly adequate.

Applying the Laplace transform to Eq. [3.5], and assuming zero initial conditions for both $y$ and $u$, yields

$$s^n Y(s) + a_{n-1}s^{n-1}Y(s) + \cdots + a_0 Y(s) = b_m s^m U(s) + b_{m-1}s^{m-1}U(s)$$

$$+ \cdots + b_0 U(s). \qquad [3.6]$$

Factoring out $Y(s)$ on the left-hand side and $U(s)$ on the right-hand side and rearranging yields

$$\frac{Y(s)}{U(s)} = \frac{b_m s^m + b_{m-1}s^{m-1} + \cdots + b_1 s + b_0}{s^n + a_{n-1}s^{n-1} + \cdots + a_1 s + a_0}$$

$$= \frac{b_m[s^m + \bar{b}_{m-1}s^{m-1} + \cdots + \bar{b}_1 s + \bar{b}_0]}{s^n + a_{n-1}s^{n-1} + \cdots + a_1 s + a_0},$$

where $\bar{b}_i = b_i/b_m$, $i = 0, 1, \ldots, m-1$. Then, letting $K = b_m$,

$$\frac{Y(s)}{U(s)} = \frac{K \prod_{i=1}^{m}(s + \beta_i)}{\prod_{i=1}^{n}(s + \alpha_i)}. \qquad [3.7]$$

The ratio $Y(s)/U(s)$ is called the transfer function between $Y$ and $U$. As we can see, it is simply a ratio of polynomials in the complex variable $s$. The coefficients are *real* numbers. This ratio of polynomials is usually represented as a single function

$$G(s) \triangleq \frac{Y(s)}{U(s)}.$$

It is then possible to write

$$Y(s) = G(s)U(s).$$

This relationship corresponds to the block diagram of Fig. 3.3.

We see that the transfer function is well defined, *except* at the roots of the denominator polynomial. There the transfer function is undefined. These so-called points of singularity are commonly referred to as "poles." To see how this terminology

**Figure 3.3 |** Block diagram of the relationship between $U(s)$ and $Y(s)$.

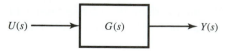

arises consider

$$G_1(s) = \frac{20(s+1)}{s+2}.$$

If $s = -1$, then $G = 0$. If $s = -2$, then $|G(s)| \to \infty$. For all other values of the Laplace variable $s$ the magnitude of $G$ is finite, and $G(s)$ is well defined. Figure 3.4 shows a plot of $\log_{10}|G(s)|$ versus the complex variable $s$. Note that by plotting $\log_{10}|G(s)|$, the zero at $s = -1$ becomes a hole or "sink." Figure 3.5 is a similar

**Figure 3.4** | $\log_{10}|G_1(s)|$ as a function of $s = \sigma + j\omega$.

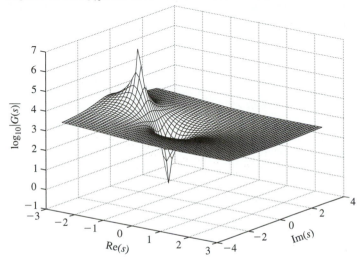

**Figure 3.5** | $\log_{10}|G_2(s)|$ as a function of $s = \sigma + j\omega$.

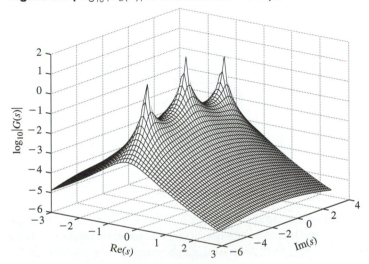

plot of

$$G_s(s) = \frac{1}{(s+2)(s+2-j2)(s+2+j2)}.$$

Here the plot looks something like a three ring circus tent.

For both these plots, we can think of stretching a flexible sheet over the $s$ plane and then at each point in the $s$ plane, adjusting the height of the sheet to the value of $|G(s)|$ at that point. Near the singularities, the sheet has to be pulled up to very large heights. As a consequence it looks like we have inserted a very long tent pole in the $s$ plane at each of the singular points. Hence the name "pole."

The fact that $Y(s)$ can be represented as the multiplication of $G(s)$ and $U(s)$ simply means that convolution in the time domain corresponds to multiplication in the $s$ domain. To see this let $u(t) = \delta(t)$. Then

$$Y(s) = G(s)\mathcal{L}\{\delta(t)\} = G(s),$$

and

$$\mathcal{L}^{-1}\{G(s)\} = g(t),$$

the impulse response of the system represented by $G(s)$. Then we know from linear system theory that

$$y(t) = \int_0^t g(t-\tau)u(\tau)\,d\tau.$$

We thus have the situation shown in Fig. 3.6. It might seem that the "end run" of finding $U(s)$ and $G(s)$, then multiplying them together to get $Y(s)$ and finally applying the inverse Laplace transform to $Y(s)$ to obtain $y(t)$ is a lot of extra work. To the contrary, it greatly simplifies the analysis by substituting multiplication for integration. This substitution of multiplication for integration is the great common strength of the Fourier, Laplace, and $Z$ transforms.

**Figure 3.6 |** Relationship between the time domain and the $s$ domain.

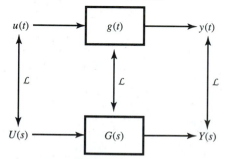

Having shown that the description of a physical system in terms of an ordinary differential equation with constant coefficients can also be represented as a transfer function, the next step is to show how this can be done for a specific system. The system chosen is an armature-controlled dc motor, and in this case, we can derive the transfer function from first principles.

# 3.3 | TRANSFER FUNCTION OF A DC MOTOR

The dc motor has been a workhorse in industry for the better part of a century. It has survived because it provides good torque at all speeds and can be manufactured easily and inexpensively. It is being replaced, to some extent, by brushless dc and ac induction motors. However, commutator dc motors are still manufactured in great quantities because for many applications, they are still the best solution.

Several of the simple control systems described in subsequent chapters use small dc motors. For that reason, the transfer function of the dc motor will be needed later. Also, having derived the transfer function of the separately excited, armature-controlled dc motor, it is only a short walk to the transfer function of the brushless dc motor. Finally, the dc motor is an exceptionally good example of how a transfer function can be derived from first principles.

In developing the transfer function of the separately excited dc motor, an equation of the form of Eq. [3.5] is never explicitly achieved. As is often the case, it proves easier to take the Laplace transform of the differential equations for the electrical and mechanical subsystems separately and then merge the resulting algebraic equations.

Figure 3.7 shows the basic electrical and mechanical components of a separately excited dc motor. The constant $K_r$ represents a restoring torque proportional to shaft displacement. That is,

$$\tau_r = K_r\theta,$$

where $\theta$ represents the "twist" or displacement of one end of the shaft relative to the other end. In many motor applications, the shaft is assumed to be perfectly rigid. In this case, there is no restoring torque and the term $K_r\theta$ will not be present. Although this term is usually missing in the derivation of the transfer function of a dc motor, it

**Figure 3.7 |** A dc motor with load.

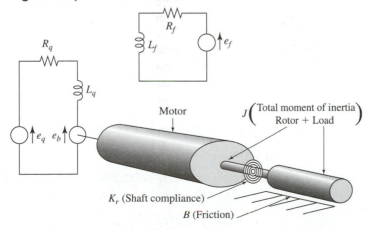

is retained in the development that follows because it appears in a system analyzed in Chapter 16.

The basic equation for the electromagnetic torque of the motor is

$$\tau_{em} = \left(\frac{ZNP}{a\pi}\right)\Phi_p i_q(t),$$ [3.8]

where, for the armature winding, $Z$ is the number of coils, $N$ is the number of turns per coil, $a$ is the number of parallel current paths, $P$ is the number of poles, $\Phi_p$ is the flux per pole, and $i_q(t)$ is the armature current.

To simplify the notation somewhat, let

$$\mathcal{K} \triangleq \left(\frac{ZNP}{a\pi}\right).$$

If $N_f$ is the number of turns and $\mathcal{R}_f$ the reluctance of the flux path of $\Phi_p$, then letting

$$\mathcal{K}_f \triangleq \frac{N_f}{\mathcal{R}_f},$$

$\Phi_p$ can be expressed as

$$\Phi_p = \mathcal{K}_f i_f(t).$$ [3.9]

The resulting equation for the electromagnetic torque is

$$\begin{aligned}
\tau_{em} &= \left(\frac{ZNP}{a\pi}\right)\Phi_p i_q(t) \\
&= \mathcal{K}\mathcal{K}_f i_f(t) i_q(t) \\
&= \mathcal{K}_{qf} i_f(t) i_q(t),
\end{aligned}$$

where

$$\mathcal{K}_{qf} \triangleq \mathcal{K}\mathcal{K}_f.$$

Referring to Fig. 3.7, the differential equation for the armature circuit is

$$e_q(t) = R_q i_q(t) + L_q i_q^{[1]}(t) + e_b(t).$$ [3.10]

The voltage $e_b(t)$ is the back electromotive force (emf) of the machine and is proportional to the speed of the motor shaft. That is,

$$e_b(t) = K_v \theta^{[1]}(t).$$ [3.11]

For an armature-controlled, separately excited dc motor, the field current is constant, and the torque produced by the motor can be expressed as

$$\tau_{em}(t) = \mathcal{K}_{qf} i_f(t) i_q(t) = \mathcal{K}_{qf} I_f i_q(t),$$ [3.12]

where $I_f$ is the constant field current. Assuming zero initial conditions and applying the Laplace transform to Eq. [3.12] yields

$$T_{em}(s) = \mathcal{K}_{qf} I_f I_q(s).$$ [3.13]

Next, assuming zero initial conditions and applying the Laplace transform to Eq. [3.10] results in

$$E_q(s) = R_q I_q(s) + L_q s I_q(s) + E_b(s). \qquad [3.14]$$

Equation [3.14] can be rearranged as

$$I_q(s) = \left[\frac{1}{L_q s + R_q}\right][E_q(s) - E_b(s)], \qquad [3.15]$$

and we see that

$$\frac{1}{L_q s + R_q}$$

is the transfer function between $E_q(s) - E_b(s)$ and the armature current $I_q(s)$.

Applying the Laplace transform to Eq. [3.11] yields

$$E_b(s) = K_v s \Theta(s).$$

Thus, we can rewrite Eq. [3.15] as

$$I_q(s) = \frac{E_q(s) - K_v s \Theta(s)}{L_q s + R_q}. \qquad [3.16]$$

If we now substitute the expression for $I_q(s)$ obtained from Eq. [3.16] into Eq. [3.13] we have

$$T_{em}(s) = \frac{\mathcal{K}_{qf} I_f [E_q(s) - K_v s \Theta(s)]}{L_q s + R_q}. \qquad [3.17]$$

We also know that

$$\tau_{mech}(t) = J\frac{d^2}{dt^2}\theta + B\frac{d}{dt}\theta + K_r\theta. \qquad [3.18]$$

Taking the Laplace transform of Eq. [3.18] yields

$$T_{mech}(s) = Js^2\Theta(s) + Bs\Theta(s) + K_r\Theta(s). \qquad [3.19]$$

Finally, equating the right-hand sides of Eqs. [3.17] and [3.19] and rearranging gives

$$G_\theta(s) = \frac{\Theta(s)}{E_q(s)} = \frac{\mathcal{K}_{qf} I_f}{(Js^2 + Bs + K_r)(L_q s + R_q) + K_v \mathcal{K}_{qf} I_f s}. \qquad [3.20]$$

By letting

$$K_m = \frac{\mathcal{K}_{qf} I_f}{J L_q},$$

we obtain the slightly simpler expression

$$G_\theta(s) = \frac{K_m}{[s^2 + (B/J)s + K_r/J](s + R_q/L_q) + K_v K_m s}. \qquad [3.21]$$

It is useful at this juncture to build a block diagram of $G_\theta(s)$. Let

$$G(s) = \frac{K_m}{[s^2 + (B/J)s + K_r/J][s + (R_q/L_q)]} \quad \text{and} \quad H(s) = K_v s.$$

Dividing numerator and denominator of the right-hand side of Eq. [3.21] by

$$[s^2 + (B/J)s + K_r/J][s + (R_q/L_q)]$$

yields

$$G_\theta(s) = \frac{G(s)}{1 + G(s)H(s)}.$$   [3.22]

This expression can be represented by the block diagram of Fig. 3.8. This block diagram resembles the block diagram we obtained in our preliminary discussion of feedback in Chapter 1. It should be emphasized that the feedback here is *internal* to the dc motor. The overall transfer function $G_\theta(s)$ between the armature voltage $E_q(s)$ and the shaft position $\Theta(s)$ is represented in the block diagram by the dotted line rectangle.

**Figure 3.8 |** Block diagram of a dc motor.

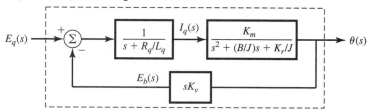

## 3.4 | TRANSFER FUNCTION OF A BRUSHLESS DC MOTOR

In this section we discuss one of the motors that is replacing the dc motor in many industrial applications, namely the brushless dc motor. Because the use of this motor continues to increase, it is worth our time to derive its transfer function. The brushless dc motor is really a synchronous motor with some internal feedback that is coupled to a power electronics circuit. The result is performance identical to that of a true dc motor with a commutator, and hence the name brushless dc motor.

Figure 3.9 shows the end views of a true dc motor and a three-phase, brushless dc motor. The stator winding of a true dc motor carries a direct current that creates a stationary B-field. The B-field of the rotor is kept orthogonal to the stator B-field by the commutator, which continually changes the direction of the current in the individual windings of the rotor as it turns.

In Fig. 3.9(b) the three stator windings of the brushless dc motor are supplied with balanced three-phase voltages, creating balanced three-phase currents in the windings. The spatial relationships of the three-phase belts combines with the temporal phase shifts of the three currents to produce a traveling current wave. This traveling current wave creates the stator B-field. In part (b) of the figure, the sinusoidal shape of this traveling current wave is indicated by the variation in the size of the dots and x's that represent the current. In the figure, the current is peaking in phase $a$.

**Figure 3.9 |** End views of (a) a dc motor and (b) a brushless dc motor.

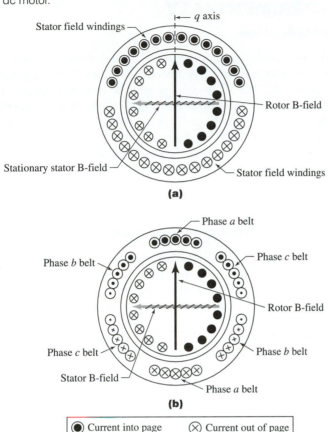

In motor operation the stator B-field leads the rotor B-field by 90°. This orthogonal relationship is maintained by an electronic circuit that utilizes shaft position as a feedback signal. This means, in effect, that the position of the $q$ axis is known. Thus, the feedback signal and the electronics replace the mechanical commutation of a true dc motor, and the B-field relationships in the brushless dc motor are identical to those in the true dc motor.

For the brushless dc motor the mechanical dynamics represented in Fig. 3.8 by

$$\frac{K_m}{s^2 + (B/J)s + K_r/J}$$

remain the same. The block in the feedback loop, $s K_v \Theta(s)$ is eliminated and the feedback signal is simply $\Theta(s)$. In the forward loop the block representing the armature winding dynamics is replaced by a gain $K_e$.

# 3.5 | FINDING TRANSFER FUNCTIONS EXPERIMENTALLY

## 3.5.1   Introduction

In the previous two sections we have seen how a transfer function can be determined theoretically from first principles. However, a difficulty remains, namely, how to find the parameters $R_q$, $L_q$, $J$, $B$, etc. For large dc motors, there are standard test procedures for determining these parameters. For fractional horsepower motors, these techniques don't work as well, primarily because the shaft friction is proportionally much larger in a small motor. Therefore, we often have to resort to more generic experimental methods for determining the parameters of transfer functions. One such technique will be introduced shortly. Before doing so, we find a simpler model for the dc motor.

## 3.5.2   Simplified Transfer Function

The transfer function of Eq. [3.21] relates the motor shaft position to armature voltage. In many applications, it is the speed of the motor that needs to be controlled. Since speed is the derivative of position, all we need to do is multiply both sides of Eq. [3.21] by the Laplace variable $s$. At the same time, we simplify the model somewhat by assuming that the shaft connecting the motor to the load is perfectly rigid. This means that there is no countertorque produced by the shaft, and thus the term $K_r/J$ is not present. With this simplifying assumption, we multiply both sides of Eq. [3.21] by $s$ to obtain:

$$\frac{\Omega(s)}{E_q(s)} = \frac{K_m}{s^2 + (B/J + R_q/L_q)s + (BR_q/JL_q + K_v K_m)},$$  [3.23]

where

$$\omega(t) \triangleq \frac{d}{dt}\theta(t) \quad \text{and} \quad \Omega(s) = \mathcal{L}\{\omega(t)\}.$$

For simple second-order transfer functions such as that in Eq. [3.23], we can often find the transfer function experimentally, as shown next.

## 3.5.3   Step Response of Simple Second-Order System

Consider the system

$$G(s) = \frac{K}{(s + p_1)(s + p_2)}$$

and assume that

$$\frac{p_2}{p_1} \geq 3.$$

This is not a very restrictive assumption because a good many systems, including the dc motor, have widely separated poles.

The step response of this system is

$$Y(s) = \frac{G(s)}{s} = \frac{K}{s(s + p_1)(s + p_2)} = \frac{A}{s} + \frac{B}{s + p_1} + \frac{C}{s + p_2},$$

where

$$A = sY(s)|_{s=0} = \frac{K}{(s + p_1)}(s + p_2)|_{s=0} = \frac{K}{p_1 p_2},$$

$$B = (s + p_1)Y(s)|_{s=-p_1} = \frac{K}{s(s + p_2)}\bigg|_{s=-p_1} = \frac{K}{p_1(p_1 - p_2)},$$

$$C = (s + p_2)Y(s)|_{s=-p_2} = \frac{K}{s(s + p_1)}\bigg|_{s=-p_2} = \frac{K}{p_2(p_2 - p_1)}.$$

Thus the step response is

$$y(t) = [A + Be^{-p_1 t} + Ce^{-p_2 t}]\mathbf{1}(t).$$

Note that $B < 0, C > 0$, and $C = -B$. Now consider Fig. 3.10. The functions defined in this figure are the total response $y(t)$,

$$y_1(t) = A + Be^{-p_1 t},$$

and

$$y_2(t) = Ce^{-p_2 t}.$$

**Figure 3.10 |** Decomposition of the step response.

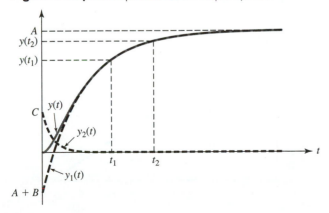

Given that $p_2$ is more than three times larger than $p_1$, we know that for large $t$,

$$y(t) \approx y_1(t) = A + Be^{-p_1 t}.$$

We next define the function

$$z(t) = A - y(t) = -Be^{-p_1 t} - Ce^{-p_2 t}.$$

This function is simply the negative of $y$ with the steady state value $A$ removed. For large $t$,

$$z(t) \rightarrow -Be^{-p_1 t} \triangleq z_1(t).$$

Note that $z(t) > 0$. This is crucial since we will shortly want to take the natural logarithm of $z(t)$, and therefore we have to have a function that is positive for all $t > 0$.
Then

$$\frac{d}{dt}\left[\ln(z_1(t))\right] = \frac{d}{dt}[\ln(-Be^{-p_1 t})]$$

$$= \frac{d}{dt}[\ln(-B) + \ln(e^{-p_1 t})]$$

$$= -p_1.$$

Our strategy will be to make a plot of $\ln z(t)$ and find the slope for large $t$. That slope will be $-p_1$, as depicted in Fig. 3.11.

Having found $p_1$, we must now find $p_2$ and $K$. There are a number of ways to attack this problem. One approach is to revisit Fig. 3.10 and note that for large $t$,

$$y(t) \approx A + Be^{-p_1 t}.$$

Since at this point we know $A$ and $p_1$, if we pick a *specific* value of $t$ near the point where $y$ reaches its steady state value, we can solve for $B$; that is,

$$B = \frac{y(t) - A}{e^{-p_1 t}}.$$

**Figure 3.11 |** Plot of $\ln z(t)$ versus $t$.

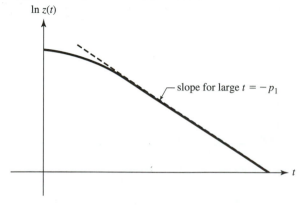

$\ln z(t)$

slope for large $t = -p_1$

$t$

If we repeat this calculation for increasing values of $t$, we should reach a point where $B$ remains nearly constant. In doing so, we have found not only $B$ but learned something about the size of $p_2$.

Once we have found $B$, we can next find

$$C = -(A + B).$$

Once $C$ is determined, we can find $p_2$ by noting that

$$p_2 = -\frac{B}{C} p_1.$$

Finally, once $p_2$ is determined, we can find

$$K = A p_1 p_2.$$

A second graphical approach is the following. Having found $B$ and then $C$ we can determine graphically

$$y_1(t) = A + B e^{-p_1 t}$$

for small values of $t$. Once we have this approximation we can also find graphically

$$y_2(t) \stackrel{\Delta}{=} y(t) - y_1(t) = C e^{-p_2 t},$$

as shown in Fig. 3.10. We then proceed as before by first making a plot of $y_2(t)$, and then finding $p_2$ from the slope of the plot at large $t$. Then it is just a matter of repeating the preceding analysis. This second method can be used as corroboration for the results obtained from the first method.

To see how these procedures play out in actual practice, we now apply them in Example 3.5.1. In the process, we introduce some laboratory equipment that we will use again later in the book.

**EXAMPLE 3.5.1**

Figure 3.12 shows a laboratory setup for recording the step response of a simple transfer function. The box in the figure provides a means of implementing simple compensators using opamps. We will discuss how transfer functions can be implemented with opamps in the next section, but our main goal in this example is to identify the transfer function from the recorded step response. The small circles on the opamps represent gold plated receptacles into which resistor and capacitor leads can be press fit to make a good electrical connection. The box also has a feedback path that leads to a summer. We will have occasion to use this feedback path later, but in this case we leave it open.

A reference input can be provided externally or internally. If the toggle switch at the lower left labeled "EXT/INT" is set to "EXT" the reference input is applied from an external source. If this same toggle switch is set to "INT," then the other toggle switch below it is used to initiate a step input. The black knob is used to adjust the amplitude of the step.

**Figure 3.12 |** Laboratory setup for measuring a step response.

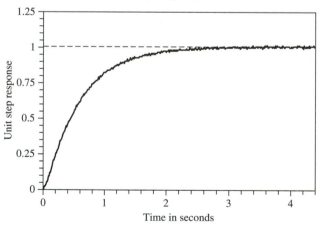

**Figure 3.13 |** Recorded step response.

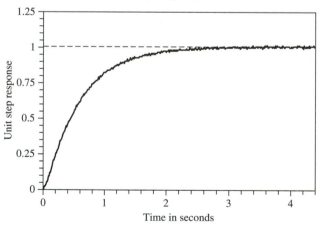

Using the opamp circuits on the box, we implement the transfer function:

$$G(s) = \frac{40}{(s+2)(s+20)}.$$

Our stated goal is to see if we can identify this transfer function from the recorded unit step response shown in Fig. 3.13.

**Figure 3.14** | $\ln z(t) = \ln[A - y(t)]$.

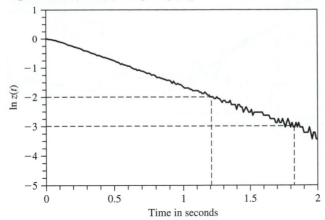

**Figure 3.15** | Plot of $B(t) = \frac{y(t)-A}{C-1.7t}$.

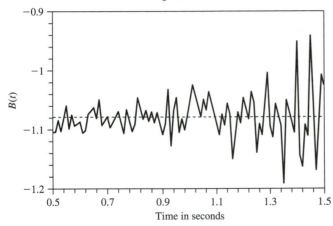

Figure 3.14 shows the function

$$\ln z(t) = \ln[A - y(t)].$$

From Fig. 3.14 we see that the slope for $0 < t < 2$ s is about $-1.7$. Thus, $p_1 = 1.7$. We also know from the time response that $A = 1.0$.

Our next goal is to find $B$. To that end we compute the function

$$B(t) = \frac{y(t) - A}{e^{-1.7t}},$$

for $0.5 < t < 1.5$, as shown in Fig. 3.15. A reasonable guess is that

$$B = -1.08.$$

**Figure 3.16** | Determining $p_2$.

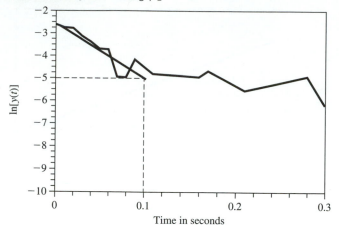

Having found $B$, we can now find

$$C = -(A + B) = -(1 - 1.08) = 0.08.$$

We next plot

$$\ln y_2(t) = \ln[y(t) - (A + Be^{-1.7t})] = \ln[Ce^{-p_2t}],$$

as shown in Fig. 3.16. From the figure, we see that the slope for small values of $t$ is roughly $-24$. This is admittedly a fairly crude estimate, but it does place the magnitude of $p_2$ at about 24.

We can now find

$$K = A \times p_1 \times p_2 = 40.8.$$

Thus, our estimate of the transfer function is

$$G(s) = \frac{41}{(s + 1.7)(s + 24)}.$$

Figure 3.17 compares the actual and estimated step responses. Given that we implemented the transfer function using resistors and capacitors whose values are only accurate within $\pm 5\%$ of the rated value, we see that we have a very accurate estimate of the actual transfer function.

**Figure 3.17 |** Comparison of measured and model responses.

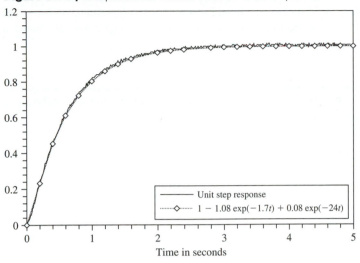

Time in seconds

# 3.6 | IMPLEMENTING TRANSFER FUNCTIONS

In Example 3.5.1, we implemented a transfer function using opamp circuits. We did so without any discussion of how such circuits are designed. That situation is now rectified, because the central theme of the book is to modify a system's behavior by adding both feedback and electronic circuits called "compensators." These compensators are themselves transfer functions of the same type used in Example 3.5.1. Thus, it is important to know how these compensators can be constructed.

The emphasis here will be on realizing a compensator with an electronic circuit. It is possible to realize a compensator using mechanical components or hydraulic components. Since there are mechanical and hydraulic equivalents for resistors and capacitors, the implementation of the compensator is formally the same. The analysis presented here concentrates on realizing transfer functions with electronic circuits, because, in most cases, this approach yields the smallest and cheapest means of producing compensation. Some alternative methods of implementing transfer functions are presented in what follows.

Finally, this is a rather lengthy section, and the reader may want to digest it in several smaller bites, and then refer back to this section later when specific compensator designs are encountered.

## 3.6.1 Passive Implementations

The network shown in Fig. 3.2 represents a simple first-order transfer function, implemented with passive components, namely, resistors and capacitors. The network shown in Fig. 3.2 is a "lead" compensator. In Chapter 7 we will see that a lead compensator can be used to improve the time response of a system in the period immediately after an input is applied. The advantage of discussing these transfer functions now is that when we encounter the mathematical representation of a lead we will have an idea of how it would actually be implemented. Higher-order transfer functions can also be implemented with passive components, as shown in Example 3.6.1.

---

**EXAMPLE 3.6.1**

Consider the passive circuit shown in Fig. 3.18. To obtain the transfer function relationship between $V_i$ and $V_o$ let

$$Z_1(s) = \frac{R_1}{R_1 C_1 s + 1} \quad \text{and} \quad Z_2(s) = R_2 + \frac{1}{C_2 s}.$$

**Figure 3.18 |** Passive lag/lead compensator.

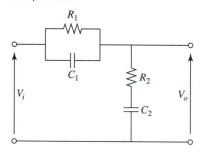

Then

$$\frac{V_o}{V_i} = \left[ \frac{Z_2(s)}{Z_1(s) + Z_2(s)} \right]$$

$$= \frac{(R_2 C_2 s + 1)/C_2 s}{[R_1/(R_1 C_1 s + 1)] + [(R_2 C_2 s + 1)/C_2 s]}$$

$$= \frac{(R_1 C_1 s + 1)(R_2 C_2 s + 1)}{(R_1 C_1 s + 1)(R_2 C_2 s + 1) + R_1 C_2 s}$$

$$= \frac{[s + 1/\tau_1][s + 1/\tau_2]}{s^2 + \beta_1 s + \beta_0},$$

where

$$\tau_1 = R_1 C_1, \quad \tau_2 = R_2 C_2, \quad \beta_1 = \frac{1}{\tau_1} + \frac{1}{\tau_2} + \frac{1}{R_2 C_1}, \quad \beta_0 = \frac{1}{\tau_1 \tau_2}.$$

Since most physical systems require relatively large amounts of power to operate properly, a transfer function implemented with passive elements is almost always used in conjunction with an amplifier, as shown in Fig. 3.19.

For the passive network to function properly the input impedance of the amplifier should be very large, since the transfer function was derived under the assumption that the output of the passive circuit is open, that is, connected in parallel with an

**Figure 3.19 |** Passive lag/lead network coupled to amplifier.

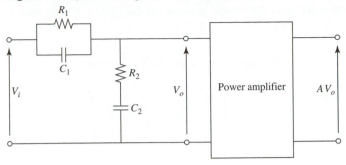

infinite impedance. In many cases, power amplifiers have a large but far from infinite look-in impedance.

One way to ensure that the output of a passive network sees a very large impedance is to connect it to an operational amplifier. A noninverting operational amplifier has a large look-in impedance and a very small output impedance. On the input side, the operational amplifier does not load down the output of the passive network, while on the output side its output impedance is much smaller than that of the power amplifier it is connected to, so that almost all the output voltage drop will be across the terminals of the power amplifier. Operational amplifiers are discussed in more detail, next.

### 3.6.2 Operational Amplifiers

A transfer function can also be implemented using an operational amplifier (opamp). An opamp is a direct coupled, high-gain amplifier. Most analysis involving opamps idealizes certain basic properties of the device.

Figure 3.20(a) shows the basic symbol used for the opamp, where $V_+$ and $V_-$ are the inputs and $V_o$ is the output. A basic property of the opamp is that the impedance looking into the input terminals is very high, so high that the input can be considered an open circuit. This leads to the circuit model of the opamp shown in Fig. 3.20(b).

The output voltage $V_o$ is $A(V_+ - V_-)$, where $A$ is a very large gain, on the order of $10^5$. It is perhaps worth mentioning that all three voltages are measured relative

**Figure 3.20 |** Symbols for opamp (a) and a controlled source model (b).

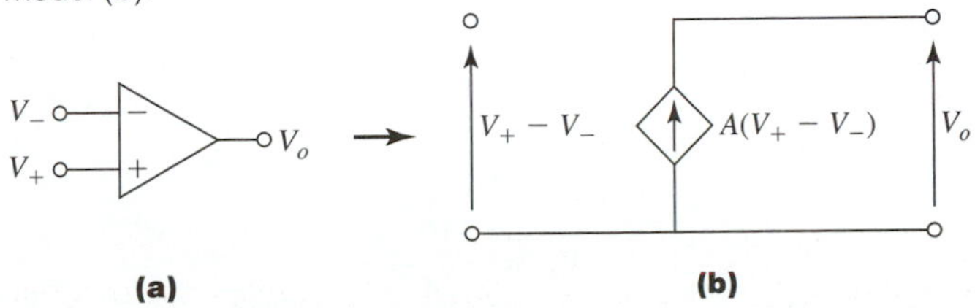

**(a)**

**(b)**

to some "ground" level, even though the input is the differential voltage $V_+ - V_-$. The ground is normally the neutral point of the dual power supply used to power the opamp, as shown in Fig. 3.21.

**Figure 3.21 |** Opamp with dual power supply.

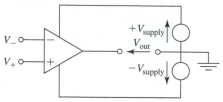

Operational amplifiers can be configured in a variety of ways. Figure 3.22 shows the inverting configuration with impedances $Z_1(s)$ and $Z_2(s)$ across the input and output, respectively. The parallel configuration is typical but series $RC$ configurations can also be used. Note that the positive input is connected to ground. Thus, relative to this same ground,

$$V_o = A(0 - V_x) = -AV_x.$$

**Figure 3.22 |** Basic inverting amplifier.

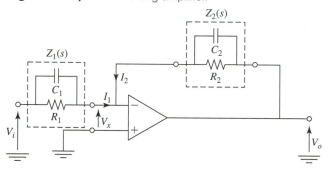

Due to the very high input impedance of the opamp, essentially no current flows into the negative input of the opamp, which means, in turn, that $I_1 = -I_2$. This implies that

$$\frac{V_i - V_x}{Z_1(s)} = -\frac{V_o - V_x}{Z_2(s)}.$$   [3.24]

Substituting

$$V_x = -\frac{V_o}{A},$$

in Eq. [3.24] yields

$$\frac{V_i - (-V_o/A)}{Z_1(s)} = -\frac{V_o - (-V_o/A)}{Z_2(s)},$$

which, after some rearrangement, yields

$$\frac{V_o}{V_i} = \frac{-Z_2(s)/Z_1(s)}{1 + [1/A] + [Z_2(s)/AZ_1(s)]}.$$

With a little work this expression can be rearranged as

$$\frac{V_o}{V_i} = \frac{-A\{Z_2(s)/[Z_1(s) + Z_2(s)]\}}{1 + A\{Z_1(s)/[Z_1(s) + Z_2(s)]\}}. \qquad \text{[3.25]}$$

Since the value of $A$ is $10^5$ or higher, as long as

$$\frac{AZ_1(s)}{Z_1(s) + Z_2(s)} \gg 1,$$

to a very good approximation

$$\frac{V_o}{V_1} = -\frac{Z_2(s)}{Z_1(s)}. \qquad \text{[3.26]}$$

Figure 3.23 shows a noninverting amplifier. For this configuration we can write

$$V_x = V_i - V_o \left[ \frac{Z_1(s)}{Z_1(s) + Z_2(s)} \right]. \qquad \text{[3.27]}$$

But

$$V_x = \frac{V_o}{A}. \qquad \text{[3.28]}$$

Then substituting Eq. [3.28] into Eq. [3.27] yields

$$\frac{V_o}{A} = V_i - V_o \left[ \frac{Z_1(s)}{Z_1(s) + Z_2(s)} \right]. \qquad \text{[3.29]}$$

**Figure 3.23 |** Noninverting operational amplifier.

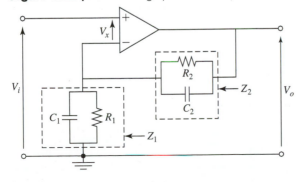

With a little work Eq. [3.29] can be written as

$$\frac{V_o}{V_i} = \frac{A}{1 + \{AZ_1(s)/[Z_1(s) + Z_2(s)]\}}.$$ [3.30]

Then for

$$\frac{AZ_1}{Z_1(s) + Z_2(s)} \gg 1,$$

we have

$$\frac{V_o}{V_i} = 1 + \frac{Z_2(s)}{Z_1(s)}.$$ [3.31]

### 3.6.3  Implementing Transfer Functions with Opamps

In this book, the implementation of a transfer function will most commonly be done using opamp circuits. The inverting opamp circuit is the easiest to use. In Examples 3.6.2 through 3.6.6 we investigate some of the compensators that we will first employ in Chapter 7.

---
**EXAMPLE 3.6.2**
---

What we will later call a "proportional plus integral (PI) compensator" is shown in Fig. 3.24(a). Then

$$G(s) = -\frac{1/(sC_2)}{[R_1/(sC_1)]/[R_1 + (1/sC_1)]} = -\frac{(C_1/C_2)[s + (1/R_1C_1)]}{s}.$$

Many analog designers do not like to have simply a capacitor between the output and the negative terminal of the opamp. They prefer to put a very large resistor in parallel with the capacitor. This moves the pole slightly away from $s = 0$. This is called a "lag" compensator. The implementation of the lag compensator and the related "lead" compensator is discussed in Example 3.6.3.

**Figure 3.24 |** (a) PI compensator and (b) lag or lead compensator.

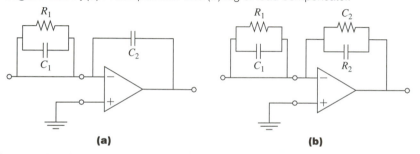

(a)                                    (b)

**EXAMPLE 3.6.3**

Consider the opamp circuit shown in Fig. 3.24(b.) Then

$$\frac{V_o(s)}{V_i(s)} = -\frac{[R_2/(C_2s)]/[R_2+(1/C_2s)]}{[R_1/(C_1s)]/[R_1+(1/C_1s)]}$$
$$= -\frac{(C_1/C_2)[s+(1/R_1C_1)]}{[s+(1/R_2C_2)]}.$$

If

$$\frac{1}{R_1C_1} < \frac{1}{R_2C_2},$$

so that the zero of the compensator at $s = -1/R_1C_1$ is closer to the origin of the $s$ plane than the pole at $s = -1/R_2C_2$, then the compensator is called a lead compensator. If

$$\frac{1}{R_1C_1} > \frac{1}{R_2C_2},$$

so that the pole is closer to the origin than the zero, then the compensator is called a lag compensator. The lag compensator is a poor man's integrator, because if $R_2C_2$ is large, the pole of the lag compensator is close to the origin.

It is possible, and often desirable, to combine several poles and zeros on a single opamp circuit. We show how that can be accomplished in Examples 3.6.4 through 3.6.6.

**EXAMPLE 3.6.4**

Consider the circuit shown in Fig. 3.25. This circuit is the implementation of a second-order low-pass filter. We now derive the transfer function as a means of increasing our skill at analyzing opamp circuits.

Noting that for an ideal opamp $V_2(s) = V_o(s)$, we write a current equation at node 1, to obtain

$$\frac{V_i(s) - V_1(s)}{R_1} = \frac{V_1(s) - V_o(s)}{R_2} + [V_1(s) - V_o(s)](C_1s), \qquad \textbf{[3.32]}$$

or

$$V_i(s)G_1 = [G_1 + G_2 + C_1s]V_1 - [G_2 + C_1s]V_o(s), \qquad \textbf{[3.33]}$$

**Figure 3.25 |** Second-order low-pass compensator using a single opamp.

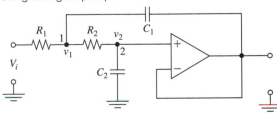

where, for convenience, we have expressed $R_1$ and $R_2$ as admittances. A similar equation at node 2 yields

$$\frac{V_1(s) - V_o(s)}{R_2} = V_o(s)(sC_2), \qquad \textbf{[3.34]}$$

where we have assumed no current flows into the positive terminal of the opamp. From Eq. [3.34] we see that

$$V_1(s) = \left[\frac{1 + sC_2}{G_2}\right] V_o. \qquad \textbf{[3.35]}$$

Substituting Eq. [3.35] into Eq. [3.33], then yields

$$V_i(s)G_1 = \left\{ [C_1 s + (G_1 + G_2)] \left[ \left(\frac{C_2}{G_2}\right) s + 1 \right] - [C_1 s + G_2] \right\} V_o(s)$$

$$= \left[ \left(\frac{C_1 C_2}{G_2}\right) s^2 + \left(\frac{C_2}{G_2}(G_1 + G_2)\right) s + G_1 \right] V_o(s).$$

Then

$$\frac{V_o(s)}{V_i(s)} = \frac{(G_1 G_2 / C_1 C_2)}{s^2 + [(1/C_1)(G_1 + G_2)]s + (G_1 G_2)/(C_1 C_2)},$$

or, equivalently

$$\frac{V_o(s)}{V_i(s)} = \frac{1/(R_1 C_1 R_2 C_2)}{s^2 + [(1/C_1)(1/R_1 + 1/R_2)]s + (1/R_1 C_1 R_2 C_2)}. \qquad \textbf{[3.36]}$$

Although it is not completely obvious from Eq. [3.36], we can determine both the coefficients in the denominator of the transfer function independently. Suppose we wish the denominator to be

$$(s + 1)(s + 10) = s^2 + 11s + 10.$$

Let $R_2 = aR_1$ and $C_2 = bC_1$. Then

$$\frac{V_o(s)}{V_i(s)} = \frac{1/(ab)\left(R_1^2 C_1^2\right)}{s^2 + [(1/R_1 C_1)(1 + 1/a)]s + \left[1/(ab) R_1^2 C_1^2\right]}.$$

Our basic strategy will be to pick $R_1$ and $C_1$ and then determine useful values of $a$ and $b$. To that end let $\alpha = 1/R_1 C_1$. Then we can write

$$\frac{V_o(s)}{V_i(s)} = \frac{\alpha^2/ab}{s^2 + [\alpha(1 + 1/a)]s + (\alpha^2/ab)}.$$

We thus have the two equations

$$\alpha\left(\frac{1 + 1}{a}\right) = 11$$

$$\frac{\alpha^2}{ab} = 10.$$

From the first of these equations we obtain

$$a = \frac{\alpha}{11 - \alpha}.$$

If we choose $\alpha = 1$, then $a = 0.1$, which is quite convenient because we can easily find resistor values that are in the ratio 1:10. Suppose we let

$$R_1 = 100 \text{ k}\Omega \quad \text{and} \quad C_1 = 10 \text{ } \mu\text{f}.$$

Then from the second equation

$$b = \frac{\alpha^2}{10a} = 1.$$

Thus,

$$R_2 = aR_1 = 10 \text{ k}\Omega \quad \text{and} \quad C_2 = bC_1 = 10 \text{ } \mu\text{f}.$$

These are all standard values of resistance and capacitance found in Table 15.1.

**Table 3.1** | Table of common capacitor and resistor values.

| $C$ $(\mu f)$ | 0.001 | 0.01 | 0.015 | 0.022 | 0.033 | 0.068 | 0.1 | 0.15 |
|---|---|---|---|---|---|---|---|---|
| $C$ $(\mu f)$ | 0.22 | 0.33 | 0.47 | 0.82 | 1.0 | 4.7 | 10 | 100 |
| $R$ $(k\Omega)$ | 10 | 11 | 12 | 13 | 15 | 16 | 18 | 20 |
| $R$ $(k\Omega)$ | 22 | 24 | 27 | 30 | 33 | 36 | 39 | 43 |
| $R$ $(k\Omega)$ | 47 | 51 | 56 | 62 | 68 | 75 | 82 | 91 |
| $R$ $(k\Omega)$ | 100 | 110 | 120 | 130 | 150 | 160 | 180 | 200 |
| $R$ $(k\Omega)$ | 240 | 270 | 300 | 360 | 390 | 430 | 470 | 510 |
| $R$ $(k\Omega)$ | 560 | 620 | 680 | 750 | 820 | 910 | 1.0 | 1.1 |
| $R$ $(M\Omega)$ | 1.3 | 1.5 | 1.8 | 2.0 | 2.2 | 2.7 | 3.0 | 3.3 |

There are many strategies for picking resistor and capacitor values. The strategy used here can be summarized as follows.

1. Couch the problem in terms of $\alpha = 1/R_1C_1$ and the multipliers $a$ and $b$.
2. Try to pick values of $a$ and $b$ that correspond to the available resistor and capacitor values.
3. Pick acceptable values $R_1$ and $C_1$ and check to see that the values for $R_2$ and $C_2$ are also acceptable and obtainable.

We may have to iterate on steps 2 and 3 a few times to get the best choice of values.

Examples 3.6.5 and 3.6.6 illustrate more complicated transfer functions that also prove very useful. They also provide an opportunity to hone our skills at analyzing opamp circuits.

**EXAMPLE 3.6.5**

Consider the bandpass filter shown in Fig. 3.26. Under ideal opamp assumptions, the voltage drop across the opamp is zero, so that node 2 is at ground. Thus, we only have to write the single current equation

$$V_i(s)G_1 - V_1G_1 = V_1(s)C_2s + (V_1 - V_o)C_1s = (C_1 + C_2)sV_1 - V_oC_1s. \qquad \text{[3.37]}$$

**Figure 3.26 |** Bandpass filter.

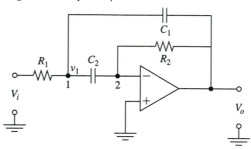

Our next task is to eliminate $V_1$ from Eq. [3.37], which we can do by noting that at node 2

$$sC_2V_1(s) = -G_2V_o(s), \qquad \text{[3.38]}$$

leading to

$$V_1(s) = -\frac{G_2V_o(s)}{sC_2}. \qquad \text{[3.39]}$$

Then, substituting Eq. [3.39] into Eq. [3.37] yields

$$V_i(s)G_1 = \left[ -\frac{G_1G_2}{C_2s} - \frac{(C_1 + C_2)G_2}{C_2} - C_1s \right] V_o(s).$$

This last equation can be rewritten as

$$\frac{V_o(s)}{V_i(s)} = \frac{-(G_1/C_1)s}{s^2 + G_2(1/C_1 + 1/C_2)s + G_1G_2/C_1C_2},$$

or alternatively

$$\frac{V_o(s)}{V_i(s)} = \frac{-(1/R_1C_1)s}{s^2 + (1/R_2C_1 + 1/R_2C_2)s + 1/R_1C_2R_2C_2}.$$

Suppose we wish to make the denominator

$$(s + 1)(s + 100) = s^2 + 101s + 100.$$

We use the same tactic as before, letting

$$R_2 = aR_1, \quad C_2 = bC_1, \quad \alpha = \frac{1}{R_1C_1}.$$

Then

$$\frac{V_o(s)}{V_i(s)} = \frac{-\alpha s}{s^2 + \alpha(1/a + 1/ab)s + \alpha^2/ab}.$$

Then we have the two equations

$$\alpha\left(\frac{b+1}{ab}\right) = 101,$$

$$\frac{\alpha^2}{ab} = 100.$$

Dividing the first equation by the second yields

$$b = 1.01\alpha - 1$$

If we let $\alpha = 1$,

$$b = 0.01,$$

and

$$a = \frac{\alpha^2}{0.01 \times 100} = 1.$$

We then choose

$$R_1 = R_2 = 100 \text{ k}\Omega, \quad C_1 = 10 \ \mu f, \quad C_2 = 0.1 \ \mu f.$$

Again, by carefully choosing $a$ and $b$, we can usually find readily available values for the resistors and capacitors.

To achieve full control of all the poles and zeros of a transfer function re-quires a more complex configuration such as that in Fig. 3.27, called a Tow-Thomas biquadratic filter (Jaeger, 1997).

**EXAMPLE 3.6.6**

Consider the Tow-Thomas biquadratic filter of Fig. 3.27. To obtain the transfer function we first note that under ideal opamp assumptions node 1 is at ground. Then at node 1,

**Figure 3.27 |** Tow-Thomas biquadratic circuit.

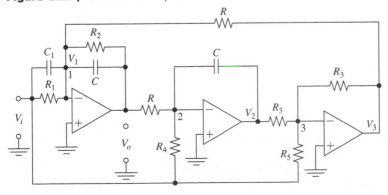

we can write the current equation

$$V_i(s)G_1 + V_i(s)C_1s + V_o(s)Cs + V_o(s)G_2 + V_3(s)G = 0. \qquad \text{[3.40]}$$

Our goal is to eliminate $V_3$ by expressing it in terms of $V_o$. As a first step, we write at node 3 the current equation

$$V_i(s)G_5 + V_2(s)G_3 + V_3(s)G_3 = 0,$$

which can be rearranged as

$$V_3(s) = -\left[ V_i(s)\frac{G_5}{G_3} + V_2(s) \right]. \qquad \text{[3.41]}$$

We now have expressed $V_3$ in terms of $V_i$ and $V_2$, so our next goal is to express $V_2$ in terms of $V_i$ and $V_o$. To that end we write, at node 2, the current equation

$$V_o(s)G + V_i(s)G_4 + V_2(s)Cs = 0,$$

which, in turn, can be rearranged as

$$V_2(s) = -\left[ V_o(s)\left(\frac{G}{Cs}\right) + V_i(s)\left(\frac{G_4}{Cs}\right) \right]. \qquad \text{[3.42]}$$

Then, by combining Eq. [3.41] and Eq. [3.42], we obtain

$$V_3(s) = -V_i(s)\left(\frac{G_5}{G_3}\right) + \left[ V_o(s)\left(\frac{G}{Cs}\right) + V_i(s)\left(\frac{G_4}{Cs}\right) \right]. \qquad \text{[3.43]}$$

Finally, substituting Eq. [3.43] into Eq. [3.40] we obtain, after some rearrangement,

$$\left[ G_1 + C_1s - \frac{GG_5}{G_3} + \frac{GG_4}{Cs} \right]V_i(s) = -\left[ Cs + G_2 + \frac{G^2}{Cs} \right]V_o(s),$$

which, after some further manipulation becomes

$$\frac{V_o(s)}{V_i(s)} = \frac{-(C_1/C)[s^2 + [(1/C_1)(1/R_1 - R_3/RR_5)]s + 1/RR_4C_1C}{s^2 + (1/R_2C)s + 1/R^2C^2}. \qquad \text{[3.44]}$$

The Tow-Thomas biquad enables us to place both poles and zeros arbitrarily. For instance, suppose we wish to implement the transfer function

$$G(s) = \frac{K(s+1-j10)(s+1+j10)}{(s+10)(s+0.01)} = \frac{K(s^2+2s+101)}{(s^2+10.01s+0.1)}.$$

We begin by letting

$$R = 300 \text{ k}\Omega, \quad C = 10 \text{ } \mu\text{f}, \quad R_2 = 10 \text{ k}\Omega.$$

Then

$$\frac{1}{R^2C^2} = \frac{1}{9} = 0.11 \quad \text{and} \quad \frac{1}{R_2C} = \frac{1}{0.1} = 10.$$

This yields a denominator polynomial of

$$s^2 + 10s + 0.11,$$

which is close enough. We next set

$$R_4 = 10 \text{ k}\Omega \quad \text{and} \quad C_1 = 0.33 \text{ }\mu\text{f.}$$

Then

$$\frac{1}{RR_4CC_1} = \frac{1}{3 \times 0.0033} = 101.$$

Finally, we choose

$$R_1 = 1.0 \text{ M}\Omega, \quad R_3 = 10 \text{ k}\Omega, \quad R_5 = 100 \text{ k}\Omega,$$

so that

$$\frac{1}{C_1}\left[\frac{1}{R_1} - \frac{R_3}{RR_5}\right] = 2.$$

Then the numerator polynomial is

$$s^2 + 2s + 101.$$

We note that the gain is

$$\frac{C_1}{C} = 0.033.$$

The gain is not of great concern because we can adjust that with a noninverting opamp, or the power amplifier that is always present.

It is possible to implement a higher-order transfer function by cascading operational amplifiers. Note that the box used in the laboratory setup of Example 3.5.1 uses this strategy by cascading two inverting opamp circuits. However, this type of circuit has its own limitation and hazard. The limitation is that only real poles and zeros can be implemented. We need a biquad to get complex poles and zeros. The hazard is that the voltage offsets in the individual opamps may cause the circuit to perform differently than expected. This is less of a problem now then in the past because opamps can be purchased at moderate cost that have very small offset voltages.

Finally, as mentioned previously, the operational amplifier can also be used in combination with a passive circuit to isolate the passive circuit from a power amplifier. Figure 3.28 shows how this could be done with a noninverting opamp. The high input impedance of the noninverting opamp isolates the network from the power amplifier.

**Figure 3.28 |** Passive network coupled through an opamp to a power amplifier.

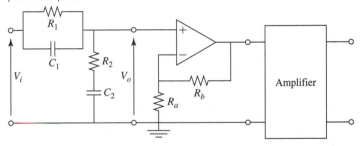

## 3.7 | REPRISE

In this chapter the concept of a transfer function has been introduced. The transfer function is nothing more than the $s$ plane representation of an ordinary differential equation with constant, real coefficients. The benefits of this representation are not yet obvious, but will become clear in subsequent chapters where the transfer function representation leads to graphical techniques for designing compensation for systems with feedback.

The transfer functions of the true dc motor and the brushless dc motor were determined from first principles. We next introduced an experimental method of finding the parameters of a transfer function.

We also investigated how to implement transfer functions using operational amplifiers and passive networks. Using opamps we were able to construct circuits that implement both real and complex poles and zeros. The transfer functions used as examples are actually "compensators" that we will subsequently use to improve the performance of real systems.

Thus, in this chapter we have developed a set of tools that will stand us in good stead in subsequent chapters, where we investigate the use of feedback and compensators to improve the performance of a system. Our first stop on this journey is the introduction of feedback, discussed in Chapter 4.

## 3.8 | PROBLEMS

### 3.8.1   Transfer Functions

These problems are drill problems for determining transfer functions from differential equations. For each equation, find the transfer function between $Y(s)$ and $U(s)$

1. $y^{[3]}(t) + 4y^{[2]}(t) + 3y^{[1]}(t) = u(t)$

2. $y^{[3]}(t) + 4y^{[2]}(t) + 3y^{[1]}(t) = u(t) + 5u^{[1]}(t)$

3. $y^{[3]}(t) + 5y^{[2]}(t) + 12y^{[1]}(t) + 8y(t) = u(t)$

4. $y^{[3]}(t) + 5y^{[2]}(t) + 12y^{[1]}(t) + 8y(t) = u(t) + 2u^{[1]}(t) + u^{[2]}(t)$

5. $y^{[3]}(t) + 5y^{[2]}(t) + 8y^{[1]}(t) + 6y(t) = u(t)$

6. $y^{[3]}(t) + 5y^{[2]}(t) + 8y^{[1]}(t) + 6y(t) = u(t) + u^{[1]}(t)$

7. $y^{[2]}(t) + 11y^{[1]}(t) + 10y(t) = u(t)$

8. $y^{[2]}(t) + 11y^{[1]}(t) + 10y(t) = u(t) + 2u^{[1]}(t)$

9. $y^{[3]}(t) + 10y^{[2]}(t) + 32y^{[1]}(t) + 32y(t) = u(t)$

10. $y^{[3]}(t) + 10y^{[2]}(t) + 32y^{[1]}(t) + 32y(t) = u(t) + 6u^{[1]}(t)$

11. $y^{[3]}(t) + 12y^{[2]}(t) + 36y^{[1]}(t) = u(t)$

12. $y^{[3]}(t) + 12y^{[2]}(t) + 36y^{[1]}(t) = u(t) + 2u^{[1]}(t)$

13. $y^{[4]}(t) + 15y^{[3]}(t) + 74y^{[2]}(t) + 135y^{[1]}(t) + 72y(t) = u(t) + u^{[1]}(t)$

**14.** $y^{[4]}(t) + 12y^{[3]}(t) + 52y^{[2]}(t) + 96y^{[1]}(t) + 64y(t) = u(t) + 2u^{[1]}(t) + u^{[2]}(t)$

**15.** $y^{[3]}(t) + 7y^{[2]}(t) + 31y^{[1]}(t) + 25y(t) = u(t)$

## 3.8.2  Transfer Functions of Passive Networks

For each network shown in Fig. 3.29 find $V_o(s)/V_i(s)$.

**Figure 3.29 |** Passive networks.

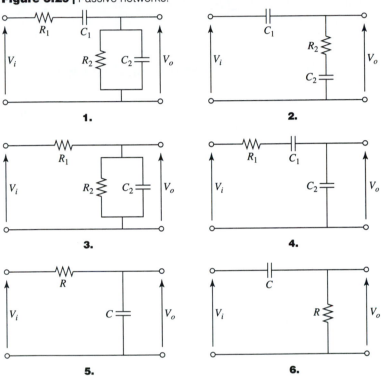

## 3.8.3  Transfer Functions—Inverting Opamp

For the inverting opamp configuration of Fig. 3.30, determine the resistor and capacitor values that will yield the listed transfer functions. The resistor and capacitor values should be chosen from Table. 15.1.

**1.** $G(s) = -\dfrac{s}{(s+10)(s+20)}$

**2.** $G(s) = -\dfrac{5s}{(s+5)(s+15)}$

**3.** $G(s) = -\dfrac{10s}{(s+1)(s+20)}$

**4.** $G(s) = -\dfrac{333s}{(s+40)(s+50)}$

**5.** $G(s) = -\dfrac{10s}{(s+1)^2}$

**6.** $G(s) = -\dfrac{10s(s+5)}{(s+1)(s+50)}$

**Figure 3.30 |** Inverting amplifier.

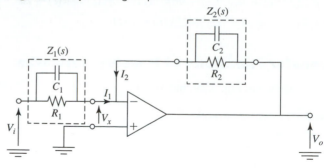

### 3.8.4   Transfer Functions—Noninverting Opamp

For the noninverting opamp configuration of Fig. 3.31, determine the resistor and capacitor values that will yield the listed transfer functions. The resistor and capacitor values should be chosen from Table. 15.1.

1.  $G(s) = \dfrac{s}{(s + 10)(s + 20)}$

2.  $G(s) = \dfrac{5s}{(s + 5)(s + 15)}$

3.  $G(s) = \dfrac{10s}{(s + 1)(s + 20)}$

4.  $G(s) = \dfrac{333s}{(s + 40)(s + 50)}$

5.  $G(s) = \dfrac{10s}{(s + 1)^2}$

6.  $G(s) = \dfrac{10s(s + 5)}{(s + 1)(s + 50)}$

**Figure 3.31 |** Noninverting amplifier.

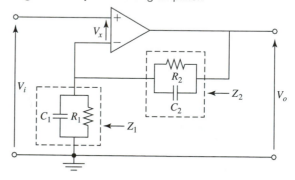

### 3.8.5   Implementing Transfer Functions Using Biquads

Use the resistor and capacitor values in Table 15.1 and biquadratic circuits of Figs. 3.26 and 3.27 to implement the listed transfer functions.

1.  Figure 3.26, $G(s) = \dfrac{10s}{(s + 10)(s + 100)}$

2. Figure 3.26, $G(s) = \dfrac{s}{(s + 1 - j2)(s + 1 + j2)}$

3. Figure 3.26, $G(s) = \dfrac{10s}{(s + 1)(s + 100)}$

4. Figure 3.27, $G(s) = \dfrac{K(s + 1)(s + 5)}{(s + 0.1)(s + 50)}$

5. Figure 3.27, $G(s) = \dfrac{K(s + 0.1)(s + 5)}{(s + 0.01)(s + 50)}$

6. Figure 3.27, $G(s) = \dfrac{K(s + 1 + j5)(s + 1 - j5)}{(s + 0.1)(s + 10)}$

## 3.8.6 Transfer Function Identification

The CD-ROM that comes with this book contains step response data for unidentified plants. For each listed file, identify the transfer function of the form

$$G_p(s) = \frac{K}{(s + a)(s + b)}.$$

| | | | | | | | |
|---|---|---|---|---|---|---|---|
| 1. | TFID1 | 2. | TFID2 | 3. | TFID3 | 4. | TFID4 |
| 5. | TFID5 | 6. | TFID6 | 7. | TFID7 | 8. | TFID8 |
| 9. | TFID9 | 10. | TFID10 | 11. | TFID11 | 12. | TFID12 |

## 3.8.7 Block Diagram Manipulation

For each problem shown in Fig. 3.32, determine the missing input or transfer function that will make the block diagram in part (b) equivalent to the block diagram in part (a).

## 3.8.8 More Challenging Problems

1. For the lag/lead transfer function of Example 3.6.1, show that the denominator factors into two real poles in the left half plane.

2. For the network of Fig. 3.33(a), find

$$T(s) = \frac{V_o(s)}{V_i(s)}.$$

Then show that the resulting poles and zeros are complex. (*Hint:* Use the star/mesh transformation.)

3. For the network of Fig. 3.33(b), find the equivalent transfer function

$$T(s) = \frac{V_o(s)}{V_i(s)}$$

in terms of $R_1$, $R_2$, $C_1$, and $C_2$. (*Hint:* Use the star/mesh transformation.)

**Figure 3.32 |** Block diagram manipulation.

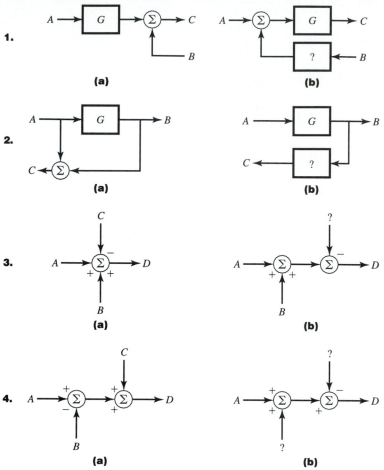

**Figure 3.33 |** Pi networks.

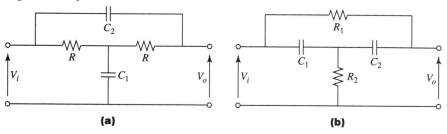

4.  Suppose in the derivation of the transfer function of the dc motor we ignore
    mechanical friction effects, and also let

$$i_q(t) = \frac{e_q(t) - e_b(t)}{R_q},$$

thereby also ignoring the dynamics of the armature winding. Find the transfer function between armature voltage and shaft position under these assumptions. Draw a block diagram of the motor and compare it to the block diagram of the brushless dc motor.

**5.** For each of the specified transfer functions make a drawing like Fig. 3.10. Note that you can probably do this with Matlab with some effort.

a. $\dfrac{16}{(s+2)(s+4)}$     b. $\dfrac{24}{(s+2)(s+6)}$     c. $\dfrac{32}{(s+2)(s+8)}$

# FURTHER READINGS

Eykhoff, P. 1974. *System Identification*. London: John Wiley.

Fitzgerald, A. E., C. Kingsley, Jr., and S. D. Umans. 1983. *Electric Machinery*. New York: McGraw-Hill.

Graupe, D. 1972. *Identification of Systems*. New York: Van Nostrand-Reinholt.

Jaeger, R. C. 1997. *Microelectronic Circuit Design*. New York: Irwin McGraw-Hill.

Melsa, J. L., and D. G. Schultz. 1969. *Linear Control Systems*. New York: McGraw-Hill.

Sedra, Adel S., and K. C. Smith. 1991. *Microelectronic Circuits,* 3rd ed. New York: Oxford University Press.

# 4 Chapter

# Introducing Feedback

## 4.1 | OVERVIEW

Chapter 1 introduced the concept of feedback in a general and qualitative way by examining some very diverse systems that all use feedback. In this chapter, we begin our investigation of feedback in earnest, developing expressions for the transfer functions that result when feedback is added and quantifying some of the effects of feedback on the performance of a physical system.

Since the entire book is essentially about feedback, our discussion of this topic is ongoing. Our purpose in this chapter is to lay the groundwork for the following chapters on root locus analysis and root locus design.

The principle use of feedback is to make a system, often called the "plant," behave "better." Better means that the system responds more rapidly and with greater accuracy to a reference input signal. This improved performance does not come without a price.

Most open-loop systems are stable for bounded reference inputs. What the open-loop system lacks normally is sufficient speed and accuracy in following the reference input applied to the system. While feedback can reshape the behavior of a system, it also has the potential to make that behavior unstable. This is an important problem, and in this chapter we will begin to quantify the effect of feedback on both the shape and stability of the system response.

Feedback also has other potential benefits. For one thing, it can improve the ability of a system to reject disturbances that may be present along with the reference input. Feedback can also change the bandwidth and overall gain of a system. These properties will be discussed in Chapter 9 when we have developed the requisite analysis tools.

The feedback strategy introduced in this chapter and used throughout the rest of the book is output feedback. That is, the output of the system is measured and fed back, possibly through a transfer function, and then subtracted from the reference input signal. The resulting error signal is then fed forward, usually through a compensator, to provide a control signal to the physical system, or plant, to be controlled.

Ideally, the error between the reference input and the system output should tend to zero with time, so that the output of the system tracks the reference input. In the best of worlds, the error tends to zero rapidly with no large excursions in the system's response.

To help quantify the relationship between feedback and stability, we introduce the Routh criterion. The Routh criterion is an algebraic procedure that identifies unstable poles. It is of most use when combined with other methods of determining stability introduced in Chapters 5, 9, 10, and 12.

We end the chapter with some examples that show how feedback can improve the steady state and transient tracking properties of a system. We will see that the behavior of the system can vary widely depending on the location of the poles of the closed-loop transfer function. This discussion paves the way for the introduction of root locus analysis in Chapter 5.

## 4.2 | BASIC FORMULATION

The general form of the output feedback problem is shown in Fig. 4.1. The effective transfer function between the input $R$ and the output $C$ can be derived by noting that

$$C(s) = E(s)G(s) = [R(s) - H(s)C(s)]G(s)$$
$$= R(s)G(s) - G(s)H(s)C(s).$$

Collecting terms in $C(s)$ on the left-hand side of the equation yields

$$[1 + G(s)H(s)]C(s) = R(s)G(s).$$

Dividing both sides by $[1 + G(s)H(s)]$ and $R(s)$ then gives

$$\frac{C(s)}{R(s)} \triangleq T_c(s) = \frac{G(s)}{1 + G(s)H(s)}. \qquad \text{[4.1]}$$

**Figure 4.1 |** Negative feedback configuration.

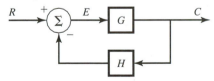

The right-hand side of Eq. [4.1] is the general expression for the closed-loop transfer function between $R$ and $C$. This is the general form in which the control problem is normally formulated. For design purposes, the transfer function $G$ in the forward loop is separated into a compensator $G_c$ and a plant $G_p$, as shown in Fig. 4.2.

**Figure 4.2 |** Negative feedback with $G$ separated into compensator and plant.

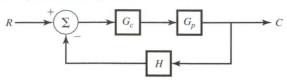

The transfer function $H$ in the feedback loop can represent many things, including a compensator to make the system perform better or the dynamics of a transducer that converts the output signal of the system to the same signal type as the reference input.

In most cases of interest $H = 1$, resulting in the block diagram of Fig. 4.3. Even for $H \neq 1$ it is possible to rework the block diagram so that the system does have unity feedback. Most of the design examples presented in Chapters 7, 11, 12, 15, and 20 assume unity feedback.

**Figure 4.3 |** Unity feedback configuration.

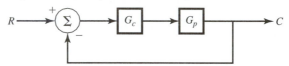

Each transfer function in Fig. 4.1 is of the general form

$$\frac{K \prod_{i=1}^{m}(s + z_i)}{\prod_{i=1}^{n}(s + p_i)},$$ [4.2]

where

$$\prod_{i=1}^{k}(s + \alpha_i) \overset{\Delta}{=} (s + \alpha_1)(s + \alpha_2) \cdots (s + \alpha_k).$$ [4.3]

That is, the numerator and denominator are polynomials in the Laplace variable $s$. These polynomials are fixed and usually given in the factored form shown. Note the gain factor $K$ present in the numerator. This gain has great importance because by varying $K$ the roots of the characteristic polynomial of the closed-loop transfer function can be changed. As previously discussed, these roots are very important because they determine the time functions that characterize the response of the closed-loop system.

Suppose for the configuration of Fig. 4.1 that $G$ and $H$ are given in factored form as ratios of polynomials in $s$. That is,

$$G(s) = \frac{g_n(s)}{g_d(s)} \quad \text{and} \quad H(s) = \frac{h_n(s)}{h_d(s)}.$$

Then the closed-loop transfer function is

$$T_c(s) = \frac{G(s)}{1 + G(s)H(s)}$$

$$= \frac{g_n(s)/g_d(s)}{1 + [g_n(s)h_n(s)]/[g_d(s)h_d(s)]}$$

$$= \frac{g_n(s)h_d(s)}{g_d(s)h_d(s) + g_n(s)h_n(s)}.$$

This final, "cleared fraction" form of $T_c$ reveals some interesting characteristics of the closed-loop transfer function. First, the numerator of $T_c$ is in factored form, and consists of the zeros of $G$ and the poles of $H$. Second, the denominator of $T_c$ is not in factored form because it consists of the sum of two factored polynomials.

Further, since $g_n$ and $h_n$ are of the form given by Eq. [4.2], either or both could potentially have multiplicative gain factors. Changing either of these gains changes the roots of the denominator polynomial.

Finally, the degree of the denominator polynomial is the same as the degree of $g_d(s)h_d(s)$. This follows easily from the fact that the degree of the numerators of both $G$ and $H$ are equal to or less than the degrees of their respective denominators. Thus the degree of $g_d h_d$ will always be equal to or greater than the degree of $g_n h_n$. As a consequence, the denominator of $T_c$ will be of the same degree as $g_d h_d$. This last point is worth remembering as the discussion proceeds.

Factoring the denominator polynomial is one of the major problems in control design because the roots of the denominator of $T_c$ determine the time functions that will show up in the time response of the closed-loop system to a reference input. This denominator polynomial is so important that it is given the name "characteristic" polynomial, because it characterizes the response of the closed-loop system.

The cleared fraction form of the closed-loop transfer function $T_c$ reveals one expression for the characteristic equation. However, the characteristic equation can also be written as

$$1 + G(s)H(s) = 0. \qquad [4.4]$$

Now

$$GH(s) = \frac{g_n(s)h_n(s)}{g_d(s)h_d(s)} = \frac{K \prod_{i=1}^{m}(s + z_i)}{\prod_{i=1}^{n}(s + p_i)}.$$

We will use this form in Chapter 5 on root locus analysis. Note from Eq. [4.4] that the characteristic polynomial is simply the loop transfer function plus one. In this form, the gain $K$ acts as a scaling factor for the term

$$\frac{\prod_{i=1}^{m}(s + z_i)}{\prod_{i=1}^{n}(s + p_i)},$$

which is just a complex number when evaluated for some particular value of $s$.

The gain $K$ will turn out to be one of the primary design variables at our disposal. Thus, it is imperative to find an efficient means of factoring the denominator of $T_c$ for a range of values of $K$. In one way or another, factoring the denominator of $T_c$ is what the rest of this book is about, and we begin that discussion in earnest in Chapter 5. For the moment, we content ourselves with an example.

**EXAMPLE 4.2.1**

Let

$$G(s) = \frac{K}{s(s+1)}, \qquad H(s) = \frac{1}{s+10}.$$

Then

$$T_c(s) = \frac{K(s+10)}{s(s+1)(s+10) + K} = \frac{K(s+10)}{s^3 + 11s^2 + 10s + K}.$$

The transfer function relationship between $C$ and $R$ is shown in Fig. 4.4.

**Figure 4.4** | Closed-loop system in cleared fraction form.

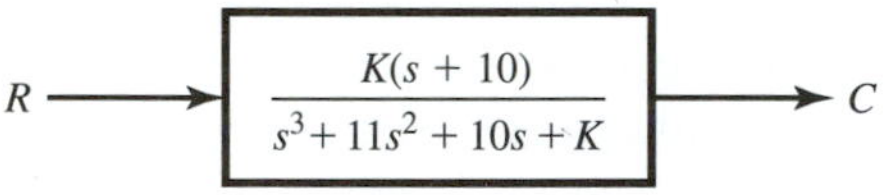

$$R \longrightarrow \boxed{\dfrac{K(s+10)}{s^3 + 11s^2 + 10s + K}} \longrightarrow C$$

It should be clear from Fig. 4.4 that changing $K$ changes the factorization of the denominator of $T_c$. Given the power of modern computer programs like MATLAB, it is an easy matter to factor the denominator of $T_c$. Once factored it is an equally routine matter to find the partial fraction expansion of $R(s)T_c(s)$ and determine the actual time response.

The specific values of the constants, or residues, in the partial fraction expansion will be of some importance in the final stages of the design process. However, earlier in the design process just the *form* of the output will be of most concern. For instance, for a bounded input, if any of the roots of the denominator are on the imaginary axis in the $s$ plane, the output will exhibit a sustained oscillation. If any of the roots of the denominator are in the right half plane, then the output will grow without bound in response to a bounded input. Thus, early in the design process it is crucial to know the factorization of the denominator of $T_c$.

To illustrate the importance of factoring the denominator of $T_c$ three specific values of $K$ are chosen.

First, let $K = 2$. Then

$$T_c(s) = \frac{2(s+10)}{(s+0.290)(s+0.688)(s+10.02)}.$$

If the input is a unit step, then

$$C(s) = \frac{2(s+10)}{s(s+0.290)(s+0.688)(s+10.02)}$$

$$= \frac{C_1}{s} + \frac{C_2}{s+0.290} + \frac{C_3}{s+0.688} + \frac{C_4}{s+10.02},$$

and the time response is

$$c(t) = [C_1 + C_2 e^{-0.290t} + C_3 e^{-0.688t} + C_4 e^{-10.02t}]\mathbf{1}(t).$$

Without finding the four residues $C_1 \ldots C_4$, the shape of the output $c(t)$ is still well characterized. It consists of a constant $C_1$ and three exponential time functions that decay to zero as $t \to \infty$. Thus, the majority of the information about the output can be determined by inspecting the *factored* denominator of $T_c$.

If the value of $K$ is now increased to 110,

$$T_c(s) = \frac{110(s + 10)}{(s - j\sqrt{10})(s + j\sqrt{10})(s + 11)}.$$

For a unit step input

$$C(s) = \frac{110(s + 10)}{s(s - j\sqrt{10})(s + j\sqrt{10})(s+11)}$$

$$= \frac{\hat{C}_1}{s} + \frac{\hat{C}_2}{s+11} + \frac{M}{s - j\sqrt{10}} + \frac{M^*}{s+j\sqrt{10}}.$$

Applying the inverse Laplace transform yields

$$c(t) = [\hat{C}_1 + \hat{C}_2 e^{-11t} + 2|M|\cos(\sqrt{10}t + \phi)]\mathbf{1}(t).$$

The residue $M$ is usually a complex number and $\phi = \underline{/M}$. Thus for $K = 110$, the output has a sustained oscillation.

Finally, for $K = 264$,

$$T_c(s) = \frac{264(s+10)}{(s-0.5 - j4.66)(s-0.05 + j4.66)(s+12)},$$

and the response to a step input is

$$c(t) = [\tilde{C}_1 + \tilde{C}_2 e^{-12t} + 2|\tilde{M}|e^{0.5t}\cos(4.66t + \theta)]\mathbf{1}(t).$$

In this case, the output expands sinusoidally without bound, certainly not a desirable response in most control applications.

The three values of gain chosen result in three very different behaviors. Also we see that increasing the gain above 110 results in an unstable response. These observations are generally true for all control systems. The gain $K$ is a potent design variable. When combined with feedback, it can markedly alter the performance of a system. But $K$ can also cause a system with feedback to become unstable. Clearly, the feedback sword has two edges. It is up to the designer to use it wisely.

As a final step in this example, the poles for all gains between zero and 264, in increments of 0.5 are computed and plotted using MATLAB. The result is shown in Fig. 4.5. We can see from Fig. 4.5 that the solutions form a locus of points. The roots of $GH$, namely, $s = 0$, $s = -1$, and $s = -10$, are marked with x's. The arrows indicate the direction of increasing gain.

An important point to be made here is that each value of $K$ results in *three* roots. For small values of $K$, such as $K = 2$, all three roots are real. For larger values of $K$,

**Figure 4.5 |** Poles of closed-loop system $0 < K < 264$.

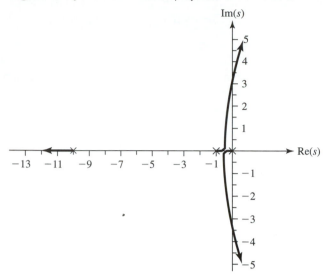

one of the roots is real and the other two are complex and conjugates of each other. The locus as a whole yields a complete picture of how the system will behave for a range of gains. This so-called root locus will be the topic of Chapter 5.

Example 4.2.1 illustrates most of the key issues associated with feedback control. One of these issues is determining the range of values of gain for which the system remains stable. As suggested at the end of the example, a complete picture of how the roots of $T_c$ vary with gain will be developed in Chapter 5. A less complete picture is available from the so called Routh criterion discussed in Section 4.3.

## 4.3 | ROUTH CRITERION

One method of determining the *general* location of roots of a polynomial is the Routh criterion. This method has application to the feedback control problem because it can yield the range of gain for which the closed-loop system is stable.

The Routh criterion is presented here without proof. The reason for this is that the Routh criterion is only of marginal use in designing a feedback control system. It is better than nothing, but it falls far short of the root locus method developed in Chapter 5. The discussion that follows simply shows how to use the Routh criterion. In this discussion, "Det" stands for determinant.

Let

$$p(s) = a_n s^n + a_{n-1} s^{n-1} + a_{n-2} s^{n-2} + \cdots + a_1 s + a_0 = 0.$$

To apply the Routh test, we first form the table:

| $s^n$ | $a_n$ | $a_{n-2}$ | $a_{n-4}$ | $\cdots$ | $a_k$ | 0 |
|---|---|---|---|---|---|---|
| $s^{n-1}$ | $a_{n-1}$ | $a_{n-3}$ | $a_{n-5}$ | $\cdots$ | $a_\ell$ | 0 |
| $s^{n-2}$ | $b_1$ | $b_2$ | $\cdots$ | | $b_i$ | 0 | 0 |
| $s^{n-3}$ | $c_1$ | $c_2$ | $\cdots$ | | $c_j$ | 0 | 0 |
| $s^{n-4}$ | $d_1$ | $d_2$ | $\cdots$ | | $d_k$ | 0 | 0 |
| $\vdots$ | | | | | | |
| $s^1$ | $e_1$ | $e_2$ | $\cdots$ | 0 | 0 | 0 |
| $s^0$ | $f_1$ | 0 | 0 | 0 | 0 | 0 |

The $b_i$'s, $c_i$'s, $d_i$'s, ... are generated by these rules:

$$b_1 = \frac{-\text{Det}\begin{bmatrix} a_n & a_{n-2} \\ a_{n-1} & a_{n-3} \end{bmatrix}}{a_{n-1}} = \frac{-(a_n a_{n-3} - a_{n-1} a_{n-2})}{a_{n-1}}$$

$$b_2 = \frac{-\text{Det}\begin{bmatrix} a_n & a_{n-4} \\ a_{n-1} & a_{n-5} \end{bmatrix}}{a_{n-1}} = \frac{-(a_n a_{n-5} - a_{n-1} a_{n-4})}{a_{n-1}}$$

$$\vdots$$

$$c_1 = \frac{-\text{Det}\begin{bmatrix} a_{n-1} & a_{n-3} \\ b_1 & b_2 \end{bmatrix}}{b_1} = \frac{-(a_{n-1} b_2 - a_{n-3} b_1)}{b_1}$$

$$c_2 = \frac{-\text{Det}\begin{bmatrix} a_{n-1} & a_{n-5} \\ b_1 & b_3 \end{bmatrix}}{b_1} = \frac{-(a_{n-1} b_3 - a_{n-5} b_1)}{b_1}$$

$$\vdots$$

$$d_1 = \frac{-\text{Det}\begin{bmatrix} b_1 & b_2 \\ c_1 & c_2 \end{bmatrix}}{c_1} = \frac{-(b_1 c_2 - c_1 b_2)}{c_1}$$

$$d_2 = \frac{-\text{Det}\begin{bmatrix} b_1 & b_3 \\ c_1 & c_3 \end{bmatrix}}{c_1} = \frac{-(b_1 c_3 - c_1 b_3)}{c_1}.$$

$$\vdots$$

The important information is in the first column of the table. Each sign change in the first column indicates a root of the polynomial in the right half plane. Two additional rules can be applied to $p(s)$ before the table is formed:

1. If any coefficient is negative, then there are roots with positive real parts.
2. If any coefficient except $a_0$ is missing from the polynomial, then there are roots with positive real parts or else roots on the imaginary axis.

The use of the Routh criterion is best illustrated with examples. The first example uses the denominator of the closed-loop transfer function from Example 4.2.1. As shown in Example 4.3.1, the Routh criterion can determine exactly the range of gains for which closed-loop poles will be in the right half of the $s$ plane.

**EXAMPLE 4.3.1**

Consider

$$p(s) = s^3 + 11s^2 + 10s + K.$$

The Routh table is

| | | | |
|---|---|---|---|
| $s^3$ | 1 | 10 | 0 |
| $s^2$ | 11 | $K$ | 0 |
| $s^1$ | $b_1$ | 0 | 0 |
| $s^0$ | $c_1$ | 0 | 0 |

Then

$$b_1 = \frac{-\text{Det}\begin{bmatrix} 1 & 10 \\ 11 & K \end{bmatrix}}{11,} = \frac{-(K-110)}{11},$$

$$b_2 = \frac{-\text{Det}\begin{bmatrix} 1 & 0 \\ 11 & 0 \end{bmatrix}}{11} = \frac{-(0-0)}{11} = 0,$$

$$c_1 = \frac{-\text{Det}\begin{bmatrix} 11 & K \\ b_1 & 0 \end{bmatrix}}{b_1} = \frac{-(-Kb_1)}{b_1} = K.$$

The completed Routh table is

| | | | |
|---|---|---|---|
| $s^3$ | 1 | 10 | 0 |
| $s^2$ | 11 | $K$ | 0 |
| $s^1$ | $\frac{-(K-110)}{11}$ | 0 | 0 |
| $s^0$ | $K$ | 0 | 0 |

The first two entries in the first column of the table are 1 and 11. For all the roots of the polynomial to be in the left half plane, the last two entries must also be positive. That is,

$$\frac{-(K-110)}{11} > 0 \quad \text{and} \quad K > 0,$$

or finally

$$0 < K < 110.$$

This result agrees with our earlier analysis for this system.

Example 4.3.1 illustrates how the Routh criterion can be used to determine the stability of a control system. Examples 4.3.2 and 4.3.3 expose some of the difficulties that can arise in applying this criterion.

**EXAMPLE 4.3.2**

Let

$$p(s) = s^3 + s^2 - 4s - 4 = (s+1)(s+2)(s-2).$$

This polynomial has roots that are negatives of each other, and the result is a zero row in the Routh table. The preliminary form of the table is

| | | | |
|---|---|---|---|
| $s^3$ | 1 | $-4$ | 0 |
| $s^2$ | 1 | $-4$ | 0 |
| $s^1$ | $b_1$ | $b_2$ | 0 |
| $s^0$ | $c_1$ | 0 | 0 |

Then

$$b_1 = \frac{-\mathrm{Det}\begin{bmatrix} 1 & -4 \\ 1 & -4 \end{bmatrix}}{1} = \frac{-[-4-(-4)]}{1} = 0,$$

$$b_2 = \frac{-\mathrm{Det}\begin{bmatrix} 1 & 0 \\ 1 & 0 \end{bmatrix}}{1} = \frac{-(0-0)}{1} = 0.$$

To proceed we must replace the row of zeros with a nonzero row. This is accomplished by forming the auxiliary equation

$$s^2 - 4.$$

This equation is formed from the row immediately above the zero row. Note that the equation contains $s^2$ and $s^0$. This is consistent with the formation of the initial rows of the Routh array, taking the highest, third highest, ... powers of $s$ for the first row and the second highest, fourth highest, ... for the second row. In this example, the second row corresponds to the second and zero powers of $s$, that is, to the polynomial $s^2 - 4s^0$. Differentiating this polynomial yields:

$$\frac{d}{ds}(s^2 - 4) = 2s.$$

This generates a new row consisting of 2 followed by zeros. The new, repaired Routh table is

| | | | |
|---|---|---|---|
| $s^3$ | 1 | $-4$ | 0 |
| $s^2$ | 1 | $-4$ | 0 |
| $s^1$ | 2 | 0 | 0 |
| $s^0$ | $c_1$ | 0 | 0 |

with

$$c_1 = \frac{-\text{Det}\begin{bmatrix} 1 & -4 \\ 2 & 0 \end{bmatrix}}{2} = \frac{-[0 - (-8)]}{2} = -4.$$

The completed Routh array is then

| | | | |
|---|---|---|---|
| $s^3$ | 1 | $-4$ | 0 |
| $s^2$ | 1 | $-4$ | 0 |
| $s^1$ | 2 | 0 | 0 |
| $s^0$ | $-4$ | 0 | 0 |

There is one sign change in the first column and hence one root in the right half plane.

We should note that another approach to the problem is the following. The auxiliary equation represents a partial factorization of the original polynomial. In this particular problem, the auxiliary equation is

$$s^2 - 4 = (s+2)(s-2).$$

We could stop at the row of zeros, form the auxiliary equation and divide it into the original polynomial to find the remaining factors. In the present case, the division would simply yield the remaining factor $s+1$.

Instead of a row of zeros, it sometimes happens that only the first element of a row in the Routh table is zero. There are two courses of action.

■ Replace the 0 by $\epsilon$, where $\epsilon$ is an arbitrarily small, positive number and proceed.
■ Return to the original polynomial, replace $s$ by $1/s$ and build a Routh table based on this new polynomial.

Example 4.3.3 illustrates these two tactics.

**EXAMPLE 4.3.3**

Consider

$$p(s) = s^4 + 3s^3 + s^2 + 3s + 2.$$

The initial Routh table is

| | | | | |
|---|---|---|---|---|
| $s^4$ | 1 | 1 | 2 | 0 |
| $s^3$ | 3 | 3 | 0 | 0 |
| $s^2$ | $b_1$ | $b_2$ | 0 | 0 |
| $s^1$ | $c_1$ | 0 | 0 | 0 |
| $s^0$ | $d_1$ | 0 | 0 | 0 |

Then

$$b_1 = \frac{-\text{Det}\begin{bmatrix} 1 & 1 \\ 3 & 3 \end{bmatrix}}{3} = \frac{-(3-3)}{3} = 0,$$

$$b_2 = \frac{-\text{Det}\begin{bmatrix} 1 & 2 \\ 3 & 0 \end{bmatrix}}{3} = \frac{-(0-6)}{3} = 2$$

Since $b_2 \neq 0$ but $b_1 = 0$, we replace $b_1$ by $\epsilon$, where $\epsilon$ is an arbitrarily small positive number. The Routh table now looks like

| | | | | |
|---|---|---|---|---|
| $s^4$ | 1 | 1 | 2 | 0 |
| $s^3$ | 3 | 3 | 0 | 0 |
| $s^2$ | $\epsilon$ | 2 | 0 | 0 |
| $s^1$ | $c_1$ | 0 | 0 | 0 |
| $s^0$ | $d_1$ | 0 | 0 | 0 |

with

$$c_1 = \frac{-\text{Det}\begin{bmatrix} 3 & 3 \\ \epsilon & 2 \end{bmatrix}}{\epsilon} = \frac{-(6-3\epsilon)}{\epsilon} = \frac{3(\epsilon-2)}{\epsilon}.$$

Since $\epsilon$ is arbitrarily small and positive, $c_1$ is negative. We next find

$$d_1 = \frac{-\text{Det}\begin{bmatrix} \epsilon & 2 \\ c_1 & 0 \end{bmatrix}}{c_1} = \frac{-(0-2c_1)}{c_1} = 2.$$

Since $d_1$ is positive and $c_1$ is negative, there are two sign changes (positive to negative back to positive), and hence two poles in the right half plane.

In this case, the zero in the first position of the row occurred late in the Routh table and hence replacing the zero by $\epsilon$ did not lead to difficult and tedious algebra. If the zero had occurred higher in the table it might have been better to use the alternative approach and create a new polynomial by replacing $s$ by $1/s$. For this example the substitution yields

$$p'(s) = p\left(\frac{1}{s}\right) = \left(\frac{1}{s}\right)^4 + 3\left(\frac{1}{s}\right)^3 + \left(\frac{1}{s}\right)^2 + 3\left(\frac{1}{s}\right) + 2.$$

Writing

$$p'(s) = 0,$$

we then obtain

$$2s^4 + 3s^3 + s^2 + 3s + 1 = 0.$$

The preliminary Routh table for this last polymonial is

| | | | | |
|---|---|---|---|---|
| $s^4$ | 2 | 1 | 1 | 0 |
| $s^3$ | 3 | 3 | 0 | 0 |
| $s^2$ | $b_1$ | $b_2$ | 0 | 0 |
| $s^1$ | $c_1$ | 0 | 0 | 0 |
| $s^0$ | $d_1$ | 0 | 0 | 0 |

Then

$$b_1 = \frac{-\text{Det}\begin{bmatrix} 2 & 1 \\ 3 & 3 \end{bmatrix}}{3} = \frac{-(6-3)}{3} = -1,$$

$$b_2 = \frac{-\text{Det}\begin{bmatrix} 2 & 1 \\ 3 & 0 \end{bmatrix}}{3} = \frac{-(-3)}{3} = 1,$$

$$c_1 = \frac{-\text{Det}\begin{bmatrix} 3 & 3 \\ -1 & 1 \end{bmatrix}}{-1} = \frac{-(3-(-3))}{-1} = 6,$$

$$c_2 = \frac{-\text{Det}\begin{bmatrix} 3 & 0 \\ -1 & 0 \end{bmatrix}}{-1} = \frac{-(0-0)}{-1} = 0,$$

$$d_1 = \frac{-\text{Det}\begin{bmatrix} -1 & 1 \\ 6 & 0 \end{bmatrix}}{6} = \frac{-(0-6)}{6} = 1.$$

The final Routh table is

| | | | | |
|---|---|---|---|---|
| $s^4$ | 2 | 1 | 1 | 0 |
| $s^3$ | 3 | 3 | 0 | 0 |
| $s^2$ | -1 | 1 | 0 | 0 |
| $s^1$ | 6 | 0 | 0 | 0 |
| $s^0$ | 1 | 0 | 0 | 0 |

This time no zeros are encountered in the first column. The two sign changes, 3 to −1 to 6 or positive to negative back to positive, signal that there are two roots in the right half plane.

## 4.4 | TRANSIENT BEHAVIOR AND STEADY STATE ERROR

So far we have concentrated on the relationship between feedback and stability. Feedback has a number of other useful properties. Some of these additional properties will be discussed in Chapter 9 when we have developed the appropriate analysis tools.

At this point we can show, however, that feedback can both improve the steady state tracking capability of a system as well as dramatically reshape the response of the system immediately after an input is applied. In Chapters 5, 6, and 7 we will begin a thorough investigation of the effects of feedback on both the transient response and steady state tracking capability of a system. For the present, we demonstrate these effects by way of an example.

**EXAMPLE 4.4.1**

Consider the system

$$G(s) = \frac{K}{s+a}.$$

If we apply a unit step input to the open-loop system, then

$$Y(s) = R(s)G(s) = \frac{K}{s(s+a)} = \frac{A}{s} + \frac{B}{s+a}.$$

It is easy enough to show that

$$A = sY(s)\big|_{s=0} = G(s)\big|_{s=0} = \left[\frac{K}{(s+a)}\right]\bigg|_{s=0} = \frac{K}{a},$$

$$B = (s+a)Y(s)\big|_{s=-a} = \left[\frac{K}{s}\right]\bigg|_{s=-a} = -\frac{K}{a}.$$

Thus,

$$\lim_{t\to\infty} y(t) = \lim_{t\to\infty} \frac{K}{a}[1 - e^{-at}]\mathbf{1}(t) = \frac{K}{a}.$$

As we can see, for a unit step input, the steady state response of the system is not in general one. Further, holding a constant, and increasing K only makes the steady state output deviate further from one.

However, if we apply feedback, as shown in Fig. 4.1, with $H = 1$, then

$$C(s) = R(s)T_c(s) = \frac{K}{s[s+(a+K)]} = \frac{A}{s} + \frac{B}{s+(a+K)},$$

where

$$A = sY(s)\big|_{s=0} = T_c(s)\big|_{s=0} = \left[\frac{K}{s+(a+K)}\right]\bigg|_{s=0} = \frac{K}{a+K},$$

$$B = [s+(a+K)Y(s)]\big|_{s=-(a+K)} = \left[\frac{K}{s}\right]\bigg|_{s=-(a+K)} = -A.$$

Thus,

$$\lim_{t\to\infty} y(t) = \lim_{t\to\infty}[A - Ae^{-at}]\mathbf{1}(t) = A.$$

As we increase the magnitude of $K$, $A$ approaches one. Thus, by making $K$ large relative to the magnitude of $a$, we can make the steady state value of the output close to the desired reference value of one.

As we have already mentioned, feedback can also be used to reshape the transient response of the system. The overriding goal throughout this book is to make the output of the closed-loop system track the reference input. One aspect of this goal has just been discussed, namely, to make the output converge to the input over time. Another part of the overall goal is to make sure the output converges *quickly* to the reference input. To that end, consider Example 4.4.2.

**EXAMPLE 4.4.2**

Let

$$G(s) = \frac{K}{s(s+4)}.$$

Again using the feedback configuration shown in Fig. 4.1, with $H = 1$, we obtain

$$T_c(s) = \frac{G}{1+G} = \frac{K}{s^2 + 4s + K}.$$

For a unit step input

$$C(s) = \frac{K}{s(s+2-\sqrt{4-K})(s+2+\sqrt{4-K})}.$$

The value of the gain $K$ is certainly a key issue in the performance of the system. For $K = 3$,

$$C(s) = \frac{K}{s(s+1)(s+3)},$$

and $T_c$ has two real roots.
   For $K = 4$,

$$C(s) = \frac{K}{s(s+2)(s+2)},$$

and the $T_c$ has two real, *repeated* roots. For $K > 4$,

$$C(s) = \frac{K}{s(s+2-j\sqrt{K-4})(s+2+j\sqrt{K-4})},$$

and $T_c$ has complex conjugate roots. It is a worthwhile MATLAB exercise to find the explicit time responses for $K = 3, 4, 8,$ and $68$, using partial fractions. These responses are shown in Fig. 4.6. As we can see from the figure, the gain has great influence on the time response. For $K = 3$, the response never overshoots the final steady state value, while for $K = 68$, the overshoot is very large, about 150% of the final steady state value. The responses for $K = 4$ and 8 look much better. It is responses like these that we will strive for beginning in Chapter 7.

**Figure 4.6 |** Step response for four values of gain $K$.

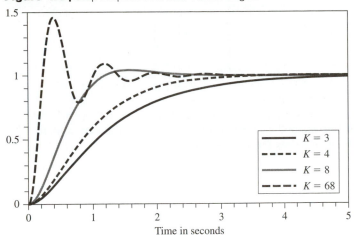

## 4.5 | REPRISE

In this chapter, we introduced the concept of feedback and took a first look at its effects. Feedback is a doubled edged sword. It leads to better performance, but it also can lead to instability if improperly applied. The key design variable discussed in this chapter is the gain $K$. By varying the gain, the performance of the system can be changed dramatically. This performance depends on the roots of the denominator of the closed-loop system. The roots of this denominator polynomial, the so called characteristic polynomial, are changed by changing $K$.

The Routh criterion was introduced to provide a means of determining the range of gains for which a system remains stable. It is of some help, but a better method of investigating the behavior of the closed-loop system, root locus analysis, is presented in Chapter 5. One example of a root locus has already been presented in Example 4.2.1. In this case, the root locus was drawn accurately using MATLAB.

The emphasis in Chapter 5 will be on developing a set of rules that enable the root locus to be correctly "sketched" very quickly by hand. Although we may ultimately wish to generate an accurate plot using a computer, the ability to rapidly sketch the root locus is a crucial design skill. By rapidly sketching a few potential root loci, a designer can very quickly decide the best way to compensate a system.

## 4.6 | PROBLEMS

### 4.6.1  Factoring Characteristic Equation

For the feedback configuration of Fig. 4.7, find and plot the roots of the characteristic polynomial for the gains specified. Then connect the plotted points. Use a calculator

**Figure 4.7** | Negative feedback configuration.

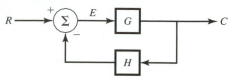

or MATLAB to factor the characteristic polynomial. You may want to calculate some additional sets of points for intermediate values of gain.

1. $GH(s) = \dfrac{K}{s\,(s+4)}$,    $K = 0.1, 0.51, 4, 20, 50$

2. $GH(s) = \dfrac{K}{(s+4)(s+8)}$,    $K = 0.1, 0.51, 4, 20, 50$

3. $GH(s) = \dfrac{K}{s(s+4)(s+8)}$,    $K = 0.1, 0.51, 3.8, 4, 4.2, 20, 50$

4. $GH(s) = \dfrac{K(s+2)}{(s+4)(s+8)}$,    $K = 0.1, 0.51, 4, 20, 50$

5. $GH(s) = \dfrac{K(s+1)}{s\,(s+4)(s+8)}$,    $K = 0.1, 0.5, 1, 1.5, 1.8, 2, 3, 4, 20, 50$

6. $GH(s) = \dfrac{K}{(s+1)(s+10)}$,    $K = 1, 5, 10, 20, 25, 50, 100$

7. $GH(s) = \dfrac{K}{(s+5)^3}$,    $K = 10, 100, 400, 580, 1000$

8. $GH(s) = \dfrac{K}{s\,(s+2)(s+40)}$,    $K = 1, 5, 50, 100$

9. $GH(s) = \dfrac{K(s+1)}{s^2(s+4)(s+60)}$,    $K = 1, 5, 10, 100, 800, 900, 2000$

10. $GH(s) = \dfrac{K(s+1)}{s^2(s+4)(s+10)}$,    $K = 1, 5, 10, 100, 200$

11. $GH(s) = \dfrac{K(s+4)}{s^2(s+2)(s+50)}$,    $K = 1, 2, 5, 50, 500$

12. $GH(s) = \dfrac{K(s+3)}{s\,(s+2)(s+10)}$,    $K = 0.5, 1, 5, 10, 20, 50$

## 4.6.2  Route Criterion—Unstable Roots

For each of these polynomials, use the Routh criterion to determine if any of the roots lie in the right half plane, then check your answer using MATLAB.

1. $s^3 - 2s^2 - 5s + 6$      2. $s^6 + 5s^5 + 6s^4 + 10s^3 + 4s + 1$

3. $s^4 + 7s^3 + 24s^2 + 58s + 40$      4. $s^4 + 5s^3 - 20s - 16$

5. $s^4 + 9s^3 + 28s^2 + 36s + 16$      6. $s^4 + 7s^3 + 14s^2 + 8s$

7. $s^5 + 9s^4 + 28s^3 + 36s^2 + 16s$      8. $s^5 - 5s^3 + 4s$

9. $s^4 + 24s^3 + 196s^2 + 624s + 640$      10. $s^4 + 2s^3 - 2s^2 - 8s - 8$

11. $s^5 + 4s^4 + s^3 + 4s^2 + 10s + 20$      12. $s^4 + s^3 + 3s^2 + 3s + 4$

### 4.6.3 Routh Criterion—Range of Stability

For each loop transfer function $GH$, use the Routh criterion to find the range of gain $K$ for which the closed-loop system has stable poles. Check with MATLAB.

1. $\dfrac{K(s+1)}{(s-2)(s+1)}$      2. $\dfrac{K}{(s-1)(s+5)(s+20)}$

3. $\dfrac{K(s+1)}{(s-1)(s-2)}$      4. $\dfrac{K}{s(s+10)(s+50)}$

5. $\dfrac{K}{(s+3)^3}$      6. $\dfrac{K}{(s+4)^4}$

7. $\dfrac{K}{s(s+1)(s+50)}$      8. $\dfrac{K(s+1)}{s^2(s+2)(s+50)}$

9. $\dfrac{K(s+3)}{s^2(s+2)(s+50)}$      10. $\dfrac{K(s+3)}{s(s+2)(s+10)(s+50)}$

11. $\dfrac{K}{s^2(s+10)}$      12. $\dfrac{K(s+1)}{s^2(s+10)(s+20)}$

### 4.6.4 Steady State Error and Transient Response

These problems are based on the feedback configuration of Fig. 4.7. For each problem, find the closed-loop transfer function $T_c(s)$ in factored form for the listed gains. Then find the closed-loop response to a unit step input for each gain, using either partial fraction expansion (P) or MATLAB (M), as indicated.

1. $G(s) = \dfrac{K(s+1)}{s^2}$, $H(s) = 1$, $K = 2, 4, 20$;    P

2. $G(s) = \dfrac{(s+1)}{s^2}$, $H(s) = K$, $K = 2, 4, 20$;    M

3. $G(s) = \dfrac{K(s+1)}{s^2(s+10)}$, $H(s) = 1$, $K = 20, 32, 50$;    P

4. $G(s) = \dfrac{(s+1)}{s^2(s+10)}$, $H(s) = K$, $K = 20, 32, 50$;    M

5. $G(s) = \dfrac{K(s+1)}{s^2(s+4)}$, $H(s) = 1$, $K = 1, 6, 20$;    P

6. $G(s) = \dfrac{K(s+1)}{s^2(s+4)}$, $H(s) = 1$, $K = 1, 6, 20$;   P

7. $G(s) = \dfrac{K}{(s+2)(s+4)}$, $H(s) = 1$, $K = 0.5, 1, 2, 10$;   P

8. $G(s) = \dfrac{K}{(s+2)(s+4)}$, $H(s) = K$, $K = 0.5, 1, 2, 10$;   P

9. $G(s) = \dfrac{K}{(s+0.1)(s+4)(s+10)}$, $H(s) = 1$, $K = 10, 30.68, 60, 100$;   M

10. $G(s) = \dfrac{K}{(s+1)(s+4)(s+10)}$, $H(s) = 1$, $K = 10, 17.04, 50, 100$;   M

11. $G(s) = \dfrac{K}{(s+1)(s+4)(s+10)}$, $H(s) = K$, $K = 10, 17.04, 50, 100$;   M

12. $G(s) = \dfrac{K}{s(s+1)}$, $H(s) = \dfrac{1}{s+20}$, $K = 2, 4.87, 10, 50$;   M

## 4.6.5  Additional Problems

1. Show that the block diagram in Fig. 4.1 is equivalent to unity feedback with forward loop transfer function

$$\tilde{G} = \frac{G}{1 + GH - G}.$$

2. Using the formulation of problem 1, find $\tilde{G}$ for each pair of $G$ and $H$.

   a. $G(s) = \dfrac{K}{s(s+1)}$, $H(s) = \dfrac{10}{s+10}$

   b. $G(s) = \dfrac{K(s+1)}{s^2}$, $H(s) = \dfrac{1}{s+5}$

   c. $G(s) = \dfrac{1}{(s+1)(s+5)}$, $H(s) = \dfrac{K}{s}$

   d. $G(s) = \dfrac{1}{s(s+10)}$, $H(s) = K$

3. For the feedback configuration of Fig. 4.8, let

$$G_p(s) = \frac{1}{s+2}.$$

**Figure 4.8 |** Unity feedback configuration.

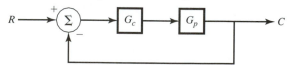

a. Let

$$G_c = K_c.$$

Find the gain $K_c$ that places the closed-loop pole at $s = -5$. Then find the closed-loop response to a unit step input using either MATLAB or partial fraction expansion.

b. Let

$$G_c = \frac{K_c(s + 2.1)}{s}.$$

Find the gain $K_c$ that places one closed-loop pole at $s = -5$. Then find the other closed-loop pole and the response of the closed-loop system to a unit step input using either MATLAB or partial fraction expansion.

4. For the feedback configuration of Fig. 4.8, let

$$G_p(s) = \frac{1}{s\,(s + 2)}.$$

a. Let

$$G_c = K_c.$$

Find the gain $K_c$ that places both closed-loop poles at $s = -1 \pm j1$. Then find the closed-loop response to a unit step input using either MATLAB or partial fraction expansion.

b. Let

$$G_c = \frac{K_c(s + 3)}{(s + p)}.$$

Find $p$ and the gain $K_c$ that places one closed-loop poles at $s = -4$, $-4$, $-q$. Then find the response of the closed-loop system to a unit step input using either MATLAB or partial fraction expansion.

5. Consider the system of Fig. 4.9.

**Figure 4.9 |** Positive feedback in inner loop.

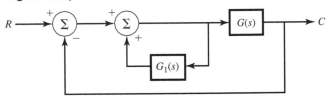

a. Find the overall closed-loop transfer function.
b. Suppose $G_1(s) \approx 1$. What is the overall transfer function in this case?

# FURTHER READINGS

D'Azzo, John J., and Constantine H. Houpis. 1988. *Linear Control System Design: Conventional and Modern*. New York: McGraw-Hill.

Franklin, Gene F., J. David Powell, and Abbas Emami-Naeini. 1991. *Feedback Control of Dynamic Systems,* 2nd ed. Reading, Mass.: Addison-Wesley.

Kuo, Benjamin C. 1982. *Automatic Control,* 4th ed. Englewood Cliffs, N.J.: Prentice-Hall.

Melsa, J. L., and D. G. Schultz. 1969. *Linear Control Systems*. New York: McGraw-Hill.

Ogata, K. 1970. *Modern Control Engineering*. Englewood Cliffs, N.J.: Prentice-Hall.

Saucedo, R., and E. E. Schiring. 1968. *Introduction to Continuous and Digital Control Systems*. New York: MacMillan.

# 5

# Root Locus Analysis

## 5.1 | OVERVIEW

In this chapter we introduce the root locus technique for factoring a polynomial. This technique is intrinsically geometric, as opposed to the algebraic approach of the Routh criterion. The root locus method enables us to rapidly sketch the locus of all solutions to the characteristic polynomial of the closed-loop transfer function $T_c$. The sketch is usually only qualitative, but even so, it offers great insight by showing how the locations of the poles of $T_c$ change as the gain is varied. The power of the root locus method is that it enables the designer to rapidly investigate the impact of various compensators on the performance of the closed-loop system.

The root locus approach can be reduced to a set of "rules." Applied in an orderly fashion, these rules quickly identify all closed-loop pole locations. Thus, the main thrust of this chapter is the development of these rules. This development requires some rethinking of the best way to express the characteristic equation. More specifically, we will express the characteristic equation in polar coordinates. In polar form, each factor in $GH$ is represented by a vector. These vectors, in turn, can be plotted in the $s$ plane, providing the designer with a picture of how each term in $GH$ affects the root locus.

## 5.2 | EXCHANGING ALGEBRA FOR GEOMETRY

The basic goal of this section is to show that it is far more insightful to think about the characteristic equation

$$1 + G(s)H(s) = 0 \qquad \text{[5.1]}$$

geometrically rather than algebraically. In Chapter 4 our approach was purely algebraic. We did gain some insight into the effects of adding feedback, but we were not able to quickly get an overall picture of how the closed-loop response would vary with changes in gain. The key to quickly achieving this global picture is to rethink the solution of the characteristic equation in terms of geometry.

### 5.2.1   Polar Formulation

As a first step in this process recall that in Chapter 4 the characteristic equation, in cleared fraction form, was

$$g_d(s)h_d(s) + g_n(s)h_n(s) = 0, \qquad \text{[5.2]}$$

where

$$G(s) = \frac{g_n(s)}{g_d(s)}, \qquad H(s) = \frac{h_n(s)}{h_d(s)}.$$

This result was obtained by clearing fractions in

$$T_c(s) = \frac{G(s)}{1 + G(s)H(s)}. \qquad \text{[5.3]}$$

Also recall from Chapter 4 that both $G$ and $H$ can be written as

$$\frac{K \prod_{i=1}^{m}(s + z_i)}{\prod_{i=1}^{n}(s + p_i)},$$

and that the gain factor $K$ of either $G$ or $H$ can be varied to change the poles of $T_c(s)$. The trouble with Eq. [5.2] is that the variable gain $K$ is buried in the second term of the sum of two polynomials, and the only obvious way to factor this expression is to use some iterative search routine. If we wanted an accurate root locus we could easily write a computer program that would substitute a series of values of $K$, factor the characteristic equation for these specific values of $K$, and plot the roots to form the root locus.

However, this is not the best way to proceed early in the design process. What we need early in the design process is a clear, *qualitative* picture of how the closed-loop poles move around as the gain is varied. In this case, the best thing to do is to rewrite Eq. [5.1] as

$$GH(s) = -1 = 1\underline{/-180°}, \qquad \text{[5.4]}$$

and then express the left-hand side of the equation in polar coordinates. If this is done, the left-hand side can be separated into a magnitude and an angle. We can then equate magnitudes and angles on both sides of the equation. Another crucial result of writing the characteristic equation in the form of Eq. [5.4] is that the gain $K$ is no longer imbedded in a polynomial but becomes a *scaling factor* for a complex number.

Putting the left-hand side of Eq. [5.4] in polar coordinates yields

$$|GH(s)|\underline{/GH(s)} = 1\underline{/-180°}, \qquad \text{[5.5]}$$

where $|GH(s)|$ is the magnitude of $GH(s)$ and $\underline{/GH(s)}$ is the symbol for its net angle, or argument. It is now possible to write two equations:

$$|GH(s)| = 1 \qquad \textbf{[5.6]}$$

and

$$\underline{/GH(s)} = -180°. \qquad \textbf{[5.7]}$$

A note in passing: we will often write $GH(s)$ in preference to $G(s)H(s)$ and some-times just $GH$.

Equation [5.7] is the *key* to the root locus, because we see that only those points in the $s$ plane for which the angle of $GH(s)$ evaluates to $-180°$ are solutions to the characteristic equation. Equation [5.6] simply shows us how to find the value of $K$ that corresponds to a *specific* solution, that is to a specific value of $s$.

The polar evaluation of $GH(s)$ can be obtained by simply substituting a particular value of $s = \sigma + j\omega$ and algebraically reducing $GH(s)$ to a magnitude and angle. There is a much more insightful way to accomplish this, however, and that is to represent each term in $GH(s)$ graphically as shown next.

## 5.2.2 Graphical Representation

Let

$$GH(s) = \frac{g_n(s)h_n(s)}{g_d(s)h_d(s)} = \frac{K \prod_{i=1}^{m}(s + z_i)}{\prod_{i=1}^{n}(s + p_i)}. \qquad \textbf{[5.8]}$$

Consider now a single term $(s + a_i)$, either a pole or a zero, from the right-hand side of Eq. [5.8]. Figure 5.1 shows the vector representation of this term. Note that by the parallelogram rule of vector addition $s + a_i$ is the vector drawn from the pole or zero location $-a_i$ to the chosen value of $s$. In polar notation, this vector can be decomposed into a length and angle, as shown by the figure. This same decomposition can be done

**Figure 5.1 |** Vector representation of $s + a_i$.

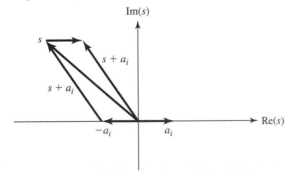

directly in Eq. [5.8]. Thus,

$$GH(s) = \frac{K \prod_{i=1}^{m}(s + z_i)}{\prod_{i=1}^{n}(s + p_i)}$$

$$= \frac{K \prod_{i=1}^{m}|s + z_i|\underline{/s + z_i}}{\prod_{i=1}^{n}|s + p_i|\underline{/s + p_i}}$$

$$= \frac{K\left[\prod_{i=1}^{m}|s + z_i|\right]\sum_{i=1}^{m}\underline{/s + z_i}}{\left[\prod_{i=1}^{n}|s + p_i|\right]\sum_{i=1}^{n}\underline{/s + p_i}}$$

$$= \left[\frac{K \prod_{i=1}^{m}|s + z_i|}{\prod_{i=1}^{n}|s + p_i|}\right] \bigg/ \sum_{i=1}^{m}\underline{/s + z_i} - \sum_{i=1}^{n}\underline{/s + p_i}. \qquad \textbf{[5.9]}$$

Equation [5.9] provides expressions that can be substituted into the left-hand side of Eqs. [5.6] and [5.7] to yield

$$\frac{K \prod_{i=1}^{m}|s + z_i|}{\prod_{i=1}^{n}|s + p_i|} = 1, \qquad \textbf{[5.10]}$$

and

$$\sum_{i=1}^{m}\underline{/s + z_i} - \sum_{i=1}^{n}\underline{/s + p_i} = -180°. \qquad \textbf{[5.11]}$$

The importance of Eqs. [5.10] and [5.11] is now illustrated with a simple example that contrasts the algebraic and geometric approaches to factoring the characteristic equation.

**EXAMPLE 5.2.1**

Let

$$G(s) = G_c(s)G_p(s),$$

with

$$G_p(s) = \frac{K_{plant}}{(s + a)(s + b)}, \qquad G_c = K, \qquad H = 1.$$

Setting $G_c(s) = K$ constitutes the simplest form of feedback compensation, namely gain compensation, where the gain by itself is used to change the location of the poles of the closed-loop transfer function. Substituting $G_c$, $G_p$, and $H$ into Eq. [5.3] and clearing fractions, yields

$$T_c(s) = \frac{G_c G_p(s)}{1 + G_c G_p(s)} = \frac{K K_{plant}}{s^2 + (a + b)s + (ab + K K_{plant})}. \qquad \textbf{[5.12]}$$

From Eq. [5.12] it is clear that changing $K$ changes the poles of the closed-loop transfer function, thereby changing the time functions that will appear in the system response. Note carefully that since the degree of the denominator is two, there will be two unique poles for *every* value of gain. Note also, as previously discussed, that the degree of $GH$ is also two.

Now let

$$K_{plant} = 1, \quad a = 2, \quad b = 4,$$

so that the characteristic equation becomes

$$s^2 + 6s + (8 + K) = 0.$$

The roots of the characteristic equation are then

$$s = -3 \pm \sqrt{1 - K}. \qquad\qquad\qquad \text{[5.13]}$$

Equation [5.13] reveals that

1. For $K = 0$, the roots of the characteristic equation are the poles of the loop transfer function.
2. For $K$ small, the closed-loop poles are real and close to $s = -2$ and $s = -4$, that is, close to the poles of $G_c G_p(s)$.
3. For $K = 1$, the system has two real poles at $s = -3$.
4. For $K > 1$, the poles are complex but all the complex poles have the *same* real part of $-3$.

Table 5.1 gives the pole locations for six specific values of gain. These values are then plotted in Fig. 5.2.

**Table 5.1** | Gains and pole locations for $s^2 + 6s + (8 + K) = 0$ for Example 5.2.1.

| Gain | Pole locations | |
|------|----------------|---|
| 0.01 | $s = -3.99,$ | $s = -2.01$ |
| 0.10 | $s = -3.95,$ | $s = -2.05$ |
| 0.50 | $s = -3.71,$ | $s = -2.29$ |
| 1.00 | $s = -3,$ | $s = -3$ |
| 2.00 | $s = -3 + j1,$ | $s = -3 - j1$ |
| 5.00 | $s = -3 + j2,$ | $s = -3 - j2$ |

We see from Fig. 5.2 that the locus of all solutions to the characteristic equation form a cross. All these solutions exist simultaneously, but it is worthwhile to think of generating the cross by writing a computer program that solves the characteristic equation repeatedly for increasing values of gain, and plots each *pair* of solutions on the computer monitor as they are computed.

As each pair of solutions is plotted on the monitor, the horizontal arms of the cross will grow toward each other, starting at the poles of $GH$. As the gain increases, the two arms will meet and begin to generate the vertical part of the cross. Eventually, the plot on the monitor will look like Fig. 5.2.

This analysis, leading to the locus of all roots of the characteristic equation, can be done algebraically for this simple example. If the characteristic equation is third order or higher, however, this approach is generally practical only on a computer.

**Figure 5.2 |** Plot of pole locations for $s^2 + 6s + (8 + K) = 0$, Example 5.2.1.

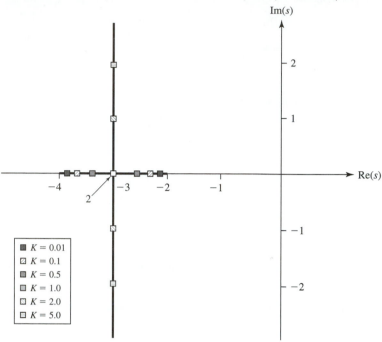

Further, the algebraic approach provides only limited insight into how the root locus might change if more poles and zeros were added. Therefore, the more intuitive geometric approach is now demonstrated for this same system.

The first step is to rewrite the characteristic equation as

$$GH(s) = -1 = 1\underline{/-180°}.$$

For this simple example we have

$$\frac{K}{(s+2)(s+4)} = 1\underline{/-180°}. \qquad \textbf{[5.14]}$$

The left-hand side is now in factored form with $K$ serving as a scaling factor. Note that the poles of $GH$ are *fixed*. It is the poles of the *closed-loop* transfer function that change with $K$. The goal is to use the fixed poles and zeros of $GH$ to find the closed-loop poles. The poles and zeros of $GH$ can be thought of as features of the landscape that serve as navigational aids in finding the closed-loop poles.

Our next step is to rewrite the left-hand side of Eq. [5.14] in polar form. This yields

$$\frac{K}{(|s+2|\underline{/\theta_1})(|s+4|\underline{/\theta_2})} = 1\underline{/-180°},$$

**Figure 5.3 |** Geometric approach to finding closed-loop poles, Example 5.2.1.

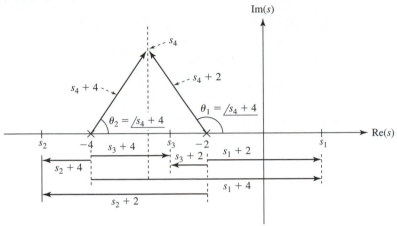

where $\theta_1 = \underline{/s+2}$ and $\theta_2 = \underline{/s+4}$. The vectors representing $s+2$ and $s+4$ can then be plotted, as shown in Fig. 5.3, for various specific values of $s$. The $\theta_1$ and $\theta_2$ shown in the figure are $\underline{/s_4 + 2}$ and $\underline{/s_4 + 4}$, respectively.

The importance of the equation

$$\underline{/G(s)H(s)} = -180°$$

should now be obvious. Only those points in the $s$ plane for which $\theta_1$ and $\theta_2$ sum to 180° are solutions of the characteristic equation. This enables us to quickly elimi-nate, as solutions to the characteristic equation, almost all the points in the $s$ plane, and just as quickly find the remaining points that do satisfy the characteristic equation.

To see how this is accomplished consider Fig. 5.3, where we have selected some specific points along the real axis at which to evaluate $GH$. The vectors $s+2$ and $s+4$ are shown for *each* of these points. For one of the selected points to be a solution to the characteristic equation, the sum of $\theta_1$ and $\theta_2$ must equal 180° at that point.

For instance, at point $s_1$

$$\frac{K}{(s_1+2)(s_1+4)} = \frac{K}{(|s_1+2|\underline{/0°})(|s_1+4|\underline{/0°})}$$

$$= \frac{K}{|s_1+2||s_1+4|}\underline{/0°}.$$

We see that $s_1$ is representative of *any* point to the right of the pole of $GH$ at $s = -2$. Thus, no point on the real axis to the right of $s = -2$ can be a solution to the characteristic equation because the angle condition cannot be satisfied. The angle is always zero, not $-180°$.

Similarly, at $s = s_2$, to the left of $s = -4$, we have

$$\frac{K}{(s_2 + 2)(s_2 + 4)} = \frac{K}{(|s_2 + 2|\underline{/180^\circ})(|s_2 + 4|\underline{/180^\circ})}$$

$$= \frac{K}{|s_2 + 2||s_2 + 4|}\underline{/-360^\circ}$$

$$= \frac{K}{|s_2 + 2||s_2 + 4|}\underline{/0^\circ},$$

and, again, the angle condition cannot be satisfied for *any* point to the left of the pole of $GH$ at $s = -4$. Thus, no point to the left of $s = -4$ can be a solution of $1 + GH = 0$.

By contrast, if we choose any point $-4 < s_3 < -2$, then

$$\frac{K}{(s_3 + 2)(s_3 + 4)} = \frac{K}{(|s_3 + 2|\underline{/180^\circ})(|s_3 + 4|\underline{/0^\circ})}$$

$$= \frac{K}{|s_3 + 2||s_3 + 4|}\underline{/-180^\circ}$$

Thus, *any* point on the real axis between the two poles of $GH$ is a solution to the characteristic equation.

At this juncture it is useful to recall the algebraic approach to this problem presented earlier and remember that for each value of $K$ there are two closed-loop poles. This is clearly shown in Table 5.1. We can think of the line segment $(-2, -4)$ as being composed of pairs of points, each associated with a specific value of $K$. These values can be computed using Eq. [5.10]. When solved for $K$, this equation becomes

$$K = \frac{\prod_{i=1}^{n} |s + p_i|}{K_{\text{plant}} \prod_{i=1}^{m} |s + z_i|}. \qquad [5.15]$$

For the simple system of this example

$$K = \frac{|s + 2||s + 4|}{1}. \qquad [5.16]$$

Selecting the point $s = -2.05$ and applying Eq. [5.16] yields the value of $K$ associated with the point $s = -2.05$. This value is simply the product of the vectors drawn from $s = -4$ and $s = -2$ to the point $s = -2.05$, or

$$K = (1.95)(0.05) = 0.0975 \approx 0.1,$$

where we have rounded to 0.1 to make the value consistent with the rounding to two decimal places in Table 5.1.

It is very important to note that this *same* value of $K$ is obtained by setting $s = -3.95$. Thus, the pair of solutions associated with $K = 0.1$ are $s = -2.05$ and $s = -3.95$.

At this juncture, we have located all the points on the real axis that solve the characteristic equation. The decision to investigate solutions along the real axis first is a considered one. As noted several times, the solutions of the characteristic equation are either real or complex conjugate pairs. Finding the real roots first is a great aid in locating the complex solutions off the real axis.

In this example, the roots off the real axis must lie on the perpendicular bisector of the line segment $(-2, -4)$ on the real axis. The points on this bisector line are the only points off the real axis where the angle constraint $\theta_1 + \theta_2 = 180°$ is satisfied. Note that this bisector passes through the point $s = -3$. For a gain $K = 1$ the characteristic equation has a double root at $s = -3$. The point $s = -3$ is a "break-out" point, a point at which the root locus breaks out of the real axis. Part of the reason for finding the root locus along the real axis first is that it helps identify potential break-out points.

---

The detailed analysis of Example 5.2.1 will prove to be justified, because in the course of this analysis every fundamental concept of the geometric approach to drawing the root locus has been exposed. The next step is to organize what has been learned into a set of "rules" that enable us to sytematically sketch the root locus in rapid fashion.

Before proceeding to the development of the rules of root locus we summarize what we have learned from Example 5.2.1.

1. First write the characteristic equation in the form

$$GH = 1\underline{/-180°}.$$

2. Plot the real poles and zeros of $GH$.
3. Plot the vectors from each pole and zero of $GH$ to a prospective solution point $s$.
4. If the sum of the angles from the zeros of $GH$ minus the sum of the angles from the poles of $GH$ is equal to $-180°$, then the point is a solution to the characteristic equation *for a specific gain*.
5. Compute the gain that places a closed-loop pole at that point by using Eq. [5.15].
6. This calculation of $K$ can *always* be made *once the angle condition has been used to identify a solution point*.

It cannot be emphasized enough that the key to the root locus is the satisfaction of the angle condition. If the angle condition is satisfied, then a gain can always be found that places a closed-loop pole (solution of the characteristic equation) at that point. That said, our next goal is to develop the rules of root locus.

## 5.3 | RULES OF ROOT LOCUS

The rules of root locus developed below are presented in the order in which we will apply them, that is roughly in their order of importance. As we have discussed already we first find the portions of the root locus on the real axis. Thus, the first rule shows us how to do just that.

**Figure 5.4 |** Angle contributions along the real axis.

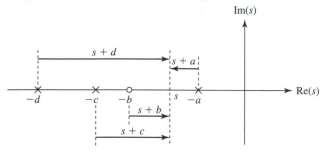

---

**Rule 5.3.1**

The root locus on the real axis is found to the left of an odd count of real poles and real zeros of *GH*.

---

Figure 5.4 shows how this rule works. Along the real axis, the angle contribution of any pole or zero is either $0°$ or $180°$. Thus, for any point $s$, the total angle contribution from the zeros of $GH$ is

$$n_{zr} \times (180°),$$

where $n_{zr}$ is the number of *real* zeros of $GH$ to the *right* of the chosen $s$. Note that the total angle contribution will either be $0°$ if $n_{zr}$ is even or $180°$ if $n_{zr}$ is odd. Similarly, the total angle contribution from the poles of $GH$ is

$$n_{pr} \times (180°),$$

where $n_{pr}$ is the number of *real* poles of $GH$ to the right of $s$. Then

$$\underline{/GH} = n_{zr}(180°) - n_{pr}(180°)$$
$$= (n_{zr} - n_{pr})(180°).$$

It is easy enough to show that if $n_{zr} - n_{pr}$ is even so is $n_{zr} + n_{pr}$, and that if $n_{zr} - n_{pr}$ is odd so is $n_{zr} + n_{pr}$. Thus,

$$\underline{/GH} = (n_{zr} + n_{pr})(180°).$$

If $n_{zr} + n_{pr}$ is odd then the net angle of $GH$ is $180°$ (or equivalently $-180°$). Thus, to find the root locus on the real axis we merely count all poles and zeros to the right of the selected point $s$. If the total count is odd, the point is on the root locus, if the count is even the point is *not* on the root locus.

It is worth noting that this rule, while easy to memorize, can be "recovered" easily if forgotten. All we have to do is draw the vectors from all the real poles and zeros of $GH$ to a particular point on the real axis and then find the net angle, which can only be $0°$ or $-180°$. Examples 5.3.1 and 5.3.2 illustrate the procedure for finding the root locus on the real axis.

**EXAMPLE 5.3.1**

Consider first

$$GH = \frac{K(s+1)}{s(s+4)(s+10)}.$$

Since the portion of the root locus on the real axis only occurs to the left of an odd count of poles and zeros, there will be no root locus to the right of the pole at $s = 0$. For any $-1 < s < 0$, however, the count is one, and so this whole interval represents solutions to the characteristic equation for a range of values of $K$. For $-4 < s < -1$, the count is two, or even, and none of the points in this portion of the real axis are solutions to the characteristic equation. For $-10 < s < -4$ the count is again odd and points on this segment of the real axis are solutions of the characteristic equation. For $-\infty < s < -10$ the count is even and none of the points in this infinite line segment are solutions. The shaded regions of Fig. 5.5 show where root locus occurs along the real axis.

**Figure 5.5** | Locating root locus on real axis in Example 5.3.1.

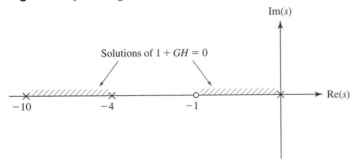

We now have divided the real axis into two regions where solutions can exist, and three regions, two of which are infinite in extent, where no solutions exist. We see that we have been able to very rapidly identify those portions of the real axis where solutions of the characteristic equation exist. This is a major step forward in drawing the root locus because the identification of the potential real roots of the characteristic equation is a great aid in finding the complex roots of the characteristic equation.

**EXAMPLE 5.3.2**

Now consider

$$GH = \frac{K(s+1)^2}{s^2(s+10)}.$$

As before, there are no solutions to the right of the poles at $s = 0$. However, there are no solutions for $-1 < s < 0$ either because of the *double* pole at the origin, making the count two in this region. Nor are there closed-loop poles for $-1 < s < -10$ since

**Figure 5.6 |** Locating root locus on the real axis for Example 5.3.2.

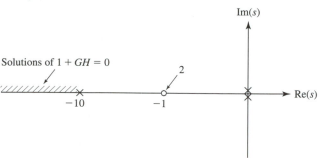

the count here is four because of the double zero at $s = -1$. In fact, the only place on the real axis where solutions exist is for $-\infty < s < -10$ where the count of poles and zeros to the right is five. The root locus on the real axis is shown in Fig. 5.6.

In both Examples 5.3.1 and 5.3.2, $GH$ is such that there will be closed-loop poles off the real axis for high gain. At this juncture, the rules of root locus that help determine the portion of the locus off the real axis have not been given. Thus, the completion of the root loci for these two examples will be deferred until Examples 5.3.5 and 5.3.8.

**Rule 5.3.2**

The root locus begins at the poles of *GH*.

To understand this rule consider the equation

$$K = \frac{\prod_{i=1}^{n} |s + p_i|}{\prod_{i=1}^{m} |s + z_i|}. \tag{5.17}$$

Suppose we choose a point $s$ near one of the poles of $GH$, for instance the pole at $s = -p_i$. Then the term $s + p_i$ in the numerator is small. The rest of the terms on the right-hand side of Eq. [5.17] will be larger but finite. The closer the chosen point is to $-p_i$ the smaller the value of the term $s + p_i$. Thus, in the limit as $s \to -p_i$ the gain $K$ goes to zero. This happens for every pole of $GH$. Since the number of poles of $T_c$ is equal to the number of poles of $GH$ one can think of each pole of $GH$ as "generating" a pole of $T_c$. That is, if we increase $K$ slightly from zero, a closed-loop pole "pops out" near each pole of $GH$. As we increase $K$ further, each closed-loop pole migrates farther and farther from its point of origin.

*Each* of these migrations generates a so called limb or branch of the root locus. If $GH$ has $n$ poles, the root locus will have $n$ branches, or limbs, with each branch describing the migration of one of the closed-loop poles as $K$ increases from zero to infinity. We now apply this rule to Example 5.3.3.

**EXAMPLE 5.3.3**

Let

$$GH = \frac{K(s+1)(s+4)}{s(s+10)}.$$

As shown in Fig. 5.7, the root locus exists to the left of the pole at the origin and between the pole at $s = -10$ and the zero at $s = -4$. Three *sets* of poles are shown in the figure for $K = 0.01$, $K = 2$, and $K = 10{,}000$, each *set* represented by small squares. Each *set* of two squares has a different shading to emphasize the point that there are two closed-loop poles for each gain. Further, it is the squares that move as the gain changes, *not* the x's and 0's that represent the poles and zeros of $GH$.

**Figure 5.7 |** Pole migration on the real axis.

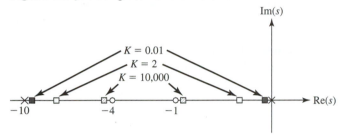

The figure is not drawn to scale, but even so, we can see that as the gain increases, the closed-loop poles initially appear near the poles of $GH$ and then migrate away. In this particular example, the total root locus is that shown in the figure. There is no root locus off the real axis. Hence as $K$ becomes arbitrarily large, the closed-loop poles are limited by the finite zeros of $GH$. In fact as $K \to \infty$ the closed-loop poles approach these finite zeros. These observations lead to the next rule.

---

**Rule 5.3.3**

The branches of the root locus end at the zeros of $GH$.

To understand this rule consider a specific point $s$ close to a finite zero, say the zero at $s = -z_i$, then the factor $|s + z_i|$ in the denominator Eq. [5.17] will be small while all the other terms are, relatively, much larger. As $s$ approaches $-z_i$, the term $|s + z_i|$ approaches zero, while all the other terms in the numerator and denominator remain finite, and $K \to \infty$. Thus, as the gain increases, the closed-loop poles migrate from the poles of $GH$ to the zeros of $GH$. Remember, the poles and zeros of $GH$ are stationary landmarks, it is the poles of $T_c$ that move as the gain changes.

A natural question at this point is what happens if there aren't any finite zeros, or if there are more poles than finite zeros? The answer is that some of the closed-loop poles migrate to so-called "zeros at infinity."

There are two ways to make $K$, as expressed in Eq. [5.17], grow. One way is to have a term $|s + z_i|$ in the denominator become very small. The other way is to have the numerator grow faster than the denominator. The two-pole, no-zero-loop transfer function in Example 5.2.1 illustrates the latter of these two possibilities. In this case, both closed-loop poles migrate to "zeros" infinitely far from the origin of the $s$ plane.

If there are not enough finite zeros to capture all the migrating closed-loop poles, then the next task is to locate these so-called zeros at infinity. The key to finding these zeros is to remember that at each point along each branch of the root locus, the angle condition must be satisfied. As the gain increases the branches of the root locus off the real axis eventually begin to straighten and approach straight-line asymptotes. The zeros at infinity lie at the end of these straight-line asymptotes.

The number of asymptotes, and hence the number of zeros at infinity is equal to the difference between the number of poles of $GH$ and the number of finite zeros of $GH$. This excess of poles over zeros will henceforward be referred to as the "pole-zero excess" (PZE). In Example 5.2.1, the root locus off the real axis consists of two straight lines extending at angles of $90°$ and $270°$ from a point midway between the two loop transfer function poles. In this case, the locus is actually *on* the asymptotes. A formula for locating the asymptotes is given by the next rule.

---

**Rule 5.3.4**

The number of branches that extend to infinity is equal to the difference between the number of poles and the number of zeros of *GH*. This number, called the pole-zero excess (PZE), is denoted by $p_{ex}$. The branches that extend to infinity approach straight-line asymptotes originating from a common point. The angles that the asymptotes make with the real axis can be computed from the formula

$$\theta_\ell = \frac{(1 + 2\ell)(180°)}{p_{ex}}, \qquad \ell = 0, 1, \ldots, p_{ex} - 1,$$

where $p_{ex}$ is the pole-zero excess of *GH*.

---

A heuristic proof of this rule can be obtained using Fig. 5.8. For points far from the origin, the angles from all the poles and zeros, as shown in part (a) of the figure,

**Figure 5.8 |** Determination of angles of asymptotes.

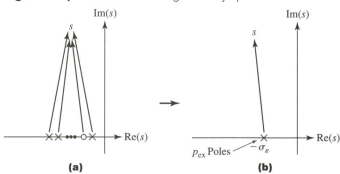

(a)            (b)

become equal. Viewed from the point $s$, far from the poles and finite zeros of $GH$, $GH$ appears to have $p_{ex}$ poles all at the point $-\sigma_i$, as shown in part (b). Thus, the straight-line asymptotes all originate from a single point on the real axis. Satisfaction of the angle condition requires that

$$-p_{ex} \times 180° = -180°, -540°, -900°, \dots$$
$$= \frac{(1 + 2\ell)(180°)}{p_{ex}}, \quad \ell = 0, 1, \dots, p_{ex} - 1.$$

The location of the point of intersection of the asymptotes with the real axis is also of interest and is given by the next rule.

---

**Rule 5.3.5**

The intersection of the asymptotes with the real axis is given by the formula

$$\sigma_i = \frac{\sum_i^n \text{Re}\{p_i\} - \sum_i^m \text{Re}\{z_i\}}{p_{ex}},$$

where the $p_i$ are the poles and the $z_i$ the zeros of $GH$.

---

The proof of this rule is tedious and not very enlightening. It can be motivated by thinking of poles as negative charge and zeros as positive charge, so that $\sigma_i$ represents the center of charge.

Example 5.3.4 illustrates rules 5.3.4 and 5.3.5.

**EXAMPLE 5.3.4**

Let

$$GH(s) = \frac{K(s+1)(s+5)}{s(s+6)(s+20)}.$$

The root locus is shown in Fig. 5.9. The single asymptote is at $\theta = -180°$. The closed-loop pole that originates from the pole of $GH$ at $s = -20$ travels along this asymptote towards a zero at $s = -\infty$.

**Figure 5.9 |** Root locus with one asymptote at $-180°$.

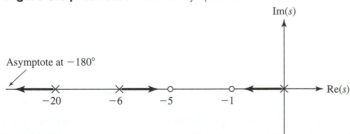

To gain a more complete understanding of Rules 5.3.4 and 5.3.5 we need Rule 5.3.6, which is crucial to sketching the root locus off the real axis.

> **Rule 5.3.6**
>
> The points at which the root locus "breaks out" of and "breaks in" to the real axis can be determined by finding the maximum and minimum points of the gain $K$ as a function of $s$ with $s$ restricted to real values.

Example 5.2.1, already analyzed in some detail, provides an illustration of a break-out point. In this case, there is a break-out point at $s = -3$. Figure 5.10 shows both the root locus and a plot of $K$ as a function of real values of $s$ between $-2$ and $-4$, with the ordinates of the two plots aligned. The maximum occurs at $s = -3$ for $K = 1$. At the point where $K = 1$ the characteristic equation has a double root at $s = -3$. This is the maximum gain for which the poles are real; higher gains result in complex roots.

**Figure 5.10 |** Gain $K$ as a function of $s$ along the real axis.

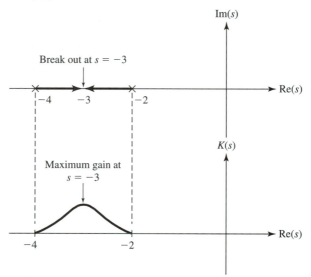

Break-in points can be determined in a similar way, by searching along the real axis for a *minimum* value of $K$. Examples 5.3.5 and 5.3.6 have break-out points and also provide the chance to use all the rules developed to this point.

**EXAMPLE 5.3.5**

Consider again Example 5.3.1. The root locus on the real axis has already been determined. In this case, closed-loop poles start at $s = -10$ and $s = -4$ and migrate toward each other. As in the case of Example 5.2.1, there will be a maximum gain somewhere along the real axis between these two starting points. Table 5.2 provides

**Table 5.2 |** Gain values along the real axis in the vicinity of the break-out point.

| s | −7.2 | −7.1 | −7.0 | −6.9 | −6.8 | −6.7 |
|---|---|---|---|---|---|---|
| K | 10.41 | 10.46 | 10.5 | 10.51 | 10.50 | 10.47 |

the gain in the region of $s = -7$, roughly the halfway point between the poles of $GH$ at $s = -10$ and $s = -4$. If $GH$ had only the two poles at $s = -10$ and $s = -4$, the break out would have been precisely at $s = -7$. However, the pole of $GH$ at $s = 0$ and the zero at $s = -1$ cause the break-out point to be just to the right of $s = -7$. Even so, the break-out point is still very close to $s = -7$, and the midpoint of the interval is thus an excellent place to start looking for the break-out point.

Since $p_{ex} = 2$, there will be two asymptotes at $\theta = \pm 90°$. The asymptotes intersect at

$$\sigma_i = \frac{-10 - 4 - (-1)}{2} = -6.5.$$

A sketch of the root locus is shown in Fig. 5.11

**Figure 5.11 |** Root locus for $GH(s) = \frac{K(s+1)}{s(s+4)(s+10)}$, Example 5.3.5.

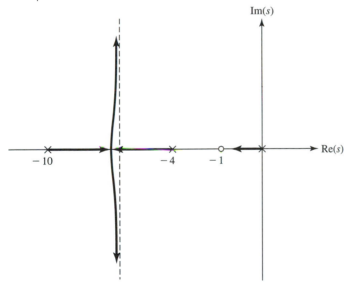

In Example 5.3.6 we consider a loop transfer function with four poles. It is perhaps worth noting that if $GH$ has five or more poles and several zeros, then sketching the root locus by hand becomes more difficult. The reason is that there will be more than one plausible root locus. Only one of them is correct, but in many cases, a fair amount of hand calculation is required to eliminate the incorrect but plausible root loci.

---

**EXAMPLE 5.3.6**

Let

$$GH = \frac{K(s+1)}{s^2(s+2)(s+20)}.$$

The first step is to find the root locus on the real axis. For $-2 < s < -1$ the count of poles and zeros to the right of $s$ is three (two poles and one zero). For $-\infty < s < -10$ the count is five (four poles and one zero). For any other locations $s$ on the real axis, the count looking to the right is even. Since there is no root locus either to the right or left of the double pole at $s = 0$, the root locus will break out of the real axis at this point. The complete root locus is shown in Fig. 5.12.

The number of asymptotes is

$$p_{ex} = 4 - 1 = 3.$$

**Figure 5.12 |** Root locus with asymptotes and zeros at infinity.

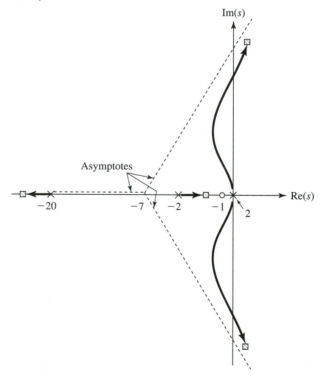

The asymptotes are at

$$\theta_\ell = \frac{(1+2\ell)(180°)}{p_{ex}}, \qquad \ell = 0, 1, \ldots, p_{ex} - 1$$

$$= \frac{(1+2\ell)(180°)}{3}, \qquad \ell = 0, 1, \ldots, 2$$

$$= 60°, 180°, 300°.$$

Also

$$\sigma_i = \frac{[0+0+(-2)+(-20)]-(-1)}{4-1}$$

$$= -7.$$

The two poles at the origin break out at $\pm 90°$.

In Example 5.3.7 we encounter a root locus that has a break-in point. It also illustrates a property that is useful in drawing more complex root loci.

**EXAMPLE 5.3.7**

Consider

$$GH(s) = \frac{Ks}{(s-0.5-j2)(s-0.5+j2)}.$$

The root locus and a plot of $K(s)$ along the negative real axis are shown in Fig. 5.13. As can be seen, the break-in point is very close to $s = -2$. The transfer function has two poles and one zero. It can be shown that in this case the root locus off the real axis is part of a circle centered at the zero. The radius of the circle is thus

$$r = \sqrt{2^2 + 0.5^2} = 2.06,$$

making the break-in point $s = -2.06$.

For simple transfer functions, especially those with no zeros, an alternative approach to finding break-out and break-in points is to solve the equation

$$\frac{dK}{ds} = 0.$$

For the problem under consideration

$$\frac{dK}{ds} = -\left[\frac{d}{ds}\frac{s^2-s+4.25}{s}\right]$$

$$= -\left[\frac{-(s^2-s+4.25)}{s^2} + \frac{2s-1}{s}\right]$$

$$= -\frac{s^2-4.25}{s^2}.$$

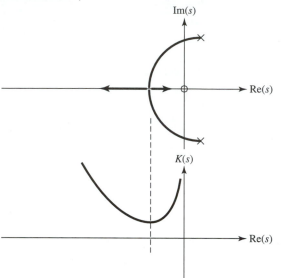

**Figure 5.13** | Gain $K$ as a function of $s$ along the real axis, Example 5.3.7.

The critical points are

$$s = \pm\sqrt{4.25} = \pm 2.06$$

The critical point of interest is $s = -2.06$. The other critical point belongs to the so-called complementary root locus discussed in Section 5.5.

One drawback to finding break-in and break-out points by the latter method is that it requires solving a polynomial in $s$ of relatively high degree *algebraically*. This is just the problem that the root locus method tries to avoid. Hence, in many cases a better approach is simply to evaluate $K$ along a stretch of real axis using Eq. [5.17] and find the *approximate* break-in or break-out point. Usually what is most important is to determine *if* the break-in and break-out points exist. Their exact locations are not of as much interest.

Examples 5.3.6 and 5.3.7 illustrate a property of all root loci that is stated in Rule 5.3.7.

**Rule 5.3.7**

The root locus is symmetric about the real axis of the $s$ plane.

This rule follows from the fact that the transfer function has real coefficients and thus so does the characteristic equation. Suppose the characteristic equation is

$$s^n + a_{n-1}s^{n-1} + \cdots + a_1 s + a_0 = 0. \qquad \text{[5.18]}$$

Conjugating both sides of Eq. [5.18] yields

$$\{s^n + a_{n-1}s^{n-1} + \cdots + a_1 s + a_0\}^* = (s^n)^* + (a_{n-1}s^{n-1})^* + \cdots + (a_1 s)^* + (a_0)^*$$
$$= (s^*)^n + a_{n-1}(s^*)^{n-1} + \cdots + a_1 s^* + a_0$$
$$= 0.$$

Hence, if $s$ satisfies the characteristic equation, so does $s^*$. Thus if any of the roots are complex, then they must come in conjugate pairs. Thus as $K$ is increased, the roots of the characteristic equation must be either real or complex conjugate pairs. Because the complex roots occur in conjugate pairs, the root locus has to be symmetric about the real axis. To illustrate this idea we complete Example 5.3.2.

**EXAMPLE 5.3.8**

For Example 5.3.2,

$$GH = \frac{K(s+1)^2}{s^2(s+10)}.$$

The root locus on the real axis has already been determined. Since $p_{ex} = 1$, there is one asymptote at $\theta = 180°$. The root locus is shown in Fig. 5.14. As we can see, the two poles of $GH$ at $s = 0$ are isolated in the sense that there is no root locus on the real axis to the right or left of $s = 0$. The same is true of the two zeros at $s = -1$. As a consequence, as the gain is increased, two closed-loop poles immediately leave the real axis at $s = 0$ and migrate to the two zeros. One travels through the second quadrant and one through the third quadrant, thereby preserving the symmetry of the root loci about the real axis.

**Figure 5.14 |** Complete root locus for $GH = \frac{K(s+1)^2}{s^2(s+10)}$.

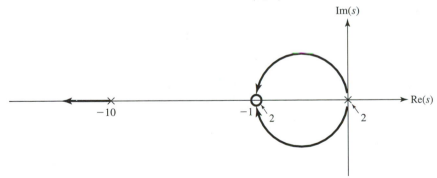

We now add one last rule. This rule is normally not employed in drawing root loci. However, there are occasions when it proves useful and for that reason we include it here.

> **Rule 5.3.8**
>
> The angle of departure of a branch of the root locus from a pole of *GH*, or the angle of arrival of a branch at a zero of *GH*, can be determined by satisfying the angle condition on a circle of small radius centered at the pole or zero in question. As this circle is made smaller, all the angles from the other poles and zeros approach exact values that are easily computed. Only the angle to the pole or zero about which this circle of small radius is constructed is then unknown.

The most important use of this rule is to compute the angle of departure from a complex pole. This angle of departure can sometimes be an aid in determining the final shape of the root locus.

**EXAMPLE 5.3.9**

Example 5.3.7 can be used to illustrate this rule. In Fig. 5.15, the radius of the circle around the pole at $s = -0.5 + j2$ is actually very small in relation to the distance to the zero and the other pole. Hence the angles to the point selected on the circle from the pole and other zero are essentially the same as if measured to the location of the pole at $s = -0.5 + j2$. In fact, as the circle shrinks in diameter the approximation becomes exact. As a consequence it is possible to write

$$\alpha - \theta_1 - \theta_2 = -180°,$$

or

$$\theta_1 = \alpha + 180° - \theta_2$$
$$= \tan^{-1}(4) + 90°$$
$$= 166°$$

**Figure 5.15 |** Determining the angle of departure.

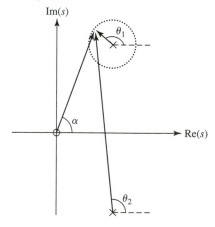

The situation is no more difficult for more complicated systems, only more tedious because more angles will have to be computed. This particular rule is not used very much because generally the root locus is only *sketched* to get a qualitative picture of the migration of closed-loop poles as the gain is varied.

We have now completed our discussion of the rules of root locus. Along the way we have worked some examples to aid our understanding of these rules. Section 5.4 is devoted to some additional examples that should help solidify our ability to use these rules.

## 5.4 | MORE EXAMPLES

The first example in this section provides us with a chance to refine our skills in finding potential break-in and break-out points. As we will see, we can often make an educated guess as to whether a break-in or break-out point is present. If we think one is present, we can also determine approximately where is it is, thereby shortening the search for its exact location.

**EXAMPLE 5.4.1**

Consider the system

$$GH(s) = \frac{K(s+2)}{s(s+1)(s+40)}.$$

The first step in drawing the root locus is to plot the poles and zeros of $GH$ in the $s$ plane and then find the root locus on the real axis. For this example, the root locus on the real axis is denoted by the shaded regions in Fig. 5.16.

**Figure 5.16 |** Root locus on the real axis.

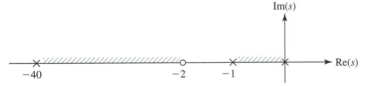

The next step is to compute the angles of the asymptotes and find $\sigma_i$ the intersection of the asymptotes with the real axis. The number of asymptotes is equal to the pole-zero excess of $GH$, in this case two, since there are three poles and one finite zero. Thus, the asymptotes occur at the angles

$$\theta_\ell = \frac{1+2\ell}{p_{ex}} \times 180° \qquad \ell = 0, 1, \ldots, p_{ex} - 1,$$

or

$$\theta_0 = \frac{1 + (2)(0)}{2} \times 180° = 90°,$$

$$\theta_1 = \frac{1 + (2)(1)}{2} \times 180° = 270°.$$

The asymptotes intersect the real axis at

$$\sigma_i = \frac{[(-1) + (-40)] - (-2)}{2} = -19.5.$$

Since there is one finite zero and three poles, two closed-loop poles will migrate to zeros at infinity, one at the "end" of each asymptote.

Two possible root loci are shown in Fig. 5.17. In both cases, the poles at $s = 0$ and $s = -1$ migrate toward each other, and then break out of the real axis. The two loci indicate the possible paths of migration after the break out.

**Figure 5.17 |** Two plausible root loci, Example 5.4.1.

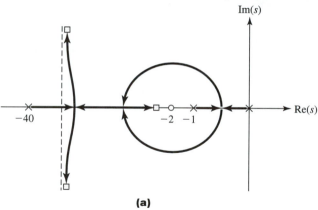

**(a)**

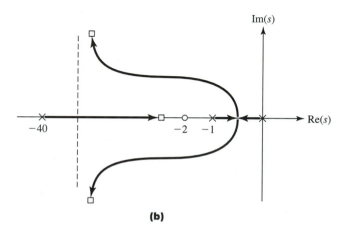

**(b)**

**Figure 5.18 |** Root locus for $GH(s) = \frac{K(s+2)}{s(s+1)}$.

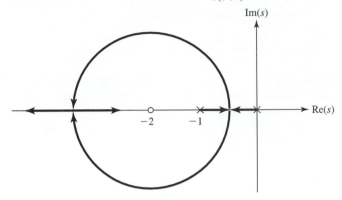

Of the two loci, that shown in Fig. 5.17(a) is by far the more probable. To rule out the case shown in Fig. 5.17(b) requires computing the gain along the real axis between $s = -40$ and $s = -2$. However, case (b) can be more or less ruled out by the following arguments. Consider first the satisfaction of the angle condition off the real axis near the origin. In this region, the angle contribution of the pole at $s = -40$ is very small. Thus near the origin the root locus should be similar to the locus for

$$GH(s) = \frac{K(s+2)}{s(s+1)}. \qquad \textbf{[5.19]}$$

The root locus for the $GH$ of Eq. [5.19] is shown in Fig. 5.18. Thus, we suspect that there is a break-in point in the neighborhood of $s = -3.5$.

On the other hand, farther away from the origin, say in a vertical strip midway between the pole of $GH$ at $s = -40$ and the zero at $s = -2$, the influence of the pole at $s = -40$ is much greater. In this region, the angle contributions of the pole of $GH$ at $s = -1$ and the zero at $s = -2$ nearly cancel each other. Thus, in this region the root locus is similar to that of

$$GH = \frac{K}{s(s+40)}. \qquad \textbf{[5.20]}$$

This root locus for the $GH$ of Eq. [5.20] has the familiar cross shape with a break-out point at $s = -20$. This leads us to the conclusion that there is probably a break-out point in the vicinity of $s = -20$.

Combining the analysis of these two approximate root loci leads us to believe that the most probable root locus is that of Fig. 5.17(a). This analysis also provides good starting points for determining the break-in and break-out points. The potential break-in point, if it exists, should be located near $s = -3.5$. This follows from the fact that the loci near the origin will be nearly a circle with a radius of approximately 1.5, centered at $s = -2$.

The break-out point should be in the region of $s = -20$, since the root locus farther from the origin should look like that of a system with poles at $s = 0$ and $s = -40$. This reasoning is confirmed by the data in Table 5.3, which shows the gains along the real

**Table 5.3 |** Search for maximum in gain, Example 5.4.1.

| $S$ | $-22$ | $-21$ | $-20$ | $-19$ | $-18$ |
|---|---|---|---|---|---|
| $K$ | 415.8 | 420 | 422.2 | 422.47 | 420.75 |

axis in the vicinity of $s = -20$. The table indicates that the peak gain occurs near $s = -19$. Thus the actual break-out point is close to that already predicted. Having found that there is a break-out point, it follows that a minimum must also exist and the correct root locus is indeed that shown in Fig. 5.17(a). We have not made a table to locate the break-in point exactly, leaving that as an exercise.

Example 5.4.2 illustrates that we occasionally have to do a little extra work to sort out the correct root locus from among several plausible candidates. In this particular example, the calculation of the angle of departure from a complex pole helps determine the correct root locus.

**EXAMPLE 5.4.2**

Draw the root locus for

$$GH = \frac{Ks}{(s - 1 - j)(s - 1 + j)(s + 2)(s + 4)}.$$

The first step in drawing the root locus is to plot the poles and zeros of $GH$. The portion of the root locus on the real axis is the shaded regions shown in Fig. 5.19.

The root locus has four poles and one finite zero. One of the limbs of the root locus will end at the finite zero. The other three limbs will end at what we have termed "zeros at infinity," that is zeros at the "end" of each of the three asymptotes.

Since the pole zero excess is three, the asymptotes are at

$$\theta = 60°, \ 180°, \ \text{and} \ 300°.$$

The asymptotes intersect at

$$\sigma_i = \frac{[0 + (1) + (1) + (-2) + (-4)] - [0]}{4 - 1}$$

$$= -1.33$$

**Figure 5.19 |** Root locus on the real axis, Example 5.4.2.

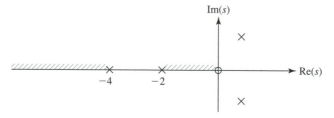

**Figure 5.20 |** Three potential root loci, Example 5.4.2.

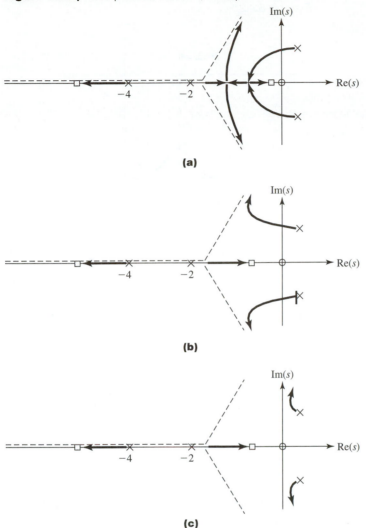

(a)

(b)

(c)

Three plausible root loci are shown in Fig. 5.20. If break-in and break-out points exist between $s = 0$ and $s = -2$, then the root locus will be that shown in Fig. 5.20(a). If there are no break-in and break-out points, the root locus will be that of either Fig. 5.20(b) or Fig. 5.20(c), depending on whether or not the locus crosses the imaginary axis.

To check for the possibility of break-in and break-out points we can calculate the gain at some representative values along the real axis. The plot will look like Fig. 5.21(a) if there are break-in and break-out points, and like Fig. 5.21(b) if there are no break-in or break-out points.

**Figure 5.21 |** Gain versus position for $s \in [-2, 0]$, Example 5.4.2.

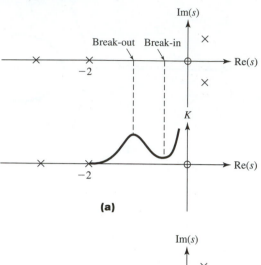

**(a)**

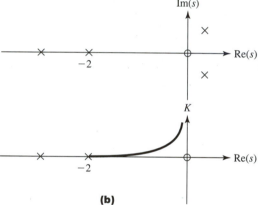

**(b)**

In Fig. 5.22, we can see how the gain would be computed for a representative point on the negative real axis. For any value of $s$ that we choose,

$$|GH(s)| = \frac{K|s|}{|s-1-j||s-1+j||s+2||s+4|} = 1,$$

and hence

$$K = \frac{|s-1-j||s-1+j||s+2||s+4|}{|s|}.$$

If we choose, for instance, $s = -1.9$, then

$$K = \frac{(\sqrt{1^2 + 2.9^2})(\sqrt{1^2 + 2.9^2})(0.1)(2.1)}{1.9} = 1.04.$$

**Figure 5.22 |** Computation of gain along the real axis, Example 5.4.2.

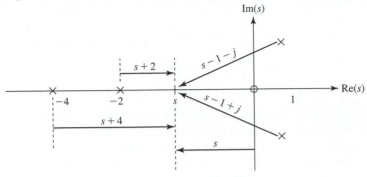

Table 5.4 summarizes the calculation of the gain on the interval $[-2, 0]$. As we see from the table, the gain increases monotonically from left to right along the negative real axis. This eliminates the locus in Fig. 5.20(a) from contention. The choice is now between the loci in Figs. 5.20(b) and 5.20(c).

Figure 5.23 shows how we would calculate the angle of departure from one of the complex poles. Somewhere on the small circle the angle condition

$$\alpha - \theta_1 - \theta_2 - \theta_3 - \theta_4 = -180°$$

**Table 5.4 |** Gain values for selected points in $[-2, 0]$, Example 5.4.2.

| $s$ | −1.6 | −1.4 | −1.2 | −1 | −0.8 | −0.6 | −0.4 | −0.2 | −0.1 |
|-----|------|------|------|-----|------|------|------|-------|--------|
| $K$ | 4.66 | 7.53 | 10.9 | 15 | 20.35 | 28.24 | 42.62 | 83.45 | 163.76 |

**Figure 5.23 |** Calculation of the angle of departure.

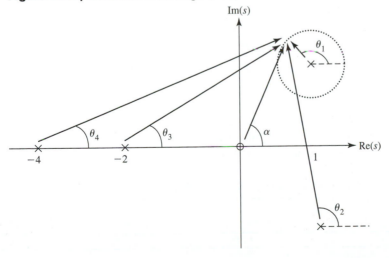

must be satisfied. As the circle shrinks in radius, all the angles except $\theta_1$ can be computed. That is,

$$\theta_1 = \tan^{-1}\frac{1}{1} + 180° - 90° - \tan^{-1}\frac{1}{3} - \tan^{-1}\frac{1}{5}$$

$$= 45° + 90° - 18.43° - 11.31°$$

$$= 105.3°.$$

Since the loci depart the complex poles in a nearly vertical direction, we are now fairly sure that the correct locus is that shown in Fig. 5.20(c).

To confirm this conjecture we investigate whether the root locus crosses the imaginary axis. We know that the root locus crosses the imaginary axis only if there is an $\omega$ for which $\underline{/GH(j\omega)} = -180°$. Figure 5.24 shows how this calculation is made.

**Figure 5.24 |** Angle calculation along the imaginary axis, Example 5.4.2.

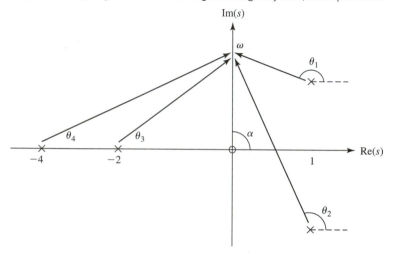

$$\underline{/GH(j\omega)} = \alpha - \theta_1 - \theta_2 - \theta_3 - \theta_4$$

$$= 90° - [180° - \tan^{-1}(\omega - 1)] - [180° - \tan^{-1}(\omega + 1)]$$

$$- \tan^{-1}\frac{\omega}{2} - \tan^{-1}\frac{\omega}{4}.$$

The value of $\underline{/GH(j\omega)}$ for some selected values of $\omega$ is shown in Table 5.5. From the table, we see that the root locus never crosses the imaginary axis and hence the correct root locus, as suspected, is that of Fig. 5.20(c).

**Table 5.5 |** Angle of loop transfer function along the imaginary axis, Example 5.4.2.

| $\omega$ | 0.1 | 1.0 | 1.8 | 2.4 | 3.2 | 3.4 |
|---|---|---|---|---|---|---|
| $\underline{/GH(j\omega)}$ | 91.4° | 112.8° | 132.8° | 136.9° | 135.5° | 134.7° |

We have now completed our main discussion of the rules of root locus for the dominant case, that of negative feedback. Occasionally, the need arises to draw a root locus for positive feedback. This is often referred to as the complementary root locus. We take a brief look at the complementary root locus in Section 5.5.

# 5.5 | NEGATIVE GAIN (COMPLEMENTARY) ROOT LOCUS

The rules of root locus developed so far are for negative feedback with $0 < K < \infty$. Suppose $-\infty < K < 0$. Then

$$1 + GH(s) = 1 + \frac{K \prod_{i=1}^{m} |s + z_i|}{\prod_{i=1}^{n} |s + p_i|} = 1 - \frac{|K| \prod_{i=1}^{m} |s + z_i|}{\prod_{i=1}^{n} |s + p_i|}. \qquad \textbf{[5.21]}$$

For $-\infty < K < 0$ the characteristic equation $1 + GH = 0$, then becomes

$$\frac{|K| \prod_{i=1}^{m} |s + z_i|}{\prod_{i=1}^{n} |s + p_i|} = 1\underline{/0°}. \qquad \textbf{[5.22]}$$

The only rules that are affected are those that involve the *angle* condition. This follows from the fact that the right-hand side of the characteristic equation is now $1\underline{/0°}$ rather than $1\underline{/-180°}$. We now restate the rules that change for the complementary root locus.

---

**Rule 5.5.1**

The root locus on the real axis is found to the left of an even count of poles and zeros.

---

This rule illustrates why the root locus for $-\infty < K < 0$ is called the complementary root locus. We see that the segments of the root locus on the real axis for the complementary root locus are the segments where root locus does *not* occur for $0 < K < \infty$. Hence the name complementary root locus.

---

**Rule 5.5.2**

The asymptotes are found from the formula

$$\theta_\ell = \frac{360° \times \ell}{p_{ex}}, \qquad \ell = 0, 1, 2, \ldots, p_{ex} - 1,$$

where $p_{ex}$ is the pole-zero excess.

---

**Rule 5.5.3**

Angles of departure and arrival must satisfy

$$\sum (\text{angles from zeros}) - \sum (\text{angles from poles}) = 0°.$$

---

In all, only three rules have changed, but they have a significant impact on the shape of the root locus. Not much use is made of the complementary root locus in this book. Despite that, two examples are included here to illustrate the drawing of the complementary root locus.

Consider again Example 5.3.7 with

$$GH(s) = \frac{Ks}{(s - 0.5 - j2)(s - 0.5 + j2)}.$$

In the complementary root locus, the locus on the real axis occurs to the left of an *even* count of poles and zeros of $GH$. Since zero is considered even, root locus on the real axis will occur only to the right of the zero at the origin. Recall from Example 5.3.7 that there were two critical points of the equation

$$\frac{dK}{ds} = 0,$$

namely, $s = \pm 2.06$. Thus the break-in point for the complementary root locus is at $s = 2.06$. After the break-in, one closed-loop pole migrates to the zero at the origin and the other to the right toward $s = +\infty$. Figure 5.25 shows both the locus for $0 < K < \infty$ and the complementary locus for $-\infty < K < 0$.

**Figure 5.25** | Root locus for $GH(s) = \frac{Ks}{(s-0.5 - j2)(s-0.5 + j2)}$, $-\infty < K < \infty$.

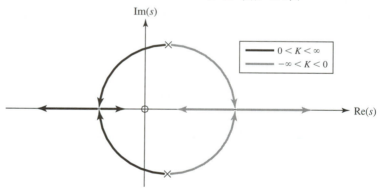

Consider again Example 5.3.1 with

$$GH = \frac{K(s+1)}{s(s+4)(s+10)}.$$

The root locus on the real axis occurs to the right of the pole at the origin, between the zero at $s = -1$ and the pole at $s = -4$, and to the left of the pole at $s = -10$. The pole-zero excess is $3 - 1 = 2$, so that there are two asymptotes at

$$\theta_0 = \frac{360° \times 0}{2} = 0,$$

$$\theta_1 = \frac{360° \times 1}{2} = 180°.$$

The root loci for both $0 < K < \infty$ and $\infty < K < 0$ are shown in Fig. 5.26.

**Figure 5.26** | Root locus for $GH = \frac{K(s+1)}{s(s+4)(s+10)} - \infty < K < \infty.$

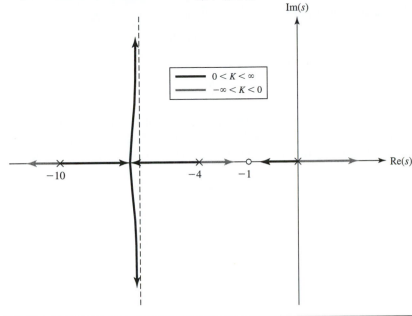

## 5.6 | POLYNOMIAL FACTORIZATION

In this brief section, we will use the rules of root locus to factor a polynomial. In this era of powerful handheld calculators and even more powerful personal computers, the reader may wonder why we are doing this. The answer is simple. We want to show that the rules of root locus can be applied to *any* unfactored polynomial. To that end, consider

$$p(s) = s^3 + 52s^2 + 512s + 1280.$$

To factor this polynomial, we first set it equal to zero and then divide both sides by $s^3 + 52s^2$ to obtain

$$1 + \frac{512s + 1280}{s^3 + 52s^2} = 0,$$

or

$$1 + \frac{512(s + 2.5)}{s^2(s + 52)} = 0.$$

We can use any subset of the terms on the left-hand side of the characteristic equation as a divisor, but the subset we have chosen leads to an easy factorization.

If we now replace 512 by $K$, we have

$$1 + \frac{K(s + 2.5)}{s^2(s + 52)} = 0.$$

This last equation looks like

$$1 + GH(s) = 0$$

for the fictitious loop transfer function

$$GH(s) = \frac{K(s + 2.5)}{s^2(s + 52)}.$$

Thus, we see that the problem of finding the roots of the characteristic polynomial of the closed-loop transfer function is a special case of factoring a polynomial. In the case of the closed-loop transfer function, the characteristic equation is already in the form

$$1 + GH(s) = 0,$$

but as we have just seen, we can always put an unfactored polynomial equation

$$s^n + \alpha_{n-1}s^{n-1} + \cdots + \alpha_1 s + \alpha_0 = 0$$

in this special form.

To complete our factorization we note that the roots we are seeking occur for $K = 512$. Examining the root locus in Fig. 5.27 we see that the polynomial will always have at least one real root, and potentially three real roots. Now all we have to do is search for a location on the root locus where $K = 512$. Table 5.6 summarizes the search. We see from the table that there is a break-out point near $s = -25$, a

**Figure 5.27 |** Root locus for polynomial factorization.

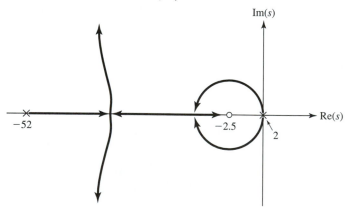

**Table 5.6 |** Values of gain along the real axis.

| $s$ | −45 | −40 | −30 | −25 | −20 | −10 | −8 | −5 | −4 |
|---|---|---|---|---|---|---|---|---|---|
| $K$ | 334 | 512 | 720 | 750 | 731 | 560 | 512 | 470 | 512 |

break-in point near $s = -5$ and *three* points where $K = 512$. Thus,

$$s^3 + 52s^2 + 512s + 1280 = (s + 4)(s + 8)(s + 40).$$

Actually, once we had found one of the real poles we could have divided out that root and solved the remaining second-order polynomial using the quadratic formula.

Few of us will ever be marooned on a desert island and have to resort to factoring polynomials by this method while waiting for a cruise ship to come and rescue us, but that is not the point. The point is that the root locus method is a graphical means of factoring polynomials, probably first investigated by Newton. We first encountered it in the control setting where the form

$$1 + G(s)H(s) = 0$$

arises naturally. As we have just seen, however, we can always put an unfactored polynomial in this form. We will have occasion to extend this idea slightly in Chapter 7 when we introduce root contours in a discussion of robust control.

## 5.7 | REPRISE

In this chaper we have developed the rules of root locus. These rules are all derived from rewriting the characteristic equation as

$$|GH(s)|\underline{/GH(s)} = 1\underline{/-180°}.$$

Then any point $s$ that is a solution of the characteristic equation must satisfy

$$|GH(s)| = 1 \quad \text{and} \quad \underline{/GH(s)} = -180°.$$

All the rules of root locus are derived from these two equations. However, as we have noted several times, it is the angle equation that is most important. To qualify as a solution, a point in the $s$ plane must satisfy the angle equation. If it does, then a gain can be found from the gain equation that will place a closed-loop pole at that solution point.

In sketching the root locus, we apply the rules in about the same order they were presented in this chapter. The first thing we do is find the root locus on the real axis. This is very easy to do and it helps us determine where break-in and break-out points might occur. We next determine the number of asymptotes from the pole-zero excess and find $\sigma_i$, the intersection of the asymptotes with the real axis.

We can then start sketching the root locus, starting at the poles of $GH$. Some of the branches will end at the finite zeros of $GH$, while remaining branches migrate to the asymptotes. We may have to compute the gain at selected points along the real axis to check for break-in and break-out points. As we have seen from the examples, we usually have a pretty good idea of where to check. Having sketched the root locus, we check to make sure it is symmetric about the real axis. If it is not, then we have made a mistake.

In this chapter, we also introduced the complementary root locus and polynomial factorization. We will not have many occasions to use the complementary root locus. It is introduced primarily to help solidify the reader's understanding of the basic ideas behind the root locus. Polynomial factorization will be of more use because we will introduce root contours in Chapter 7. Also, polynomial factorization is really what the root locus is, at bottom, all about. It just so happens that in the case of feedback control, the characteristic equation is already in the appropriate form. All we have to do is apply the rules. It should be clear, however, that we can put any unfactored polynomial in this form by dividing the polynomial by the sum of any subset of its terms.

In this day and age when computers are ubiquitous, it may seem that a graphical technique like root locus is outdated. To see why that is not the case consider the allegory of the cave in Book VII of Plato's *Republic*. There Socrates describes the following scene.

A group of citizens, representative of mankind as whole, sit chained in a cave facing one wall of the cave. They cannot turn their heads to see that behind them is a low wall behind which runs a roadway, and farther up a great fire burns perpetually. Other citizens carry various items from everyday life back and forth along the roadway. These items cast shadows on the far wall of the cave.

To the citizens chained in place, this endless sequence of shadows is reality. A philosopher's duty, according to Socrates, is to break free of the chains, assess the situation, and then find the narrow passageway that leads out of the cave to the real world. His second duty it to return to the cave and free his fellow prisoners.

If the reader wonders what Plato has to do with computers and the root locus, then consider this modern version of the allegory of the cave. You sit in front of a computer screen. Poles and zeros flash onto the screeen, and then the root locus for that set of poles and zeros appears very briefly, followed by a new set of poles and zeros and, very briefly, another root locus, and so on.

Depending on your background and aptitude, you may, after a while, begin to make some sense of the patterns. Maybe you finally begin to formulate a set of rules that enables you to quickly make a mental sketch of the root locus the minute the poles and zeros appear.

In other words, by trial and error, you find the rules of root locus. So, when we formulate the rules of root locus, we are looking for the same thing as Socrates: the clearest, simplest explanation of the phenomena we see around us. Our goal here is considerablly narrower than that of Socrates, but it is the same fundamental goal.

The rules of root locus give us a clear, precise understanding of the endless patterns that can be created by an infinite set of characteristic equations. We could, eventually, learn to design without these rules, and other analysis tools that we will develop later. But our level of skill would never be as high or our understanding as great.

With our knowledge of the rules of root locus in hand, our next goal is to be able to predict with reasonable accuracy the time response for a *specific* set of closed-loop poles. That is the subject of Chapter 6. There we determine figures of merit that will aid us in predicting both the transient and steady state responses of the closed-loop system to a step input. We will then be in a position to begin designing control strategies in Chapter 7.

# 5.8 | PROBLEMS

## 5.8.1 Applying the Rules of Root Locus

For each loop transfer function $GH(s)$, use the rules of root locus to *sketch* the root locus, then check your solution with MATLAB.

1. $\dfrac{K(s+2)}{s(s+1)}$

2. $\dfrac{K(s+1)}{s(s+2)}$

3. $\dfrac{K}{(s+3)^3}$

4. $\dfrac{K}{(s+3)^4}$

5. $\dfrac{10K(s+10)}{s(s+4)(s+20)}$

6. $\dfrac{10K(s+8)}{s(s+4)(s+30)}$

7. $\dfrac{10K(s+10)}{s(s+4)(s+40)}$

8. $\dfrac{10K(s+6)}{s(s+4)(s+40)}$

9. $\dfrac{K}{(s+2)(s+4)(s+10)}$

10. $\dfrac{10K}{(s+1)(s+4)(s+20)}$

11. $\dfrac{10K}{(s+1)(s+5)(s+30)}$

12. $\dfrac{K(s+2)}{s^2}$

13. $\dfrac{K(s+1)(s+2)}{s^3(s+30)(s+40)}$

14. $\dfrac{K(s+1)(s+3)}{s(s+2)^2(s+10)}$

15. $\dfrac{K(s+5)}{s(s+2)(s+40)}$

16. $\dfrac{K(s+2)}{s(s+1)(s+10)(s+20)}$

17. $\dfrac{K(s+1)}{(s-j4)(s+j4)(s+6)(s+10)}$

18. $\dfrac{Ks}{[(s+1)^2+1](s+2)(s+4)}$

19. $\dfrac{Ks}{[(s+2)^2+1](s+3)(s+5)}$

20. $\dfrac{K}{s(s+1)(s+10)}$

21. $\dfrac{K}{s(s+10)(s+40)}$

22. $\dfrac{K(s+2)}{s(s+1)(s+40)}$

23. $\dfrac{K(s+3)}{s(s+2)(s+50)}$

24. $\dfrac{K(s+3)}{s^2(s+5)(s+50)}$

25. $\dfrac{K(s+2)}{s^2(s+8)}$

26. $\dfrac{K(s+1)}{s^2(s+4)(s+40)}$

27. $\dfrac{K}{s(s+6)(s+20)}$

28. $\dfrac{K(s+1)}{s(s+5)(s+15)(s+30)}$

29. $\dfrac{K(s+4)}{s(s+1)(s+20)}$

30. $\dfrac{K(s+2)}{s(s+1)(s+40)}$

31. $\dfrac{K(s+2)}{[(s-1)^2+1]}$

32. $\dfrac{K}{s(s+1)(s+10)}$

33. $\dfrac{K(s+2)}{[(s+1)^2+1](s+20)(s+40)}$

34. $\dfrac{K(s+3)}{s(s+2)(s+15)}$

35. $\dfrac{K(s+1)}{s^2(s+3)(s+10)}$

36. $\dfrac{K(s+1)}{s^2(s+3)(s+10)}$

**37.** $\dfrac{K(s+1)}{s^2(s+20)(s+40)}$

**38.** $\dfrac{K(s+2)}{s^2(s+3)(s+10)}$

**39.** $\dfrac{K(s+2)(s+3)}{s^2(s+1)(s+30)(s+40)}$

**40.** $\dfrac{K(s+2)}{s(s+1)(s+20)(s+30)}$

**41.** $\dfrac{K(s+1)}{s(s+5)(s+6)(s+20)}$

**42.** $\dfrac{K(s+2)}{s(s+1)(s+21)}$

**43.** $\dfrac{K(s+2)}{s^2(s+25)(s+50)}$

**44.** $\dfrac{K(s+1)}{[(s-1)^2+1](s+10)(s+20)}$

## 5.8.2  Stability

For each loop transfer function, sketch the root locus and complete any additional tasks requested. Then check your result with MATLAB.

**1.** Let

$$G(s) = \frac{K}{s+1} \quad \text{and} \quad H(s) = \frac{s+2}{s-4}.$$

Find the range of gain $K$ for which the system is stable.

**2.** Let

$$G(s) = K\frac{s-2}{s+2}, \qquad H = 1.$$

Find the range of gain for which the system is stable.

**3.** Let

$$GH(s) = K\frac{s-1}{(s+1)(s+2)}$$

a.  Find the gain for which the closed-loop system has a pole at $s = 0$
b.  For the gain of part (a) find the other closed-loop pole.

**4.** Let

$$GH(s) = K\frac{s+1}{s(s-2)}$$

Find the range of gain for which the closed-loop system is stable.

**5.** Let

$$GH(s) = K\frac{s+1}{s(s-2)(s+40)}.$$

Find the range of gain for which the closed-loop system is stable.

**6.** Let

$$GH(s) = \frac{K(s+1)}{s^2(s+2)(s+4)}.$$

Find the range of gain for which the closed-loop system is stable.

### 5.8.3  Angles of Departure and Arrival

For each loop transfer function, find all angles of departure and arrival and *sketch* the root locus. Then check your result with MATLAB.

1. $\dfrac{K(s+2)}{[(s+1)^2+1](s+20)(s+30)}$

2. $\dfrac{K[(s+4)^2+16](s+10)}{s[(s+2)^2+4]}$

3. $\dfrac{K(s+3)}{[(s+1)^2+11](s+15)(s+20)}$

4. $\dfrac{K[(s+2)^2+40](s+10)}{s[(s+3)^2+45]}$

5. $\dfrac{K(s+4)^2}{s(s+1)(s+30)}$

6. $\dfrac{K[(s+4)^2+16](s+10)}{s[(s+2)^2+4]}$

7. $\dfrac{K[(s+2)^2+4]}{s^2(s+20)}$

8. $\dfrac{K(s+4)(s+8)}{[(s+2)^2+4](s+30)}$

### 5.8.4  Polynomial Factorization

Factor each polynomial using the rules of root locus. Then check your result using MATLAB.

1. $s^3+9s^2+20s+12$
2. $s^3+22s^2+152s+320$
3. $s^4+11s^3+41s^2+61s+30s^3+22s^2+152s+320$
4. $s^4+17s^3+80s^2+100s$
5. $s^4+23s^3+174s^2+472s+320$
6. $s^3-3s^2+4s+8$
7. $s^4+13s^3+76s^2+192s+128$
8. $s^5+71s^4+1470s^3+9400s^2+8000s$

### 5.8.5  Complementary Root Locus

For each loop transfer function $GH(s)$, use the rules of root locus to *sketch* the complementary root locus. Then check your answer with MATLAB.

1. $\dfrac{K(s+2)}{s(s+1)}$

2. $\dfrac{K(s+1)}{s(s+2)}$

3. $\dfrac{K}{(s+3)^3}$

4. $\dfrac{K}{(s+3)^4}$

5. $\dfrac{10K(s+10)}{s(s+4)(s+20)}$

6. $\dfrac{10K(s+8)}{s(s+4)(s+30)}$

7. $\dfrac{10K(s+10)}{s(s+4)(s+40)}$

8. $\dfrac{10K(s+6)}{s(s+4)(s+40)}$

9. $\dfrac{K}{(s+2)(s+4)(s+10)}$

10. $\dfrac{10K}{(s+1)(s+4)(s+20)}$

### 5.8.6  Additional Problems

1. Discuss why in root locus Rule 1, we don't have to consider the angle contributions of complex poles or zeros of $GH$.

2. Locate the break-in point in Example 5.4.1.

3. Write a short MATLAB program to plot the root locus for each $GH$ listed below. Use the MATLAB statement 'plot(X,Y,'bd')' to plot a diamond at each point on the root locus. Discuss why the diamonds are farther apart for low gain than they are for high gain.

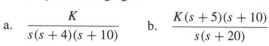

a. $\dfrac{K}{s(s+4)(s+10)}$   b. $\dfrac{K(s+5)(s+10)}{s(s+20)}$

c. $\dfrac{K(s+3)}{s(s+1)(s+40)}$   d. $\dfrac{K}{(s+5)^3}$

4. Let

$$GH(s) = \frac{K(s+2)}{s(s+1)(s+30)}.$$

Use the rules of root locus to find the gain for which the closed-loop system has two poles with real part $-2$. Find the third closed-loop pole for this gain.

5. Let

$$GH(s) = \frac{K(s+3)}{s(s+1)(s+15)}.$$

Use the rules of root locus to find the gain for which the closed-loop system has two poles with imaginary part $-5$. Find the third closed-loop pole for this gain.

6. Let

$$GH(s) = \frac{K(s+3)}{s(s+1)(s+15)}.$$

Use the rules of root locus to find the find the gain for which the closed-loop system has two poles on the rays through the origin of the $s$ plane that make angles of $\pm45°$ with the negative real axis. Find the third closed-loop pole for this gain.

## FURTHER READINGS

D'Azzo, John J., and Constantine H. Houpis. 1988. *Linear Control System Design, Conventional and Modern.* New York: McGraw-Hill.

Franklin, Gene F., J. David Powell, and Abbas Emami-Naeini. 1991. *Feedback Control of Dynamic Systems,* 2nd ed. Reading, Mass.: Addison-Wesley.

Kuo, Benjamin C. 1982. *Automatic Control,* 4th ed. Englewood Cliffs, N.J.: Prentice-Hall.

Ogata, K. 1970. *Modern Control Engineering.* Englewood Cliffs, N.J.: Prentice-Hall.

Saucedo, R., and E. E. Schiring. 1968. *Introduction to Continuous and Digital Control Systems.* New York: MacMillan.

# Chapter 6

# Quantifying Performance

## 6.1 | OVERVIEW

Chapter 5 introduced root locus analysis as a means of getting a complete picture of how the closed-loop poles move as the gain is changed. What we need now is a method of interpreting the time domain output of the closed-loop system for specific sets of poles on the root locus.

We could select a set of poles, find the associated gain, apply a specific input, and look at the time response. However, this is a tedious process that might have to be repeated many times. It would be preferable to be able to estimate the time response with reasonable accuracy without having to do any computation. That is, we would like to get *close* to the exact solution with minimum computational effort.

One could argue that given the computing power available today this is a quaint and outdated idea. There is a grain of truth in this last statement, but as we discussed in the reprise to Chapter 5 we do not want to fall into the trap of the allegory of the cave. If we can find a way to simply look at the root locus and gauge the time response for a particular reference input then we have greatly increased our design skills.

We have already seen that the root locus does provide some qualitative information about the time response. We know that the impulse response of a system with all real poles will certainly be different than that of a system that has complex poles, since in the latter case the response will be oscillatory while in the former case there will be no oscillation. At this juncture, however, it is not easy with our present knowledge to examine a root locus and say definitively just how much oscillation could be expected for a given set of complex poles.

We clearly need to develop quantitative measures of the performance of a closed-loop system. On the surface, this looks like a challenging goal, since we would like the closed-loop system to respond well to all inputs. Experience has shown, however, that we can get a very good idea of the response of a system to an arbitrary input by measuring its response to certain test inputs. The most useful test inputs are the unit step and unit ramp. If a system responds satisfactorily to both unit step and unit ramp inputs we can say with good confidence that it will respond well to any input.

We now have to quantify what we mean by the qualitative statement "responds well." We do this with numbers called figures of merit. Figures of merit describe quantitatively the performance of the closed-loop system. For example, if the input is a unit step, and the closed-loop response converges to 0.9, then we can say that there is a 10% error in steady state accuracy. As another example, if the system responds to a step input by overshooting its final steady value by 100% and oscillates for several seconds before stabilizing, we would say that the system is not very stable. The amount of overshoot and the duration of the oscillations could be used to quantify the stability of the system.

There are a number of figures of merit that help specify system performance. As one might guess they are related to our characterization of a good response in Chapter 1. There we said that the response of a system could be well characterized by the speed of its transient response, its steady state accuracy, and its stability. The figures of merit developed in this chapter quantify these three aspects of the time response of a closed-loop system.

It is possible to obtain figures of merit, expressible as simple formulas, that characterize the speed and stability of the response, *if* a very simple closed-loop transfer function is used and *if* we choose the appropriate input function. The simple transfer function that we will choose will be only an approximation to the actual closed-loop transfer function. Nonetheless, decades of experience with control systems have shown that this simple transfer function captures the response of more complex systems with good accuracy.

As a consequence, the formulas derived from this simple transfer function are accurate enough when applied to two more complex systems to make them very useful. In short, being able to compute the figures of merit from simple formulas is too attractive a feature to be discarded, even if the values obtained from the formulas are not perfectly accurate.

In Section 6.2 figures of merit related to speed of response and stability are developed in terms of a simple, normalized second-order transfer function and a unit step input. It is probably not obvious at this point why the unit step is the preferred test input. We will try to point out its utility as a test input as the discussion proceeds. Our first order of business, however, is to select a nominal closed-loop transfer function of minimum complexity. We do that next.

## 6.2 | NORMALIZED SECOND-ORDER SYSTEM

Consider the simple closed-loop transfer function

$$T_{N2}(s) = \frac{\omega_n^2}{s^2 + 2\zeta\omega_n s + \omega_n^2}. \qquad \text{[6.1]}$$

The parameters $\zeta$ and $\omega_n$ are called the "damping ratio" and "natural frequency," respectively. This seems to be an overly simple model, since it has only two poles and no zeros. Real closed-loop transfer functions are, in general, more complicated. However, if a closed-loop system has five poles, it very often happens that all five poles do not contribute equally to the closed-loop response. In many cases, one or two poles dominate the response. In that case, the model given by Eq. [6.1] can describe the behavior of a more complicated system quite accurately. The other feature of $T_{N2}$ that makes it valuable is that its response to a unit step input yields simple formulas for several useful figures of merit.

The poles of $T_{N2}$ can be found by applying the quadratic formula. However, it is a useful exercise to factor the characteristic equation using the root locus method developed in Chapter 5. To that end, consider the characteristic equation of this transfer function,

$$s^2 + 2\zeta\omega_n s + \omega_n^2 = 0,$$    [6.2]

which can be rearranged as

$$\left(s^2 + \omega_n^2\right) + 2\zeta\omega_n s = 0.$$    [6.3]

Dividing both sides by $s^2 + \omega_n^2$ yields

$$1 + \frac{2\zeta\omega_n s}{s^2 + \omega_n^2} = 0.$$    [6.4]

By fixing $\omega_n$ and letting $\zeta$ play the role of the variable gain, this equation becomes $1 + GH = 0$ for the *fictitious* loop transfer function

$$GH(s) = \frac{2\zeta\omega_n s}{s^2 + \omega_n^2} = \frac{2\zeta\omega_n s}{(s - j\omega_n)(s + j\omega_n)}.$$

The root locus of this "system" is shown in Fig. 6.1. For $\zeta = 0$, the system has two purely imaginary poles $s = \pm j\omega_n$. Recall from Chapter 5 that if $GH$ has two poles and one zero, the root locus off the real axis forms portions of a circle whose center is the zero of $GH$. The break-in point occurs when the gain

$$\zeta = \frac{|s - j\omega_n||s + j\omega_n|}{2\omega_n|s|}\bigg|_{s=-\omega_n} = \frac{\sqrt{\omega_n^2 + \omega_n^2}\sqrt{\omega_n^2 + \omega_n^2}}{2(\omega_n)(\omega_n)} = 1.$$

Thus, for $0 < \zeta < 1$, the normalized second-order transfer function of Eq. [6.2] has

**Figure 6.1 |** Root locus for $s^2 + 2\zeta\omega_n s + \omega_n^2 = 0$.

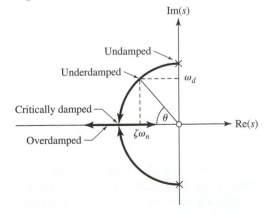

complex conjugate poles, and for $\zeta > 1$ two real poles. We can thus classify the response as undamped ($\zeta = 0$), underdamped ($0 < \zeta < 1$), or overdamped ($\zeta > 1$). For $\zeta = 1$, we say the system is critically damped. Critical damping corresponds to the fastest response that has no overshoot.

We will see shortly that the values of $\zeta$ of most interest are those between zero and one. The reason is that very often the best design has dominant complex conjugate poles. Choosing a design that has dominant complex poles generally produces a response that reacts quickly to changes in the reference input. The trick is to make sure the response is also stable. As it turns out, the stability can be accurately predicted from the damping ratio.

## 6.3 | STEP RESPONSE OF $T_{N2}$

The most common inputs used to test the efficacy of a control system design are the step and ramp inputs. In many industrial applications the input is a series of steps of different magnitude that move the system from one set point to the next. Ideally, we would like the system to move rapidly between set points with little oscillation. The step, because of its discontinuity, is a very good test of not only a system's "reaction time" but also its stability. When presented with a step input, the closed-loop system has a tendency to overreact, overshooting the final value of the step. Once it has overshot the steady state value, the system has to reverse itself. If the system is not properly designed, it may then undershoot the steady state value, and then overshoot it again. In a word, the system may oscillate. Thus, the amount of overshoot and any oscillations are measures of the closed-loop system's stability.

The other usual test input, the ramp $r(t) = t\mathbf{1}(t)$, is a reasonable measure of how well the system will track a rapidly varying input. Recall the antiaircraft gun example of Fig. 1.5. The control system in this case must be very fast since the aircraft may take evasive action, varying its velocity to prevent being targeted by the antiaircraft gun. For this system we would add to the unit step, two additional test inputs, the unit ramp and the unit parabolic input $r(t) = \frac{1}{2}t^2\mathbf{1}(t)$, to test the gun's response to both constant velocity and accelerating targets.

Our strategy will be to initially design the gun's response to these three standard test inputs and then measure the gun's response to a more representative input that simulates the actual path of an aircraft taking evasive action. We use this latter response to alter the gun's response to our three standard inputs.

After a few more iterations we get a satisfactory response to our representative input. In this process we gain some engineering expertise at correlating the gun's response to standard inputs to that of an input that represents how a target aircraft will actually maneuver. The benefit is that it is ultimately more efficient to design using a small number of standard test inputs.

However, by far the most common test input is the unit step. The reason, as discussed earlier, is that the discontinuity of the step at $t = 0$ makes the step one of the toughest signals for a system to track. Further, by using the unit step as the input to $T_{N2}$ we can find closed-form expressions for a useful set of figures of merit. Thus, our next goal is to find the step response of $T_{N2}$ in closed form.

To simplify the following expressions, we let

$$\omega_d \overset{\Delta}{=} \omega_n \sqrt{1 - \zeta^2}.$$

For $0 < \zeta < 1$, the frequency at which the time response oscillates will turn out to be $\omega_d$, as we see next.

Applying a unit step input to the transfer function of Eq. [6.1] yields

$$C(s) = \frac{1}{s} \frac{\omega_n^2}{(s + \zeta\omega_n - j\omega_d)(s + \zeta\omega_n + j\omega_d)}$$

$$= \frac{C_1}{s} + \frac{M}{s + \zeta\omega_n - j\omega_d} + \frac{M^*}{s + \zeta\omega_n + j\omega_d}.$$

We first find

$$C_1 = sC(s)|_{s=0} = \left( \frac{\omega_n^2}{s^2 + 2\zeta\omega_n s + \omega_n^2} \right)\Bigg|_{s=0} = 1.$$

The fact that $C_1 = 1$ means that $\lim_{t \to \infty} c(t) = 1$. Thus, the system will exhibit no steady state error to a unit step input. The discussion of steady state accuracy later in the chapter shows how this residue could have been evaluated by inspection.

The remaining residue to be determined is

$$M = \left[ \frac{(s + \zeta\omega_n - j\omega_d)\omega_n^2}{s(s + \zeta\omega_n - j\omega_d)(s + \zeta\omega_n + j\omega_d)} \right]\Bigg|_{s=-\zeta\omega_n + j\omega_d}$$

$$= \frac{\omega_n^2}{(-\zeta\omega_n + j\omega_d)(j2\omega_d)}$$

$$= \frac{\omega_n^2}{2\left[ -\omega_d^2 - j\zeta\omega_n\omega_d \right]}.$$

Then, since $\omega_d = \omega_n \sqrt{1 - \zeta^2}$, we can write

$$M = \frac{1}{2[-(1 - \zeta^2) - j\zeta\sqrt{1 - \zeta^2}]}$$

$$= \frac{1}{2[\sqrt{1 - \zeta^2}][-\sqrt{1 - \zeta^2} - j\zeta]}$$

$$= \frac{-\sqrt{1 - \zeta^2} + j\zeta}{2\sqrt{1 - \zeta^2}}.$$

Referring to Fig. 6.2 we see that

$$-\sqrt{1 - \zeta^2} + j\zeta = e^{j\gamma},$$

where

$$\gamma = \tan^{-1}\left[ \frac{-\zeta}{\sqrt{1 - \zeta^2}} \right].$$

**Figure 6.2 |** The angles $\gamma$ and $\theta$ used in the unit step response of $T_{N2}$.

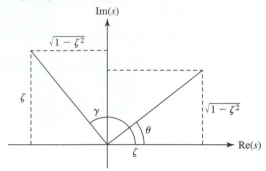

We note for future use that

$$\gamma = \frac{\pi}{2} + \theta,$$

with

$$\theta = \tan^{-1}\left(\frac{\sqrt{1-\zeta^2}}{\zeta}\right).$$

Thus, we have

$$M = \frac{e^{j\gamma}}{2\sqrt{1-\zeta^2}}.$$

Finally, we apply the inverse Laplace transform to obtain

$$
\begin{aligned}
c(t) &= \mathcal{L}^{-1}\{C(s)\} \\
&= \mathcal{L}^{-1}\left\{\frac{1}{s}\right\} + \mathcal{L}^{-1}\left\{\frac{M}{s + \zeta\omega_n - j\omega_d}\right\} + \mathcal{L}^{-1}\left\{\frac{M^*}{s + \zeta\omega_n + j\omega_d}\right\} \\
&= [1 + 2|M|e^{-\zeta\omega_n t}\cos(\omega_d t + \gamma)]\mathbf{1}(t) \\
&= \left[1 + \frac{e^{-\zeta\omega_n t}}{\sqrt{1-\zeta^2}}\cos(\omega_d t + \gamma)\right]\mathbf{1}(t).
\end{aligned}
$$

An alternative representation more common in the literature is

$$c(t) = \left[1 - \frac{e^{-\zeta\omega_n t}}{\sqrt{1-\zeta^2}}\sin(\omega_d t + \theta)\right]\mathbf{1}(t) \qquad \textbf{[6.5]}$$

with $\theta$ as defined in Fig. 6.2. This sine representation is easily obtained from the cosine representation by using

$$\cos\left(x + \frac{\pi}{2}\right) = -\sin x.$$

Having found the step response of $T_{N2}$ in closed form, we are now in a position to define some useful figures of merit. For the step response of $T_{N2}$, we will be able to find closed form expressions for these figures of merit, as shown next.

## 6.4 | FIGURES OF MERIT

Given either formula for the step response it is now possible to derive formulas for the figures of merit shown in Fig. 6.3. These figures of merit are the time to peak $t_p$, the rise time $t_r$, the settling time $t_s$, and percent overshoot (PO). Time to peak is self-explanatory, it is simply the time it takes to reach the peak value $C_{\max}$. We now discuss the other figures of merit briefly, indicating what aspect of the response they measure.

One definition of rise time, that shown in the figure, is the time it takes the response to reach 63% of its final value. Another common definition is the time it takes the response to rise from 10 to 90% of its final value. Rise time and time to peak measure the speed of response.

The settling time is defined in terms of a band about the final value, and is the time at which the response enters, and stays within, the band. The band is typically defined as the final value plus or minus 3 to 5%. Settling time is a measure of system stability and to some extent of speed of response.

Percent overshoot is defined as

$$\text{PO} = \frac{C_{\max} - \lim_{t \to \infty} c(t)}{\lim_{t \to \infty} c(t)} \times 100. \qquad \textbf{[6.6]}$$

Percent overshoot is a measure of system stability.

The figures of merit defined here can be measured for any system response, either experimentally or by simulation. What is really needed, however, is a means of predicting these values beforehand. This, in turn, requires formulas for the figures

**Figure 6.3 |** Figures of merit for underdamped response.

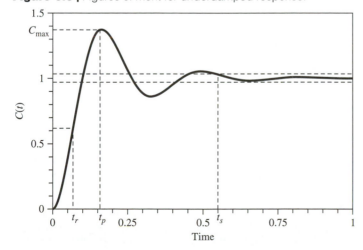

of merit. As discussed earlier, we can find such formulas for the figures of merit for $T_{N2}$, as defined by Eq. [6.1], for a step input. Those formulas are now developed.

### 6.4.1 Period of Oscillation $T_d$

The period of oscillation for a step input to $T_{N2}$, as given by Eq. [6.5], is

$$T_d = \frac{2\pi}{\omega_d} = \frac{2\pi}{\omega_n\sqrt{1-\zeta^2}}. \qquad \text{[6.7]}$$

### 6.4.2 Time to Peak $t_p$

The time to peak $t_p$ is given by

$$t_p = \frac{\pi}{\omega_d} = \frac{\pi}{\omega_n\sqrt{1-\zeta^2}}. \qquad \text{[6.8]}$$

This result can be obtained by differentiating Eq. [6.5] with respect to $t$ to obtain

$$\frac{d}{dt}c(t) = \frac{e^{-\zeta\omega_n t}}{\sqrt{1-\zeta^2}}[\zeta\omega_n \sin(\omega_d t + \theta) - \omega_d \cos(\omega_d t + \theta)]. \qquad \text{[6.9]}$$

Equating the right-hand side of Eq. [6.9] to zero then yields

$$\zeta\omega_n \sin(\omega_d t + \theta) - \omega_n\sqrt{1-\zeta^2}\cos(\omega_d t + \theta) = 0,$$

or

$$\tan(\omega_d t + \theta) = \frac{\sqrt{1-\zeta^2}}{\zeta} = \tan\theta. \qquad \text{[6.10]}$$

Since the tangent function repeats every $\pi$ radians, the maxima and minima occur when

$$\omega_d t = k\pi, \qquad k = 0, \pm 1, \pm 2, \ldots. \qquad \text{[6.11]}$$

The first maximum occurs for $k = 1$, making

$$t_p = \frac{\pi}{\omega_d} = \frac{\pi}{\omega_n\sqrt{1-\zeta^2}}. \qquad \text{[6.12]}$$

This is a very useful figure of merit. For one thing, it is easy to remember. Further, as $t_p$ decreases, so does $t_r$. In most cases, properly specifying $t_p$ is sufficient to guarantee a satisfactory rise time.

### 6.4.3 Percent Overshoot PO

For $0 < \zeta < 1$ the response will be underdamped. We can find a formula for percent overshoot as follows. Substituting the right-hand side of Eq. [6.12] into Eq. [6.5], yields

$$c_{\max} = c(t_p) = 1 - \frac{e^{-\zeta\omega_n(\pi/\omega_n\sqrt{1-\zeta^2})}}{\sqrt{1-\zeta^2}}\sin\left(\omega_d\frac{\pi}{\omega_d} + \theta\right)$$

$$= 1 + \frac{e^{-(\zeta\pi/\sqrt{1-\zeta^2})}}{\sqrt{1-\zeta^2}} (\sin\theta)$$

$$= 1 + e^{-(\zeta\pi/\sqrt{1-\zeta^2})},$$

where we have used the fact that $\sin\theta = \sqrt{1-\zeta^2}$.

If for the normalized second-order system of Eq. [6.5], we let

$$c_{ss} = \lim_{t\to\infty} c(t),$$

then the steady state response to a unit step input is $c_{ss} = 1$. Then

$$PO = \frac{c_{max} - c_{ss}}{c_{ss}} \times 100 = e^{-(\zeta\pi/\sqrt{1-\zeta^2})} \times 100. \qquad [6.13]$$

Note that PO depends only on the damping ratio $\zeta$.

The most convenient way to remember the relationship between percent overshoot and damping ratio is given in Fig. 6.4, which shows PO as a function of $\zeta$. Note that $\zeta = 0.5$ yields a PO of about 17%, while $\zeta = 0.7$ results in PO $\approx 4\%$. Thus for $\zeta > 0.7$, the system is essentially critically damped. In general, 20% is about the maximum tolerable overshoot. Thus, adequately compensated systems generally have $\zeta \geq 0.5$.

## 6.4.4 Settling Time $t_s$

Settling time is defined as the time at which the response settles to within some percentage of the final steady state value. A typical requirement is that the response be within 5% of the final steady state value, although smaller percentages can be specified. It is possible to get a good approximation to $t_s$ as follows. The times at

**Figure 6.4 |** Percentage overshoot versus $\zeta$ for step input to $T_{N2}$.

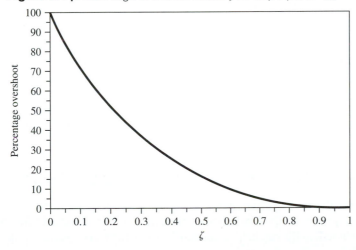

which $c(t)$ alternately reaches minima and maxima is given by the formula

$$t_k = \frac{k\pi}{\omega_n \sqrt{1 - \zeta^2}}, \quad k = 1, 2, \ldots. \tag{6.14}$$

Then $t_s$ can be approximated by finding the smallest $k$ for which $c(t_k)$ remains within some percentage of its final value of one. That is,

$$|c(t_k) - 1| = e^{-\zeta \omega_n t_k} \leq \frac{X}{100}, \tag{6.15}$$

where $X$ is a given percentage.

Taking the natural logarithm of both sides of Eq. [6.15] and then multiplying through by $-1$, yields

$$\zeta \omega_n t_k \geq -\ln \frac{X}{100}. \tag{6.16}$$

Substituting the expression for $t_k$ on the right-hand side of Eq. [6.14] into the left-hand side of Inequality [6.16] then gives

$$\frac{\zeta \omega_n k\pi}{\omega_n \sqrt{1 - \zeta^2}} \geq -\ln \frac{X}{100}. \tag{6.17}$$

Solving for $k$ then yields

$$k \geq \frac{\sqrt{1 - \zeta^2}}{\zeta \pi} \left( -\ln \frac{X}{100} \right). \tag{6.18}$$

Finally, using the value of $k$ from Inequality [6.18] in Eq. [6.14], we have

$$t_s \approx t_k = \frac{-\ln(X/100)}{\zeta \omega_n}. \tag{6.19}$$

For $X = 5$, this becomes

$$t_s = \frac{3}{\zeta \omega_n}.$$

### 6.4.5   Rise Time $t_r$

As previously discussed, there are various definitions of rise time. It is possible to derive a formula for rise time for $T_{N2}$. However, the formula is reasonably complicated and of limited use since rise time is strongly correlated to time to peak. Since $t_p$ is easy to compute, it will serve as the measure of speed of response.

Part of the reason for making this choice is the fact that $T_{N2}$ has only the two parameters $\zeta$ and $\omega_n$. As a consequence, specifying values for four or five figures of merit, all of which depend on the same two parameters, is futile. Therefore, if we can only pick two figures of merit, $t_p$ and PO turn out to be useful choices, as discussed next.

## 6.5 | FIGURES OF MERIT—A DISCUSSION

As we have discussed before, effective control can be summed up as satisfactory transient response, adequate steady state accuracy, and good stability. The figures of merit discussed so far can help us quantify two of the three qualitative descriptors, namely, "satisfactory" transient response and "good" stability. Time to peak and rise time quantify the transient response, while PO and settling time are measures of stability.

If we reduce the time to peak, we automatically reduce the rise time. Similarly, if we limit the overshoot we usually end up with a satisfactory settling time. Since PO depends only on $\zeta$, while $t_p$ depends on both $\zeta$ and $\omega_n$, it is possible to specify both percent overshoot and time to peak. This is done by first picking a value of $\zeta$ that will give the desired percent overshoot. Using this value of $\zeta$, $\omega_n$ can be determined from Eq. [6.8]. These ideas can best be illustrated with Example 6.5.1.

**EXAMPLE 6.5.1**

Figure 6.5 shows a large dish antenna whose azimuthal angle $\theta$ and elevation angle $\phi$ can be changed, allowing the antenna to point in any direction. Let us assume $\theta$ is controlled by a large dc motor. An appropriate model is Eq. [3.21], repeated here for convenience:

$$G_\theta(s) = \frac{K_m}{[s^2 + (B/J)s + K_r/J](s + R_q/L_q) + K_v K_m s}. \qquad [6.20]$$

For the purposes of this example, we will select the numbers for ease of computation by letting

$$G_\theta(s) = \frac{10}{s(s+4)(s+50)}. \qquad [6.21]$$

If we add gain compensation and unity feedback, as shown in Fig. 6.6, then

$$T_c(s) = \frac{10K}{s^3 + 54s^2 + 200s + 10K}. \qquad [6.22]$$

Suppose we increase the gain until the closed-loop system has a pair of dominant complex poles with a damping ratio $\zeta = 1/\sqrt{2}$, as shown in Fig. 6.7. The point where the root locus crosses the line of constant damping ratio can be found by searching along the line until the angle condition is satisfied. It is easy enough to verify that the crossing point is $s = -1.92 + j1.92$. The gain to place the complex poles of the

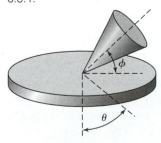

**Figure 6.5 |** Satellite tracking antenna for Example 6.5.1.

**Figure 6.6 |** Gain compensation with unity feedback for Example 6.5.1.

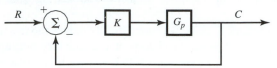

**Figure 6.7 |** Satisfying angle condition along line of constant damping for Example 6.5.1.

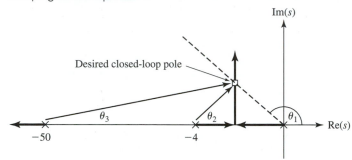

closed-loop transfer function at $s = -1.92 \pm j1.92$ is

$$K = \left[ \frac{|s||s+4||s+50|}{10} \right]_{s=-1.92+j1.92} = 36.98 \rightarrow 37.$$

The third closed-loop pole is on the negative real axis to the left of $s = -50$. We can find it by simply evaluating $K$ for some points along this portion of the real axis until we finally find $K = 37$. We do not have to search far. The third pole is at $s = -50.16$. Thus, to a very good approximation

$$T_c(s) = \frac{37}{(s+1.92 - j1.92)(s+1.92+j1.92)(s+50.16)}.$$

The unit step response in partial fraction form is

$$C(s) = \frac{A}{s} + \frac{B}{s+50.16} + \frac{M^*}{s+1.92+j1.92} + \frac{M}{s+1.92-j1.92}.$$

With a little work we find

$$A = 1, \qquad B = -0.0032, \qquad M = 0.7365\underline{/2.3163} \text{ rad.}$$

Thus,

$$c(t) = [1 - 0.0032e^{-50.2t} + 1.473e^{-1.92t}\cos(1.92t + 2.3163)]\mathbf{1}(t).$$

A plot of the step response is shown in Fig. 6.8. As we can see, the values obtained from the formulas for time to peak and PO are very close to the actual values taken from the time response. The results are not always this good. If the pole of the plant at $s = -50$ were moved in to $s = -10$, we would get a lower damped frequency and more overshoot than predicted by the formula.

**Figure 6.8 |** Unit step response for Example 6.5.1 with $K = 37$.

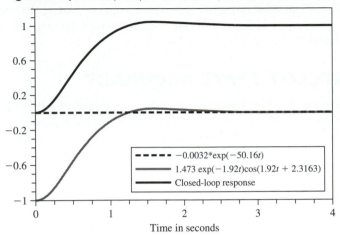

An accurate root locus plot is shown in Fig. 6.9. From the plot, we see that the pole of the plant at $s = -50$ has very little influence on the root locus near the origin, which is why the time response is very close to what we expect from the formulas. We will not always be so fortunate, as we will see in Chapter 7.

**Figure 6.9 |** Accurate root locus for Example 6.5.1 with $K = 37$.

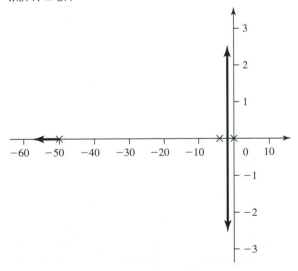

The other component of good control, namely, adequate steady state accuracy, can be achieved independently of the the two parameters $\zeta$ and $\omega_n$. It depends on the plant poles and zeros and the overall gain. Quantification of steady state accuracy is considered next.

## 6.6 | STEADY STATE ACCURACY

The traditional approach to steady state accuracy is to formulate it in terms of specific reference inputs, namely the unit step, the unit ramp and the unit parabolic function. Steady state accuracy is simply how close the system finally comes to matching the reference input. This is most easily formulated as the error between the two signals. That is, we let

$$e(t) = r(t) - c(t).$$ **[6.23]**

As usual, it will prove to be most useful to consider the Laplace transforms of these three quantities. In what follows, we first develop expressions for steady state accuracy for the closed-loop transfer function. We then consider the special case of unity feedback and find that we can express steady state accuracy in terms of the open-loop transfer function.

### 6.6.1   Closed-Loop Formulation

Given the closed-loop transfer function $T_c(s)$, we can write

$$E(s) = R(s) - C(s) = R(s)[1 - T_c(s)].$$

Let $e_{ss} \triangleq \lim_{t \to \infty} e(t)$. Using the final value theorem we obtain

$$e_{ss} = \lim_{s \to 0} s E(s) = \lim_{s \to 0} s R(s)[1 - T_c(s)].$$

If the reference input is a unit step function, then

$$e_{ss} = \lim_{s \to 0} s \left( \frac{1}{s} \right)[1 - T_c(s)] = 1 - \lim_{s \to 0} T_c(s).$$

If $T_c$ is a ratio of polynomials in the Laplace variable $s$, then we can write

$$e_{ss} = 1 - T_c(0).$$

Thus, zero steady state error to a step input requires that

$$T_c(0) = 1.$$

If $r(t) = t\mathbf{1}(t)$, a ramp input, then

$$e_{ss} = \lim_{s \to 0} s \left( \frac{1}{s^2} \right)[1 - T_c(s)] = \lim_{s \to 0} \left[ \frac{1 - T_c(s)}{s} \right].$$

If $T_c(0) \neq 1$, then the steady state error to a ramp is infinite. Thus, keeping the steady state error to a ramp finite requires that the system exhibit zero steady state error to a step. Given that the system has zero steady state error to a step, the expression listed previously for $e_{ss}$ is still indeterminate. Applying L'Hospital's rule yields

$$e_{ss} = -\lim_{s \to 0} \frac{d}{ds} T_c(s). \qquad [6.24]$$

Equation [6.24] is useful in its own right, but we can turn it into a much better result with just a little work. Let

$$T_c(s) = \frac{K \prod_{i=1}^{m}(s + z_i)}{\prod_{i=1}^{n}(s + p_i)},$$

and then write

$$\frac{d}{ds} \ln T_c(s) = \frac{1}{T_c(s)} \frac{d}{ds} T_c(s). \qquad [6.25]$$

Next, supposing that the closed-loop system has no error to a step input, so that $\lim_{s \to 0} T_c(s) = 1$, we have

$$\lim_{s \to 0} \left[ \frac{d}{ds} \ln T_c(s) \right] = \lim_{s \to 0} \left[ \frac{1}{T_c(s)} \frac{d}{ds} T_c(s) \right] = \lim_{s \to 0} \left[ \frac{d}{ds} T_c(s) \right].$$

Thus

$$e_{ss} = -\lim_{s \to 0} \left[ \frac{d}{ds} \ln T_c(s) \right]. \qquad [6.26]$$

What makes this development important is that the right-hand side of Eq. [6.26] leads to this simple (and pleasing) result:

$$-\lim_{s \to 0} \left[ \frac{d}{ds} \ln T_c(s) \right] = -\lim_{s \to 0} \frac{d}{ds} \left[ \ln \frac{K \prod_{i=1}^{m}(s + z_i)}{\prod_{i=1}^{n}(s + p_i)} \right]$$

$$= -\lim_{s \to 0} \frac{d}{ds} \left[ \ln K + \sum_{i=1}^{m} \ln(s + z_i) - \sum_{i=1}^{n} \ln(s + p_i) \right]$$

$$= \left[ \sum_{i=1}^{n} \frac{1}{p_i} - \sum_{i=1}^{m} \frac{1}{z_i} \right].$$

Thus, we have the very useful formula

$$e_{ss} = \left[ \sum_{i=1}^{n} \frac{1}{p_i} - \sum_{i=1}^{m} \frac{1}{z_i} \right], \qquad [6.27]$$

which expresses the steady state error to a ramp input in terms of the poles and zeros of the closed-loop transfer function $T_c(s)$. It is worth noting that the formula for $e_{ss}$ for a ramp input does not depend on the gain of $T_c$.

**EXAMPLE 6.6.1**

Consider again the satellite tracking antenna of Example 6.5.1. Using Eq. [6.22] it, is easily seen that $T_c(0) = 1$, and the system should exhibit zero steady state error to a step input. However, consider what happens if we move the gain to the feedback

**Figure 6.10 |** Antenna configuration with gain in feedback loop, Example 6.6.1.

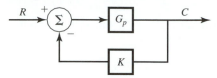

loop, as shown in Fig. 6.10. For this configuration

$$T_c(s) = \frac{10}{s^3 + 54s^2 + 200s + 10K}.$$

The reader should verify that the same gain as before is required to place the closed-loop poles at the same locations as in Example 6.5.1. For this system, the steady state error is not zero since $T_c(0) \neq 1$. Indeed,

$$T_c(0) = \frac{1}{K} = \frac{1}{37} = 0.027.$$

and

$$e_{ss} = 1 - T_c(0) = 0.973.$$

Thus, we see that where we add the gain is crucial to the steady state accuracy.

We can also see that with *either* configuration, steady state error to a ramp input will not be zero. If we keep the gain in the forward loop then the steady state error to a ramp is finite and can be computed from Eq. [6.27] to be

$$e_{ss} = \frac{1}{50.2} + \frac{1}{1.92 - j1.92} + \frac{1}{1.92 + j1.92} = 0.541.$$

The fact that $T_c$ has no zeros means that the steady error to a ramp input cannot be zero.

From Example 6.6.1 we gain some appreciation for the advantages of unity feedback. Indeed, in the design Chapters 7, 11, 12, 15, and 20, we will normally assume unity feedback. In the context of the present discussion, unity feedback makes it possible to express the steady state error in terms of the loop transfer function, as discussed next.

### 6.6.2   Unity Feedback Formulation

Recall that for

$$T_c(s) = \frac{G(s)}{1 + G(s)H(s)},$$

with $H \neq 1$, the general expression for steady state error becomes

$$e_{ss} = \lim_{s \to 0} s R(s) \left[ 1 - \frac{G(s)}{1 + G(s)H(s)} \right]$$

$$= \lim_{s \to 0} s R(s) \left[ \frac{1 + G(s)H(s) - G(s)}{1 + G(s)H(s)} \right].$$

This expression is not very enlightening. However, if $H(s) = 1$, then this expression for steady state error simplifies to

$$e_{ss} = \lim_{s \to 0} s R(s) \left[ \frac{1}{1 + G(s)} \right]. \qquad [6.28]$$

Equation [6.28] is very simple, and leads to the concept of error constants. Error constants are figures of merit for closed-loop steady state accuracy that can be expressed in terms of the forward loop transfer function $G$. Three of these error constants are of great importance as discussed next.

Suppose

$$G(s) = \frac{K \prod_{i=0}^{m}(s + z_i)}{s^{\ell} \prod_{i=0}^{n-\ell}(s + p_i)}. \qquad [6.29]$$

We assume that there are $\ell$ poles at the origin, where $\ell$ is an integer. The remaining poles are assumed to be strictly in the left half of the $s$ plane. Equation [6.28] is now applied to three specific reference inputs, namely, the step, ramp, and parabolic functions.

For the unit step input,

$$e_{ss} = \lim_{s \to 0} s \left( \frac{1}{s} \right) \left[ \frac{1}{1 + G(s)} \right] = \frac{1}{1 + \lim_{s \to 0} G(s)}. \qquad [6.30]$$

Defining

$$K_p \triangleq \lim_{s \to 0} G(s),$$

we can then write

$$e_{ss} = \frac{1}{1 + K_p}. \qquad [6.31]$$

$K_p$ is called the position error constant, a name that makes sense since it measures the ability of the closed-loop system to track a steady output that can be thought of as position.

For instance, the input signal could be the new azimuth angle $\theta$ for the satellite tracking radar dish of Example 6.5.1. The larger $K_p$, the better the dish will align with the desired azimuth. For perfect alignment we must have $K_p \to \infty$. This in turn requires that $G$ have at least one pole at $s = 0$. If there are no poles at $s = 0$, then using Eq. [6.29], we see that

$$K_p = \lim_{s \to 0} \frac{K \prod_{i=0}^{m}(s + z_i)}{\prod_{i=0}^{n}(s + p_i)} = \frac{K \prod_{i=0}^{m} z_i}{\prod_{i=0}^{n} p_i},$$

and the steady state error to a step input is finite. In the case of the antenna system, there is a single pole at the origin, so if we use unity feedback, the system will exhibit zero error to a step input.

For a ramp input,

$$e_{ss} = \lim_{s \to 0} s \left( \frac{1}{s^2} \right) \left[ \frac{1}{1 + G(s)} \right] = \frac{1}{\lim_{s \to 0} s G(s)} \qquad [6.32]$$

Following the pattern we used for the step input, we define

$$K_v \overset{\Delta}{=} \lim_{s \to 0} s G(s), \qquad [6.33]$$

and then write

$$e_{ss} = \frac{1}{K_v}. \qquad [6.34]$$

$K_v$ is called the velocity error constant. For our satellite tracking example, $K_v$ represents the long-term error in tracking a steadily changing azimuth angle.

We see that if the forward loop transfer function $G$ has no poles at $s = 0$, then

$$K_v = 0,$$

and

$$e_{ss} = \frac{1}{K_v} = \infty.$$

If $G$ has one pole at $s = 0$, then $K_v$ and $e_{ss}$ will both be finite. To have no steady state error to a ramp input, $G$ must have two or more poles at $s = 0$.

If we continue on along the same path, the next logical reference input is $r(t) = \frac{1}{2}t^2 \mathbf{1}(t)$ the parabolic input. For this choice of $r(t)$,

$$e_{ss} = \lim_{s \to 0} s \left( \frac{1}{s^3} \right) \left[ \frac{1}{1 + G(s)} \right] = \frac{1}{\lim_{s \to 0} s^2 G(s)} = \frac{1}{K_a},$$

where

$$K_a \overset{\Delta}{=} \lim_{s \to 0} s^2 G(s).$$

As we might expect, $K_a$ is called the acceleration constant and, in terms of our satellite example, represents the acceleration of a time varying azimuth angle. It follows from our previous discussion that if $G$ has one or fewer poles at $s = 0$, then the steady state error to the parabolic input will be infinite. If $G$ has two poles at $s = 0$, then the steady state error will be finite, and three or more poles at the origin are required to make the steady state error equal to zero.

**Table 6.1** | Steady state error versus system type for step, ramp, and parabolic inputs.

| Input/system type | 0 | 1 | 2 | 3 |
|---|---|---|---|---|
| $1/s$ | Finite | 0 | 0 | 0 |
| $1/s^2$ | $\infty$ | Finite | 0 | 0 |
| $1/s^3$ | $\infty$ | $\infty$ | Finite | 0 |

At this juncture, it should be clear that the analysis can be repeated for any input of the form

$$R(s) = \frac{1}{s^k}, \quad k = 1, 2, \ldots.$$

In practice, the only cases of interest are $k \leq 3$. This development can be consolidated into a table as follows. Let the number of poles of $G$ at $s = 0$ designate the system type. Thus if $G$ has no poles at $s = 0$, it is called type 0, if it has one it is called type 1, and so on. Table 6.1 then summarizes our development of error constants.

**EXAMPLE 6.6.2**

Suppose we revisit the satellite tracking antenna and this time add some additional compensation in the forward loop, namely,

$$G_c(s) = \frac{K(s+1)}{s},$$

as shown in Fig. 6.11. In Chapter 7 we will see that this is called a proportional plus integral (PI) compensator. It is primarily used to improve the steady state error characteristics of a system. The overall forward loop transfer function is now

$$G_c G_p(s) = \frac{10K(s+1)}{s^2(s+4)(s+50)}.$$

An accurate root locus for this system is shown in Fig. 6.12. Note that the root locus shows only three of the four branches. The fourth branch is to the left of $s = -50$ and is not shown. We see from the root locus that the dominant poles never have a damping ratio of $\zeta = 1/\sqrt{2}$. The largest damping ratio occurs for dominant poles at

**Figure 6.11** | Antenna configuration with added compensation, Example 6.6.2.

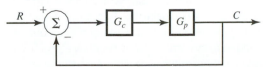

**Figure 6.12** | Accurate root locus for Example 6.6.2.

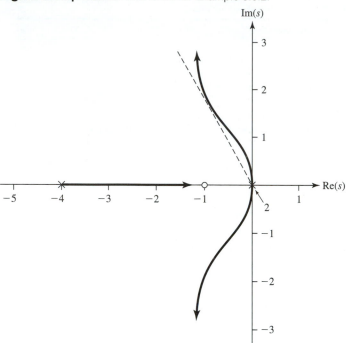

$s = -1 \pm j1.917$, for a gain of $K = 42.6$. For this gain

$$T_c(s) = \frac{42.6(s+1)}{(s+1-j1.917)(s+1+j1.917)(s+1.183)(s+50.18)}.$$

The damping ratio for the dominant poles is

$$\zeta = \cos[\tan^{-1}(1.917)] = 0.463.$$

From the formula for PO to a unit step input we compute

$$PO = \exp\left[\frac{-(0.4525)(\pi)}{\sqrt{1-0.4625^2}}\right] \times 100 = 19.4\%.$$

The actual PO, as shown in Fig. 6.13(a), is closer to 50%. Thus, the formula is not particularly accurate in this instance. Part of the problem is the closed-loop pole at $s = -1.813$.

By way of contrast, the unit ramp response is shown in Fig. 6.13(b). This response if very smooth and the output is closing to its steady state value after 4 s. This is another example of why the unit step is often the primary input for testing the tracking response of the closed-loop system. The discontinuity at $t = 0$ is very difficult to track, more so than the rapidly changing, but continuous unit ramp.

**Figure 6.13 |** Step (a) and ramp (b) responses for the closed-loop system of Example 6.6.2.

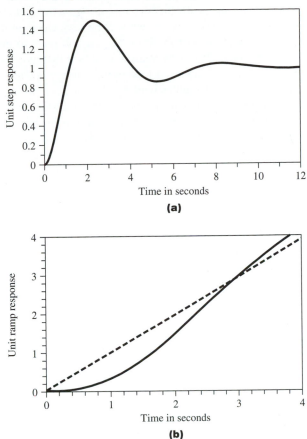

(a)

(b)

# 6.7 | REPRISE

In this chapter, we have developed quantitative measures of system performance called figures of merit. The figures of merit can be easily measured from the actual or simulated response of a system of any complexity. Further, they measure the three properties of a system's response that are of most interest, namely, the quickness of the transient response, the stability of the system, and its ability to track the reference input.

We next found that for a simplified closed-loop transfer function, which we called $T_{N2}$, we could obtain closed-loop expressions for the figures of merit. We then found that the value of a particular figure of merit, as computed from the formula, was a reasonably good estimate of that same figure of merit for a system of greater complexity than $T_{N2}$.

This makes the formulas valuable because they enable us to make a very good first estimate of where the dominant poles of the closed-loop system should be. As we shall see in Chapter 7, this means that our first design will be close to the mark. We may have to iterate once or twice, but we will be very close on the first try. In short, the formulas for the figures of merit of $T_{N2}$ are too good to give up even if they are only approximations. Part of the reason for this is that most systems can be compensated in a way that yields a closed-loop transfer function with two, *dominant* complex poles. In this case, the formulas work quite well.

In this chapter, we also developed formulas for computing the steady state error of the closed-loop system to step, ramp, and parabolic inputs, using both the closed-loop transfer function and the loop transfer function. For the closed-loop transfer function, we found that we could specify the steady state error to both a step and ramp input if the closed-loop transfer function had at least one zero. In later chapters, we will make use of this formula by modifying $T_{N2}$ slightly so that it has a zero and an adjustable gain.

For unity feedback, we also found that we could express the steady state error in terms of the forward loop transfer function. More specifically, we were able to express the steady state error in terms of the error constants $K_p$, $K_v$ and $K_a$. By defining the system type to be the number of poles of $G$ at $s = 0$, we were then able to see by inspection the steady state error of the closed look system to input functions of the form $1/s^\ell$.

Finally, we noted that since $T_{N2}$ has only two parameters, $\zeta$ and $\omega_n$, it is not possible to specify independently the rise time, time to peak, settling time, and percent overshoot of $T_{N2}$. We then concluded that time to peak and PO could be specified independently in terms of $\zeta$ and $\omega_n$. As we will see in Chapter 7, it is possible in the majority of design situations to get a satisfactory response by simply specifying the time to peak and the percent overshoot. In practically every case encountered in practice, reducing the time to peak reduces the rise time. Further, if the percent overshoot is less than 20%, the response of most systems does not oscillate. By making $\zeta \geq 0.7$, the percent overshoot can be held under 20%. Thus, for the root locus design presented in Chapter 7 the specifications will be given in terms of time to peak and percent overshoot.

We have now assembled a sufficient set of tools to begin designing control systems. In Chapter 7 we begin to do so, combining root locus analysis with the figures of merit developed in this chapter.

# 6.8 | PROBLEMS

## 6.8.1  Time Response

For the feedback configuration of Fig. 6.14, find the specified dominant closed-loop poles, and then plot the response to a unit step input for each transfer function $G$ listed.

**1.** $\dfrac{K}{(s+1)(s+5)}$, $\zeta = \dfrac{1}{\sqrt{2}}$

**2.** $\dfrac{K}{(s+1)(s+5)}$, $\omega_d = 4$ rad/s

**Figure 6.14 |** Unity feedback configuration.

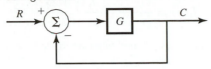

3. $\dfrac{K}{(s+5)(s+10)}$, $\omega_d = 5$ rad/s

4. $\dfrac{K}{(s+5)(s+10)}$, $\zeta = 0.8$

5. $\dfrac{K}{(s+20)(s+40)}$, $\zeta = 1.0$

6. $\dfrac{K}{(s+20)(s+40)}$, $\omega_d = 10$ rad/s

7. $\dfrac{K}{(s+1)(s+3)}$, $\omega_d = 10$ rad/s

8. $\dfrac{K}{(s+1)(s+3)}$, $\omega_d = 2$ rad/s

9. $\dfrac{K}{(s+1)(s+3)}$, $\zeta = 0.9$

10. $\dfrac{K}{s(s+1)(s+30)}$, $\zeta = \frac{1}{\sqrt{2}}$

11. $\dfrac{K}{s(s+1)(s+30)}$, $\zeta = 0.4$

12. $\dfrac{K}{s(s+1)(s+30)}$, $\zeta = 0.2$

13. $\dfrac{K}{s(s+1)(s+30)}$, $\omega_d = 15$ rad/s

14. $\dfrac{K(s+0.5)}{s(s+5)(s+20)}$, $\zeta = 0.6$

15. $\dfrac{K(s+0.5)}{s(s+5)(s+20)}$, $\zeta = 0.8$

16. $\dfrac{K(s+1)}{s(s+4)(s+10)}$, $\zeta = 0.8$

17. $\dfrac{K(s+1)}{s(s+4)(s+20)}$, $\zeta = 0.5$

18. $\dfrac{K(s+1)}{s(s+4)(s+30)}$, $\omega_d = 10$ rad/s

## 6.8.2 Steady State Accuracy

For the feedback configuration of Fig. 6.14, assume the closed-loop transfer function is

$$T_c(s) = \frac{G(s)}{1 + G(s)}.$$

Determine the unknown parameters necessary to achieve the desired closed-loop steady state accuracy. Then find and plot the unit step and unit ramp responses.

1.
$$T_c(s) = \frac{K(s+\delta)}{(s+\sigma - j\omega_d)(s+\sigma + j\omega_d)},$$

with $\omega_n = 5$ rad/s, $\zeta = 0.8$, and zero steady state error to both step and ramp inputs.

2.
$$T_c(s) = \frac{K(s+\delta)}{(s+\sigma - j\omega_d)(s+\sigma + j\omega_d)},$$

with $\omega_n = 5$ rad/s, $\zeta = 0.8$, zero steady state error to step input, and 10% error to a ramp input.

**3.**

$$T_c(s) = \frac{K(s + \delta)}{(s + \sigma - j\omega_d)(s + \sigma + j\omega_d)},$$

with $\omega_n = 5$ rad/s, $\zeta = 1/\sqrt{2}$, and zero steady state error to both step and ramp inputs.

**4.**

$$T_c(s) = \frac{K(s + \delta)}{(s + \sigma - j\omega_d)(s + \sigma + j\omega_d)},$$

with $\omega_n = 5$, $\zeta = 1/\sqrt{2}$, zero steady state error to step input, and 5% error to a ramp input.

**5.**

$$T_c(s) = \frac{K(s + \delta)}{(s + \sigma - j\omega_d)(s + \sigma + j\omega_d)(s + 20)},$$

with $\omega_n = 10$, $\zeta = 1/\sqrt{2}$, and zero steady state error to both step and ramp inputs.

**6.**

$$T_c(s) = \frac{K(s + \delta)}{(s + \sigma - j\omega_d)(s + \sigma + j\omega_d)(s + 20)},$$

with $\omega_n = 5$, $\zeta = 1/\sqrt{2}$, zero steady state error to step input and 1% error to a ramp input.

**7.**

$$T_c(s) = \frac{K(s + \delta)}{(s + \sigma - j\omega_d)(s + \sigma + j\omega_d)(s + 20)},$$

with $\omega_n = 5$, $\zeta = 0.6$, and zero steady state error to both step and ramp inputs.

**8.**

$$T_c(s) = \frac{K(s + \delta)}{(s + \sigma - j\omega_d)(s + \sigma + j\omega_d)(s + 20)},$$

with $\omega_n = 5$, $\zeta = 0.6$, zero steady state error to step input, and 1% error to a ramp input.

**9.**

$$T_c(s) = \frac{K(s + \delta)}{(s + \sigma - j\omega_d)(s + \sigma + j\omega_d)(s + 20)},$$

with $\omega_n = 8$, $\zeta = 0.9$, and zero steady state error to both step and ramp inputs.

**10.**

$$T_c(s) = \frac{K(s + \delta)}{(s + \sigma - j\omega_d)(s + \sigma + j\omega_d)(s + 20)},$$

with $\omega_n = 8$, $\zeta = 0.9$, zero steady state error to step input, and 1% error to a ramp input.

### 6.8.3 Comparing Actual Response to Nominal Response

For each of these problems, find the gain that yields the desired dominant poles. Then compare the response of the system to that of $T_{N2}(s)$ with the *same* dominant poles for the specified input. Use MATLAB (M) or partial fraction expansion (P), as directed, to find the time response.

1. $G(s) = \dfrac{K}{s(s+2)(s+20)}$, $H = 1$, $\omega_n = 3$, step; M

2. $G(s) = \dfrac{K}{s(s+2)(s+20)}$, $H = 1$, $\zeta = 0.8$, step; M

3. $G(s) = \dfrac{K}{s(s+2)}$, $H = \dfrac{1}{s+20}$, $\zeta = 0.8$, step; M

4. $G(s) = \dfrac{K}{s(s+1)(s+10)}$, $H = 1$, $\zeta = 0.2$, step and ramp; M

5. $G(s) = \dfrac{K}{s(s+2)}$, $H = 1$, $\zeta = 0.6$, step; P

6. $G(s) = \dfrac{K(s+1)}{s(s+0.2)(s+20)}$, $H = 1$, $\zeta = 1/\sqrt{2}$, step and ramp; P

7. $G(s) = \dfrac{K}{s(s+4)(s+30)}$, $H = 1$, $\zeta = 1/\sqrt{2}$, step and ramp; M

8. $G(s) = \dfrac{K(s+2)}{s(s+4)(s+30)}$, $H = 1$, $\zeta = 1/\sqrt{2}$, step and ramp; M

9. $G(s) = \dfrac{K}{(s+2)(s+4)}$, $H = 1$, $\zeta = 1/\sqrt{2}$, step and ramp; P

10. $G(s) = \dfrac{1}{s+2}$, $H = \dfrac{K}{s+4}$, $\zeta = 1/\sqrt{2}$, step and ramp; P

### 6.8.4 Additional Problems

1. Consider the system shown in Fig. 6.15 with

$$G(s) = \frac{0.1}{(s - j10)(s + j10)}.$$

A control engineer decides to compensate the system by letting

$$H(s) = Ks.$$

**Figure 6.15** | Unity feedback configuration.

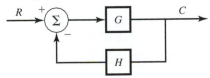

He claims that he can critically damp the system and get great performance.
a.   Find the minimum gain that will give a system with two real poles.

A second engineer says he doesn't think the system will track a step input very well.

b.   Explain why the second engineer thinks this.

The first engineer then says he can improve the performance by increasing the gain in the feedback loop. The second engineer diasgrees and says the additional gain should go in the forward loop.

c.   Determine which engineer is right.

**Figure 6.16 |** Closed-loop control system.

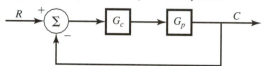

2.   For the system shown in Fig. 6.16, let

$$G_p(s) = \frac{10}{(s+2)(s+10)}.$$

a.   If we wish to have zero steady state error to a unit step input which of these compenstors should we choose for $G_c(s)$:

(i) $\dfrac{K_c(s+0.01)(s+4)}{(s+0.1)(s+20)}$,   (ii) $\dfrac{K_c(s+0.01)(s+10)}{s(s+20)}$,   (iii) $\dfrac{K_c(s+0.01)}{s+0.05}$?

b.   Suppose $G_c = K_c$, a variable gain. For what value of $K_c$ will the root locus cross the line of constant damping $\zeta = 1/\sqrt{2}$, as shown in Fig. 6.17?

**Figure 6.17 |** Line of constant damping $\zeta = 1/\sqrt{2}$.

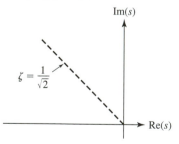

3.   For the dish antenna of Example 6.5.1 move the pole at $s = -50$ to $s = -10$ and find the step response using MATLAB.

4.   For the dish antenna of Example 6.6.2 find the time response by partial fraction expansion.

5.  For $T_{N2}(s)$, what is the maximum error in settling time that results from using Eq. [6.19] with $X = 5$? With $X = 3$? Note your answer will be in terms of the parameters of $T_{N2}(s)$.

6.  Show that $c(t_k) = e^{-\zeta \omega_n t}$, where $t_k$ is defined by Eq. [6.14].

**Figure 6.18** | Nested feedback loops.

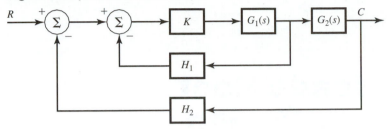

7.  For the system of Fig. 6.18, let

$$G_1(s) = \frac{5}{s+2} \quad \text{and} \quad G_2(s) = \frac{10}{s}.$$

The specifications for the closed-loop transfer function are

a.  $\omega_n = 10$ rad/s
b.  $\zeta = 0.7$
c.  Zero steady state error to a step input

Find the constants $K$, $H_1$, and $H_2$.

8.  Could we use $t_p$ and $t_s$ instead of $t_p$ and PO to specify the speed and stability of a system's performance? Explain your answer.

## FURTHER READINGS

D'Azzo, John J., and Constantine H. Houpis. 1988. *Linear Control System Design, Conventional and Modern.* New York: McGraw-Hill.

Franklin, Gene F., J. David Powell, and Abbas Emami-Naeini. 1991. *Feedback Control of Dynamic Systems,* 2nd ed. Reading, Mass.: Addison-Wesley.

Kuo, Benjamin C. 1982. *Automatic Control,* 4th ed. Englewood Cliffs, N.J.: Prentice-Hall.

Melsa, J. L., and D. G. Schultz. 1969. *Linear Control Systems.* New York: McGraw-Hill.

Ogata, K. 1970. *Modern Control Engineering.* Englewood Cliffs, N.J.: Prentice-Hall.

Saucedo, R., and E. E. Schiring. 1968. *Introduction to Continuous and Digital Control Systems.* New York: MacMillan.

# 7 Chapter

# Cascade Root Locus Design

## 7.1 | OVERVIEW

This is the first chapter devoted to control system design. In Chapters 5 and 6 we laid the groundwork for design techniques based on root locus analysis. In the end, root locus analysis will not prove to be the best design method. That honor is reserved for the Bode design method.

Nonetheless, root locus design is very intuitive. The root locus provides a portrait of all possible closed-loop pole locations over a range of gains. When that portrait is combined with the figures of merit developed in the Chapter 6, it is easy to decide on good pole locations for the closed-loop system.

Additionally, proportional plus integral plus derivative (PID) control is still widely used in industrial applications. PID control is best understood from the root locus perspective. Finally, a knowledge of root locus design will prove most beneficial when Bode design is introduced in Chapter 11.

The root locus design procedures developed in this chapter are based on shaping the three aspects of a system's response discussed at length, in Chapter 6, namely, the speed, stability, and steady state accuracy of the closed-loop response. Both PID and "lead/lag" compensation are developed in this chapter. The two approaches are closely related, as will become evident.

The design procedures will use the figures of merit developed in Chapter 6. The formulas for the figures of merit were derived for a simple system with two poles and no zeros. The systems in this chapter will have three or more poles, as well as zeros. In spite of this, their behavior will be dominated, in almost all cases, by a single pair of complex poles. For that reason, the formulas from Chapter 6 prove to be reasonably accurate measures of the behavior of these more complex systems, and are of great help in starting the design process off in the right direction.

The specifications used in this chapter are time to peak, percent overshoot, and the error constants $K_p$ and $K_v$. Time to peak and percent overshoot are used to determine the damping ratio and natural frequency of the dominant poles. Despite the elementary nature of the specifications, the low-order PID and lead/lag compensators introduced in this chapter provide excellent performance. Part of the reason is that the overall compensator consists of the cascade of two simple compensators each with a specific purpose.

PID control, for instance, consists of a proportional plus derivative (PD) compensator cascaded with a proportional plus integral (PI) compensator. The purpose of the PD compensator is to improve the transient response while maintaining the desired stability. The purpose of the PI compensator is to improve the steady state accuracy of the system without degrading the stability. Since speed of response, accuracy, and stability are what we need for a satisfactory response, generally the cascade of a PD and a PI will suffice.

Lead/lag compensation is very similar to PD/PI, or PID, control. The lead compensator plays the same role as the PD controller, reshaping the root locus to improve the transient response. In like manner, lag and PI compensation are very similar and have the same purpose: to improve the steady state accuracy of the closed-loop system. Both PID and lead/lag compensation, can be used successfully, and they can be combined. We can, for instance, design a lead/PI compensator.

The approach taken in this chapter is to place the compensation in the forward loop in "cascade" with the plant and to assume unity feedback. Although some systems of interest do not have unity feedback, these systems can be put in an equivalent configuration that has unity feedback. As shown in Chapter 6, steady state error analysis is much easier if the system has unity feedback.

The chapter proceeds as follows. PD compensation is first introduced, followed by lead compensation. We show that PD compensation is an idealization of lead compensation. We then introduce PI compensation, followed by lag compensation. Again, we show that lag compensation is merely a slight variation on PI compensation.

We then introduce a general PD/PI (lead/lag) compensation methodology and illustrate it with examples. In the process, we show that PID compensation is equivalent to PD/PI compensation. Most of the crucial concepts are developed through examples.

## 7.2 | PROPORTIONAL PLUS DERIVATIVE COMPENSATION

Consider the block diagram of Fig. 7.1. The block labeled $G_p$ represents some physical system, or "plant," whose response to a family of reference inputs is to be improved. The block labeled $G_c$ represents the compensator to be designed to improve the overall

**Figure 7.1 |** Cascade compensation with unity feedback.

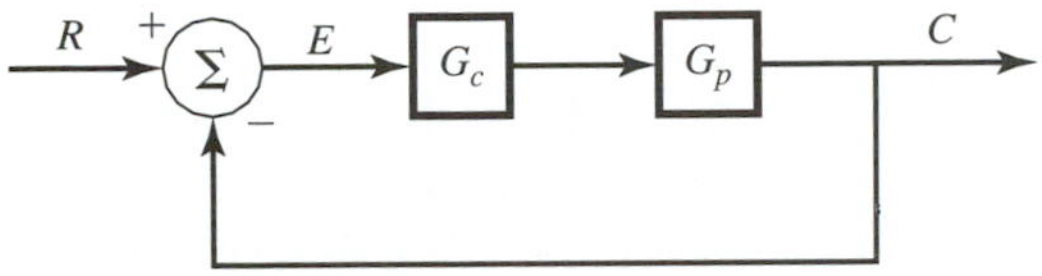

system response. The simplest form of compensation is gain compensation, where $G_c$ is merely an amplification of the error signal fed forward from the summer. This is the subject of example 7.2.1.

**EXAMPLE 7.2.1**

Let

$$G_p(s) = \frac{10}{s(s+1)}. \qquad \text{[7.1]}$$

Our goal is to improve the transient response of this system. The system is type 1, and, based on the steady state error analysis of Chapter 6, we know that the closed-loop system will exhibit zero steady state error to a step input. The design specifications are very modest: achieve a transient response that has no more than 5% overshoot. As we will see, this is about the best that can be expected from simple gain compensation.

The root locus for $G_c = K_c$ is shown in Fig. 7.2. To achieve the design specification, we choose a damping ratio of $\zeta = 1/\sqrt{2}$. The location of the closed-loop poles is the intersection of rays from the origin at angles $\pm 45°$ to the negative real axis with the vertical section of the root locus. Simple geometry shows that to achieve the specified damping ratio the closed-loop poles will be at $s = -0.5 \pm j0.5$.

The gain required to place the poles at $s = -0.5 \pm j0.5$ is

$$K = \frac{1}{|G_p(s)|\big|_{s\,=\,-0.5+j0.5}} = \frac{|-0.5 + j0.5|\,|(1 - 0.5) + j0.5|}{10} = 0.05.$$

**Figure 7.2 |** Root locus for simple gain compensation for Example 7.2.1.

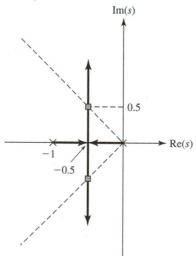

With simple gain compensation, the resulting closed-loop system will be precisely the normalized second-order system of Eq. [6.1]. Thus, the percent overshoot will be exactly that predicted by Eq. [6.13], less than 4%. The time to peak is

$$t_d = \frac{\pi}{\omega_d} = \frac{\pi}{0.5} \approx 6 \text{ s.}$$

The response is quite slow, but it is the best that can be achieved with such a simple compensator.

The primary problem with the response obtained in Example 7.2.1 is that in order to achieve a response with minimal overshoot we have to settle for a very slow transient response. What we would like to do is somehow speed up the transient response without causing a large increase in the overshoot. To that end we introduce a zero into the system by letting

$$G_c = K_c(s + a).$$

Whether such a compensator can be realized easily is a question that we will subsequently have to address, but for the moment the focus is on improving the transient response.

**EXAMPLE 7.2.2**

Suppose we use the same plant as in Example 7.2.1 and let

$$G_c = K_c(s + a).$$

The root locus with the zero added is shown in Fig. 7.3. As can be seen, the root locus

**Figure 7.3 |** Root locus with PD compensation for Example 7.2.2.

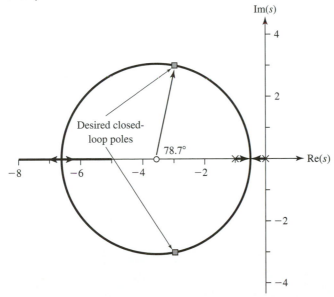

**Figure 7.4 |** Satisfaction of angle condition at $s = -3 + j3$ for Example 7.2.2.

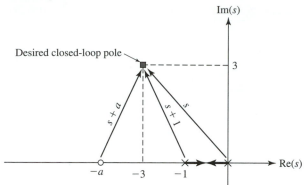

off the real axis will be a circle centered at the zero, whose radius is the distance from the zero to the break-out point on the real axis.

Our goal is to make the root locus pass through the points $s = -3 \pm j3$. The closed-loop system will now have a zero, but the damping ratio of the closed-loop poles at $s = -3 \pm j3$ will remain the same. As shown in Fig. 7.3, the zero must be at $s = -3.6$ to guarantee that the root locus passes through the desired points.

This location was determined by satisfying the angle condition at $s = -3 + j3$. In other words, we must have

$$\underline{/G_c G_p(s)}\Big|_{s = -3+j3} = -180°.$$

Each component of $G_c G_p$, evaluated at $s = -3 + j3$ is shown in Fig. 7.4.

Satisfaction of the angle condition then requires that

$$\underline{/G_c G_p(s)}\Big|_{s = -3+j3} = \underline{/s+a} - \underline{/s+1} - \underline{/s} = -180°.$$

Since two of the three angles are known, it is an easy matter to find

$$\underline{/s+a} = \underline{/s+1} + \underline{/s} - 180°$$

$$= \left(180° - \tan^{-1}\frac{3}{2}\right) + \left(180° - \tan^{-1}\frac{3}{3}\right) - 180°$$

$$= 123.7° + 135° - 180°$$

$$= 78.7°.$$

Then, by simple trigonometry we have

$$a = 3 + \frac{3}{\tan 78.7°} = 3.6.$$

The gain required to place the poles of the closed loop transfer function at $s = -3 \pm j3$ is

$$K_c = \frac{|s|\,|s+1|}{10|s+3.6|}\Big|_{s = -3+j3} = 0.5.$$

**Figure 7.5** | Block diagram of PD control.

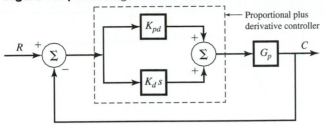

It is worth noting from Fig. 7.3 that the PD compensator reduces the pole/zero excess of the overall system from two to one.

Figure 7.5 shows how the PD compensator might be achieved. The compensator consists of two parallel branches, one containing a gain or proportionality term $K_{pd}$ and the other the derivative term $K_d s$. The controller is then

$$G_c(s) = K_{pd} + K_d s = K_d \left( s + \frac{K_{pd}}{K_d} \right).$$

It should be clear that

$$K_d = K_c = 0.5.$$

It is then an easy matter to find

$$K_{pd} = 3.6 \times K_d = 1.8.$$

The closed-loop transfer function is

$$T_c(s) = \frac{5(s + 3.6)}{(s + 3 - j3)(s + 3 + j3)},$$

and the step response

$$C(s) = \frac{1}{s} + \frac{M}{s + 3 - j3} + \frac{M^*}{s + 3 + j3}.$$

In this case,

$$M = -0.5 - j0.3333 = 0.601\underline{/-2.55} \text{ rad,}$$

so that

$$c(t) = [1 + 1.202e^{-3t} \cos(3t - 2.55)]\mathbf{1}(t).$$

The time response is shown in Fig. 7.6. As we see from the figure, the response is very close to what we might expect from the formulas for the figures of merit. That is, the presence of the zero has not noticeably altered the response.

**Figure 7.6 |** Time response for PD compensation.

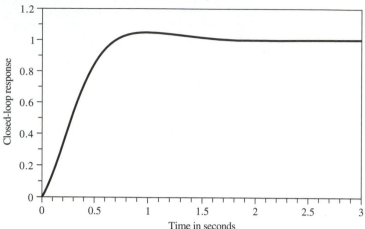

It is worthwhile at this juncture to find the impulse response function of the PD compensator. Applying the inverse Laplace operator yields

$$g_{pd}(t) = \mathcal{L}^{-1} \left\{ K_d \left( s + \frac{K_{pd}}{K_d} \right) \right\}$$
$$= K_d \mathcal{L}^{-1}\{s\} + K_{pd}\mathcal{L}^{-1}\{1\}$$
$$= K_d \delta'(t) + K_{pd}\delta(t),$$

where $\delta'(t)$ is the derivative of $\delta(t)$, sometimes called the doublet. Thus, the impulse response function of the PD compensator contains both an impulse and the derivative of an impulse. For that reason, the PD compensator is an idealization. However, it is possible to construct more realistic compensators that behave very much like the ideal PD compensator. One such approximation, called a lead compensator, is discussed next.

## 7.3 | CASCADE LEAD COMPENSATION

The lead compensator discussed in Example 7.3.1 has the same purpose as the PD compensator: to improve the transient response of the closed-loop system by reshaping the root locus. The lead compensator consists of a zero and a pole with the zero closer to the origin of the $s$ plane than the pole. The zero of the lead compensator, like the zero of the PD, reshapes a portion of the root locus to achieve the desired transient response. The pole of the lead compensator is placed far enough to the left that it does not have much influence on the portion of the root locus being reshaped by the zero. The pole does, of course, influence the *overall* shape of the root locus, but its impact on the portion being reshaped by the zero is minimal.

The pole of the lead compensator serves another important purpose. A pure PD compensator cannot be implemented using opamps. A lead compensator is one of the simplest approximations to a PD compensator, and is, by contrast, very easy to implement with opamps.

**EXAMPLE 7.3.1**

Consider again

$$G_p = \frac{10}{s(s+1)}.$$

The design specifications this time are a little more specific:

1.  PO $\leq$ 20%.
2.  $t_p \leq 1.0$ s.

To achieve the desired $t_p$, we place the closed-loop poles at $s = -3 \pm j3$. Note that the damping ratio of these closed-loop poles remains the same as in Example 7.2.2, namely $\zeta = 1/\sqrt{2}$. We might expect that the overshoot will remain at 4%; however, this expectation will not be fulfilled. The presence of the pole and zero of the lead compensator will cause the formula for percent overshoot to be too optimistic.

The general form of the lead compensator is

$$G_c(s) = \frac{K_c(s+a)}{s+b}, \tag{7.2}$$

with $0 < a < b$. The poles and zeros of the plant and the compensator are shown in Fig. 7.7.

For the root locus to pass through $s = -3 \pm j3$, we must have

$$\underline{/G_c\,G_p(s)}\big|_{s=-3\pm j3} = -180°.$$

The angle contributions $\theta_1$ and $\theta_2$ due to the poles of $G_p$ are known. The angles of

**Figure 7.7** | Angle contributions of $G_c$ and $G_p$ at $s = -3 + j3$ for Example 7.3.1.

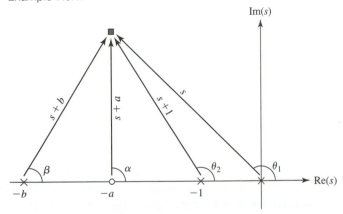

the zero and pole of the compensator, $\alpha$ and $\beta$, are as yet unknown. However, at $s = -3 + j3$ it must be true that

$$\alpha - \beta - \theta_1 - \theta_2 = -180°. \qquad [7.3]$$

Equation [7.3] can be rewritten as

$$\alpha - \beta = \theta_1 + \theta_2 - 180° = 78.7°.$$

Since the plant transfer function is the same one we used in designing the PD compensator, in Example 7.2.2, we see that on the left-hand side of the equation we have simply replaced the angle of the zero of the PD compensator by the *net* angle contribution of the lead compensator. Like the PD compensator, the lead compensator must contribute 78.7° at $s = -3 + j3$ in order for the root locus to pass through this point. We see that there are an infinite number of choices that will work. Each different choice will yield a different root locus plot and a different gain.

The next step is to choose the location of either the pole or the zero of the lead compensator. In this example, we place the zero at $s = -3$. Whether this is a good choice remains to be seen. However, having selected the location of the zero, we can find the compensator pole by simple trigonometry. With $\alpha = 90°$,

$$\beta = 90° - 78.7° = 11.3°.$$

Then,

$$b = 3 + \frac{3}{\tan 11.3°} = 3 + 15 = 18.$$

The compensator is thus,

$$G_c(s) = \frac{K_c(s+3)}{s+18},$$

and the only remaining task is to determine the gain of the compensator.

From Fig. 7.7 we have

$$K_c = \left( \frac{|s| |s+1| |s+18|}{10|s+3|} \right) \Bigg|_{s = -3 + j3} = 7.8.$$

The gain calculation can be done directly from Fig. 7.7 since each of the terms in the expression for $K_c$ is the length of one of the vectors in the figure. The calculation can also be done by directly substituting $s = -3 + j3$ in the expression for $K_c$ and "grinding out" the result.

The disadvantage of the second method is that it does not provide a "sanity check" on the result, whereas calculating the gain from the vector diagram of Fig. 7.7 does. If we use the vector diagram, the relative lengths of the vectors used in the computation of $K_c$ are clearly displayed, so that a glaring mistake in the value of $K_c$ will be easy to catch.

The final design is then

$$G_c(s) = \frac{7.8(s+3)}{s+18}.$$

Although the design is complete, we include some additional analysis that should help reinforce the concepts of root locus analysis from Chapter 5. The first step is

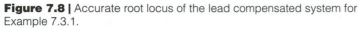

**Figure 7.8 |** Accurate root locus of the lead compensated system for Example 7.3.1.

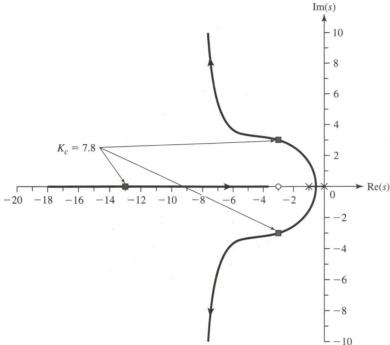

to find the other closed-loop pole. Two of the closed-loop poles are already known, namely, the poles at $s = -3 \pm j3$. However, the lead compensator introduces a third closed-loop pole. An accurate root locus of the compensated system is shown in Fig. 7.8. Because the compensator has a pole at $s = -18$, there will be a third closed-loop pole on the real axis somewhere between the compensator pole at $s = -18$ and the compensator zero at $s = -3$.

The easiest way to locate this third closed-loop pole is to repetitively solve for the gain along the real axis. That is, solve the equation

$$K_c = \frac{|s|\,|s+1|\,|s+18|}{10|s+3|}$$

for values of $s$ in the interval $(-18, -3)$. The vector quantities involved in this calculation are shown in Fig. 7.9. The results of this repetitive computation are shown in Table 7.1. This table shows the gain at selected points in the interval $(-18, -3)$. We see from the table that for $s = -13$, $K_c = 7.8$. Thus, the third closed-loop pole is at $s = -13$.

**Table 7.1 |** Gain $K_c$ along the real axis for Example 7.3.1.

| $s$ | $-16$ | $-15$ | $-14$ | $-13$ | $-12$ |
|---|---|---|---|---|---|
| $K_c$ | 3.69 | 5.25 | 6.62 | 7.8 | 8.8 |

**Figure 7.9** | Computing $K_c$ on line segment $-18 < s < -3$.

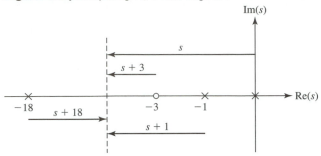

It may seem that this is simply a trial-and-error process, but it is not. It is a convergent search, because as the trial point is moved to the right the gain increases. If a trial point yields a gain greater than 7.8, the next trial point should be to the left of the one that yielded the gain larger than 7.8. Thus, the search will converge, and generally it takes no more than five or six trials to arrive at the desired gain. Note that the process would be no more difficult if there were additional poles and zeros, just more tedious.

The closed-loop transfer function can now be written down in the factored form

$$T_c(s) = \frac{C(s)}{R(s)} = \frac{78(s+3)}{(s+3-j3)(s+3+j3)(s+13)},$$

where the plant and compensator gains have been combined into the composite gain of 78.

For a step input,

$$C(s) = \frac{1}{s}T_c(s) = \frac{1}{s}\frac{78(s+3)}{(s+3-j3)(s+3+j3)(s+13)}$$

$$= \frac{A_1}{s} + \frac{A_2}{s+13} + \frac{M}{s+3-j3} + \frac{M^*}{s+3+j3}.$$

The coefficient $A_1$ must be 1.0 because the system is type 1. The other coefficients are

$$A_2 = \frac{s+13}{1}\frac{78(s+3)}{s(s+3-j3)(s+3+j3)(s+13)}\bigg|_{s=-13}$$

$$= 0.55$$

and

$$Me^{j\phi} = \frac{s+3-j3}{1}\frac{78(s+3)}{s(s+3-j3)(s+3+j3)(s+13)}\bigg|_{s=-3+j3}$$

$$= \frac{(j3)(78)}{(-3+j3)(j6)(10+j3)}$$

$$= 0.88\underline{/-2.65}\text{ rad}.$$

**Figure 7.10 |** Response of the compensated system for
Example. 7.3.1.

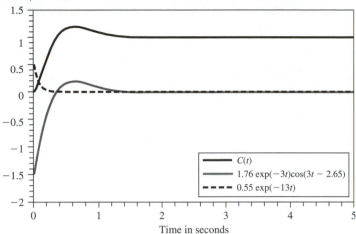

Time in seconds

Then, applying the inverse Laplace transform,

$$c(t) = [1 + A_2 e^{-13t} + 2Me^{-3t} \cos(3t + \phi)]\mathbf{1}(t)$$
$$= [1 + 0.55e^{-13t} + 1.76e^{-3t} \cos(3t - 2.65)]\mathbf{1}(t).$$

The individual components of $c(t)$ plus the overall response are shown in Fig. 7.10. We note that the term $0.55e^{-13t}$ influences the response immediately after the step is applied and accounts for the overshoot being around 20%, whereas the formula for PO predicts about 4% overshoot.

---

Example 7.3.1 illustrates the power of the geometric interpretation of $G_c G_p(s)$. By sketching the vectors that represent the poles and zeros of $G_c$ and $G_p$, it is easy to see the effect of each vector component at any point in the $s$ plane. This makes the design procedure very straightforward. In Chapter 11 we will find that the Bode design technique is superior to root locus design. But even when the design is done using a Bode plot, a sketch of the root locus of the compensated system will prove helpful in revealing how the compensation does its job.

The transient response obtained in Example 7.3.1 is satisfactory. However, the decomposition of the time response shows that the third pole at $s = -13$ does impact the response. As a consequence, the formula for percent overshoot proved too optimistic. If we wish to further reduce the percent overshoot, we could redo the design using a larger damping ratio, say, $\zeta = 0.8$.

An alternative approach is given in Example 7.3.2. This alternative design is based on the idea of trying to make the final closed-loop transfer function as close as possible to the normalized second order transfer function $T_{N2}$.

**EXAMPLE 7.3.2**

Consider again the plant of Example 7.3.1. Our goal will be to add compensation that makes $T_c$ look as much like

$$T_{N2}(s) = \frac{\omega_n^2}{s^2 + 2\zeta\omega_n^2 s + \omega_n^2}$$

as possible. As in Example 7.3.1, we will place the closed-loop poles at $s = -3 \pm j3$ so that $t_p \approx 1.0$ s. This time, however, our approach will be to cancel the plant pole at $s = -1$ with a zero and add a pole at $s = -6$, as shown in Fig. 7.11.

Referring to part(b) of Fig. 7.11, we see that the gain necessary to place poles at $s = -3 \pm j3$ is

$$K_c = \frac{|s+6||s|}{10}\bigg|_{s=-3+j3} = \frac{\sqrt{3^2+3^2} \times \sqrt{3^2+3^2}}{10} = 1.8$$

The closed-loop transfer function is

$$T_c(s) = \frac{18/[s(s+6)]}{1 + 18/[s(s+6)]} = \frac{18}{s^2 + 6s + 18}.$$

This is just $T_{N2}$ for $\omega_n = 3\sqrt{2}$ and $\zeta = 1/\sqrt{2}$. Assuming perfect cancellation, the

**Figure 7.11 |** Lead compensation with exact cancellation for Example 7.3.2.

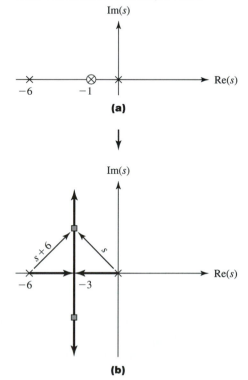

**Figure 7.12** | Angle contributions at $s = x + j3$ with $s = -1.1$ for Example 7.3.2.

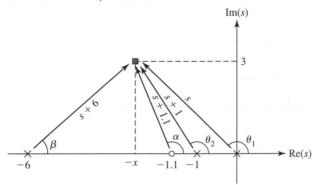

overshoot is reduced from 20% to less than 4% and the gain drops from 7.8 to 1.8. Thus, the new design is in some ways superior to the first attempt. It certainly requires less gain.

Since perfect cancellation cannot be achieved, it is worthwhile to see how the performance of the system is affected when we have only near cancellation. Suppose, as shown in Fig. 7.12, that the zero, intended to be a $s = -1.0$, is actually at $s = -1.1$.

The root locus will no longer pass through $s = -3 + j3$ but it will intersect a horizontal line through $s = -j3$, as shown in the figure. That is, there will be complex roots of the form $s = -x \pm j3$, where $|x| \approx 3$. We can find $x$, because at the point where the root locus intersects the horizontal line through $s = j3$ we must have

$$\alpha - \beta - \theta_1 - \theta_2 = -180°.$$

The quickest way to do this is simply to evaluate the net angle of $G_cG_p$ for some trial values of $x$. For instance if $x = -2.98$, then

$$
\angle G_c G_p(s)\Big|_{s=-2.98+j3} = \left(180° - \tan^{-1}\frac{3}{1.88}\right) - \left(180° - \tan^{-1}\frac{3}{1.98}\right)
$$
$$
- \left(180° - \tan^{-1}\frac{3}{2.98}\right) - \tan^{-1}\frac{3}{3.02}
$$
$$
= 122.07° - 123.42° - 134.81° - 44.81°
$$
$$
= -180.97°.
$$

This angle is too large, but in one guess we are very close to the actual crossing point, and also very close to $s = -3 + j3$. So we choose $x = -2.97$ and reevaluate to obtain

$$
\angle G_c G_p(s)\Big|_{s=-2.97+j3} = \left(180° - \tan^{-1}\frac{3}{1.87}\right) - \left(180° - \tan^{-1}\frac{3}{1.97}\right)
$$
$$
- \left(180° - \tan^{-1}\frac{3}{2.97}\right) - \tan^{-1}\frac{3}{3.03}
$$
$$
= 121.94° - 123.29° - 134.71° - 44.71°
$$
$$
= -180.78°.
$$

**Table 7.2 |** Search for closed-loop pole $s = x + j3$ for Example 7.3.2.

| $x$ | −2.95 | −2.92 | −2.93 |
|---|---|---|---|
| $\angle G_c G_p$ | −180.41° | −179.85° | −180.03° |

Continuing in this way we generate Table 7.2. We settle for closed-loop poles at $s = -2.93 \pm j3$.

The gain required to place the closed-loop poles at $s = -2.93 \pm j3$ is

$$K_c = \left( \frac{|s|\,|s+1|\,|s+6|}{10|s+1.1|} \right)\Bigg|_{s=-2.93+j3} = 1.827. \qquad \text{[7.4]}$$

Thus, the final compensator is

$$G_c(s) = \frac{1.83\,(s+1.1)}{s+6}.$$

The root locus is shown in Fig. 7.13.

The third closed-loop pole can be determined by searching along the real axis to the left of the zero at $s = -1.1$. Table 7.3 summarizes this search. Based on the

**Figure 7.13 |** Accurate root locus with near cancellation of plant pole for Example 7.3.2.

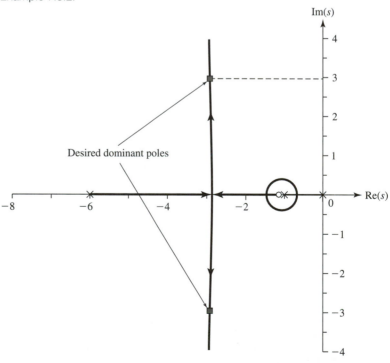

**Table 7.3 |** Gain $K_c$ along the real axis in Example 7.3.2.

| $s$ | $-1.2$ | $-1.15$ | $-1.145$ | $-1.144$ | $-1.435$ | $-1.43$ |
|---|---|---|---|---|---|---|
| $K_c$ | 1.152 | 1.67 | 1.79 | 1.818 | 1.832 | $-1.846$ |

table, we settle for a third pole at $s = -1.1436$, and a closed-loop transfer function

$$T_c(s) = \frac{18.3(s+1.1)}{(s+1.1436)(s+2.928-j3)(s+2.928+j3)}.$$

The time response of the system to a unit step input is

$$c(t) = [1 + 0.05727e^{-1.1436t} + 1.4645e^{-2.928t}\cos(3t+2.379)]\mathbf{1}(t).$$

The individual terms of $c(t)$, plus the overall response are shown in Fig. 7.14. The time response is very close to that for perfect cancellation.

**Figure 7.14 |** Time response with near pole/zero cancellation for Example 7.3.2.

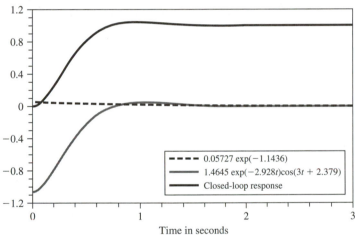

Time in seconds

Thus, our tactic of making $T_c$ as similar as possible to $T_{N2}$ seems to work quite well. For one thing, since the closed-loop pole at $s = -1.1436$ is very close to the zero of the compensator at $s = -1.1$, the residue associated with this pole is very small. Hence the term $0.05727e^{-1.1436t}$ has very little impact on the overall time response, even though its time constant is quite large.

It is possible to make a lead compensator look very much like the PD compensator of Example 7.2.1. By moving the pole of the lead compensator of Example 7.3.1 to the left and the zero to the right, the complex poles will break back into the real axis, as shown in example 7.3.3.

**EXAMPLE 7.3.3**

For the same plant previously considered, namely

$$G_p(s) = \frac{10}{s(s+1)},$$

let the pole of the lead compensator be at $s = -30$. We wish to find the zero of the compensator and the time response.

Calculations similar to those done for the previous two lead compensator designs show that the angle from the pole at $s = -30$ is $\beta = 6.34°$. Then

$$\alpha = 78.7° + 6.34° = 85.04°,$$

so that

$$a = 3 + \frac{3}{\tan \alpha} = 3 + \frac{3}{\tan 85.04°} = 3.26.$$

The gain required to place closed-loop poles at $s = -3 \pm j3$ is

$$K_c = \left. \frac{|s|\,|s+1|\,|s+30|}{10|s+3.26|} \right|_{s=-3+j3} = 13.8.$$

The root locus is shown in Fig. 7.15. The portion of the root locus to the right of the

**Figure 7.15 |** Lead compensation that approximates PD control for Example 7.3.3.

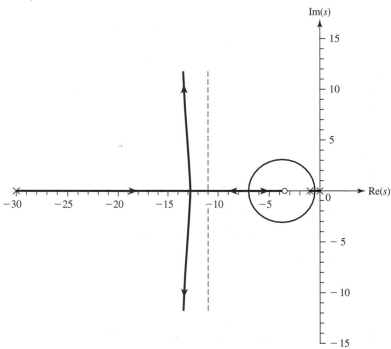

vertical dotted line looks very much like the root locus for the PD compensator. There will be a third pole between $s = -30$ and $s = -3$ but closer to $s = -30$. This pole will have a very small time constant that will not effect the performance of the closed-loop system very much. One obvious disadvantage of this design is the large increase in gain.

# 7.4 | PROPORTIONAL PLUS INTEGRAL COMPENSATION

The purpose of lead and PD compensation is to improve the transient response, typically to make that response faster without introducing instability. This compensation does nothing, however, to improve the steady state accuracy of the response.

Improvement in steady state accuracy is achieved by lag or PI compensation. PI compensation is discussed in this section and lag compensation in Section 7.5. Unlike PD compensation, PI compensation is relatively easy to implement. As with the lead and PD compensators, PI compensation is most easily understood through specific examples.

Before proceeding to the examples, however, consider Fig. 7.16, which shows that PI compensation can be thought of as a parallel combination of a proportional gain $K_{pi}$, and an integral term, $K_i/s$. The overall compensator is

$$G_c(s) = K_{pi} + \frac{K_i}{s} = \frac{K_{pi}s + K_i}{s} = \frac{K_{pi}(s + K_i/K_{pi})}{s}. \qquad [7.5]$$

The PI compensator adds a pole and a zero, with the pole being at the origin. This pole at the origin increases the system type by one. The lag compensator discussed in Section 7.5 differs from the PI compensator only in that the pole of the lag is near but not at the origin. Thus the lag compensator will not increase the system type but does provide an increase in steady state accuracy.

The traditional approach to PI and lag compensation is to put the zero of the compensator very close to the pole of the compensator. This strategy can work, but it also can backfire, as we see in Example 7.4.1.

**Figure 7.16 |** Proportional plus integral control.

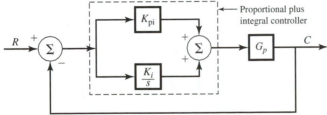

**EXAMPLE 7.4.1**

For the unity feedback configuration of Fig. 7.1. let

$$G_p(s) = \frac{1}{(s+1)(s+5)}.$$

The specifications are:

1.  $t_p = 1$ s.
2.  $e_{ss} < 5\%$ for a step input.

Gain compensation seems a potential candidate here, because as shown in Fig. 7.17, with gain compensation the root locus will pass through the points $s = -3 \pm j3$. The gain required to put closed-loop poles at $s = -3 \pm j3$ is

$$K_c = \left. \frac{|s+1||s+5|}{1} \right|_{s=-3+j3} = 13$$

Since $\zeta = 1/\sqrt{2}$ and $\omega_d = 3$ rad/s, the transient portion of the response should meet the specifications. However, $G_p$ is type 0, and the steady state error to a step input is

$$e_{ss} = \frac{1}{1 + K_p} = \frac{5}{18}.$$

Thus,

$$\lim_{t \to \infty} c(t) = \lim_{t \to \infty}[r(t) - e(t)] = r_{ss} - e_{ss} = 1 - \frac{5}{18} = 0.72,$$

yielding a 28% steady state error, which does not meet the specifications.

Now consider adding a PI compensator, as shown in Fig. 7.18. The zero of the compensator, is shown in its traditional location very close to the origin at $s = -0.1$.

**Figure 7.17 |** Root locus for gain compensation for Example 7.4.1.

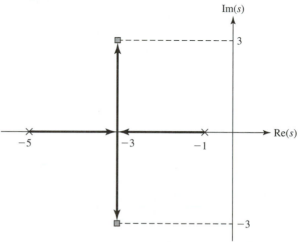

**Figure 7.18 |** Computation of gain $K_{pi}$ for PI compensation for Example 7.4.1.

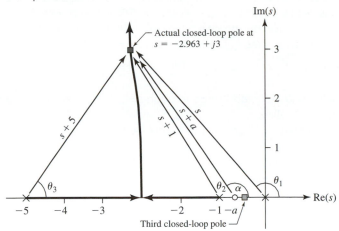

From the figure, it is clear that the root locus can no longer pass exactly through the points $s = -3 \pm j3$. However, the root locus does pass very close to these points.

The reason is that in the vicinity of $s = -3 + j3$, the angles from the zero and the pole of the compensator are nearly equal. Thus, at $s = -3 + j3$ the *net* angle contribution of the compensator will be nearly zero. Table 7.4 shows that with the compensator added the root locus intersects a horizontal line through $s = j3$ for $x = -2.963$. Thus for all practical purposes we might as well assume that the root locus passes through $s = -3 + j3$, and that is what is traditionally done.

**Table 7.4 |** Search for root locus crossing of the vertical line through $j3$ for Example 7.4.1.

| Re{$x + j3$} | $-2.95$ | $-2.96$ | $-2.97$ | $-2.963$ |
|---|---|---|---|---|
| $\angle G_c G_p(x + j3)$ | $-179.7°$ | $-179.93°$ | $-180.19°$ | $-180.00°$ |

We are now in a position to compute the gain required to place the poles at $s = -2.963 \pm j3$. This calculation is illustrated in Fig. 7.18. Recall that

$$a = \frac{K_i}{K_{pi}} = 0.1,$$

and that $K_{pi}$ is the gain of the compensator. Then

$$K_{pi} = \frac{\sqrt{2.963^2 + 3^2} \times \sqrt{1.963^2 + 3^2} \times \sqrt{2.037^2 + 3^2}}{\sqrt{2.863^2 + 3^2}} = 13.21.$$

The gain computed earlier for simple gain compensation was 13. Thus the gain has only changed by about 1.6%. That is because

$$\frac{|s|}{|s + 0.1|}\bigg|_{s = -0.2963 + j3} = \frac{4.217}{4.147} = 1.016.$$

What is traditionally done is to design the lead or PD portion of the compensator first and then assume that the PI or lag compensator does not perturb the closed-loop pole locations. In this simple example, instead of PD or lead compensation we simply used gain compensation but the idea is the same. Thus, the PI compensator is simply added without changing the gain. That is, our compensator would be

$$G_c = \frac{13(s + 0.1)}{s},$$

and the root locus is *assumed* to pass through $s = -3 + j3$. As we can see, this is a very good approximation.

If we use the slightly larger gain of 13.2 obtained originally, we have

$$K_i = 0.1 \times K_{pi} = 1.32.$$

The PI compensator is then,

$$G_c = 13.2 + \frac{1.32}{s} = \frac{13.2(s + 0.1)}{s}.$$

The placement of the zero of the PI compensator at $s = -0.1$ is not entirely arbitrary. There are practical limitations to its location that depend on how it is implemented. If we implement the compensator with an operational amplifier, there are limits to the size of the resistors and capacitors that can be used without upsetting the ideal opamp assumptions that are usually made. As the performance of opamps continues to improve, however, these restrictions are becoming less stringent.

In addition, the location of the zero influences the magnitude of the relevant error constants. In the case of Example 7.4.1, the placement of the zero influences the magnitude of $K_v$.

An accurate root locus of the compensated system is shown in Fig. 7.19. As we can see, in the vicinity of $s = -3 \pm j3$, the locus barely differs from that drawn for the gain compensation case.

The step response of the closed-loop system, as shown in Fig. 7.20, is

$$c(t) = [1 - 0.26285e^{-0.07433t} + 1.039e^{-2.963t} \cos(3t + 2.358)]\mathbf{1}(t).$$

Note that the coefficient of the closed-loop pole near the origin is quite large. As a consequence, the effect of this pole persists for a long time, as shown in the figure. This is a fairly typical response if the zero of the PI compensator is placed near the origin.

It may be possible to mitigate the slow creep to steady state by increasing the natural frequency of the dominant complex poles. This will increase the overall gain and drive the third closed-loop pole near origin closer to the zero at $s = -0.1$. This *may* decrease the coefficient of this term in the response. However, this is not a sure bet because the overall gain, which figures in the computation of the coefficient, will also increase.

Further, it may not be desirable to increase the natural frequency. That is, the chosen natural frequency may the most desirable for the specific application. In that case, another alternative is to move the zero away from the origin. Doing so means that we will have to account for the angle contributions of both the pole and zero of the PI compensator. Nonetheless, it may be worthwhile to do so.

**Figure 7.19 |** Root Locus for PI compensation for Example 7.4.1.

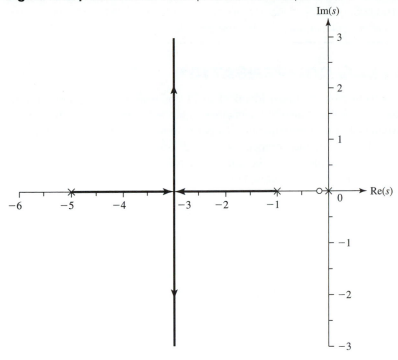

**Figure 7.20 |** Time response for PI compensation for Example 7.4.1.

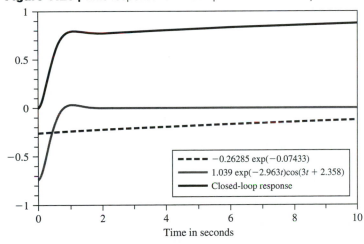

In the present case, suppose we cancel the plant pole at $s = -1$ with the zero of the PI compensator. Assuming perfect cancellation

$$G_cG_p(s) = \frac{K_c}{s(s+5)}.$$

For a gain of $K_c = 15.25$, the system will have complex poles at $s = -2.5 \pm j3$. The closed-loop system is now $T_{N2}$ with $\omega_d = 3$ rad/s and $\zeta = 0.64$. The time to peak will again be about 1.0 s, and the percent overshoot will be about 10%. This is a far better result than we obtained by placing the zero close to the origin.

## 7.5 | LAG COMPENSATION

Lag compensation is almost identical to PI compensation. The only difference is that the pole of the compensator is close to but not at the origin. The pole close to the origin is a near approximation to a perfect integrator. The decision about where to place the zero of the compensator is the same as that for the PI compensator discussed in Example 7.4.1. The same system used to illustrate the PI compensator is now reconsidered for lag compensation.

**EXAMPLE 7.5.1**

For the same plant used in Example 7.4.1, namely,

$$G_p(s) = \frac{1}{(s+1)(s+5)},$$

we now design a lag compensator for the same specifications given in that example.

The lag compensator is of the form

$$\frac{K_c(s+a)}{s+b}, \qquad \qquad \textbf{[7.6]}$$

where $a > b > 0$. The traditional lag compensator has the pole and zero close to the origin. As we saw in Example 7.4.1, however, this did not lead to a satisfactory response. Therefore, we choose to place the pole of the lag close to the origin to obtain a close approximation to the pure integrator present in the PI compensator, but use the zero of the lag to cancel the pole of the plant at $s = -1$. Then

$$G_c G_p(s) = \frac{K_c(s+1)}{s+b} \frac{1}{(s+1)(s+5)} = \frac{K_c}{(s+b)(s+5)}.$$

The root locus will have the familiar cross shape. The break-out point is at

$$s = -b - \frac{5-b}{2}.$$

If we choose $s = -0.1$ for the compensator pole location then the break-out point is at $s = -2.55$. In this case, we can place the closed-loop poles at $s = -2.55 \pm j3$. The gain required to do so is

$$K_c = |s + 0.1| \, |s + 5| \big|_{s = -2.55 + j3} = 2.45^2 + 3^2 = 15.0025 \rightarrow 15.$$

For the chosen poles and zeros,

$$K_p = \lim_{s \to 0} \frac{15}{(s+0.1)(s+5)} = 30,$$

and the steady state error to a step input is

$$e_{ss} = \frac{1}{1 + K_p} = 0.03,$$

**Figure 7.21 |** Time response for the lag compensator for Example 7.5.1.

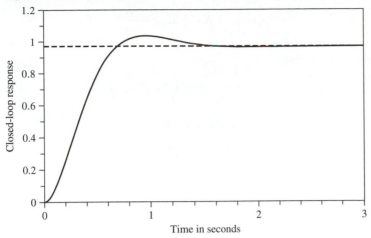

exceeding the specified value of 5%. The response to a unit step input is

$$c(t) = [0.9676 + 1.270e^{-2.55t}\cos(3t + 2.437)]\mathbf{1}(t),$$

as shown in Fig. 7.21. The time to peak is almost exactly 1 s, and the overshoot is under 10%.

## 7.6 | PID AND LEAD/LAG COMPENSATION

In this section we combine PD and lead compensators with PI and lag compensators and formulate an overall design strategy. That strategy can best be developed through some examples. Before doing so we discuss PID control and show that it is equivalent to cascading a PD compensator with a PI compensator.

A PID controller, often referred to as a "three-term" controller, is shown in Fig. 7.22. This is the most prevalent compensator in process control. The compensator is "tuned" by adjusting three parameters $K_P$, $K_I$, and $K_D$.

**Figure 7.22 |** PID compensation.

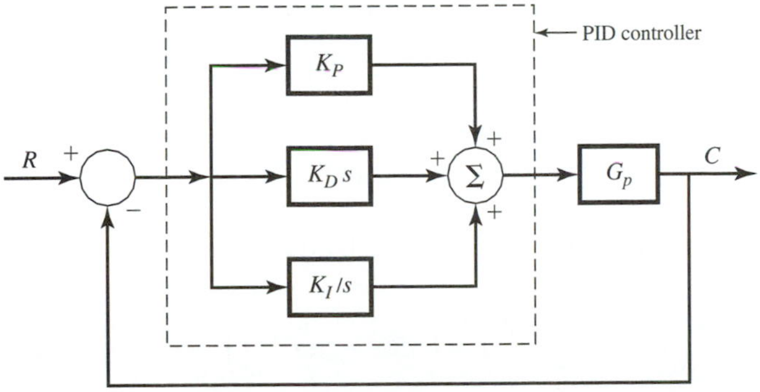

The PID compensator can be written:

$$G_{\text{PID}} = K_P + K_D s + \frac{K_I}{s}. \qquad [7.7]$$

Now consider a PD compensator cascaded with a PI compensator. The overall transfer function is then

$$G_{\text{PD}}(s) G_{\text{PI}}(s) = (K_{\text{pd}} + K_d s)\left( K_{\text{pi}} + \frac{K_i}{s} \right)$$

$$= (K_{\text{pd}} K_{\text{pi}} + K_d K_i) + (K_d K_{\text{pi}})s + \frac{K_{\text{pd}} K_i}{s}. \qquad [7.8]$$

Equating constants between Eqs. [7.7] and [7.8], reveals that

$$K_P = K_{\text{pd}} K_{\text{pi}} + K_d K_i, \qquad K_I = K_{\text{pd}} K_i, \qquad K_D = K_d K_{\text{pi}}.$$

Thus, a PID compensator is completely equivalent to cascading a PD compensator with a PI compensator. In Example 7.6.1 we design a PID compensator by combining the PD and PI compensation techniques discussed earlier.

---

**EXAMPLE 7.6.1**

Consider again the plant

$$G_p(s) = \frac{1}{(s+1)(s+5)},$$

and let the design specifications be:

1. $t_p \approx 0.5$ s.
2. PO $\leq 10\%$.
3. $e_{ss} \leq 10\%$ for a ramp input.

To meet the specifications on $t_p$ requires $\omega_d > 6.28$ rad/s. We let $\omega_d = 7$ rad/s. To meet the specification on percent overshoot, we will choose a large damping ratio of $\zeta = 1/\sqrt{2}$. We then do a preliminary design based on perfect pole/zero cancellation. In reality, we cannot achieve perfect cancellation. However, we saw in Example 7.5.1 that the results for near cancellation are very close to those achieved with perfect cancellation. With this preliminary design in hand, we next check to see if the specification on accuracy is met.

With our strategy mapped out, we now let

$$G_c(s) = (K_{\text{pd}} + K_d s)\left( K_{\text{pi}} + \frac{K_i}{s} \right) = \frac{K_c(s+1)(s+z_1)}{s}.$$

The zero at $s = -z_1$ represents the PD portion of the compensator, whereas the zero at $s = -1$ and the pole at the origin represent the PI portion of the compensator.

For the root locus to pass through $s = -7 + j7$, we must satisfy the angle condition at this point, as shown in Fig. 7.23. In what by now should be a routine calculation, we have

$$\alpha = \left( 180° - \tan^{-1} \frac{7}{7} \right) + \left( 180° - \tan^{-1} \frac{7}{2} \right) - 180° = 60.95°.$$

**Figure 7.23 |** Determining the angle of zero of the PD compensator for Example 7.6.1.

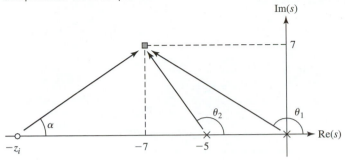

This places the zero of the PD compensator at $s = -10.9$. The gain required to place the closed loop poles at $s = -7 \pm j7$ is $K_c = 9$.

With the compensator complete we now determine

$$K_v = \lim_{s \to 0} sG_cG_p(s) = \lim_{s \to 0} s\frac{9(s + 10.9)}{s(s + 5)} = 19.6.$$

Thus, the steady state error to a ramp input is

$$e_{ss} = \frac{1}{K_v} = 0.051,$$

or about 5%, which more than meets the specification of 10%.

The response to a unit step input is then

$$c(t) = [1 + 1.04e^{-7t} \cos(7t - 2.864)]\mathbf{1}(t).$$

The step response is shown in Fig. 7.24. The overshoot is about 5% and the time to peak less than half a second. The specifications have clearly been met.

**Figure 7.24 |** Time response of the PID-compensated system for Example 7.6.1.

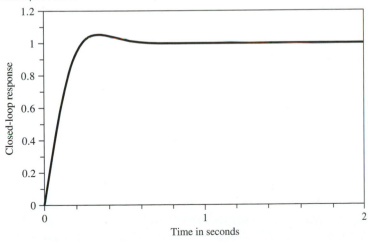

The last step is to determine the values of the three parameters in the PID representation. First note that

$$G_{PID} = \frac{K_c(s+1)(s+z_1)}{s} = K_c(z_1 + 1) + \frac{K_c z_1}{s} + K_c s.$$

Thus

$$K_D = K_c = 9,$$

$$K_I = K_c z_1 = 9 \times 10.9 = 98,$$

$$K_p = K_c(z_1 + 1) = 107.$$

A pure PD compensator is virtually impossible to implement with analog electronics. A PI compensator, on the other hand, can be implemented without too much difficulty using opamps. As a consequence, a viable and effective alternative to a pure PID compensator is a lead/PI compensator, as discussed in Example 7.6.2.

**EXAMPLE 7.6.2**

Consider again the plant of example 7.6.1. The compensator to be designed will be of the form

$$G_c(s) = \frac{K_c(s+z_1)}{(s+p_1)} \frac{s+z_2}{s}.$$

This is the cascade of a lead compensator with a PI compensator. Our first try is

$$G_c(s) = \frac{K_c(s+1)(s+5)}{s(s+14)}.$$

In other words, we cancel both the plant poles to achieve

$$G_c G_p(s) = \frac{K_c}{s(s+14)}.$$

The closed-loop transfer function will then be $T_{N2}$ with $\omega_n$ and $\zeta$ determined by the value of $K_c$ that we choose. Letting

$$K_c = |s| |s+14| \big|_{s=-7+j7} = 98$$

yields a closed-loop transfer function of the form $T_{N2}$ with damping ratio $\zeta = 0.707$, $\omega_d = 7$ rad/s, and $\omega_n = 7\sqrt{2}$ rad/s. This more than meets the specifications for $t_p$ and PO, but

$$K_v = \lim_{s \to 0} s G_c G_p(s) = 7.$$

We see that this compensator meets all the specifications except that on accuracy. To improve the accuracy we move the lead compensator pole to the left to $s = -36$, and adjust the gain so that the closed-loop poles are at $s = -18 \pm j8$. This increases $K_c$ to 388. If we can obtain this much gain, then $K_v$ increases to 10.78, so that the steady state error is

$$e_{ss} = \frac{1}{K_v} = 0.093.$$

The damping ratio of the dominant complex poles is 0.91. Since the closed-loop transfer function is of the form $T_{N2}$, the formulas for time to peak and percent overshoot are exact. Thus, $t_p = 0.39$ s, and the overshoot will be less than 3%. This more than meets the specifications.

In reality we cannot obtain perfect pole/zero cancellation. However, near cancellation usually is sufficient. In the present case, we can get an idea of how robust the design is by simply perturbing the pole and zero locations slightly and then evaluating the time response to see how much it changes.

To that end we move the zeros slightly away from the plant poles to $s = -1.1$ and $s = -4.8$. We could relocate the pole of the lead compensator to make the root locus pass exactly through $s = -18 + j8$, but that really isn't necessary or in keeping with what we are trying to accomplish. What we really want to know is whether imperfect cancellation leads to a radical change in the system response. Thus we leave the pole of the lead compensator at $s = -36$ and the gain at $K_c = 388$. In so doing, we will achieve dominant complex poles very close to $s = -18 \pm j8$, and since we have far less overshoot than required by the specifications, the design should still be more than adequate. We thus choose

$$G_c(s) = \frac{388(s + 1.1)(s + 4.8)}{s(s + 36)}.$$

We note that the steady state error to a ramp actually improves slightly to 8.8%. The time response to a unit step input is shown in Fig. 7.25.

**Figure 7.25 |** Step response of lead/PI design for Example 7.6.2.

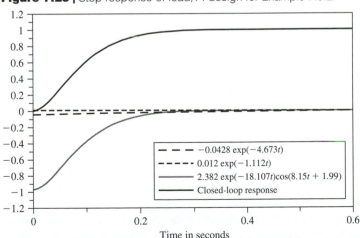

**Figure 7.26 |** Root locus of lead/PI design for Example 7.6.2.

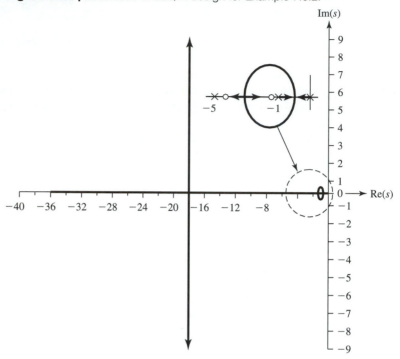

The overshoot is less than half a percent, so that the system is essentially critically damped. The time to peak is about 0.4 s. The root locus is shown in Fig. 7.26. As might be expected, the root locus away from the area near the origin looks almost exactly like the locus for the case of perfect pole/zero cancellation.

## 7.7 | ROBUST STABILITY

We introduce here the idea of robust stability. This is an idea that has been an implicit part of control theory from its very beginnings, but has received a lot of very explicit attention over the last decade. In Chapter 9, we discuss robust control using frequency domain techniques. The development here is more limited but it does provide an introduction to the subject. It also gives us a chance to see how we can use some simple optimization techniques to help us decide on the "best" choice of compensation.

By robust stability we mean that the compensated system remains stable despite any uncertainties in the model. In Chapter 12, we broaden this definition to include high-frequency and low-frequency noice rejection, but for the moment we will concentrate on model uncertainty.

Most of the the model uncertainty resides with the plant transfer function. There will be some inaccuracy in the compensator we design simply due to the tolerances of the components used, but this is minimal compared to the uncertainty in the plant parameters.

It is very common for the exact location of one or more of the plant poles or zeros to be known only within a range of values. Such uncertainty is termed structural uncertainty. This means that we know the basic model structure, e.g., a transfer function with a certain number of poles and zeros, but we may be uncertain about some of the parameters of the model. Our interest here is in structural uncertainty, and we analyze it in the context of Example 7.7.1, using a variation of the root locus technique called root contour.

**EXAMPLE 7.7.1**

Consider the plant transfer function

$$G_p(s) = \frac{1}{s(s+1)(s+\gamma)},$$

where $\gamma$ is not known exactly, but we can say that $-70 < \gamma < -50$. We introduce the lead compensator

$$G_c(s) = \frac{K_c(s+1)}{(s+10)},$$

with the intent of adjusting the gain so that the compensated system has dominant complex poles with a damped frequency of 4 rad/s. Figure 7.27 shows the root locus

**Figure 7.27 |** Root locus for $\gamma = 60$ for Example 7.7.1.

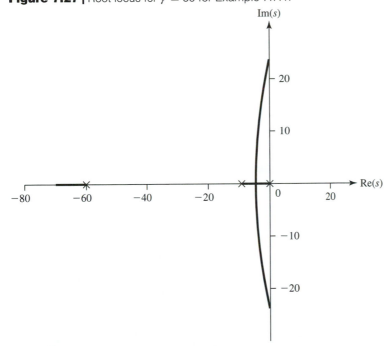

for $\gamma = 60$. The gain that places the dominant poles in the desired locations is $K_c = 2270$. The gain that causes the system to become unstable is $K = 40{,}000$. It is pretty clear that absolute stability is not much of an issue, but *relative* stability and performance may be worth investigating.

One way to analyze the relative stability would be to redraw the root locus for a range of values of $\gamma$ and look at the gain required to achieve the desired closed-loop poles for each value of $\gamma$. This can be done, but it could be a lot of work since we have a continuous range of values for $\gamma$. Even if we look only at the end points and midpoint of the range of values, of $\gamma$, we are still in for a lot of drawing. For instance, what happens if we design for one value of $\gamma$ but the actual value is different from the value we have assumed? To answer this question we introduce the idea of a root contour.

The characteristic equation for the system is

$$s^3 + (10 + \gamma)s^2 + 10\gamma s + K_c = 0.$$

We can rearrange this equation as

$$1 + \frac{\gamma s(s + 10)}{s^3 + 10s^2 + K_c}.$$

If we *fix* $K_c$, and vary $\gamma$, we can investigate how the closed-loop poles vary with $\gamma$. We choose three values of $K_c$, the values required to achieve the desired closed-loop poles with $\gamma = 50$, 60, and 70. The respective values are 1870, 2270, and 2680.

For any of these values of $K_c$ the root contour for $0 < \gamma < \infty$ has the form of the sketch shown in Fig. 7.28. An accurate root contour for all three gains for $0 < \gamma < 70$ is shown in Fig. 7.29. As can be seen the contours overlap for larger values of $\gamma$. Since we are only interested in $50 < \gamma < 70$, an accurate root contour for the three chosen values of gain is shown in Fig. 7.30, with $\gamma$ limited to this range of values.

We can see where the name root contour comes from. For the complex poles there are three sets of root locus plots, one for each gain. The same is true for the real

**Figure 7.28 |** Root contour for fixed $K_c$ and $\gamma$ variable for Example 7.7.1.

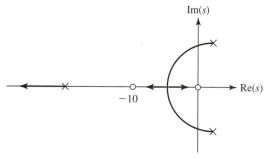

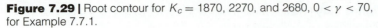

**Figure 7.29 |** Root contour for $K_c = 1870$, 2270, and 2680, $0 < \gamma < 70$, for Example 7.7.1.

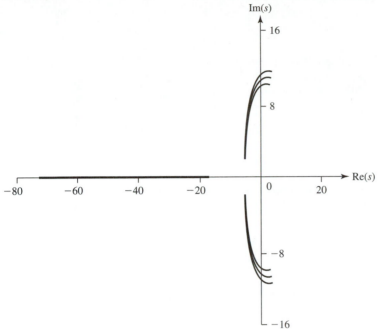

pole, but here the three plots are almost identical. The contours are distinguished by the weight and shade of the lines. For $K_c = 1870$, the contours are the thin black lines. For $K_c = 2270$, the contours are light gray and thicker. For $K_c = 2680$, the contours are an even lighter gray and thicker yet.

The root contour makes is very clear what our choices are in terms of *relative* stability. If we design under the assumption that $\gamma = 50$, then we guarantee that

$$0.78 < \zeta < 0.93,$$

where $\zeta$ is the damping ratio based on the location of the dominant poles. The downside to this design is that if $\gamma = 70$, $\omega_d = 2$ rad/s, and $t_p$ will be half of what we want.

If we design using $\gamma = 60$ then

$$0.86 < \zeta < 0.69,$$

and the speed of response, as specified by $t_p$, will be between 75% and 125% of our target.

If we design using $\gamma = 70$ then

$$0.78 < \zeta < 0.53,$$

and the speed of response will be between 100% and 150% of the target.

**Figure 7.30 |** Root contour for $K_c = 1870$, 2270, and 2680, $50 < \gamma < 70$ for Example 7.7.1.

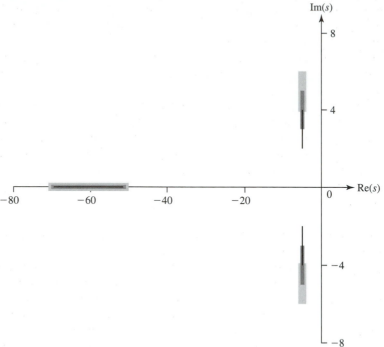

Thus, the root contour technique has helped us sort out and quantify the design trade-offs. Which design we choose will depend on our relative weighting of control effort (gain), speed of response (damped frequency $\omega_d$), and percent overshoot (damping ratio). One way to quantify the choice is to define a "cost function" by assigning weighting coefficients to these three quantities. The optimal design would be the design that minimizes the cost function. For instance; consider the cost function

$$c(\omega_d, \zeta, K_c) = 0.5 \left( \frac{|\omega_d - 4|}{4} \right) + 0.25 \left( \frac{|\zeta - 0.8|}{0.8} \right) + 0.25 \left( \frac{K_c}{1870} \right).$$

For each of the three gains, we can take values from the root contour for $50 < \gamma < 70$, and compute, for each $\gamma$, the values of $\omega_d$ and $\zeta$. If we substitute these values in the cost function, we get the graph shown in Fig. 7.31. This provides us with another means of chosing our controller.

Of course, there are an infinite number of cost functions that we could choose. This particular cost function puts the largest weighting coefficient on speed of response. For this cost function, the best choice of gain appears to be $K_c = 2270$. A different cost function could easily lead to a different choice of $K_c$.

**Figure 7.31** | Cost functions for $K = 1870$, $2270$, and $2680$ for Example 7.7.1.

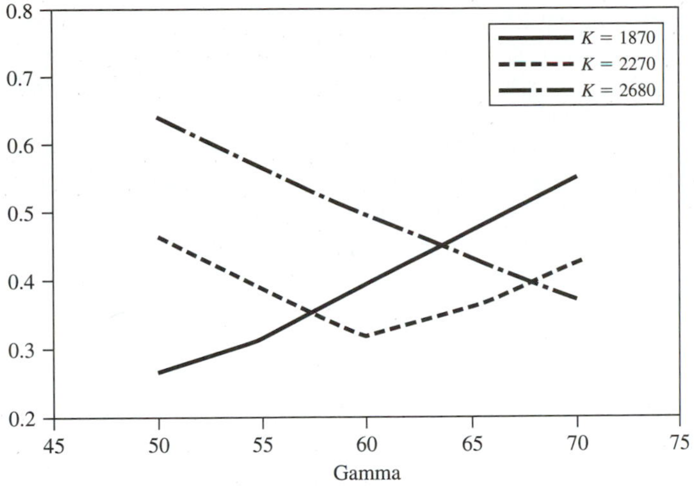

# 7.8 | Reprise

In this chapter, we have introduced design techniques based on root locus analysis that use the figures of merit developed in Chapter 6. The advantage of root locus design is that it is very intuitive. The root locus plot provides the designer with a picture of all potential closed-loop pole locations. This picture, when combined with the figures of merit, makes it an easy matter to find a good compensator using very simple specifications. The choice in this chapter was to specify the time to peak and the percent overshoot. Since percent overshoot depends only on $\zeta$, once an appropriate value of $\zeta$ is chosen, the natural frequency $\omega_n$ can be determined from the formula for $t_p$.

The design procedures have been explained through examples. The overriding principle is the use of pole/zero cancellation to make the closed-loop transfer function as close as possible to the normalized second-order transfer function $T_{N2}$. The actual implementation of the compensator will result in near, but not perfect pole/zero cancellation. The assumption is that the response for near cancellation will be essentially the same as that for perfect cancellation. We have not provided a rigorous analysis to support this assumption, but the examples in this chapter suggest that the assumption is generally true.

Although the primary purpose of the chapter was to introduce the fundamental skills necessary to do root locus design, the techniques presented are effective for the vast majority of design problems encountered. The Bode design technique introduced in Chapter 11 is generally superior to the root locus design method. However, the two approaches are related and the intuition developed in this chapter will stand us in good stead when we discuss Bode design in Chapter 11. In addition, the root locus design skills learned here are of great utility in designing digital compensators.

Another goal of the chapter was to introduce PID control. As we have seen, PID control is an idealization of lead/lag control and can best be thought of as the cascade of PD and PI compensators. PID control is still used in a great many industrial applications, and hence it is important to understand how such a compensator is designed. In many cases lead/lag control, which is very similar to PID control, is easier to implement and therefore a good choice.

Finally, we introduced the root contour method as a way of designing a compensator when there is some uncertainty in the model of the plant to be controlled. Generally we know the structure of the plant with reasonable but not perfect accuracy. For the purposes of this book, that structure is either a transfer function or a state model. However, it often happens that there is some uncertainty in one or more of the parameters of the model. In Example 7.7.1, we discussed a transfer function where the location of one pole was uncertain. The root contour method was effective in laying bare the performance of a family of potential compensators. To help us make the best choice, we introduced a simple optimization strategy.

Now that we have developed some design expertise, we are ready to try our hand at a real design. In Chapter 8 we will go through the complete design cycle. We will begin by proposing a model for the plant to be controlled. This model will turn out to be a transfer function whose exact pole locations are unknown. We will then identify the pole locations, design a compensator, and finally implement the compensator using opamp circuits.

## 7.9 | Problems

The problems in Sections 7.9.1 through 7.9.8 are based on the feedback configuration of Fig. 7.32. Design the proposed compensator for the given plant and specifications, and complete any other stated requirements.

**Figure 7.32 |** Cascade compensation with unity feedback.

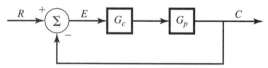

### 7.9.1   Lag Compensation

1. $G_p = \dfrac{10}{(s+1)(s+3)(s+30)}$      $G_c = \dfrac{K(s+0.1)}{s+b}$.

   a.   Damping ratio $\zeta = 1/\sqrt{2}$
   b.   Steady state error to a step input less than 10%

2. $G_p = \dfrac{10}{(s+3)(s+30)}$      $G_c = \dfrac{K(s+b)}{s+0.1}$.
   a.   Damping ratio $\zeta = 1/\sqrt{2}$
   b.   Steady state error to a step input less than 5%

3.  $G_p(s) = \dfrac{1}{(s+3)(s+30)}$    $G_c(s) = \dfrac{K_c(s+0.5)}{s+b}$.

    a.  Damping ratio $\zeta = 0.8$
    b.  Steady state error to a step input less than 10%
    c.  Find the time response to a step input using partial fraction expansion.

4.  $G_p(s) = \dfrac{1}{(s+1)(s+5)}$    $G_c(s) = \dfrac{K_c(s+0.1)}{s+b}$.

    Design $G_c$ so that the closed-loop system has poles at $s = -3 \pm j3$, and the steady state error to a step is less than 5%.

5.  $G_p(s) = \dfrac{1}{(s+1)(s+10)}$    $G_c(s) = \dfrac{K_c(s+a)}{s+0.1}$.

    For $a = 0.5, 1, 2$, adjust $K$ so that the closed-loop system has dominant complex poles with a damping ratio $\zeta = 0.8$. Find $K_p$ for each value of $a$.

## 7.9.2  PI Compensation

1.  $G_p = \dfrac{1}{(s+2)(s+4)}$    $G_c(s) = K_{pi} + \dfrac{K_i}{s}$.

    a.  Find $K_{pi}$ and $K_i$ so that the closed-loop system has poles at $s = -x \pm j3$ and $K_i/K_{pi} = 0.2$.
    b.  Determine the steady state error for $r(t) = t1(t)$.
    c.  Find the closed-loop transfer function $T_c(s)$ in factored form.
    d.  Find and plot the closed-loop response.

2.  $G_p = \dfrac{1}{(s+2)(s+4)}$    $G_c(s) = K_{pi} + \dfrac{K_i}{s}$.

    a.  Find $K_{pi}$ and $K_i$ so that the closed-loop system has poles at $s = -x \pm j3$ and $K_i/K_{pi} = 0.1$.
    b.  Determine the steady state error for $r(t) = t1(t)$.
    c.  Find the closed-loop transfer function $T_c(s)$ in factored form.
    d.  Find and plot the unit step response.

3.  $G_p = \dfrac{1}{(s+2)(s+4)}$    $G_c(s) = K_{pi} + \dfrac{K_i}{s}$.

    a.  Find $K_{pi}$ and $K_i$ so that the closed-loop system has poles at $s = -x \pm j3$ and $K_i/K_{pi} = 2$.
    b.  Determine the steady state error for $r(t) = t1(t)$.
    c.  Find the closed-loop transfer function $T_c(s)$ in factored form.
    d.  Find and plot the unit step response.

4.  $G_p = \dfrac{1}{(s+2)(s+4)}$    $G_c(s) = K_{pi} + \dfrac{K_i}{s}$.

    a.  Find $K_{pi}$ and $K_i$ so that the closed-loop system has poles at $s = -x \pm j3$ and $K_i/K_{pi} = 0.5$.
    b.  Determine the steady state error for $r(t) = t1(t)$.

c.  Find the closed-loop transfer function $T_c(s)$ in factored form.

d.  Find the unit step response by partial fraction expansion.

5.  $G_p = \dfrac{1}{(s+2)(s+8)}$     $G_c(s) = K_{pi} + \dfrac{K_i}{s}$.

a.  Closed-loop system has exactly two poles at $s = -4 \pm j4$.

b.  Sketch the unit step response of the system of part a.

c.  Suppose when implemented the zero of the PI compensator is at $a - 0.1$, where $-a$ is the desired zero location. Find the poles of the closed-loop system for the gain of part (a) and the unit step response by partial fraction expansion. Check with MATLAB.

6.  $G_p = \dfrac{1}{(s+1)(s+5)}$     $G_c = \dfrac{K_c(s+a)}{s}$.

For $a = 1.0, 0.8, 0.5,$ and $0.2,$

a.  Find the gain that places the dominant poles at $s = -x \pm j3$. Note that you have to find $x$ to do this.

b.  For $a = 0.8, 0.5, 0.2$ find the third closed-loop pole.

c.  Find the time response by partial fraction expansion.

7.  $G_p = \dfrac{1}{(s+1)(s+10)}$     $G_c = \dfrac{K_c(s+a)}{s}$.

a.  $T_p \le 0.6$ s.

b.  PO $\le 20\%$.

c.  $K_v \ge 10$.

8.  $G_p = \dfrac{1}{(s+2)(s+6)}$     $G_c = \dfrac{K_c(s+a)}{s}$.

a.  $T_p \le 1$ s.

b.  PO $\le 20\%$.

c.  $K_v \ge 7$.

9.  $G_p = \dfrac{1}{(s+3)(s+7)}$     $G_c = \dfrac{K_c(s+a)}{s}$.

a.  $T_p \le 0.5$ s.

b.  PO $\le 20\%$.

c.  $K_v \ge 7$.

10.  $G_p(s) = \dfrac{10}{(s+4)(s+20)}$.

Consider two compensators

$$G_{c_1}(s) = \frac{K_c(s+0.5)}{s} \quad \text{and} \quad G_{c_2}(s) = \frac{K_c(s+4)}{s}.$$

It is desired that the closed-loop system have complex dominant poles with a damping ratio of $\zeta = 0.8$.

a.  Which choice of compensator will yield the smallest steady state error for $r(t) = t\mathbf{1}(t)$?

b. Without doing any calculations, which system do you suppose will have the shortest settling time for a unit step input?

11. Redesign the PI compensator of Example 7.4.1 so that the dominant poles are at $s = -3 \pm j4$, and then find the step response using MATLAB.

### 7.9.3 Lead Compensation

1. Find the time response for the compensator of Example 7.3.3.

2. $G_p = \dfrac{10}{s(s+0.5)(s+20)}$     $G_c = \dfrac{K(s+b)}{s+10}$.

    a. Find $b$ so that the closed-loop system has poles at $s = -3 \pm j3$.
    b. Find the gain that places closed-loop poles at $s = -3 \pm j3$.
    c. Find $K_v$.

3. $G_p = \dfrac{5}{s(s+1)}$     $G_c = \dfrac{K(s+4)}{s+b}$.

    Find $b$ and $K$ so that
    a. $t_p \approx 0.785$ s.
    b. $\zeta = 0.8$.

4. $G_p = \dfrac{5}{s(s+1)(s+10)}$     $G_c = \dfrac{K_c(s+a)}{s+b}$.

    a. Suppose $t_p = 0.785$ s and $\zeta = 0.8$. Find the location of the dominant complex poles.
    b. Find the general location of the zero of the compensator for the closed-loop poles determined in part (a).
    c. Let $b = 186$ and find $K_c$ and $a$ to place the dominant poles at the desired location.
    d. Find the other two closed-loop poles.
    e. Write down the factored form of the closed-loop transfer function.
    f. Find the unit step response by partial fraction expansion.

5. $G_p = \dfrac{1}{s(s+1)}$     $G_c = \dfrac{K_c(s+3)}{s+18}$.

    For $K_c = 78$,

$$T_c(s) = \frac{78(s+3)}{(s+3-j3)(s+3+j3)(s+13)}.$$

Find $T_c(s)$ for $K_c = 70$ and $K_c = 86$. For each of the three gains, find $c(t)$ by partial fraction expansion and then plot the time response for 5 s.

6. $G_p = \dfrac{1}{s(s+1)}$     $G_c = \dfrac{K_c(s+3)}{s+18}$.

    For $K_c = 78$,

$$T_c(s) = \frac{78(s+3)}{(s+3-j3)(s+3+j3)(s+13)}.$$

Find $T_c(s)$ for $K_c = 62$ and $K_c = 94$. For each of the three gains, find $c(t)$ by partial fraction expansion and then plot the time response for 5 s.

7.  $G_p = \dfrac{1}{s(s+1)}$     $G_c = \dfrac{K_c(s+1)}{s+6}$.

For $K_c = 18$,

$$T_c(s) = \frac{18}{(s+3-j3)(s+3+j3)}.$$

Find $T_c(s)$ for $K_c = 16$ and $K_c = 20$. For each of the three gains plot the time response for 5 s.

8.  $G_p = \dfrac{1}{s(s+1)}$     $G_c = \dfrac{K_c(s+1)}{s+6}$.

For $K_c = 18$,

$$T_c(s) = \frac{18}{(s+3-j3)(s+3+j3)}.$$

Find $T_c(s)$ for $K_c = 14$ and $K_c = 22$. For each of the three gains plot the time response for 5 s.

9.  $G_p = \dfrac{10}{s(s+4)(s+10)}$     $G_c = \dfrac{K_c(s+a)}{s+b}$.

Using pole cancellation such that the closed-loop system has dominant poles at $s = -4 \pm j3$. Using MATLAB to plot step response.

10. $G_p(s) = \dfrac{1}{s^2}$     $G_c(s) = K_c \dfrac{s+a}{s+b}$.

Design a compensator that meets the specifications:
a.  Time to peak $t_p$ less than 1 s.
b.  PO less than 15%.

11. $G_p(s) = \dfrac{1}{s^2}$     $G_c(s) = \dfrac{K_c(s+a)}{s+b}$.

Design a compensator using near pole/zero cancellation that results in a closed-loop transfer function with poles near $s = -3 \pm j3$.

12. $G_p(s) = \dfrac{1}{(s+3)(s+10)}$     $G_c(s) = \dfrac{K_c(s+a)}{s+b}$.

Design a compensator that places the dominant closed-loop poles at $s = -4 + j3$.

### 7.9.4  PD Compensation

1.  $G_p = \dfrac{1}{s(s+1)}$     $G_c = K_{pd} + K_d s$.

a.  Add a PD compensator, finding $K_{pd}$ and $K_d$ so that the closed-loop system has poles at $s = -3 \pm j2$.
b.  Determine the steady state error for $r(t) = t1(t)$.

c.　Find the closed-loop transfer function $T_c(s)$ in factored form.

d.　Find the unit step response using MATLAB.

2.　$G_p = \dfrac{1}{s(s + 0.5)}$ 　　　$G_c = K_{pd} + K_d s$.

a.　Add a PD compensator, finding $K_{pd}$ and $K_d$ so that the closed-loop system has poles at $s = -3 \pm j2$.

b.　Determine the steady state error for $r(t) = t1(t)$.

c.　Find the closed-loop transfer function $T_c(s)$ in factored form.

d.　Find the unit step response using MATLAB.

3.　$G_p = \dfrac{1}{s(s + 0.5)}$ 　　　$G_c = K_{pd} + K_d s$.

a.　Add a PD compensator, finding $K_{pd}$ and $K_d$ so that the closed-loop system has poles at $s = -4 \pm j3$.

b.　Determine the steady state error for $r(t) = t1(t)$.

c.　Find the closed-loop transfer function $T_c(s)$ in factored form and the unit step response using MATLAB.

4.　$G_p(s) = \dfrac{1}{(s + 0.1)(s + 1)(s + 20)}$ 　　　$G_c = K_{pd} + K_d s$.

a.　Closed-loop system has dominant poles at $s = -4 \pm j3$.

b.　Find the closed-loop transfer function in factored form and the unit step response using MATLAB.

## 7.9.5　Lead/Lag Compensation

1.　$G_p = \dfrac{1}{s(s + 0.5)}$ 　　　$G_c = \dfrac{K_c(s + 1.5)}{s + p_1}$.

a.　Find $K_c$ and $p_1$ so that the closed-loop system has poles at $s = -3 \pm j2$.

b.　Determine the steady state error for $r(t) = t1(t)$.

c.　Add a lag filter,

$$\frac{s + z_1}{s + p_2},$$

in cascade with the lead compensator so that the steady state error to a ramp is 2%.

d.　Find the closed-loop transfer function $T_c(s)$ in factored form.

e.　Find the unit step response using MATLAB.

2.　$G_p = \dfrac{1}{(s + 1)(s + 2)}$ 　　　$G_c(s) = \dfrac{K_c(s + 1)(s + z_2)}{(s + 0.2)(s + 20)}$.

a.　Closed-loop poles at $s = -3 \pm j2$.

b.　Determine the steady state error for $r(t) = 1(t)$.

c.　Find the closed-loop transfer function $T_c(s)$ in factored form.

d.　Find the unit step response using MATLAB.

3. $G_p = \dfrac{10}{s(s+1)(s+10)}$   $G_c(s) = \dfrac{K_c(s+1)(s+z)}{(s+12)(s+p)}$.

   a.  Closed-loop system has poles at $s = -3 \pm j2$.
   b.  The closed-loop system tracks a ramp input within 1%.
   c.  Find the closed-loop transfer function $T_c(s)$ in factored form.

4. $G_p = \dfrac{1}{s(s+0.5)}$   $G_c = \dfrac{K_c(s+0.5)(s+z)}{(s+0.1)(s+p)}$.

   a.  Closed-loop poles at $s = -3 \pm j2$.
   b.  The steady state error to a ramp input is less or equal to 5%.
   c.  Find the closed-loop transfer function $T_c(s)$ in factored form.
   d.  Find the unit step response.

5. $G_p = \dfrac{1}{s(s+0.5)(s+10)}$   $G_c = \dfrac{K_c(s+z_1)(s+z_2)}{(s+20)(s+p)}$.

   a.  Closed-loop transfer function has two of its poles at $s = -3 \pm j2$.
   b.  Find the closed-loop transfer function $T_c(s)$ in factored form.
   c.  Determine the unit step response.

6. $G_p = \dfrac{1}{s(s+0.2)(s+0.5)}$   $G_c = \dfrac{K_c(s+z_1)(s+z_2)}{(s+p_1)(s+30)}$.

   a.  Closed-loop transfer function has poles at $s = -4 \pm j3$.
   b.  The closed-loop transfer function has a exactly three poles.

7. $G_p = \dfrac{1}{s(s+0.1)(s+5)}$   $G_c = \dfrac{K_c(s+z_1)(s+0.2)}{(s+p_1)(s+30)}$.

   a.  Closed-loop transfer function has *dominant* poles at $s = -4 \pm j3$.
   b.  Closed-loop system has *exactly* four poles.

8. $G_p = \dfrac{1}{s(s+0.1)(s+5)}$   $G_c = \dfrac{K_c(s+z_1)(s+1)}{(s+p_1)(s+30)}$.

   a.  Closed-loop transfer function has *dominant* poles at $s = -4 \pm j3$.
   b.  Closed-loop system has *exactly* four poles.

9. $G_p = \dfrac{1}{s(s+0.1)(s+5)}$   $G_c = \dfrac{K_c(s+z_1)(s+1)}{(s+20)(s+p_1)}$.

   a.  Closed-loop transfer function has *dominant* poles at $s = -4 \pm j3$.
   b.  Closed-loop system has *exactly* four poles.

### 7.9.6   Lead/PI Compensation

1. $G_p = \dfrac{1}{(s+1)(s+2)}$   $G_c(s) = \dfrac{K_c(s+1)(s+z_2)}{s(s+10)}$.

   a.  Closed-loop transfer function has poles at $s = -3 \pm j2$.
   b.  Determine the steady state error for $r(t) = t\mathbf{1}(t)$.

c.  Find the closed-loop transfer function $T_c(s)$ in factored form.
d.  Find the unit step response.

2.  $G_p = \dfrac{1}{(s+1)(s+2)}$        $G_c(s) = \dfrac{K_c(s+2)(s+z_2)}{s(s+10)}$.

a.  Closed-loop transfer function has poles at $s = -3 \pm j2$.
b.  Determine the steady state error for $r(t) = t\mathbf{1}(t)$.
c.  Find the closed-loop transfer function $T_c(s)$ in factored form.
d.  Find the unit step response by partial fraction expansion.

3.  $G_p = \dfrac{1}{(s+2)(s+5)}$        $G_c(s) = \dfrac{K_c(s+2)(s+5)}{s(s+10)}$.

a.  Closed-loop transfer function has poles at $s = -5 \pm j4$.
b.  Suppose when implemented the zero at $s = -5$ is really at $s = -5.1$. For the gain of part (a), find the closed-loop poles.
c.  Compare the responses of the systems of part (a) and part (b).

4.  $G_p = \dfrac{1}{(s+0.5)^2}$.

a.  Consider first the compensator

$$G_c(s) = \frac{K_c(s+0.5)^2}{s(s+a)}.$$

Find $K_c$ and $a$ so that that the dominant closed-loop poles are at $s = -4 \pm j2$. Then evaluate the steady state error to a ramp input.
b.  Now consider the compensator

$$G_c(s) = \frac{K_c(s+0.5)(s+0.1)}{s(s+a)}.$$

Find $K_c$ and $a$ so that that the dominant closed-loop poles are at $s = -4 \pm j2$. Then evaluate the steady state error to a ramp input.

5.  $G_p(s) = \dfrac{1}{(s+1)(s+2)(s+20)}$        $G_c(s) = \dfrac{K_c(s+2)(s+z_1)}{s(s+40)}$.

a.  Assuming $\zeta = 1/\sqrt{2}$ and that the free zero of the compensator is at $s = -1.5$, what is the largest damped frequency that the dominant complex poles can have?
b.  Assuming $\zeta = 1/\sqrt{2}$, and that the zero of the compensator is moved close to the origin, what is the largest damped frequency (approximately) that the dominant complex poles can have?

6.  $G_p = \dfrac{1}{(s+1)^2}$        $G_c(s) = \dfrac{K_c(s+1)(s+z_1)}{s(s+20)}$.

Design $G_c$ so that the closed-loop transfer function has poles at $s = -5 \pm j4$.

7.  $G_p = \dfrac{1}{(s+1)^2}$        $G_c(s) = \dfrac{K_c(s+1)(s+z_1)}{s(s+20)}$.

Design $G_c$ so that the closed-loop transfer function has poles a $s = -8 \pm j6$.

8.  $G_p(s) = \dfrac{10}{(s+1)(s+2)}$     $G_c(s) = \dfrac{K_c(s+z_1)(s+z_2)}{(s+p_1)(s+15)}$.

    a.  Dominant poles at $s = -4 \pm j2$.
    b.  Zero steady state error to a step input.
    c.  Closed-loop system has three poles.
    d.  Find the step response.

9.  $G_p(s) = \dfrac{6}{(s+2)(s+3)}$     $G_c(s) = \dfrac{K_c(s+z_1)(s+z_2)}{(s+p_1)(s+15)}$.

    a.  Dominant poles at $s = -4 + j2$.
    b.  Zero steady state error to a step input.
    c.  Closed-loop system has three poles.
    d.  Find the step response.

### 7.9.7  PID Compensation

1.  $G_p = \dfrac{1}{s(s+0.5)}$     $G_c = K_{pd} + K_d s$.

    a.  Add a PD compensator, finding $K_{pd}$ and $K_d$ so that the closed-loop system has poles at $s = -3 \pm j2$.
    b.  Determine the steady state error for $r(t) = t\mathbf{1}(t)$.
    c.  Add a PI compensator $K_{pi} + K_i/s$ in cascade with the PD compensator.
    d.  Find the coefficients $K_D$, $K_I$, and $K_p$ of the equivalent PID compensator.
    e.  Find the unit step response.

2.  $G_p = \dfrac{1}{s(s+0.5)}$     $G_c(s) = \dfrac{K_c(s+a)^2}{s}$.

    a.  Closed-loop transfer function has poles at $s = -3 \pm j2$.
    b.  Determine the steady state error for $r(t) = (1/2)t^2\mathbf{1}(t)$.
    c.  Find the closed-loop transfer function $T_c(s)$ in factored form.
    d.  Estimate the step response based on $\omega_d$ and $\zeta$.
    e.  Find the unit step response.

3.  $G_p(s) = \dfrac{10}{(s+1)(s+2)(s+20)}$     $G_c(s) = K_p + \dfrac{K_I}{s} + K_D s$.

    Design a compensator that meets the following specifications.
    a.  The closed-loop system has dominant poles with a damped frequency of 5 rad/s and $\zeta > 0.707$.
    b.  The closed-loop system exhibits zero steady state error to a unit step input.
    c.  The closed-loop transfer function has exactly two poles.

### 7.9.8  Root Contour

For these problems a (short) MATLAB program must be written to generate the closed-loop poles for the root contour so that $\omega_d$ and $\zeta$ can be determined and substituted into the cost function.

1. For Example 7.7.1, change the cost function to

$$c(\omega_d, \zeta, K_c) = 0.5\left(\frac{|\omega_d - 4|}{4}\right) + 0.25\left(\frac{|\zeta - 0.8|}{0.8}\right) + 0.25\left(\frac{|K_c - 1870|}{1870}\right).$$

2. For Example 7.7.1, change the cost function to

$$c(\omega_d, \zeta, K_c) = 0.34\left(\frac{|\omega_d - 4|}{4}\right) + 0.33\left(\frac{|\zeta - 0.8|}{0.8}\right) + 0.33\left(\frac{|K_c - 1870|}{1870}\right).$$

3. Let $G_p(s) = \dfrac{5}{s(s + \gamma)}$    $G_c(s) = \dfrac{K_c(s + 5)}{s + 30}$.

Suppose $2 < \gamma < 4$.

   a. For the end points and midpoint of the interval on $\gamma$, find the gains that yield dominant closed-loop poles with $\omega_d = 3$ rad/s.
   b. Use the root contour method to determine the range of damping ratios and the range of $\omega_d$ for the three gains of part (a).

## 7.9.9  Additional Problems

1. For the PD compensator design of Example 7.2.2, find the gain $K_{critical}$ for which the closed-loop transfer function is critically damped. Then find the minimum damping ratio for $0 < K < K_{critical}$.

2. For Example 7.3.1, Consider the two compensators

$$G_1(s) = \frac{K_c(s + 2)}{s + p_1} \quad \text{and} \quad G_2(s) = \frac{K_c(s + 3.3)}{s + p_2}.$$

   a. Find $p_1$ and $p_2$ and the associated gains.
   b. Write a short MATLAB program to draw an accurate root locus for these two designs.
   c. Compute $K_v$ for these two designs and compare with the $K_v$ from the example.

3. For Example 7.3.3, find the third closed-loop pole and then find the response of the closed-loop system to a unit step input by partial fraction expansion.

4. For Example 7.4.1, leave the zero of the compensator at $s = -0.1$, and reduce the damping ratio to 0.5. Find the compensator gain and then plot the unit step response of the closed-loop system using MATLAB.

5. For Example 7.3.2, leave the gain at 1.8 and find the closed-loop pole locations and the step response.

6. For Example 7.6.2, let the compensator be

$$G_c(s) = \frac{K_c(s + 1)(s + z_1)}{s(s + 11)}.$$

   a. Find $K_c$ and $z_1$.
   b. Find $K_v$ and compare with Examples 7.6.1 and 7.6.2.
   c. Find the unit step response and compare with Examples 7.6.1 and 7.6.2.

7. Consider the "smart" missile shown in Fig. 7.33. The missile has a TV camera in its nose that relays a picture to the pilot. The pilot then directs the missile by centering the target on a display in the cockpit with a joystick. The signal from the pilot then causes the guidance system of the missile to move toward the target. Let the dynamics of the the missile and its control system be

$$G_p(s) = \frac{200}{s(s+5)(s+15)}.$$

For the unity feedback, cascade compensation configuration of Fig. 7.32, design the compensator $G_c$ to these specifications.
a. $K_v > 5$
b. $t_p \leq 1$ s
c. $10\% < \text{PO} < 40\%$

**Figure 7.33 |** Smartbomb system.

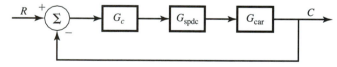

8. Figure 7.34 shows a block diagram of a speed controller for an automobile, where

$$G_{\text{spdc}}(s) = \frac{10}{(s+3)(s+3.2)} \qquad G_{\text{car}}(s) = \frac{1}{s+2.5}.$$

Design a controller $G_c$ that meets these specifications.
a. $K_p \geq 10$
b. $\zeta \geq 0.5$
c. The response to a step input is critically damped.

**Figure 7.34 |** Block diagram of automobile speed control.

9. Consider the system shown in Fig. 7.35, where the plant has a feedback loop. Let

$$G_1(s) = \frac{1}{s^2} \qquad G_2(s) = \frac{120s + 100}{s^2 + 12s + 72}.$$

Design a controller $G_c$ to meet these specifications
a. $t_p \leq 0.5$ s

**Figure 7.35 |** Multiloop control.

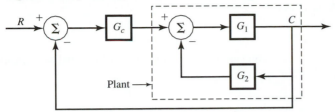

b.  PO ≤ 15%
c.  $t_s < 2$ s to ±10% of final value
d.  $K_p > 9$

**10.** Consider the missile control system of Fig. 7.36. $G_t$ and $G_m$ are the thruster and missile dynamics given by

$$G_t(s) = \frac{12}{s + 10} \qquad G_m(s) = \frac{5}{(s + 1.2)(s - 1)}.$$

Note that the missile has an unstable pole. $K_r$ is the adjustable gain of the rate gyro, and $K_s$ the adjustable gain of the veritcal gyro, sometimes called a stable platform. By adjusting $K_r$ and $K_s$, stablize the missile and try to obtain a set of dominant complex poles with a damping ratio of 0.5, and $K_p > 9$.

**Figure 7.36 |** Multiloop missile control.

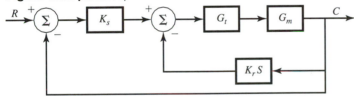

**11.** Figure 7.37 shows a unity feedback loop for the pitch control of an aircraft where

$$G_{flap}(s) = \frac{4000}{s + 8} \qquad G_p(s) = \frac{(s + 6)(s + 15)}{s(s + 3 - j12)(s + 3 + j12)}.$$

**Figure 7.37 |** Pitch control of aircraft.

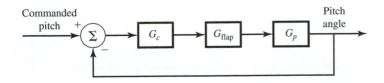

Design a compensator to meet these specifications.

a.   $K_v \geq 130$
b.   PO $\leq 15\%$
c.   $t_p \leq 0.7$ s

12.   The roll characteristics of a missile about its longitudinal axis, as shown in Fig. 7.38, are given by

$$G_m(s) = \frac{1}{s(s+15)}.$$

Design a compensator $G_c$ to meet these specifications.

a.   $K_v \geq 100$
b.   $t_p \leq 0.4$ s
c.   PO $\leq 20\%$

**Figure 7.38 |** Roll control of missile.

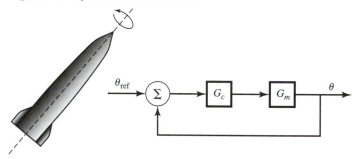

13.   Consider Fig. 7.39, which shows a high-speed magnetic levitation train. On curves, it is necessary to bank the train to match the bank of the turn. The block diagram shows how this might be accompished with a rate gyro. $R$ is a bank command in degrees and $C$ is the acutal amount of bank in degrees. Since the train is floating its dynamics have been modeled as

$$G_{\text{maglev}}(s) = \frac{1}{Js^2}.$$

**Figure 7.39 |** Roll control of MagLev train.

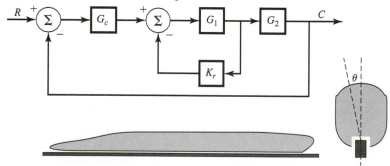

In the figure, these dynamics are broken down into

$$G_1(s) = \frac{1}{J_s} \quad \text{and} \quad G_2(s) = \frac{1}{s}.$$

We do not need to know the value of $J$. Simply assume that the ratio

$$\frac{K_r}{J}$$

is known.

Design the control system $G_c$ to these specifications.

a. System critically damped with zero steady state error to a step input.
b. Rise time to 90% of final value less than 0.2 s.
c. $K_v \geq 50$.

# FURTHER READINGS

D'Azzo, John J., and Constantine H. Houpis. 1988. *Linear Control System Design; Conventional and Modern.* New York: McGraw-Hill.

Franklin, Gene F., J. David Powell, and Abbas Emami-Naeini. 1991. *Feedback Control of Dynamic Systems,* 2nd ed., Reading, Mass.: Addison-Wesley.

Kuo, Benjamin C. 1982. *Automatic Control.* Englewood Cliffs, N.J.: Prentice-Hall.

Melsa, James L., and Donald G. Schultz. 1969. *Linear Control Systems.* New York: McGraw-Hill.

Ogata, Katsuhiko. 1970. *Modern Control Engineering.* Englewood Cliffs, N.J.: Prentice-Hall.

Saucedo, Roberto., and Earl E. Schiring. 1968. *Introduction to Continuous and Digital Control Systems.* New York: MacMillan.

# 8
## Chapter

# Motor Speed Control
## *A Case Study*

## 8.1 | OVERVIEW

In Chapter 7 we had our first taste of design, using root locus analysis to design a variety of compensators. With that design experience in hand, we are now ready for a case study that will take us through the entire design cycle. The essential steps in the design cycle are modeling, identification, design, and implementation. Along the way, we will do a lot of analysis and later some simulation, but these four steps are the crucial ones.

We have already looked briefly at the first stage of the design cycle in Chapter 3, where we found the model for a separately excited dc motor. We will put that model to work in this chapter by considering the control of a fractional horsepower, separately excited dc motor.

However, as noted in Chapter 3, to make the model useful for a particular motor requires finding the parameters of the model specific to that motor. If the dc motor were of large horsepower, we could make some standard tests to find these parameters. In the case of a fractional horsepower dc motor, the friction effects are too large to let us do these tests accurately. Therefore, we will have to resort to an another approach.

This process of identifying the parameters of a model whose basic structure is known arises almost every time we design a control system, and for that reason is worthy of our attention. Very seldom are we lucky enough to have an accurate model of the plant at the start of the design.

In this chapter, we will employ two different identification techniques based on the recorded step response of the plant. One of these techniques was discussed in Chapter 3. The other technique will be introduced in this chapter. Both will be applied to the system shown in Fig. 8.1. The system consists of a fractional horsepower, separately excited dc motor and a cylinder that can be attached to one shaft end of the motor to change the moment of inertia of the system.

On a small scale, this system is representative of a very common industrial application, namely a large-horsepower dc or induction motor maintaining speed

**Figure 8.1 |** Separately excited dc motor with attachable cylinder.

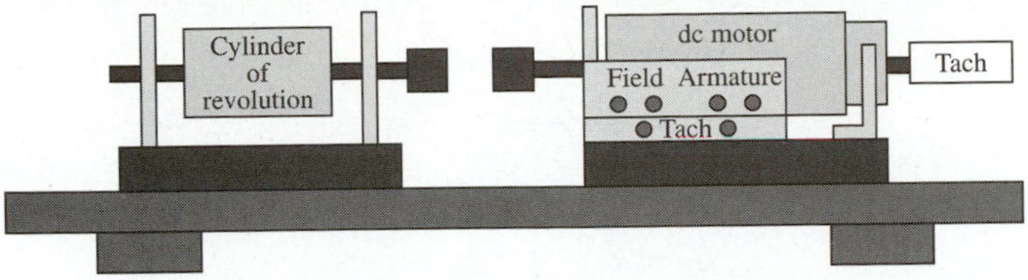

control of a large load. We will use the method introduced in this chapter to identify the parameters of the transfer function without the cylinder attached and the method from Chapter 3 to identify the parameters when the cylinder is attached.

Once we have identified the transfer function of the system we can proceed to the final two phases of the design cycle, the design of a suitable controller and the implementation of that controller on the actual system. In the case of speed control of the dc motor, the control will prove to be quite easy. We will look at integral control and PI control. Both will prove quite satisfactory. Indeed, one important lesson to be learned from this chapter is that if we have a good model of the plant to be controlled, and have correctly identified the parameters of that model, then the design of the controller is relatively easy. As a bonus, the results from the implementation of the control will shed some light on the model that we have chosen.

Our goal in Section 8.2 is to develop a new identification technique that is more general than the one in Chapter 3. With this new technique in hand, we can then measure the step responses of the motor and identify the parameters of the two transfer functions just discussed.

## 8.2 | A NEW IDENTIFICATION PROCEDURE

The identification technique developed in this section is more powerful than that discussed in Chapter 3. The latter technique was only appropriate for a transfer function with two poles and no zeros. The technique developed here can, theoretically, be used for transfer functions with an arbitrary number of poles and zeros.

In practice, there are limits to the order of the transfer function whose parameters can successfully be identified. On the other hand, this technique will enable us to identify the parameters of a transfer function with one or two zeros and as many as three poles. This is a definite improvement over the identification technique introduced in Chapter 3.

Consider a transfer function of the form

$$
\begin{aligned}
G(s) &= \frac{K_0 \prod_{i=1}^{2}(1 + \gamma_i s)}{\prod_{i=1}^{3}(1 + \tau_i s)} \\
&= \frac{K_0(1 + (\gamma_1 + \gamma_2)s + \gamma_1 \gamma_2 s^2)}{1 + (\tau_1 + \tau_2 + \tau_3)s + (\tau_1 \tau_2 + \tau_1 \tau_3 + \tau_2 \tau_3)s^2 + (\tau_1 \tau_2 \tau_3)s^3} \\
&= \frac{K_0 + b_1 s + b_2 s^2}{1 + a_1 s + a_2 s^2 + a_3 s^3},
\end{aligned}
$$

where

$$b_1 = K_0(\gamma_1 + \gamma_2),$$
$$b_2 = K_0\gamma_1\gamma_2,$$
$$a_1 = \tau_1 + \tau_2 + \tau_3,$$
$$a_2 = \tau_1\tau_2 + \tau_1\tau_3 + \tau_2\tau_3,$$
$$a_3 = \tau_1\tau_2\tau_3.$$

For the purposes of this development, we have included two zeros in the transfer function. In point of fact, zeros are reasonably rare in transfer functions, and in this development we will have occasion to point out that the analysis is greatly simplified if one or both of the zeros is missing.

Now consider the unit step response of the LTI system represented by $G(s)$. That is, let

$$y_u(t) = \int_0^\infty g(t - \tau)\mathbf{1}(\tau)\,d\tau.$$

Suppose that the response is that shown in Fig. 8.2. Using the final value theorem we can write

$$\lim_{t\to\infty} y_u(t) = \lim_{s\to 0} s\frac{G(s)}{s}$$
$$= \lim_{s\to 0} G(s)$$
$$= \lim_{s\to 0} \frac{K_0 + b_1s + b_2s^2}{1 + a_1s + a_2s^2 + a_3s^3}$$
$$= K_0.$$

Now define

$$y_1(t) = \int_0^t [K_0 - y_u(\tau)]\,d\tau.$$

**Figure 8.2 |** Step response of unknown system $G(s)$.

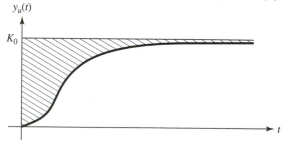

Taking the Laplace transform of both sides of the equation yields

$$Y_1(s) = \frac{1}{s}\left[\frac{K_0}{s} - Y_u(s)\right]$$

$$= \frac{1}{s}\left[\frac{K_0}{s} - \frac{G(s)}{s}\right]$$

$$= \frac{1}{s^2}[K_0 - G(s)].$$

Note that the shaded area in Fig. 8.2 is

$$\lim_{t\to\infty} y_1(t) \overset{\Delta}{=} K_1$$

$$= \lim_{s\to 0} s Y_1(s)$$

$$= \lim_{s\to 0} \frac{1}{s}[K_0 - G(s)].$$

We express this last result in terms of the original formulation of $G(s)$ by writing

$$K_0 - G(s) = K_0 - \frac{K_0 + b_1 s + b_2 s^2}{1 + a_1 s + a_2 s^2 + a_3 s^3}$$

$$= \frac{K_0 + a_1 K_0 s + a_2 K_0 s^2 + a_3 K_0 s^3 - K_0 - b_1 s - b_2 s^2}{1 + a_1 s + a_2 s^2 + a_3 s^3}$$

$$= \frac{(a_1 K_0 - b_1)s + (a_2 K_0 - b_2)s^2 + a_3 K_0 s^3}{1 + a_1 s + a_2 s^2 + a_3 s^3}.$$

We now find

$$\lim_{s\to 0} \frac{1}{s}[K_0 - G(s)] = \lim_{s\to 0} \frac{1}{s} \frac{(a_1 K_0 - b_1)s + (a_2 K_0 - b_2)s^2 + a_3 K_0 s^3}{1 + a_1 s + a_2 s^2 + a_3 s^3}$$

$$= a_1 K_0 - b_1.$$

At this juncture we have the two equations

$$K_0 = \lim_{s\to 0} G(s),$$

$$K_1 = K_0 a_1 - b_1.$$

We have made some headway, because if $b_1 = 0$, as is often the case, then after finding $K_1$ by numerical integration, we could immediately find $a_1$, thereby identifying a transfer function of the form

$$G(s) = \frac{K_0}{1 + \tau_1 s}.$$

To compress the notation somewhat we now let

$$K_0 - G(s) = \frac{(a_1 K_0 - b_1)s + (a_2 K_0 - b_2)s^2 + a_3 K_0 s^3}{1 + a_1 s + a_2 s^2 + a_3 s^3}$$

$$= \frac{K_1 s + (a_2 K_0 - b_2)s^2 + a_3 K_0 s^3}{1 + a_1 s + a_2 s^2 + a_3 s^3}$$

$$\triangleq G_1(s).$$

We next define

$$y_2(t) = \int_0^t [K_1 - y_1(\tau)]\, d\tau.$$

Then

$$Y_2(s) = \frac{1}{s}\left[\frac{K_1}{s} - Y_1(s)\right]$$

$$= \frac{1}{s}\left[\frac{K_1}{s} - \frac{G_1(s)}{s^2}\right]$$

$$= \frac{1}{s^2}\left[K_1 - \frac{G_1(s)}{s}\right].$$

Now

$$K_1 - \frac{G_1(s)}{s} = K_1 - \frac{K_1 s + (a_2 K_0 - b_2)s^2 + a_3 K_0 s^3}{s(1 + a_1 s + a_2 s^2 + a_3 s^3)}$$

$$= K_1 - \frac{K_1 + (a_2 K_0 - b_2)s + a_3 K_0 s^2}{1 + a_1 s + a_2 s^2 + a_3 s^3}$$

$$= \frac{K_1 + a_1 K_1 s + a_2 K_1 s^2 + a_3 K_1 s^3 - K_1 - (a_2 K_0 - b_2)s - a_3 K_0 s^2}{1 + a_1 s + a_2 s^2 + a_3 s^3}$$

$$= \frac{(a_1 K_1 - a_2 K_0 + b_2)s + (a_2 K_1 - a_3 K_0)s^2 + a_3 K_1 s^3}{1 + a_1 s + a_2 s^2 + a_3 s^3}.$$

It then follows that

$$\lim_{t \to \infty} y_2(t) \triangleq K_2$$

$$= \lim_{s \to 0} s\left[\frac{1}{s^2}\frac{(a_1 K_1 - a_2 K_0 + b_2)s + (a_2 K_1 - a_3 K_0)s^2 + a_3 K_1 s^3}{1 + a_1 s + a_2 s^2 + a_3 s^3}\right]$$

$$= \lim_{s \to 0}\left[\frac{1}{s}\frac{(a_1 K_1 - a_2 K_0 + b_2)s + (a_2 K_1 - a_3 K_0)s^2 + a_3 K_1 s^3}{1 + a_1 s + a_2 s^2 + a_3 s^3}\right]$$

$$= \lim_{s \to 0}\left[\frac{(a_1 K_1 - a_2 K_0 + b_2) + (a_2 K_1 - K_0 a_3)s + a_3 K_1 s^2}{1 + a_1 s + a_2 s^2 + a_3 s^3}\right]$$

$$= a_1 K_1 - a_2 K_0 + b_2.$$

We now have the three equations

$$K_0 = \lim_{s \to 0} G(s),$$

$$K_1 = a_1 K_0 - b_1,$$

$$K_2 = a_1 K_1 - a_2 K_0 + b_2.$$

We can see at this point that we have more unknowns than equations. We will address that point shortly, but it is worth noting that if $b_1 = b_2 = 0$, then the equations become

$$K_0 = \lim_{s \to 0} G(s),$$

$$K_1 = a_1 K_0,$$

$$K_2 = a_1 K_1 - a_2 K_0,$$

and we could at this stage identify a transfer function of the form

$$G(s) = \frac{K_0}{(1 + \tau_1 s)(1 + \tau_2 s)},$$

*if* we can find $K_2$. Further, if there are no zeros in the transfer function, then the equations can be solved recursively.

To find $K_2$, we first have to find $y_1(t)$ by numerical integration. We note that we can write for any $t_n$,

$$y_1(t_n) \approx \sum_{i=1}^{n} [K_0 - y_u(t_i) \Delta t],$$

as shown in Fig. 8.3. We could do the integration graphically by making a careful plot of the unit step response. This is a tedious process but it can be done. The other alternative is to capture the response and then write a MATLAB program to do not only the numerical integration to find $y_1(t)$ but also the series of such integrations that will be necessary if we carry out subsequent iterations of this algorithm.

Most digitizing oscilloscopes now have the capability to capture responses and also transfer those responses to portable storage mediums, such as floppy disks.

**Figure 8.3 |** Determination of $y_1$ from step response.

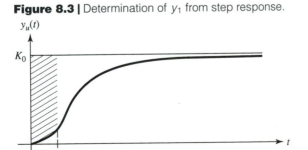

**Figure 8.4 |** Determination of $K_2$ from the plot of $y_1(t)$.

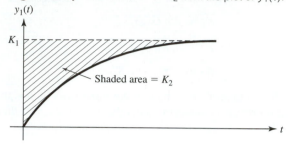

Thus, it is not hard to capture the data as a file that can be used with a MATLAB program.

Assuming that we find $y_1(t)$ by numerical integration, we next note that the shaded area in Fig. 8.4 is

$$\lim_{t\to\infty} y_2(t) = \lim_{t\to\infty} \int_0^t [K_1 - y_1(\tau)]\, d\tau = K_2.$$

A this point, we have gone far enough to identify the transfer function of the separately excited dc motor. The sequence of iterations discussed next will enable us to identify the parameters of higher-order models.

For the next iteration we define

$$y_3(t) = \int_0^t [K_2 - y_2(\tau)]\, d\tau.$$

In keeping with our previous analysis, we now write

$$K_1 - \frac{G_1(s)}{s} = \frac{(a_1K_1 - a_2K_0 + b_2)s + (a_2K_1 - a_3K_0)s^2 + a_3K_1s^3}{1 + a_1s + a_2s^2 + a_3s^3}$$

$$= \frac{K_2s + (a_2K_1 - a_3K_0)s^2 + a_3K_1s^3}{1 + a_1s + a_2s^2 + a_3s^3}$$

$$\overset{\Delta}{=} G_2(s).$$

Then

$$Y_3(s) = \frac{1}{s}\left[\frac{K_2}{s} - Y_2(s)\right]$$

$$= \frac{1}{s}\left[\frac{K_2}{s} - \frac{G_2(s)}{s^2}\right]$$

$$= \frac{1}{s^2}\left[K_2 - \frac{G_2(s)}{s}\right].$$

Once more we expand

$$
K_2 - \frac{G_2(s)}{s} = K_2 - \frac{K_2 s + (a_2 K_1 - a_3 K_0)s^2 + a_3 K_1 s^3}{s(1 + a_1 s + a_2 s^2 + a_3 s^3)}
$$

$$
= K_2 - \frac{K_2 + (a_2 K_1 - a_3 K_0)s + a_3 K_1 s^2}{1 + a_1 s + a_2 s^2 + a_3 s^3}
$$

$$
= \frac{K_2 + a_1 K_2 s + a_2 K_2 s^2 + a_3 K_2 s^3 - K_2 - (a_2 K_1 - a_3 K_0)s - a_3 K_1 s^2}{1 + a_1 s + a_2 s^2 + a_3 s^3}
$$

$$
= \frac{(a_1 K_2 - a_2 K_1 + a_3 K_0)s + (a_2 K_2 - a_3 K_1)s^2 + a_3 K_2 s^3}{1 + a_1 s + a_2 s^2 + a_3 s^3}.
$$

Then

$$
\lim_{t\to\infty} y_3(t) \triangleq K_3
$$

$$
= \lim_{s\to 0} s \left[ \frac{1}{s^2} \frac{(a_1 K_2 - a_2 K_1 + a_3 K_0)s + (a_2 K_2 - a_3 K_1)s^2 + a_3 K_2 s^3}{1 + a_1 s + a_2 s^2 + a_3 s^3} \right]
$$

$$
= \lim_{s\to 0} \left[ \frac{1}{s} \frac{(a_1 K_2 - a_2 K_1 + a_3 K_0)s + (a_2 K_2 - a_3 K_1)s^2 + a_3 K_2 s^3}{1 + a_1 s + a_2 s^2 + a_3 s^3} \right]
$$

$$
= \lim_{s\to 0} \left[ \frac{(a_1 K_2 - a_2 K_1 + a_3 K_0) + (a_2 K_2 - a_3 K_1)s + a_3 K_2 s^2}{1 + a_1 s + a_2 s^2 + a_3 s^3} \right]
$$

$$
= a_1 K_2 - a_2 K_1 + a_3 K_0.
$$

We complete this iteration by noting that

$$
K_3 \triangleq \lim_{t\to\infty} y_3(t)
$$

is the shaded area shown in Fig. 8.5.

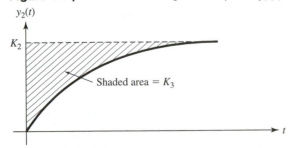

**Figure 8.5 |** Determination of $K_3$ from the plot of $y_2(t)$.

We now have the four equations

$$K_0 = \lim_{s \to 0} G(s),$$

$$K_1 = a_1 K_0 - b_1,$$

$$K_2 = a_1 K_1 - a_2 K_0 + b_2,$$

$$K_3 = a_1 K_2 - a_2 K_1 + a_3 K_0,$$

in the five unknowns $a_1, a_2, a_3, b_1,$ and $b_2$. We still do not have enough equations to solve for all the coefficients of our original transfer function. However, if we do one more iteration we could solve for the coefficients of

$$\bar{G}(s) = \frac{1 + b_1 s}{1 + a_1 s + a_2 s^2 + a_3 s^3}.$$

In order to solve for all the coefficients of our original transfer function, we would have to do two more iterations.

We will do the next iteration. In doing so, we will discover a pattern that will enable us to write down the results of the following iteration by inspection. Before proceeding we point out that if the $b_i$ are all zero, then we have

$$K_0 = \lim_{s \to 0} G(s),$$

$$K_1 = a_1 K_0,$$

$$K_2 = a_1 K_1 - a_2 K_0,$$

$$K_3 = a_1 K_2 - a_2 K_1 + a_3,$$

and we could at this juncture identify a transfer function with three poles and no zeros, using equations that can be solved recursively.

For the next iteration, proceeding in what by now should be a familiar pattern, we define

$$y_4(t) = \int_0^t [K_3 - y_3(\tau)] \, d\tau.$$

Again, in keeping with our previous analysis, we now note that

$$
\begin{aligned}
K_2 - \frac{G_2(s)}{s} &= \frac{(a_1 K_2 - a_2 K_1 + a_3 K_0)s + (a_2 K_2 - a_3 K_1)s^2 + a_3 K_2 s^3}{1 + a_1 s + a_2 s^2 + a_3 s^3} \\
&= \frac{K_3 s + (a_2 K_2 - a_3 K_1)s^2 + a_3 K_2 s^3}{1 + a_1 s + a_2 s^2 + a_3 s^3} \\
&\overset{\Delta}{=} G_3(s).
\end{aligned}
$$

Then, as before,

$$Y_4(s) = \frac{1}{s}\left[\frac{K_3}{s} - Y_3(s)\right]$$

$$= \frac{1}{s}\left[\frac{K_3}{s} - \frac{G_3(s)}{s^2}\right]$$

$$= \frac{1}{s^2}\left[K_3 - \frac{G_3(s)}{s}\right].$$

We next find

$$K_3 - \frac{G_3(s)}{s} = K_3 - \frac{K_3 s + (a_2 K_2 - a_3 K_1)s^2 + a_3 K_2 s^3}{s(1 + a_1 s + a_2 s^2 + a_3 s^3)}$$

$$= K_3 - \frac{K_3 + (a_2 K_2 - a_3 K_1)s + a_3 K_2 s^2}{1 + a_1 s + a_2 s^2 + a_3 s^3}$$

$$= \frac{K_3(1 + a_1 s + a_2 s^2 + a_3 s^3) - [K_3 + (a_2 K_2 - a_3 K_1)s + a_3 K_2 s^2]}{1 + a_1 s + a_2 s^2 + a_3 s^3}$$

$$= \frac{(a_1 K_3 - a_2 K_2 + a_3 K_1)s + (a_2 K_3 - a_3 K_2)s^2 + a_3 K_3 s^2}{1 + a_1 s + a_2 s^2 + a_3 s^3}.$$

Again, the next step is to find

$$\lim_{t\to\infty} y_4(t) \triangleq K_4$$

$$= \lim_{s\to 0} s\left[\frac{1}{s^2}\frac{(a_1 K_3 - a_2 K_2 + a_3 K_1)s + (a_2 K_3 - a_3 K_2)s^2 + a_3 K_3 s^2}{1 + a_1 s + a_2 s^2 + a_3 s^3}\right]$$

$$= \lim_{s\to 0}\left[\frac{1}{s}\frac{(a_1 K_3 - a_2 K_2 + a_3 K_1)s + (a_2 K_3 - a_3 K_2)s^2 + a_3 K_3 s^3}{1 + a_1 s + a_2 s^2 + a_3 s^3}\right]$$

$$= \lim_{s\to 0}\left[\frac{(a_1 K_3 - a_2 K_2 + a_3 K_1) + (a_2 K_3 - a_3 K_2)s + a_3 K_3 s^2}{1 + a_1 s + a_2 s^2 + a_3 s^3}\right]$$

$$= a_1 K_3 - a_2 K_2 + a_3 K_1$$

$$\triangleq K_4.$$

Then, as before,

$$K_4 \triangleq \lim_{t\to\infty} y_4(t)$$

is the shaded area shown in Fig. 8.6.

We now have the five equations.

$$K_0 = \lim_{s\to 0} G(s),$$

$$K_1 = a_1 K_0 - b_1,$$

$$K_2 = a_1 K_1 - a_2 K_0 + b_2,$$

$$K_3 = a_1 K_2 - a_2 K_1 + a_3 K_0,$$

$$K_4 = a_1 K_3 - a_2 K_2 + a_3 K_1.$$

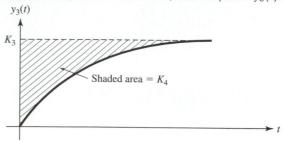

**Figure 8.6 |** Determination of $K_4$ from the plot of $y_3(t)$.

The last four equations are in terms of the five unknowns $a_1, a_2, a_3, b_1,$ and $b_2$. Thus, to solve for all five variables we would have to define

$$y_5(t) = \int_0^t [K_4 - y_4(\tau)] \, d\tau,$$

and repeat this analysis to obtain another equation in the five variables. Although we could do this, we won't because it should be clear from the last two equations that the next iteration will yield

$$K_5 = a_1 K_4 - a_2 K_3 + a_3 K_2.$$

The only remaining question is the numerical stability of the technique, and that will almost certainly be dependent on the specific identification problem. Nonetheless, as already noted, we have gone far enough to find

$$\bar{G}(s) = \frac{K_0 + b_1 s}{1 + a_1 s + a_2 s^2 + a_3 s^3}, \qquad \textbf{[8.1]}$$

or

$$\hat{G}(s) = \frac{K_0}{1 + a_1 s + a_2 s^2 + a_3 s^3}. \qquad \textbf{[8.2]}$$

This is a great improvement over the identification technique presented in Chapter 3 because transfer functions of the form given by Eqs. [8.1] and [8.2] are sufficient to model a very large family of real physical systems.

In the case of the transfer function we are currently seeking to identify, namely,

$$G(s) = \frac{K_0}{(1 + \tau_1 s)(1 + \tau_2 s)} = \frac{K_0}{1 + (\tau_1 + \tau_2)s + \tau_1 \tau_2 s},$$

our new technique is more than adequate. We will have to find $y_1(t)$ by numerical integration, followed by a second integration to find $K_2$. We do so in the next section.

# 8.3 | IDENTIFICATION FOR DC MOTOR WITHOUT CYLINDER

## 8.3.1 Data Measurement

Before we can identify the parameters of the motor we need to measure the step response. Figure 8.7 shows in block diagram form how this measurement is made. The step is initiated from a menu driven laboratory support software package. The step output reaches the input to the power amplifier via a digtial-to-analog conversion board resident in an output slot in the computer. The output of the power amplifier is then connected to the armature winding of the motor. When the step input is applied to the motor, changes in the armature voltage and the tachometer voltage will be captured by the digitizing oscilloscope.

**Figure 8.7 |** Block diagram of the setup to measure the step response of a motor.

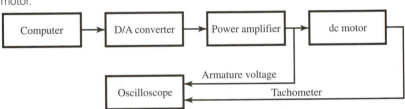

The actual laboratory setup is shown in Fig. 8.8. The "thick" wires, or leads, represent multiconductor pairs. The thinner wires at the ends represent the individual conductors. The connections for the field winding, armature winding, and tachometer are brought from the motor to the front panel on the motor mount so that the connections can be made conveniently.

Note that we need a low-power dc supply to provide the excitation for the field winding of the motor and a much higher power amplifier to supply power to the armature winding. The speed of the motor is measured by a dc tachometer. This is merely a small dc motor connected to one shaft end of the separately excited motor. When driven by the separately excited motor it operates as a generator and produces 3 V per thousand revolutions per minute (rpm).

The digital-to-analog converter is housed in the computer and connected to the panel shown in the figure by a ribbon cable. The panel is merely a convenience. It makes the connections to the motor easier since the panel accepts the type of cables typically used in a laboratory.

## 8.3.2 Transfer Function without Cylinder Attached

The step response of the separately excited dc motor without the cylinder attached is shown in Fig. 8.9. The oscilloscope that captured the response had a floppy disk drive. The data was transferred to a floppy disk and thence to a data file where it could be read by a MATLAB routine written to do the required numerical integrations. We now employ the identification algorithm discussed in Section 8.3.1.

**Figure 8.8 |** Actual laboratory setup for measuring the step response of a motor.

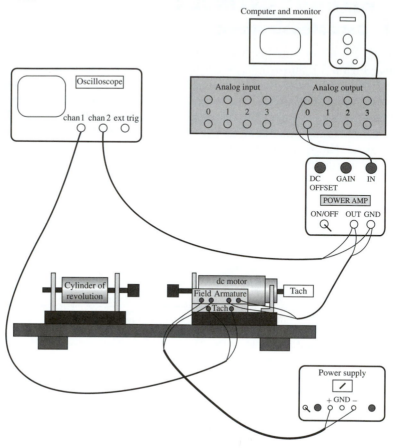

**Figure 8.9 |** Step response of dc motor without cylinder attached.

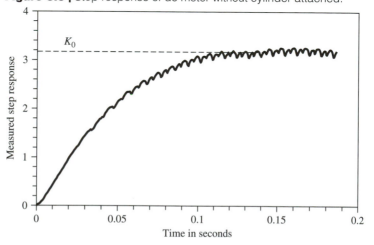

Since the transfer function of the motor has two poles and no zeros we only need the equations

$$K_0 = \lim_{s \to 0} G(s),$$

$$K_1 = a_1 K_0,$$

$$K_2 = a_1 K_1 - a_2 K_0.$$

Figure 8.10(a) shows the function

$$f_0(t) = K_0 - y_u(t).$$

**Figure 8.10** | Functions (a) $f_0(t) = K_0 - y_u(t)$ and (b) $y_1(t) = \int_0^\infty f_0(\tau)\, d\tau$.

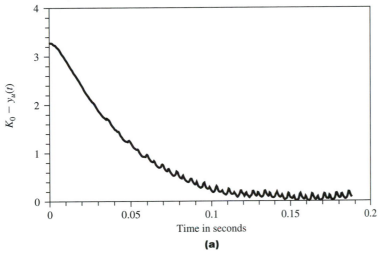

(a)

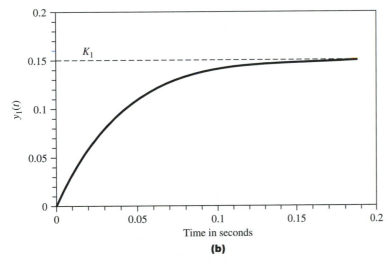

(b)

From $f_0$, we generate the function

$$y_1(t) = \int_0^\infty [K_0 - y_u(\tau)]\, d\tau,$$

shown in Fig. 8.10(b). The steady state value is $K_1$.

We next generate

$$f_1(t) = K_1 - y_1(t),$$

as shown in Fig. 8.11(a). We need to integrate this function to find

$$K_2 = \lim_{t \to \infty} f(t) = \int_0^t [K_1 - y_1(\tau)]\, d\tau.$$

**Figure 8.11 |** Functions (a) $f_1(t) = [K_1 - y_1(t)]$ and (b) $y_2(t) = \int_0^\infty f_1(\tau)\, d\tau$.

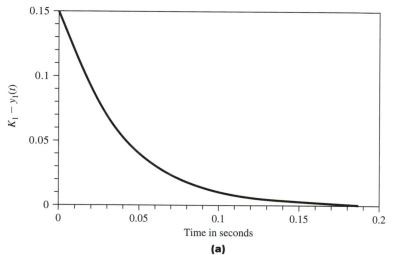

**(a)**

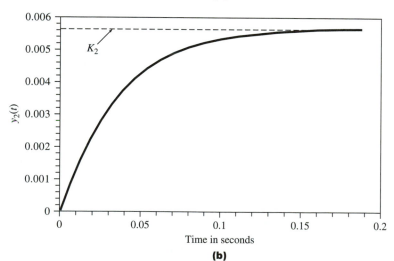

**(b)**

Figure 8.11(b) shows the function

$$y_2(t) = \int_0^\infty [K_1 - y_1(\tau)]\, d\tau.$$

The steady state value of this function is $K_2$.

We now have generated

$$K_0 = 3.25656 \qquad K_1 = 0.149778 \qquad K_2 = 0.00566667.$$

Using this data, it is a simple matter to find

$$a_1 = \frac{K_1}{K_0} = 0.0459927,$$

and

$$a_2 = \frac{a_1 K_1 - K_2}{K_0} = 0.000372503.$$

Finally,

$$\begin{aligned}
G(s) &= \frac{K_0}{1 + a_1 s + a_2 s^2} \\
&= \frac{K_0/a_2}{s^2 + (a_1/a_2)s + 1/a_2} \\
&= \frac{8678}{s^2 + 122.565s + 2664.888} \\
&= \frac{8678}{(s + 28.3)(s + 94.3)}.
\end{aligned}$$

A comment about this technique is in order. The identification procedure assumes a unit step input. In fact, in order to achieve a response with a steady state value of 3 V, a step input of approximately 30 V had to be applied to the armature winding. Therefore, the gain we derived is 30 times too large. Thus, our final estimate of the transfer function is

$$G(s) = \frac{289}{(s + 28.3)(s + 94.3)}.$$

In Chapter 9 we will use frequency response methods to reidentify this transfer function, and obtain good agreement with the model found here.

### 8.3.3 Transfer Function with Cylinder Attached

We can use the same experimental setup to find the step response of the motor with the cylinder attached. Figure 8.12 is a plot of the step response with the cylinder attached.

Now define

$$x(t) = y_{\text{ss}} - y(t).$$

Fig. 8.13(a) is a graph of $x(t)$, while part (b) is a graph of $\ln x(t)$. We know that $p_1$

**Figure 8.12** | Measured step response with a cylinder attached.

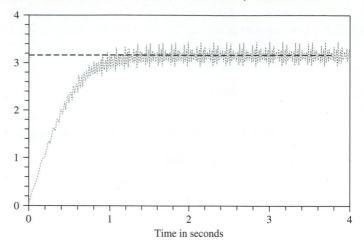

**Figure 8.13** | Measuring $p_1$ from the step response.

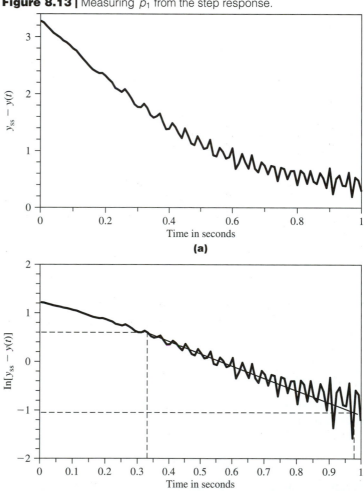

(a)

(b)

is simply the negative of the slope of the graph in part (b) of the figure. Thus,

$$p_1 \approx 2.5.$$

Our next goal is to determine

$$B = \frac{-K}{p_1(p_2 - p_1)}.$$

We do this by recalling that as the step response nears its steady state value,

$$y(t) \approx A + Be^{-p_1 t}.$$

We know that $A = 3.15$, and we have an estimate of $p_1$. Thus, one way to find $B$ is to measure some values of $y(t)$ near the steady state and compute

$$B = \frac{y(t) - A}{e^{-p_1 t}}.$$

We start by using $p_1 = 2.5$. Table 8.1 shows the results for data taken from Fig. 8.14, for several values of $p_1$.

We have chosen to add some additional estimates of $p_1$ for the following reason. We know that $|B| > |A|$. However, the value of $B$ computed using $p_1 = 2.5$ yields magnitudes of $B$ that are too small, as can be seen from Table 8.1. The dc motor is not

**Table 8.1** | Estimates of $B$ based on several values of $p_1$.

| Time | 0.5 | 0.6 | 0.7 | 0.8 |
|------|------|------|------|------|
| $B(p_1 = 2.5)$ | −3.14 | −2.91 | −2.30 | −2.22 |
| $B(p_1 = 3.0)$ | −4.03 | −3.93 | −3.27 | −3.31 |
| $B(p_1 = 3.2)$ | −4.46 | −4.43 | −3.76 | −3.88 |
| $B(p_1 = 3.6)$ | −5.44 | −5.64 | −4.97 | −5.34 |

**Figure 8.14** | Estimating $B$.

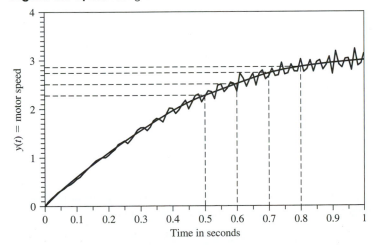

**Figure 8.15 |** First model of a step response.

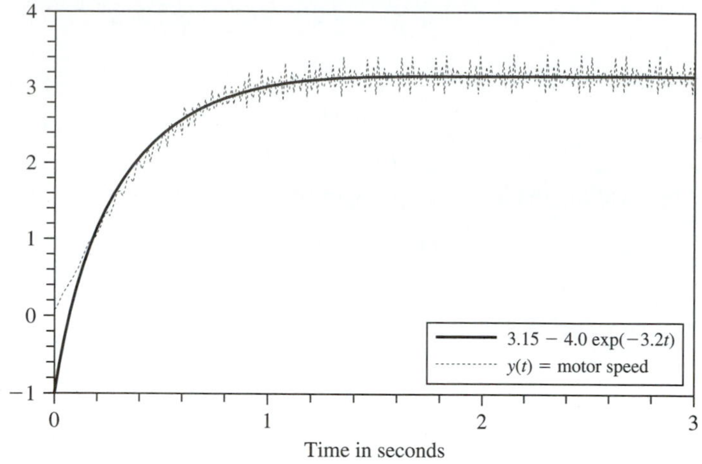

Time in seconds

perfectly linear, and our estimate of $p_1$ may be just that, an estimate. For that reason, we have chosen some larger values and repeated the computation of $B$. The values for $p_1 = 3.2$ are the most consistent.

At this point, we have a pretty good estimate of $B$ and a refined estimate of $p_1$. We see from Fig. 8.15 that the function

$$f(t) = 3.15 - 4.0e^{-3.2t}$$

fits the measured step response very well for $t > 0.5$ s.

The next task is to find $p_2$. We know that

$$A + B + C = 0,$$

and that $A = 3.15$, $B \approx -4.0$. Thus

$$C = -(A + B) = -(3.15 - 4.0) = 0.85.$$

Knowing $C$, there are a couple of ways to find $p_2$. One way is to note that

$$\frac{|B|}{|C|} = \frac{p_2}{p_1}.$$

Thus, we have

$$p_2 = p_1 \frac{|B|}{|C|} = 3.2\frac{4.0}{0.85} = 15.1 \rightarrow 15.$$

Another way to find $p_2$ is to form the function

$$z(t) = y(t) - [A + Be^{-p_1t}],$$

as shown in Fig. 8.16(a). Figure 8.16(b) is a plot of $\ln z(t)$ versus time. Then $p_2$ is the negative of the slope of this curve or about 12. We now have

$$12 < p_2 < 15.$$

**Figure 8.16 |** Plots of (a) $z(t) = Ce^{-p_2 t}$ and (b) $\ln z(t)$.

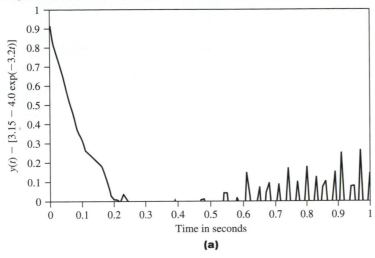

(a)

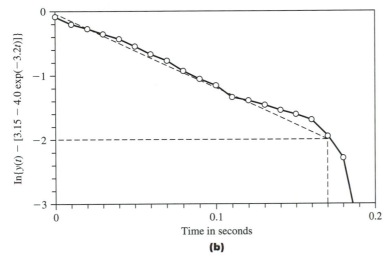

(b)

The analysis we have done so far has narrowed our search for values of $p_1$, $p_2$, and $B$. What we have to do next is try some different values for these three parameters to find the best fit with the measured response. This process, otherwise known as engineering, can easily be done using a package like MATLAB. Figure 8.17 shows our final choice for $y(t)$, namely,

$$y(t) = 3.15 - 4e^{-3.2t} + 0.85e^{-15t}.$$

Knowing $A$, $p_1$, and $p_2$ we can now find

$$K = A p_1 p_2 = (3.15)(3.2)(15) = 151.$$

**Figure 8.17 |** Plot of $y(t)$ and the final model of $y(t)$.

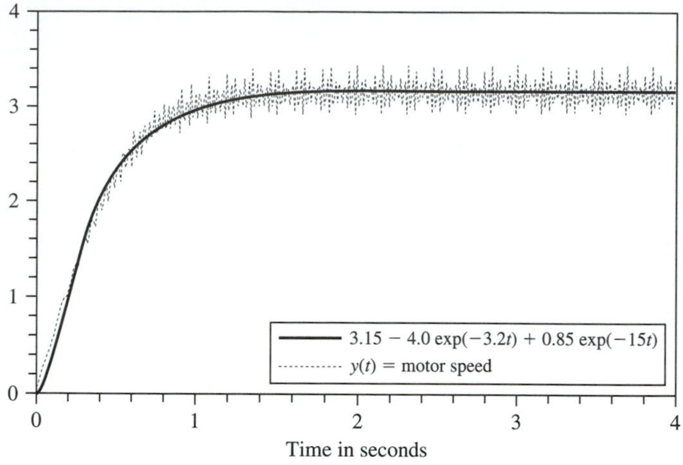

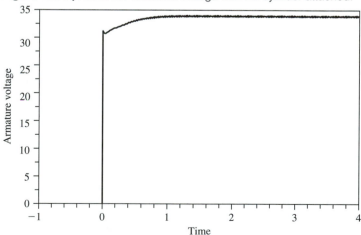

As discussed in the identification of the parameters for the motor *without* the cylinder attached, the input to the armature winding was approximately 30 V. A plot of the armature voltage with the cylinder attached is shown in Fig. 8.18. Thus, the gain for the transfer function is too large by a factor of 30. We can see that the voltage has a transient and then settles at around 32 V. In determining our final model for the motor, we reduce the gain by a factor of 30.

The reader may ask why we didn't reduce the gain by a factor of 32. The answer is that we have not been able to identify the pole locations of the transfer function with enough precision to warrant dividing by 32 instead of 30. The values we have determined for $p_1$, $p_2$, and $B$ may be within 10% of the "correct" values. Furthermore, we know that the motor dynamics are mildly nonlinear. For that reason as well,

**Figure 8.18 |** Plot of the armature voltage with the cylinder attached.

we shouldn't try to compute $K$ to three decimal places. Thus, our final choice for the model of the motor with the cylinder attached is

$$\frac{\Omega(s)}{V_q(s)} = \frac{5}{(s + 3.2)(s + 15)}.$$

At this juncture we have accurate transfer functions for the dc motor, both with and without the cylinder attached. Having found these two transfer functions, our next goal is to compare the simulated response and the actual response for some simple compensation strategies.

## 8.4 | COMPENSATOR DESIGN AND IMPLEMENTATION

Now that we have identified the parameters in the two transfer functions, we are ready to design and implement the compensators for the control of the dc motor both with and without the cylinder attached. In most instances we would probably design the compensator and then simulate its response first before actually trying it on the actual system. This would definitely be the policy if the system was of high power or costly to build. For a fractional horsepower motor mounted on rails, however, there is little chance of catastrophe, so we will forego the simulation phase and proceed directly from the design to the implementation.

The two control strategies we will try are integral control and PI control. Both strategies will yield very good results. In addition, we will use integral control to reinforce our understanding of how increasing the type of the forward-loop transfer function improves the tracking capabilities of the closed-loop system.

## 8.5 | INTEGRAL CONTROL

Figure 8.19 shows in block diagram form how we implement speed control using unity feedback and cascade compensation. The box in the figure was first introduced in Chapter 3. To achieve some economy of language, we will henceforward, on occasion, refer to this feedback and compensation box as the "FAC."

**Figure 8.19 |** Block diagram of a laboratory setup for speed control of a dc motor.

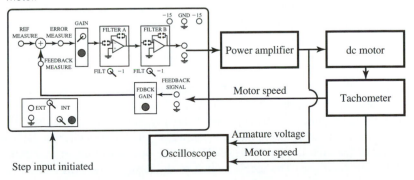

**Figure 8.20** | Laboratory setup for speed control of a dc motor.

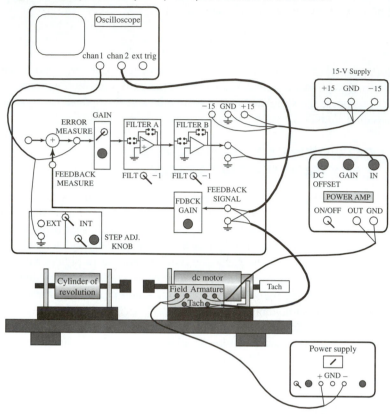

The actual laboratory setup is shown in Fig. 8.20. There is a good deal of equipment in this figure. For one thing, we have to supply ±15 V to the FAC to operate the opamps. We also need a separate power supply for the field winding of the separately excited dc motor.

The FAC subtracts the reference input from the feedback signal and feeds the error signal forward through a gain stage and then two opamp stages. The opamp circuits can be used to add compensation. Pins protrude from the schematic of the inverting opamp stages printed on the surface of the box. These pins connect to the actual opamps inside the box.

Resistors and capacitors can be press fit into the receptacles on the top of the pins to create simple compensators. The compensator is activated by moving the toggle switch below the opamp stage to "Filt." If the toggle switch is moved to the "−1" position the opamp stage provides a gain of −1.

The reference input can be supplied externally, say from an analog-to-digital (A/D) converter linked to a computer, or internally. The toggle switch in the bottom left corner of the box, labeled "EXT/INT" lets the user select either an internal or external reference input. The toggle switch to the right of the "EXT/INT" toggle switch enables the user to initiate a step response manually. The size of the step is controlled by the potentiometer (the black knob in the figure) below the toggle switch.

What the FAC does is relieve us of the tedium of building up the summer and the gain and the opamp circuits on a breadboard. This frees us to concentrate on the control aspects of the implementation. One could argue that there is something to be gained by building the circuit up on a breadboard, but the gain would be mostly in our understanding of analog circuit implementation not the effect of the control.

Before proceeding a few points are worth considering. Note that the tachometer signal is fed not only to the feedback input on the box but also to the oscilloscope so that we can record the step response. In the laboratory setup, the terminals for the armature winding, field winding, and tachometer have all been routed to the panel mounted beside the motor. This makes it easier to make the connections in the laboratory.

The "thicker" leads are bundles of individual conductors. In the case of the $\pm 15$-V supply for the FAC, there are three conductors in the bundle. The thinner leads at each end of the bundles are individual leads or wires. By showing the connections in bundles we are able to reduce the clutter in the picture somewhat.

We will now use this laboratory setup to investigate integral control. We will use the configuration shown in Fig. 8.21 on one of the opamp stages and leave the toggle switch on the other opamp stage on "$-1$."

For integral control we put a $1$-$\mu$F capacitor across the feedback path and a $1$-M$\Omega$ resistor in the forward path, yielding

$$-G_c(s) = -\frac{1/Cs}{R} = -\frac{1/RC}{s} = -\frac{1}{s}.$$

The second opamp circuit then inverts this signal so that the output has the right polarity.

We will collect three sets of data with the goal of showing that the forward loop gain times the area under the curve of the error signal $e(t)$ is constant. We first set the power amp to near full power. Data is first collected with the gain at the output of opamp stage "B" on the FAC set to 8 V. The measured step and error responses are shown in Fig 8.22(a). The second set of data is collected with the output of opamp stage "B" set to 10 V, and the third set of data with the output set to 12 V. Note that we never change the gain of the power amplifier. The measured step and error responses

**Figure 8.21 |** Opamp configuration for integral control.

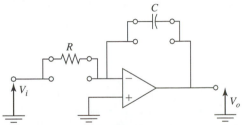

**Figure 8.22 |** Responses for (a) 8 V, (b) 10 V, and (c) 12 V.

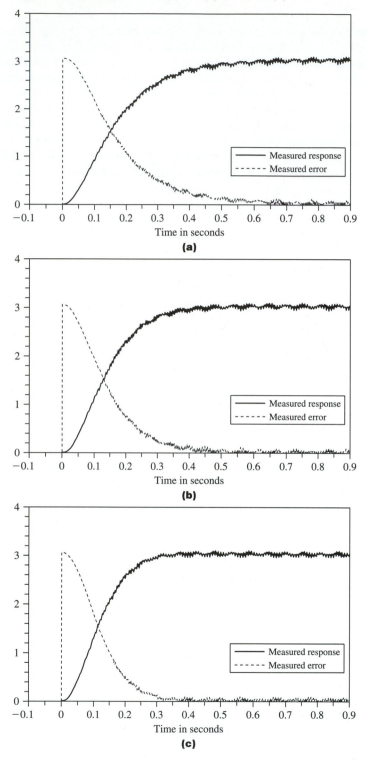

(a)

(b)

(c)

are shown in parts (b) and (c) of Fig. 8.22. The final step is to integrate the error curves. This is easily done in MATLAB. Writing the program is a good exercise.

For $i = 1, 2,$ and 3, let $K_i$ be the gain at the output of opamp "B" and $A_i$ the area under the error curve for our three trials. Then we have

$$K_1 = 8.0 \text{ V} \qquad A_1 = 0.57892,$$
$$K_2 = 10 \text{ V} \qquad A_2 = 0.4658,$$
$$K_3 = 12 \text{ V} \qquad A_3 = 0.3954.$$

Since the gain of the power amplifier was held constant, the forward gain on the FAC is proportional to the total forward gain.

What we expect find is that

$$K_1 A_1 = K_2 A_2 = K_3 A_3.$$

That is in fact the case, since

$$K_1 A_1 = 4.631 \qquad K_2 A_2 = 4.658 \qquad K_3 A_3 = 4.74.$$

Thus, even though the error signal itself decays to zero, there is still a constant voltage, proportional to $A_i K_i$, applied by the power amplifier to the armature winding of the motor. This is why integral control manages to make the steady state error to a step equal to zero even though the error signal itself is zero. We see that we get the same voltage applied to the motor in all cases, because, if we lower the gain, the area under the error curve increases proportionately.

## 8.6 | PI CONTROL

We now investigate PI control for the dc motor with the cylinder attached. The laboratory setup is the same as that for integral control in Fig. 8.20, except that the cylinder is attached and the controller is that shown in Fig. 8.23.

**Figure 8.23** | Opamp configuration for PI control.

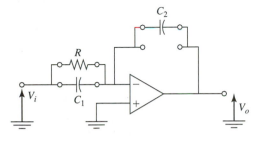

The compensator implemented on the first opamp stage is

$$-G_c(s) = -\frac{1/C_2 s}{R/C_1 s/R + 1/C_1 s} = -\frac{(C_1/C_2)[s + (1/RC_1)]}{s}.$$

The second opamp stage is set to $-1$ so that the two stages together yield the desired compensator $G_c(s)$.

**Figure 8.24 |** Actual and simulated responses PI control.

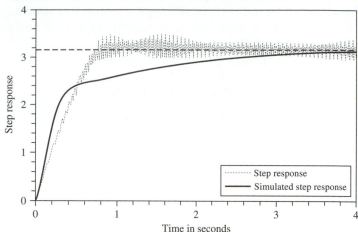

If we choose

$$C_1 = C_2 = 10 \ \mu\text{F} \quad \text{and} \quad R = 100 \ \text{k}\Omega,$$

we obtain, from the first opamp stage,

$$-G_c(s) = -\frac{s+1}{s}.$$

The step response using this compensator, along with the simulated response, is shown in Fig. 8.24. We see from the figure the actual response is better than the simulated response. The simulated response is what we would expect for the zero of the PI compensator close to the origin.

The fact that the actual response is different indicates that our model is not perfect. Indeed, a better model of the dc motor would take into account some of the motor's nonlinearities, in particular, the saturation of the armature winding under heavy load. In this instance, nonlinearity is not necessarily bad, since the response is better than we would expect from the simulation.

## 8.7 | REPRISE

In this chapter we have done a complete design. We started with the transfer function of a dc motor, as derived in Chapter 3. Then we developed a new technique for identifying the parameters of the transfer function. This technique proved more general than that presented in Chapter 3, being, theoretically at least, capable of identifying the parameters of transfer functions with zeros and three or more poles.

The only drawback to the technique was the fact that the succession of integrations required to identify the parameters makes this new technique potentially numerically unstable. Nonetheless it proved more than adequate for our purposes. In that regard, it is a worthwhile addition to our design tool bag.

We then completed the design cycle by designing two compensators and then implementing them on the actual dc motor, both with and without the cylinder attached. Both compensators worked very well. Thus, at this juncture in the book, we have in our control tool bag not only the root locus design method, but two techniques for identifying the parameters of a transfer function, plus the ability to implement our control designs using opamps.

In Chapter 9 we start the next stage of our journey by beginning a study of frequency domain methods for analyzing and compensating control systems. The next four chapters are really the heart of this book, and by the end of Chapter 12 we will have greatly improved our design skills.

# 8.8 | PROBLEMS

The CD-ROM that comes with this book contains step responses for six separately excited dc motors, both with and without the cylinder attached. For instance, for motor 1, the files are mtr1step (no cylinder) and mtr1stepc (cylinder attached). The step responses used in the examples in the chapter are mtr6step and mtr6stepc. These step responses can be used to gain some experience in model identification.

1. Use the data mtr6step to find the transfer function for motor 6 by the method presented in Chapter 3. Compare with the model found by the method developed in this chapter.

2. Use the data mtr6stepc and the identification method presented in this chapter to find the transfer function for the motor with the cylinder attached.

3. Use the data for any of the other motors and find the transfer function by both the method presented in this chapter and that presented in Chapter 3.

4. The step response for each of three gains used in the integral control example is overdamped. Letting $K$ represent the composite gain of the transfer function, the compensator, and the power amplifier, determine the gain that drives the poles at $s = -28.3$ and $s = 0$ to the break-out point. Find the response of the closed-loop system to a 3.15-V step input. Compare it to the actual response in Fig. 8.24. Do you think the poles in the recorded response are close to the break-out point?

5. Move the zero in the PI control to $s = -3$, and adjust the gain so that the poles at $s = -3$ and $s = -15$ just meet. Compare the response to that found experimentally.

6. The input voltage to the dc motor to produce the step responses in this chapter was on the order of 30 V. Assuming that the poles identified by both methods are correct, let the transfer function in each case be

$$G_m(s) = \frac{K}{(s + p_1)(s + p_2)},$$

and the input be $A\mathbf{1}(t)$, where $A = 30$. Use the partial fraction expansion of the response to determine $K$ for the motor with and without the cylinder. Note that this same approach can be used for any of the other motors.

7. For the identification of the motor with the cylinder attached, write a short MATLAB program to evaluate the function

$$B = \frac{-K}{p_1(p_2 - p_1)}$$

in the region near steady state. Use the data mtrstep6c on the CD-ROM at the back of the book.

8. The CD-ROM at the back of the book contains files that contain step responses for transfer functions of the form:

$$G(s) = \frac{K(1 + \tau s)}{(1 + \tau_1 s)(1 + \tau_2 s)}.$$

Write a MATLAB program and identify the transfer functions. You may have to find, or write, a MATLAB routine to smooth the data in the step response files:

a. p2zid1
b. p2zid2
c. p2zid3
d. p2zid4

9. The CD-ROM at the back of the book contains files that contain step responses for transfer functions of the form:

$$G(s) = \frac{K}{(1 + \tau_1 s)(1 + \tau_2 s)(1 + \tau_3 s)}$$

Write a MATLAB program to identify the transfer functions. You may have to find, or write, a MATLAB routine to smooth the data in the step response files:

a. p3id1
b. p3id2
c. p3id3
d. p3id4

10. The CD-ROM at the back of the book contains files that contain step responses for transfer functions of the form

$$G(s) = \frac{K(1 + \tau s)}{(1 + \tau_1 s)(1 + \tau_2 s)(1 + \tau_3 s)}.$$

Write a MATLAB program to identify the transfer functions. You may have to find, or write, a MATLAB routine to smooth the data in the step response files:

a. p3zid1
b. p3zid2
c. p3zid3
d. p3zid4

11. Reconsider the data collection for the PI compensator. Suppose we continue to lower the voltage out of the box by lowering the gain of the amplifier. What will happen to the area under the curve? From a practical standpoint what happens if we continue lowering the gain?

12. Experimentally, the second pole of the transfer function with the cylinder attached was in the interval $-15 < s < -12$. Leave the zero of the PI at $s = -1$, and assume

$$G_c G_p(s) = \frac{15K_c(s + 1)}{s(s + 3.2)(s + \gamma)}.$$

Find the gains for which the closed loop system is critically damped for the second pole at $\gamma = 12$ and $\gamma = 15$. Then do a root contour for $12 < \gamma < 15$.

13. For the transfer function with the cylinder attached, let $p_1 = 3.2$ and $p_2 = 12$. Compare the step response using these parameters to the measured step response.

14. Write a MATLAB routine to integrate the error signal for integral control.

15. Find the values of the step response with the cylinder attached for $t = 0.75, 0.85, 0.95$, and $1.05$ s, and build a table similar to Table 8.1, for $p = 3.0, 3.1, 3.3$, and $3.4$. Then try to find a model of the step response that is better than the one in the text example.

# FURTHER READINGS

Eykhoff, P. 1974. *System Identification*. London: John Wiley.

Graupe, D. 1972. *Identification of Systems*. New York: Van Nostrand-Reinholt.

Hsia, T. C. 1977. *System Identification*. Lexington, Mass.: Lexington Books, D. C. Heath.

Rake, H. 1981. *Step Response and Frequency Response Methods*. IFAC System Identification Tutorial. Oxford: Pergamon Press.

Unbehauen, Heinz, and Ganti P. Rao. 1987. *Identification of Continuous Systems*. Amsterdam: North Holland.

# 9

## Chapter

# Frequency Response

### 9.1 | OVERVIEW

In this chapter we introduce the frequency domain analysis of a transfer function using Bode magnitude and phase plots. This analysis, combined with the Nyquist criterion introduced in Chapter 10, lays the groundwork for Bode design in Chapter 11.

Frequency domain analysis is another example of a strategy that we have used before. Our real interest is how the closed-loop system behaves in the time domain, but we find that the easiest way to predict this behavior is to examine the loop transfer function $GH$ in the $s$ domain. We have already used this strategy in root locus analysis. There we wanted to factor the characteristic equation

$$1 + GH(s) = 0,$$

and we found that the best thing to do was to rewrite the equation as

$$GH(s) = 1\underline{/-180°},$$

with $GH$ isolated on the left-hand side of the equation. In Chapter 6 we found it useful, for the unity feedback case, to express the steady state error characteristics of the closed-loop system's time response in terms of the structure of $G_c G_p(s)$. More specifically, we related the number of poles of $G_c G_p(s)$ at $s = 0$ to the steady state accuracy of the closed-loop system for a particular set of reference input functions.

In this chapter we will look at the loop transfer function in yet another way, but our ultimate goal will be the same: to use the loop transfer function to understand the time response of the closed-loop system.

### 9.2 | STEADY STATE RESPONSE TO SINUSOIDAL INPUTS

In this section we will discover that the steady state response of a physical system to sinusoidal inputs can be used to identify the transfer function of the physical system. We will see later in the chapter that we can use this new approach in conjunction with the two identification techniques we have studied previously. By combining these techniques we can find better models for the physical systems we want to control.

For this analysis we assume that all the poles and zeros of the transfer function are in the left half of the $s$ plane. For simplicity we will also assume that there are no repeated poles. There is no real loss of generality in assuming this, just a significant simplification in the notation.

Consider the system of Fig. 9.1. Suppose that the model of the plant can be adequately represented by

$$G(s) = \frac{g_n(s)}{g_d(s)},$$

with

$$g_n(s) = K \prod_{i=1}^{m}(s + z_i) \quad \text{and} \quad g_d(s) = \prod_{i=1}^{n}(s + p_i),$$

where $m$ and $n$ are integers with $m \le n$. We also assume without any great loss of generality that the $p_i$ are real, positive and distinct. This assumption is not very restrictive. Almost all physical systems are open-loop stable. Further, any system with right half plane poles cannot be analyzed by the technique presented next.

**Figure 9.1 |** Block diagram representation of the system.

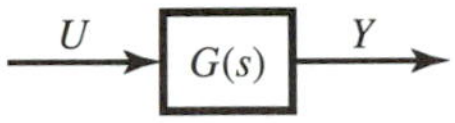

Let the input to the system of Fig. 9.1 be

$$u(t) = \begin{cases} A \cos \omega t & \text{if } t \ge 0 \\ 0 & \text{otherwise.} \end{cases}$$

The Laplace transform of $u(t)$ is

$$U(s) = \frac{As}{s^2 + \omega^2},$$

and the Laplace transform of the output can be written:

$$Y(s) = \frac{M}{s - j\omega} + \frac{M^*}{s + j\omega} + F(s), \qquad \text{[9.1]}$$

where $M^*$ is the conjugate of $M$ and

$$F(s) = \sum_{i=1}^{n} \frac{C_i}{s + p_i}, \qquad \text{[9.2]}$$

with

$$C_i = (s + p_i)Y(s)\big|_{s=-p_i} = (s + p_i)U(s)G(s)\big|_{s=-p_i}.$$

Then $y(t)$ is the inverse Laplace transform of the right-hand side of Eq. [9.1].

The inverse transform of $F(s)$ is

$$f(t) = \sum_{i=1}^{n} C_i e^{-p_i t}.$$

We do not need to solve for the $C_i$ because we are interested in the steady state response. If all the $p_i > 0$, the time functions in $f(t)$ will decay to zero as $t \to \infty$.

The residue $M$ is another matter because it is part of the steady state response. We now solve for $M$, and we will find the expression for $M$ very insightful. To that end,

$$M = (s - j\omega)Y(s)\big|_{s=j\omega}$$

$$= (s - j\omega)\frac{As}{s^2 + \omega^2}G(s)\Big|_{s=jw}$$

$$= \frac{AG(j\omega)}{2}.$$

Almost without exception, $M$ is a complex number and we will find it convenient to express it in polar form as

$$M = \frac{A|G(j\omega)|e^{j\theta}}{2},$$

where $\theta = \underline{/G(j\omega)}$.

Then

$$y(t) = \mathcal{L}^{-1}\{Y(s)\} = \mathcal{L}^{-1}\left\{\frac{M}{s - j\omega} + \frac{M^*}{s + j\omega} + F(s)\right\}$$

$$= A|G(j\omega)|\left[\mathcal{L}^{-1}\left\{\frac{e^{j\theta}}{2(s - j\omega)}\right\} + \mathcal{L}^{-1}\left\{\frac{e^{-j\theta}}{2(s + j\omega)}\right\}\right]$$

$$+ \mathcal{L}^{-1}\left\{\sum_{i=1}^{n}\frac{C_i}{s + p_i}\right\}$$

$$= A|G(j\omega)|\left[\frac{e^{j(\omega t+\theta)} + e^{-j(\omega t+\theta)}}{2}\right] + \sum_{i=1}^{n} C_i e^{-p_i t}.$$

Then, using the identity

$$\cos\phi = \frac{1}{2}\{e^{j\phi} + e^{-j\phi}\},$$

we obtain

$$y(t) = A|G(j\omega)|\cos(\omega t + \theta) + \sum_{i=1}^{n} C_i e^{-p_i t}.$$

Since we have assumed all the $p_i > 0$, the steady state response is

$$\lim_{t\to\infty} y(t) \overset{\Delta}{=} y_{ss}(t) = A|G(j\omega)|\cos(\omega t + \theta).$$

This analysis can be summarized as follows. If a sinusoidal input is applied to a system all of whose poles have a negative real part, the steady state response is a scaled, phase-shifted version of the input. The scaling factor is $|G(j\omega)|$, and the phase shift $\theta$ is the phase of $G(j\omega)$.

Computing $G(j\omega)$ for a range of frequencies $\omega$ determines the frequency response of the system. One of the important uses of the frequency response is to identify the transfer function $G$. Several examples of transfer function identification are given later in the chapter.

## 9.3 | BODE PLOTS

We now wish to find a means of quickly plotting $G(j\omega)$ for a range of frequencies. For a given frequency $\omega$, $G(j\omega)$ is just a complex number and there are several alternative plots that can be drawn. One alternative is a polar plot of magnitude and angle. That approach proves useful in Chapter 10 on Nyquist theory.

In this chapter we will place the magnitude and angle of $G(j\omega)$ on the same semi-log plot. Specifically, the abscissa along which the frequency is plotted will be logarithmic and the ordinates along which the magnitude and phase of $G(j\omega)$ are plotted will be linear. However, the magnitude plot will be effectively logarithmic since $|G(j\omega)|$ will be converted to decibels. That is,

$$|G(j\omega)|(\text{dB}) \triangleq 20 \log_{10}|G(j\omega)|. \qquad [9.3]$$

The fact that both magnitude and frequency are plotted on logarithmic scales will provide excellent scale compression. Scale compression is something a root locus plot does not provide, which is one of several reasons why the Bode design technique, introduced in Chapter 11, is in most ways superior to root locus design.

A necessary design skill is the ability to plot $|G(j\omega)|$ rapidly. We can do so by using an asymptotic magnitude plot. Thus, we next discuss techniques for rapidly drawing asymptotic Bode magnitude and phase plots of a given $G(j\omega)$.

Although the asymptotic Bode phase plots are of little use for Bode design, we include them for completeness.

### 9.3.1 Time Constant Form of *G(s)*

The general form of the transfer functions we encounter in enginneering problems is

$$G(s) = \frac{K \prod_{i=1}^{m}(s + z_i)}{s^\ell \prod_{i=1}^{n-\ell}(s + p_i)}. \qquad [9.4]$$

It will prove convenient to rewrite $G(s)$ as

$$G(s) = \left( \frac{K \prod_{i=1}^{m} z_i}{\prod_{i=1}^{n-\ell} p_i} \right) \left[ \frac{\prod_{i=1}^{m}(1 + s/z_i)}{s^\ell \prod_{i=1}^{n-\ell}(1 + s/p_i)} \right] \qquad [9.5]$$

The right-hand side of Eq. 9.5 is sometimes called the 'time constant' form of the transfer function, because we can write, for example,

$$1 + \frac{s}{p_i} = 1 + \tau_{p_i} s,$$

where $\tau_{p_i}$ is the time constant of the pole at $s = -p_i$.

In time constant form $G(s)$ consists of a gain term

$$K' = \frac{K \prod_{i=1}^{m} z_i}{\prod_{i=1}^{n-\ell} p_i},$$

plus terms of the form

$$\frac{1}{s^{\ell}}, \quad 1 + \frac{s}{z_i}, \quad \text{and} \quad 1 + \frac{s}{p_i}.$$

Infrequently, we encounter repeated poles or zeros, leading to terms of the form

$$\left(1 + \frac{s}{z_i}\right)^k \quad \text{and} \quad \left(1 + \frac{s}{p_i}\right)^k,$$

where $k$ is an integer, usually 2.

In time constant form, all of these terms are particularly easy to plot on semi-log graph paper, because we can obtain convenient low-frequency and high-frequency approximations for each term.

For instance, if $s = j\omega$ in Eq. [9.5], and we let $\omega$ approach zero, then

$$G(j\omega) \rightarrow \left(\frac{K \prod_{i=1}^{m} z_i}{\prod_{i=1}^{n-\ell} p_i}\right)\left(\frac{1}{s^{\ell}}\right), \qquad \text{[9.6]}$$

because all the terms of the form

$$1 + \frac{s}{z_i} \quad \text{and} \quad 1 + \frac{s}{p_i}$$

approach their limiting values of 1. Thus, the low-frequency asymptotic approximation of $G(j\omega)$ is

$$\frac{K'}{s^{\ell}}.$$

The fact that the individual terms $|1 + j\omega/z_i|$ and $|1 + j\omega/p_i|$ have magnitude 1 as $\omega$ approaches zero is very convenient. Since $\log_{10}(1) = 0$, the individual asymptotic plots of these components of $|G(j\omega)|$ will "break-off" the 0-dB line on the magnitude plot.

The term

$$\frac{1}{s^{\ell}}$$

will prove to be simply a straight line passing through the 0-dB line at a slope of

$$-20 \times \ell \text{ dB/decade,}$$

while the gain term is simply a horizontal line of magnitude

$$20 \log_{10} \left( \frac{K \prod_{i=1}^{m} z_i}{\prod_{i=1}^{n-\ell} p_i} \right) \text{ dB.}$$

Once we plot all the individual terms of $G$, we can then simply *add* up their contributions at each frequency to obtain the complete Bode magnitude plot.

Having outlined the procedure for drawing an asymptotic Bode magnitude plot, we next show how to rapidly plot the asymptotic approximation of the various terms we are likely to encounter in engineering problems.

### 9.3.2 Simple Real Pole

Consider the term

$$\frac{1}{1 + j\omega/p_i}. \qquad\qquad [9.7]$$

We have already noted that if $\omega$ is small the magnitude is close to one. If we now let $\omega$ beceome large, we can write

$$20 \log_{10} \left| \frac{1}{1 + j\omega/p_i} \right| \approx 20 \log_{10} \left| \frac{1}{j\omega/p_i} \right|$$

$$= 20 \log_{10}(p_i/\omega)$$

$$= 20 \log_{10} p_i - 20 \log_{10} \omega.$$

Letting

$$y = 20 \log_{10} \left| \frac{1}{1 + j\omega/p_i} \right|,$$

we can write

$$y = 20[\log_{10} p_i] - 20[\log_{10} \omega].$$

If we now plot this equation on semi-log graph paper we get a straight line. This line crosses the 0-dB line at $\omega = p_i$, where $p_i$ is referred to as the "break" frequency.

The asymptotic Bode magnitude plot of a single real pole of the form [9.7] can now be drawn as follows.

1. Assume the magnitude is 0 dB up to the break frequency $p_i$.
2. Starting at $p_i$ plot a straight line of slope $-20$ dB/decade.

Setting $\omega = p_i$, we find that at the break frequency $p_i$

$$\left| \frac{1}{1 + j\omega/p_i} \right| = \frac{1}{|1 + jp_i/p_i|} = \frac{1}{\sqrt{2}} = -3 \text{ dB.}$$

Figure 9.2(a) shows the actual and asymptotic magnitude plots for a simple pole, for the normalized frequency $\hat{\omega} = \omega/p_i$. We see that the maximum error in the asymptotic plot is 3 dB and occurs at the break frequency $\omega = p_i$. The break frequency is also referred to as the "corner" frequency.

**Figure 9.2 |** Actual and asymptotic magnitude and phase plots of a single pole.

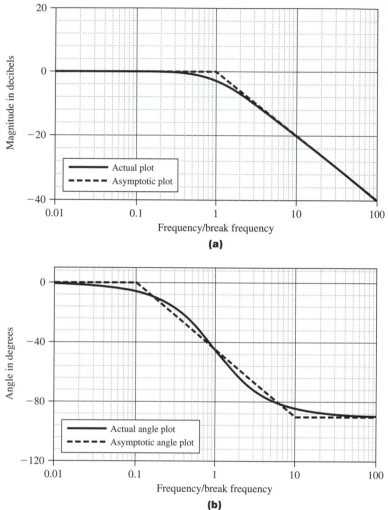

(a)

(b)

The Bode phase plot also has an asymptotic approximation. It is not used as much as the magnitude plot for a couple of reasons. One is the nonlinear nature of the arctangent function, which makes the approximation less accurate. Another is that a reasonably good approximation to the phase at a particular frequency can be obtained from an inspection of the magnitude plot in the vicinity of that frequency.

To develop an asymptotic approximation for the phase of a single pole we write

$$\frac{1}{1 + j\omega/p_i} = \frac{1}{\sqrt{1 + (\omega/p_i)^2}\underline{/\tan^{-1}(\omega/p_i)}} = \frac{1}{\sqrt{1 + (\omega/p_i)^2}}\underline{/-\tan^{-1}(\omega/p_i)}.$$

As $\omega \to 0$, $\underline{/G(j\omega)}$ approaches zero, and as $\omega \to \infty$,

$$\underline{/G(j\omega)} = -\lim_{\omega \to \infty} \tan^{-1} \frac{\omega}{p_i} \to -90°.$$

At $\omega = p_i$,

$$\underline{/G(jp_i)} = -\tan^{-1}(1) = -45°.$$

The phase can then be approximated by assuming it is zero for frequencies up to a decade below the break frequency and $-90°$ for all frequencies more than a decade greater than the break frequency. These two asymptotes are then connected by a straight line, as shown in in Fig. 9.2(b).

### 9.3.3 Simple Real Zero

The development of the asymptotic magnitude and phase plots for a simple zero parallels that for the simple pole. In the case of the zero, the magnitude plot rises 20 dB/decade as $\omega \to \infty$.

The asymptotic and actual magnitude plots of a single zero are shown in Fig. 9.3(a). Again, the maximum error occurs at the break frequency $z_i$ and is 3 dB.

The asymptotic and actual phase plots of the zero are shown in Fig. 9.3(b). As before, the phase is assumed to be zero for all frequencies a decade below the break frequency $z_i$ and 90° for all frequencies a decade above $z_i$. A straight line then connects the two asymptotic approximations, as shown in the figure.

### 9.3.4 Qualitative Vector Analysis

It often proves useful, especially in drawing the Nyquist plots in Chapter 10, to be able to do a quick, qualitative analysis of the contribution of each component of a transfer function to the overall frequency response. Consider the vector representation of

$$\frac{1}{j\omega + p_i} = \frac{1}{\sqrt{\omega^2 + p_i^2}} \underline{/-\theta}.$$

As $\omega \to \infty$, the magnitude of the simple pole, which is inversely proportional to the length of the vector in Fig. 9.4, shrinks to zero while its phase angle, the negative of the angle $\theta$ in the figure, approaches $-90°$. This qualitative analysis is a very useful companion to the Bode magnitude and phase plots developed in this chapter. We will utilize it again later in the chapter.

### 9.3.5 Composite Asymptotic Magnitude Plots

At this juncture it is worthwhile to construct a composite asymptotic Bode magnitude plot for a simple transfer function with no repeated poles or zeros. The procedure is first outlined and then followed by an example.

1. Put the transfer function with all simple poles and zeros in the form of Eq. [9.5].
2. Construct the asymptotic magnitude plot by plotting the individual magnitude plots of the poles and zeroes and then combining the contributions of each component at each frequency.

**Figure 9.3 |** Actual and asymptotic magnitude and phase plots of a single zero.

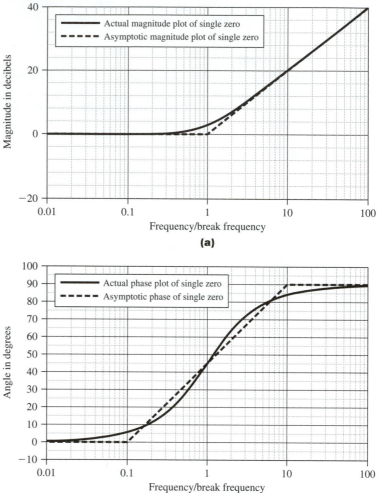

(a)

(b)

The second step is easy because the magnitude is plotted in decibels, a logarithmic quantity, and the magnitude contributions of individual poles and zeros can simply be added together at each frequency. That is,

$$20 \log_{10} |G(j\omega)| = 20 \log_{10} K + \sum_{i=1}^{m} 20 \log_{10} \left| 1 + \frac{j\omega}{z_i} \right| - \sum_{i=1}^{n} 20 \log_{10} \left| 1 + \frac{j\omega}{p_i} \right|.$$

For the asymptotic plot this is particularly easy because the plots of the individual poles and zeros consist of straight-line segments.

**Figure 9.4** | Vector representation for qualitative analysis of $G(j\omega)$.

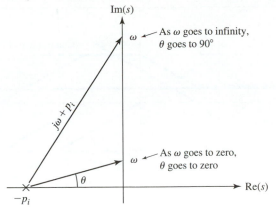

EXAMPLE 9.3.1

Let

$$G(s) = \frac{500(s+2)}{(s+10)(s+50)}.$$

Our goal is to determine the asymptotic magnitude plot.

The first step is to put $G(s)$ in the form

$$G(s) = \frac{2(500)}{10(50)} \frac{(1+s/2)}{(1+s/10)(1+s/50)} = \frac{2(1+s/2)}{(1+s/10)(1+s/50)}.$$

The plots of the individual components

$$K = 2, \quad |1+j\omega/2|, \quad \frac{1}{|1+j\omega/10|}, \quad \text{and} \quad \frac{1}{|1+j\omega/50|}$$

are shown in Fig. 9.5(a), along with the composite asymptotic magnitude plot. The *actual* magnitude and phase plots as well as the asymptotic magnitude plot are shown in Fig. 9.5(b).

The phase is computed from

$$\underline{/G(j\omega)} = \tan^{-1}\frac{\omega}{2} - \tan^{-1}\frac{\omega}{10} - \tan^{-1}\frac{\omega}{50}$$

at the frequencies shown in Table 9.1. A smooth curve is then passed through the calculated points. As indicated earlier, the important asymptotic plot is the magnitude plot. It can be drawn very easily and rapidly, and it will form the basis for the Bode design techniques introduced in Chapter 11.

Note that at the frequency $\omega = 0.2$ rad/s, one decade below the break frequency of the zero at $s = -2$, the total phase of $G(j\omega)$ is only 4.3° away from 0°. Indeed, the

**Figure 9.5 |** (a) Individual and composite asymptotic magnitude plots and (b) actual phase and magnitude plots.

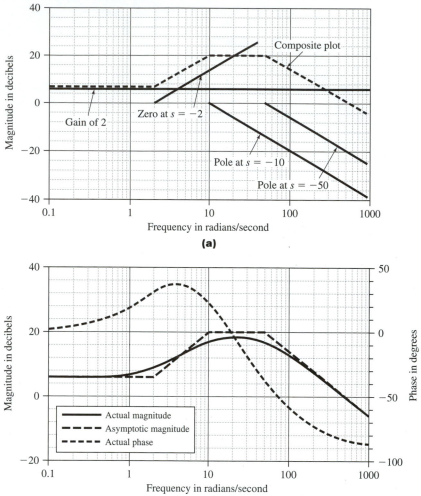

(a)

(b)

**Table 9.1 |** Phase of $G(s) = 500\frac{(s+2)}{(s+10)(s+50)}$ for Example 9.3.1.

| $\omega$ | 0.2 | 0.4 | 0.6 | 0.8 | 1 | 2 | 3 |
|---|---|---|---|---|---|---|---|
| $\underline{/G(j\omega)}$ | 4° | 9° | 13° | 16° | 20° | 31° | 36° |
| $\omega$ | 4 | 5 | 10 | 20 | 50 | 100 | 200 |
| $\underline{/G(j\omega)}$ | 37° | 36° | 22° | −90° | −36° | −59° | −74° |

**Figure 9.6 |** Asymptotic phase values from the vector representation of the transfer function.

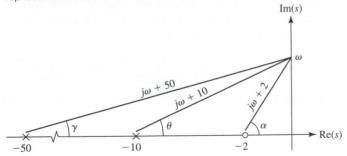

calculation for $\omega = 0.2$ rad/s is

$$\underline{/G(j0.2)} = \tan^{-1}\frac{0.2}{2} - \tan^{-1}\frac{0.2}{10} - \tan^{-1}\frac{0.2}{50}$$
$$= 5.7° - 1.15° - 0.23° = 4.3°.$$

What this analysis tells us is that $\underline{/G(j0.2)}$ is nearly zero and mainly determined by the zero at $s = -2$. The two poles contribute only $-1.4°$ of phase. Note further that the slope of the magnitude plot is 0 dB/decade on both sides of $\omega = 0.2$. One can, therefore, associate a phase of $0°$ with a slope of 0 dB/decade.

By contrast, at high frequencies, $\underline{/G(j\omega)}$ is almost $-90°$, the value to which the phase tends as $\omega \to \infty$. There are a couple of ways to see this. One is to examine the vector diagram shown in Fig. 9.6, and note that as $\omega \to \infty$, the angle of the zero tends to $90°$ and the angle of each pole to $-90°$. Thus, in the limit, the phase of the zero cancels the phase contribution of one of the poles, and what is left is the phase of the other pole.

An accurate calculation at $\omega = 500$ rad/s yields

$$\underline{/G(j500)} = \tan^{-1}\frac{500}{2} - \tan^{-1}\frac{50}{10} - \tan^{-1}\frac{500}{50}$$
$$= 89.8° - 88.9° - 84.3° = -83.4°,$$

or nearly $-90°$. We see from this calculation that at frequencies a decade above the largest pole or zero, the contributions from the simple poles and zeros approach $-90°$ and $90°$, respectively. Note from the Bode magnitude plot that at $\omega = 500$ rad/s, the slope is $-20$ dB/decade for at least a decade on both sides of $\omega$. Thus, it is possible to associate a phase of $-90°$ with a slope of $-20$ dB/decade. The ability to estimate the phase of $G(j\omega)$ from the slope of the magnitude plot in the vicinity of a specific frequency is a very useful skill that will come into play when Bode design is introduced in Chapter 11.

## 9.3.6  Bode Plot of Repeated Real Poles

The asymptotic Bode plots discussed to this point cover the vast majority of the cases ever encountered. However, there are two additional plots that need to be considered. One is the plot of a repeated pole of the form

$$\frac{1}{(1 + j\omega/p_i)^2} = \frac{1}{1 + (\omega/p_i)^2} \underline{\bigg/ -2\tan^{-1}\frac{\omega}{p_i}}.$$

The magnitude at low frequency is obtained from

$$\lim_{\omega \to 0} \left| \frac{1}{(1 + j\omega/p_i)^2} \right| = \lim_{\omega \to 0} \frac{1}{[1 + (\omega/p_i)^2]} = 1.$$

Converting to decibels yields a value of 0 dB.

To find the limiting or asymptotic magnitude at high frequency we follow the same procedure we used for the single pole, noting that as $\omega$ becomes very large

$$\left| \frac{1}{1 + (\omega/p_i)^2} \right| \approx \lim_{\omega \to \infty} \frac{p_i^2}{\omega^2}.$$

Converting to decibels yields

$$20\log_{10} \left| \frac{1}{1 + (\omega/p_i)^2} \right| = 40\log_{10} p_i - 40\log_{10}(\omega).$$

We again let

$$y = 20\log_{10} \left| \frac{1}{1 + (\omega/p_i)^2} \right|,$$

to obtain the equation

$$y = 40\log_{10} p_i - 40\log_{10} \omega. \qquad \textbf{[9.8]}$$

Plotted on semi-log graph paper, Eq. [9.8] is a straight line that crosses the 0-dB line at $p_i$. As before, $p_i$ is called the break frequency.

The asymptotic plot is drawn by letting the magnitude be 0 dB until the break frequency $p_i$ is reached, and then constructing a straight-line asymptote of slope $-40$ dB/decade through the break frequency. The maximum error occurs at the break frequency $p_i$, where

$$20\log_{10} \left| \frac{1}{1 + (\omega/p_i)^2} \right| = 20\log_{10} \left[ \frac{1}{1 + (p_i/p_i)^2} \right]$$

$$= 20\log_{10}(1) - 20\log_{10}(2)$$

$$= -6 \text{ dB}.$$

The actual and asymptotic bode magnitude plots, along with the actual phase plot, for a double pole are shown in Fig. 9.7. Again, the easiest way to draw the phase plot is simply to compute the phase at five or six points around the break frequency and then sketch a smooth curve through these points.

**Figure 9.7 |** Bode magnitude and phase plots of a double pole.

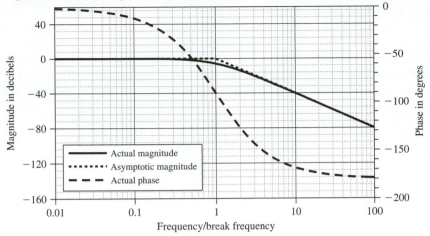

**Figure 9.8 |** Vector representation of the double pole.

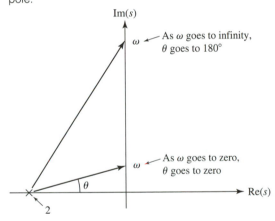

Figure 9.8 shows the vector representation of the double pole. Only one vector is shown but there are really two vectors drawn from the same point. As the frequency increases,

$$\angle \frac{1}{(1+s/p_i)^2} = -2\theta$$

goes from zero to $-180°$, while the magnitude of the double pole shrinks to zero.

Note that as the frequency gets very large, the magnitude on the Bode plot approaches the straight-line asymptote with slope $-40$ dB/decade. The angle "flattens" out as it approaches a horizontal asymptote at $-180°$. Thus, if we pick a frequency high enough that the slope of the magnitude plot is $-40$ dB/decade for at least a decade above and below this chosen frequency, we will be in the flat part of the phase curve and we can be sure that the actual phase is very close to $-180°$.

If we were to now repeat this analysis for a triple pole, we would see the slope approaching $-60$ dB/decade at high frequency and the phase flattening out as it approaches an asymptote at $-270°$. We will use these ideas a little later in the chapter when we introduce system identification using the Bode magnitude and phase plots.

We can analyze one or more poles at $s = 0$ in the same fashion, by noting that

$$20 \log_{10} \left| \frac{1}{(j\omega)^\ell} \right| = 20 \log_{10} \left( \frac{1}{\omega^\ell} \right) = -20 \times \ell \log_{10} \omega.$$

If we let

$$y = 20 \log_{10} \left| \frac{1}{(j\omega)^\ell} \right|,$$

then we can write

$$y = -20 \times \ell \log_{10} \omega,$$

which, when plotted on semi-log graph paper is a straight line of slope $-20 \times \ell$ dB/decade that crosses the 0-dB line at $\omega = 1$ rad/s.

The phase contribution is

$$\left/ \frac{1}{(j\omega)^\ell} \right. = -\ell \times 90°,$$

or $-90°$ of phase contribution from each pole at the origin, for *all* frequencies.

Single or multiple zeros at the origin can be similarly analyzed. The term $(j\omega)^\ell$ when transferred to the Bode magnitude plot is a line of slope $20 \times \ell$ passing through the 0-dB line at $\omega = 1$ rad/s. Each zero at the origin contributes $90°$ of phase at all frequencies.

### 9.3.7 Phase and Magnitude Plots of Complex Poles

We now consider the case of a pair of complex conjugate poles of the form

$$\frac{\sigma^2 + \omega_d^2}{(s + \sigma - j\omega_d)(s + \sigma + j\omega_d)} = \frac{\sigma^2 + \omega_d^2}{s^2 + 2\sigma s + \sigma^2 + \omega_d^2} = \frac{\omega_n^2}{s^2 + 2\zeta\omega_n s + \omega_n^2},$$

where $\omega_n^2 = \sigma^2 + \omega_d^2$ and $\zeta = \cos\theta$, $\theta = \tan^{-1}(\omega_d/\sigma)$.

The asymptotic behavior can be investigated in a manner similar to that used previously for the single pole and double pole. For low frequencies,

$$\lim_{\omega \to 0} \frac{\omega_n^2}{(j\omega)^2 + 2\zeta\omega_n(j\omega) + \omega_n^2} = \frac{\omega_n^2}{\omega_n^2} = 1.$$

Thus, the magnitude at low frequency is again 0 dB.

For high frequencies,

$$y = 20 \log_{10} \left| \frac{\omega_n^2}{(j\omega)^2 + 2\zeta\omega_n(j\omega) + \omega_n^2} \right| \approx 20 \log_{10} \frac{\omega_n^2}{\omega^2}$$

$$= 40 \log_{10} \omega_n - 40 \log_{10} \omega.$$

Once again, the semi-log graph of $y$ is a straight line whose intercept with the 0-dB line is at $\omega_n$.

We will find that for large damping ratios $\zeta$ the asymptotic magnitude plot of the complex poles can be approximated quite well by that of a double pole with break frequency $\omega_n$. However, if $\zeta$ is small the magnitude plot of the complex poles will have a "hump" with the peak of the hump occuring close to $\omega_n$. Thus, we next investigate the behavior of the magnitude plot of the complex poles for frequencies in the vicinity of $\omega_n$.

We know that

$$\left| \frac{\omega_n^2}{(j\omega)^2 + 2\zeta\omega_n(j\omega) + \omega_n^2} \right| = \frac{\omega_n^2}{\sqrt{\left(\omega_n^2 - \omega^2\right)^2 + (2\zeta\omega_n\omega)^2}}. \qquad [9.9]$$

The peak magnitude occurs when the denominator of this expression is minimized. Differentiating the denominator with respect to $\omega$ yields

$$\frac{d}{d\omega}\sqrt{\left(\omega_n^2 - \omega^2\right)^2 + (2\zeta\omega_n\omega)^2} = \frac{\frac{1}{2}\left[-4\left(\omega_n^2 - \omega^2\right)\omega + 8\zeta^2\omega_n^2\omega\right]}{\left[\left(\omega_n^2 - \omega^2\right) + (2\zeta\omega_n\omega)^2\right]^{3/2}}$$

The derivative is equal to zero if

$$-4\left(\omega_n^2 - \omega^2\right)\omega + 8\zeta^2\omega_n^2\omega = 0, \qquad [9.10]$$

or

$$\omega = \omega_n\sqrt{1 - 2\zeta^2} \overset{\Delta}{=} \omega_r, \qquad [9.11]$$

where $\omega_r$ is the frequency at the peak magnitude. The frequency $\omega_r$ is called the resonant frequency.

We can see from Eq. [9.11] that the smaller $\zeta$, the closer $\omega_r$ gets to $\omega_n$. It is also clear from Eqs. [9.10] and [9.11] that if $\zeta > 1/\sqrt{2}$, then the peak magnitude occurs for $\omega = 0$.

In actual practice, this expression for $\omega_r$ is of most use for systems with a pair of complex poles for which the damping ratio $\zeta$ is very small. For such systems, both the peak magnitude $M_r$ and the resonant frequency $\omega_r$ can be measured from experimental data, as shown in Fig. 9.9.

To see this, first note that

$$M_r = \frac{G_{\max} - G_0}{G_0}.$$

For the complex pair of poles under consideration here $G_0 = 1$, and hence $M_r$ is simply the maximum value of the magnitude plot. That is,

$$M_r = \frac{\omega_n^2}{\sqrt{\left(\omega_n^2 - \omega_r^2\right)^2 + (2\zeta\omega_n\omega_r)^2}}. \qquad [9.12]$$

**Figure 9.9 |** Measurement of $M_r$ and $\omega_r$.

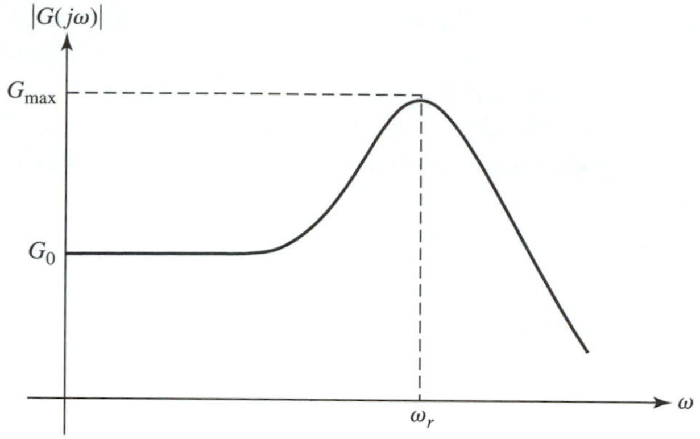

Substituting the expression for $\omega_r$ from Eq. [9.11] into Eq. [9.12] eliminates both $\omega_r$ and $\omega_n^2$, leaving, after a little work,

$$M_r = \frac{1}{2\zeta\sqrt{1-\zeta^2}}. \qquad\qquad [\mathbf{9.13}]$$

Thus, measuring $M_r$ enables us to determine $\zeta$. Once $\zeta$ is known, the natural frequency $\omega_n$ can be determined using the measurement of $\omega_r$ and Eq. [9.11].

The formulas just developed are important, but were obtained only after considerable algebraic manipulation. By contrast, the qualitative analysis developed earlier can be used to easily show why, and approximately where, the peak magnitude occurs. The first step is to put the transfer function in the form

$$\frac{\omega_n^2}{s^2 + 2\zeta\omega_n s + \omega_n^2} = \frac{\sigma^2 + \omega_d^2}{(s + \sigma - j\omega_d)(s + \sigma + j\omega_d)}$$

$$= \frac{\sigma^2 + \omega_d^2}{(|s + \sigma - j\omega_d|\underline{/\theta_1})(|s + \sigma + j\omega_d|\underline{/\theta_2})}$$

$$= \frac{\sigma^2 + \omega_d^2}{(\ell_1\underline{/\theta_1})(\ell_2\underline{/\theta_2})}$$

$$= \frac{\sigma^2 + \omega_d^2}{\ell_1\ell_2}\underline{/-(\theta_1 + \theta_2)}.$$

The individual components are the vector quantities of Fig. 9.10. If $\zeta$ is small, then as $\omega$ approaches the vicinity of $\omega_n\sqrt{1 - 2\zeta^2}$, that is approaches the neighborhood of

**Figure 9.10 |** Vector representation of two complex conjugate poles.

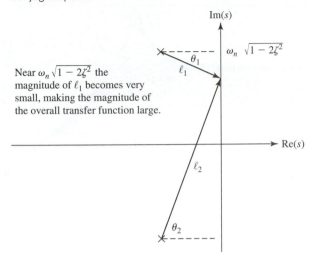

Near $\omega_n \sqrt{1 - 2\zeta^2}$ the magnitude of $\ell_1$ becomes very small, making the magnitude of the overall transfer function large.

$\omega_n$, the length of $\ell_1$ shrinks to its minimum value, causing the magnitude of

$$\frac{\sigma^2 + \omega_d^2}{\ell_1 \ell_2},$$

to reach a maximum, provided $0 < \zeta < 1/\sqrt{2}$. If $\zeta$ is large, then it is no longer the case that $\ell_1$ becomes small. In this case the maximum occurs at $\omega = 0$. The size of the peak in the magnitude increases as $\zeta$ decreases. As $\zeta \to 0$, the peak becomes arbitrarily large. All these points are easily seen from the graphical analysis.

Figure 9.11 shows the normalized magnitude and phase plots for a pair of complex poles for a range of values of $\zeta$. By normalizing the frequency to $\omega/\omega_n$, Fig. 9.11 can be used to construct the magnitude and phase plots for complex poles with arbitrary $\omega_n$ for any of the damping ratios shown in the figure.

The form of the phase plot can be deduced from the vector representation of the two complex poles shown in Fig. 9.10. At $\omega = 0$, the angle contributions from the two poles exactly cancel each other. As $\omega \to \infty$, the angle contribution from each pole approaches $-90°$, so that the total angle contribution of the pair is $-180°$. The transition from $0°$ to $-180°$ is very fast for low damping ratios because the angle contribution of the pole in the second quadrant changes rapidly due to its proximity to the imaginary axis.

An examination of Fig. 9.11(a) reveals that the hump in the magnitude plot is significant only if $\zeta \leq 0.5$ and that for $\zeta \geq 0.7$ there is no hump at all. If $\zeta$ is large, a very good approximation to the asymptotic magnitude plot would be that of a double pole with break frequency $\omega_n$.

**Figure 9.11 |** Normalized magnitude and phase plots of $\dfrac{\omega_n^2}{s^2 + 2\zeta\omega_n s + \omega_n^2}$ for various $\zeta$.

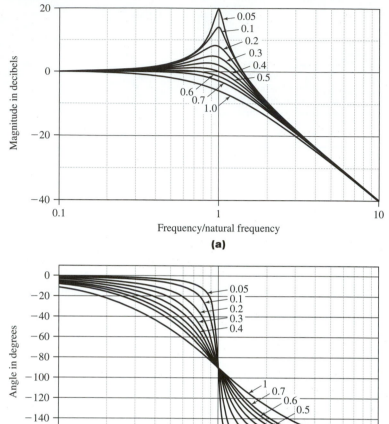

(a)

(b)

**EXAMPLE 9.3.2**

Let

$$G(s) = \frac{396}{(s+2-j19.8)(s+2+j19.8)}.$$

In this example, we present alternative methods of constructing the magnitude and phase plots for a given pair of complex poles.

One method is simply to compute and plot the magnitude and phase of the pair of poles for some frequencies around the natural frequency $\omega_n$, and then draw a

**Table 9.2 |** Magnitude and phase values for $G(s)$ of Example 9.3.2.

| % $\omega_n$ | 30 | 40 | 50 | 60 | 80 | 90 |
|---|---|---|---|---|---|---|
| $\omega$ | 5.97 | 7.96 | 9.95 | 11.94 | 15.92 | 17.9 |
| $|G(j\omega)|$ | 1.09 | 1.18 | 1.32 | 1.54 | 2.54 | 3.8 |
| $|G(j\omega)|$ dB | 0.8 | 1.51 | 2.42 | 3.73 | 8.16 | 11.6 |
| % $\omega_n$ | 100 | 110 | 120 | 130 | 150 | 200 |
| $\omega$ | 19.9 | 21.89 | 23.88 | 25.87 | 29.85 | 39.8 |
| $|G(j\omega)|$ | 4.97 | 3.28 | 2.0 | 1.36 | 0.78 | 0.33 |
| $|G(j\omega)|$ dB | 13.9 | 10.32 | 6 | 2.64 | −2.18 | −9.6 |

smooth curve throught the plotted points. The pair of complex poles has a damping ratio $\zeta = 0.1$, and a natural frequency $\omega_n = 19.9$ rad/s. This makes the effect of the "hump" in the magnitude plot significant. The peak of the hump is at

$$\omega_r = \omega_n\sqrt{1 - 2\zeta^2} = \sqrt{396}\sqrt{1 - 2(0.1)^2} = 19.7 \text{ rad/s},$$

and, as discussed earlier, for small damping ratios the peak occurs almost exactly at $\omega_n$. Table 9.2 provides the magnitude and phase values necessary to sketch the magnitude and phase plots accurately.

An alternative approach is to use Fig. 9.11 to calculate these same values. For instance, the magnitude for $\omega = 0.5\omega_n$ is approximately 3 dB. Therefore, the value 3 dB would be plotted at the frequency

$$\omega = 0.5\omega_n = 0.5 \times 19.9 = 9.95 \text{ rad/s}.$$

Examining Table 9.2, we see clearly that this is a viable alternative to direct calculations.

A similar set of angle calculations, based on Fig. 9.11(b), are shown in Table 9.3. By comparison an exact calculation yields

$$\angle G(j9.95) = \tan^{-1}\left(\frac{19.8 + 9.95}{2}\right) - \tan^{-1}\left(\frac{19.8 - 9.95}{2}\right)$$

$$= 86.15° - 78.52° = 7.63°,$$

which is in very good agreement with the value from the table.

**Table 9.3 |** Computation of phase using normalized phase plot for Example 9.3.2.

| % $\omega_n$ | 30 | 40 | 50 | 80 | 100 | 150 | 200 | 400 |
|---|---|---|---|---|---|---|---|---|
| $\omega$ (rad/s) | 6.0 | 8.0 | 10.0 | 15.9 | 19.9 | 29.9 | 39.8 | 59.7 |
| $\angle G(j\omega)$ | −2° | −4° | −10° | −23° | −90° | −165° | −173° | −180° |

# 9.4 | TRANSFER FUNCTION IDENTIFICATION

In this section the Bode analysis techniques developed in Sections 9.1 to 9.3 are put to work identifying a transfer function from the Bode magnitude and phase plots.

**Figure 9.12 |** Bode phase and magnitude plots for an unknown system.

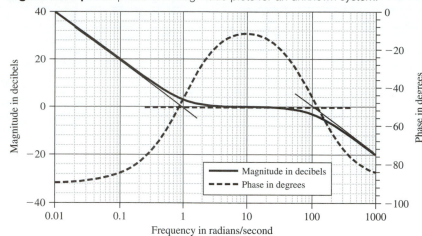

The identification focuses on generating the asymptotic Bode magnitude plot from the actual magnitude plot. The poles and zeros of the transfer function occur at the intersection of these asymptotes.

The Bode phase plot can then be used to corroborate the transfer function identified from the asymptotic magnitude plot. A few iterations may be required to refine the identification. The process is best illustrated with examples.

**EXAMPLE 9.4.1**

Consider the Bode phase and magnitude plots shown in Fig. 9.12. Asymptotes at 0 dB/decade and −20 dB/decade have been added as shown in the figure. The low-frequency asymptote has a slope of −20 dB/decade, indicating there is a pole at $s = 0$. The high-frequency asymptote also has a slope of −20 dB/decade. At middle frequencies, the slope approaches 0 dB/decade, indicating the presence of a zero. The presence of the zero can also be detected by noting that the phase starts out at −90° but then moves back toward −10° before again decreasing toward −90°.

The intersection of the asymptotes indicate that there is a zero at $s = -1$ and a pole at $s = -100$. The transfer function is then

$$G(s) = \frac{K(s+1)}{s(1+s/100)}.$$

The gain can be determined by noting that as $\omega \to 0$,

$$20\log_{10}\left|\frac{K(1+j\omega)}{j\omega(1+j\omega/100)}\right| \to 20\log_{10} K - 20\log_{10}\omega.$$

As we know this is the equation of a straight line that is, in fact, the low-frequency asymptote shown in Fig. 9.12 that passes through the 0-dB line at $\omega = 1$ rad/s. We can thus write

$$0 = 20 \log_{10} K - 20 \log_{10} 1 = 20 \log_{10} K,$$

showing that

$$K = 1.$$

An alternative choice is to do the evaluation at $\omega = 0.01$ rad/s, in which case we have

$$40 = 20 \log_{10} K - 20 \log_{10} 0.01 = 20 \log_{10} K + 40,$$

which again yields $K = 1$.

Although $K = 1$ if the transfer function is written in *time constant form*, we also can write

$$G(s) = \frac{100(s+1)}{s(s+100)}.$$

The identification of the transfer function in Example 9.4.1 was quite easy because the poles and zeros were widely separated. In Example 9.4.2 the identification is a little more difficult because two of the poles are separated by less than 1 decade in frequency.

**EXAMPLE 9.4.2**

Consider first the Bode magnitude and phase plots shown in Fig. 9.13. Asymptotes of slope −20 dB/decade and −40 dB/decade have been added. It is clear that there are poles at or near $s = -1$, $s = -100$, and $s = -500$. There is also a zero somewhere between the pole at $s = -1$ and the pole at $s = -100$. We can tell this from the way the phase begins to increase again for frequencies between 10 and 100 rad/s. Our

**Figure 9.13 |** Bode phase and magnitude plots for an unknown system.

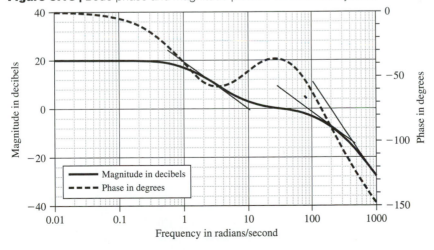

preliminary guess at the transfer function is

$$G(s) = \frac{10(1 + s/\gamma)}{(1 + s)(1 + s/90)(1 + s/500)}.$$

Looking a little more closely at the Bode magnitude plot we see that the plot is 3 dB above the asymptotes at $\omega = 10$ rad/s and 3 dB below at $\omega = 100$ rad/s. This tells us that the zero is probably around $s = -10$. We now compute the phase at $\omega = 100$ rad/s, and find that for $\gamma = 10$

$$\angle G(j100) = \tan^{-1}10 - \tan^{-1}100 - \tan^{-1}1 - \tan^{-1}0.2 = 61.4°,$$

which matches the phase shown in Fig. 9.13.

So our final estimate, aided by the phase computation, is

$$G(s) = \frac{10(1 + s/10)}{(1 + s)(1 + s/100)(1 + s/500)} = \frac{50,000(s + 10)}{(s + 1)(s + 100)(s + 500)}.$$

Our next two examples of transfer function identification use real data obtained for the separately excited dc motor studied in Chapter 8. In this case, the data will be less perfect than in Examples 9.4.1 and 9.4.2.

**EXAMPLE 9.4.3**

Figure 9.14 is the plot of the Bode magnitude and phase data for the separately excited dc motor first presented in Chapter 8. The data were collected with the cylinder detached. From these data we can extract the transfer function

$$G_{mtr}(s) = \frac{0.1122}{(1 + s/26)(1 + s/100)} = \frac{292}{(s + 26)(s + 100)}. \qquad \textbf{[9.14]}$$

In this case, we get a model that is very close to that obtained in Chapter 8.

**Figure 9.14 |** Bode magnitude and phase plots for a dc motor.

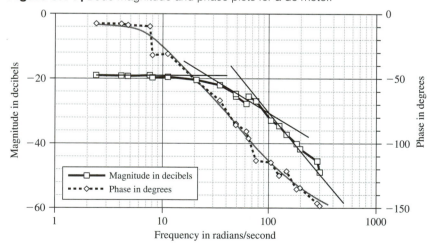

**Figure 9.15 |** Bode magnitude and phase plots for a dc motor with a cylinder attached.

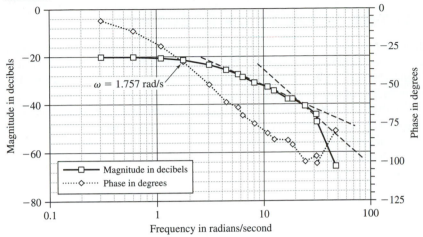

Figure 9.15 shows the Bode magnitude and phase plots for the dc motor with the cylinder attached. As we can see, there is clearly a pole between $s = -2.7$ and $s = -3$. If we look at the point where the plot has dropped 3 dB from its low-frequency value, we would probably put the pole at $s = -3$. This is close to the location we found in Chapter 8. The location of the second pole is not easy to determine from the data but appears to be around $s = -20$, putting it to the left of the value $s = -15$ obtained in Chapter 8.

It is tempting to try to determine the location of the second pole from the phase data, which appears to be pretty good at low frequency. Thus we could pick a frequency and phase, assume a pole at $s = -3$, and try to estimate the location of the second pole. For instance, for $\omega = 1.757$ rad/s the total phase is $-34.22°$. The phase due to the pole at $s = -3$ is

$$\theta_1 = \tan^{-1} \frac{1.757}{3} = -30°.$$

Thus, the phase contribution of the second pole, at $\omega = 1.757$ rad/s is

$$\theta_2 = 34.2° - 30° = -4.2°,$$

and consequently the location of the second pole can be estimated to be

$$p_2 = \frac{1.757}{\tan(4.2°)} = 24.$$

However, this approach doesn't prove to be very useful because if we repeat this computation for the first six data points we find that the estimate of the magnitude of the second pole keeps increasing. Thus, we settle for the model

$$G(s) = \frac{6}{(s+3)(s+20)},$$

a model close to the one we found in Chapter 8.

## 9.5 | THE EFFECTS OF FEEDBACK

When we introduced feedback in Chapter 4, the primary emphasis was on determining the effect of feedback on stability. We then moved on to root locus analysis and design. Now that we have introduced frequency response analysis we can extend our understanding of the effects of feedback.

Our discussion of the effects of feedback in Chapter 4 was mostly qualitative. With the frequency domain skills that we have acquired in this chapter we can now quantify some of the effects of feedback. For instance, we can use feedback to change the bandwidth of a system. We can also quantify the relative sensitivities of the open-loop and closed-loop systems to changes in parameters of the respective transfer functions. Further, we will see that feedback can help a system cancel the effects of unwanted disturbances. These last two topics are to some extent inter-related as we shall see.

### 9.5.1  The Effect of Feedback on Bandwidth

Consider the simple plant transfer function

$$G_p(s) = \frac{K}{s + a}. \qquad [9.15]$$

This transfer function can represent such disparate systems as a dc motor or an operational amplifier. In Fig. 9.16, nonunity feedback has been added to this plant. The closed-loop transfer function for this system is

$$T_c(s) = \frac{K}{s + (a + KK_1)}.$$

Suppose that $K$ is large but not known with great precision and has a "nominal" value of $K = 10^6$. Further let $a = 100$ rad/s. The open-loop frequency response is shown in Fig. 9.17. Using the usual definition of bandwidth as the half power point (3 dB down from the dc gain), we see that the open-loop bandwidth is 100 rad/s, and the dc gain is $10^4$. The frequency response of the closed-loop system, also shown in Fig. 9.17 for $K_1 = 0.1$, has a bandwidth of $10^5$ rad/s and a dc gain of 10.

Thus, we see that by applying feedback we can change an open-loop system that has a narrow bandwidth and a large, but imprecise gain into a closed-loop system with a small, but very precise, gain and a very large bandwidth. Indeed the frequency

**Figure 9.16 |** Block diagram representation of a system with feedback.

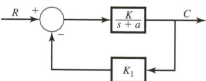

**Figure 9.17** | Open-loop and closed-loop frequency responses.

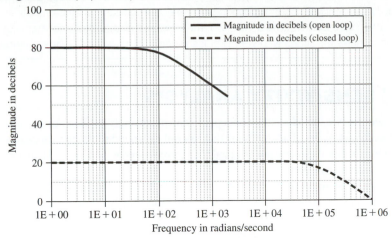

response of the closed-loop system is a very good approximation to the frequency response of a $\delta$ function, that is, perfectly flat over a very large frequency range. We note that the product of the gain and bandwidth is constant.

**EXAMPLE 9.5.1**

Recall the transfer function relationship of the noninverting operational amplifier given by Eq. [3.28], namely,

$$\frac{V_o(s)}{V_i(s)} = \frac{A}{1 + A[Z_1/(Z_1 + Z_2)]}. \qquad \textbf{[9.16]}$$

In the derivation in Chapter 3, we assumed that $A$ was a large constant. In fact, a reasonable model of the dynamics of an opamp is

$$A(s) = \frac{K}{s + a},$$

with

$$K \gg a.$$

Then

$$\frac{V_o(s)}{V_i(s)} = \frac{K/(s + a)}{1 + [K/(s + a)][Z_1/(Z_1 + Z_2)]}$$

$$= \frac{K}{s + \{a + K[Z_1/(Z_1 + Z_2)]\}}.$$

This is precisely the system of Fig. 9.16, with

$$K_1 = \frac{Z_1}{Z_1 + Z_2}.$$

If we let $K = 10^6$, $a = 100$, $Z_1 = 100 \text{ k}\Omega$, and $Z_2 = 910 \text{ k}\Omega$, then we have the closed-loop system whose frequency response is shown in Fig. 9.17. Thus, using opamps we can obtain a transfer function with a very precise gain of 10 and a bandwidth of $10^5$ rad/s. Since the transfer functions of the electromechanical systems considered in this book have bandwidths below 100 rad/s, we see that operational amplifiers can provide transfer functions with very precise gains and essentially infinite bandwidth.

## 9.6 | SENSITIVITY ANALYSIS

In this section, we introduce the concept of sensitivity analysis. Sensitivity analysis is an aid in designing feedback systems that not only respond to the reference input in a satisfactory way but also are not affected to any great degree by unwanted disturbances that may also be present.

Consider again the system of Fig. 9.16 and let $K_1 = 1$. Suppose we are interested in how changes in the gain $K$ affect the closed-loop transfer function

$$T_c(s) = \frac{K}{s + (a + K)}.$$

Suppose we let $\Delta T_c$ and $\Delta K$ represent small changes in $T_c$ and $K$, respectively. Then a useful way to define the sensitivity of the closed-loop transfer function to changes in $K$ might be

$$S_K^{T_c} \triangleq \frac{\Delta T_c / T_c}{\Delta K / K} = \frac{K}{T_c} \frac{\Delta T_c}{\Delta K} \rightarrow \frac{K}{T_c} \frac{\partial T_c}{\partial K}.$$

We use the symbol for partial differentiation here because $T_c$ is a function of $s$ and $a$ as well as $K$.

An alternative definition found in the literature is

$$S_K^{T_c} \triangleq \frac{\partial \ln T_c}{\partial \ln K} = \frac{(\partial \ln T_c)/\partial K}{(\partial \ln K)/\partial K} = \frac{(1/T_c)(\partial T_c/\partial K)}{(1/K)(\partial K/\partial K)} = \frac{K}{T_c} \frac{\partial T_c}{\partial K},$$

which amounts to the same thing. For the simple system of Fig. 9.16,

$$S_K^{T_c} = \frac{K}{T_c} \frac{\partial T_c}{\partial K}$$

$$= \frac{K}{K/[s + (a + K)]} \left[ \frac{\partial}{\partial K} \frac{K}{s + (a + K)} \right]$$

$$= [s + (a + K)] \left[ \frac{-K}{[s + (a + K)]^2} \frac{\partial [s + (a + K)]}{\partial K} + \frac{1}{s + (a + K)} \frac{\partial K}{\partial K} \right]$$

$$= [s + (a + K)] \left[ \frac{-K}{[s + (a + K)]^2} + \frac{1}{s + (a + K)} \right]$$

$$= [s + (a + K)] \left[ \frac{-K + [s + (a + K)]}{[s + (a + K)]^2} \right]$$

$$= \frac{s + a}{[s + (a + K)]} \qquad\qquad \textbf{[9.17]}$$

**Figure 9.18 |** Plot of $20 \log_{10} |S_K^{T_c}(s)|$.

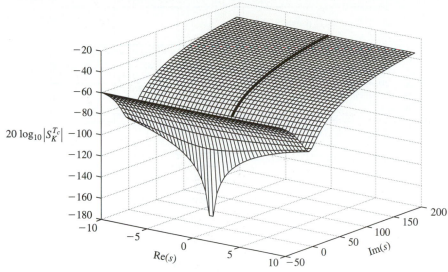

By contrast,

$$S_K^{G_p} = \frac{K}{G_p} \frac{\partial G_p}{\partial K} = \frac{K}{K/(s+a)} \frac{\partial}{\partial K} \frac{K}{s+a} = 1.$$

We see that the sensitivity of the closed-loop system to changes in $K$ decreases as $K$ increases, whereas for the open-loop system no matter what value of $K$ we choose the sensitivity is the same and very poor at that.

One of the problems with the sensitivity measure $S_K^{T_c}$ of Eq.[9.17] is that it is a function of $a$, $s$, and $K$. If we choose values for $a$ and $K$, and eliminate the phase of $S_K^{T_c}(s)$ by plotting $20 \log_{10} |S_K^{T_c}(s)|$, we have a function of the real and imaginary parts of $s$, whose plot is a surface in three-dimensional space. Such a plot is shown in Fig. 9.18, for

$$S_K^{T_c} = \frac{s+a}{s+(a+K)},$$

with $a = 1$ and $K = 1000$.

We could take a slice of this surface by fixing either the real or imaginary part of the Laplace variable $s$. Given the development in this chapter, we see that one logical choice is to let $s = j\omega$. The heavy dark line in Fig. 9.18 represents the intersection of $20 \log_{10} |S_K^{T_c}(s)|$ with a vertical plane that passes through the imaginary axis of the $s$ plane. In other words, the heavy dark line represents the Bode magnitude plot of $|S_K^{T_c}(s)|$. By noting the "flatness" of the three-dimensional plot, we see that it offers almost no advantage over the simpler Bode magnitude plot.

**Figure 9.19 |** Frequency responses of $S_K^{T_c}(j\omega)$ and $S_K^{G_p}(j\omega)$.

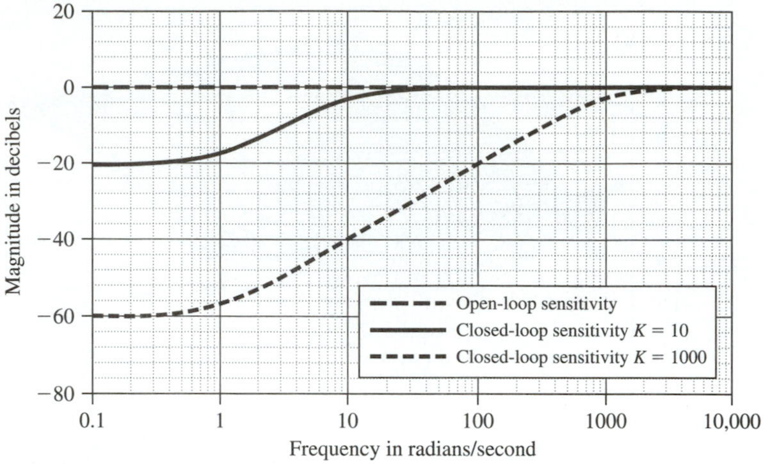

Using the Bode magnitude plot of $|S_K^{T_c}(s)|$, we can easily see the effect of $K$ on sensitivity in this simple example. If we set $a = 1$ and $K = 0.1$, then

$$\left|S_K^{T_c}(j\omega)\right| = \frac{|j\omega + 1|}{|j\omega + 1.1|} \approx 1.$$

The sensitivity of the closed-loop system is just about the same as that of the open-loop system.

If $K$ is increased to 100, however, then

$$\left|S_K^{T_c}(j\omega)\right| = \frac{|j\omega + 1|}{|j\omega + 101|},$$

and it is clear that the sensitivity will improve, especially for smaller values of $\omega$. The sensitivities of the closed-loop system for $K = 10$ and 1000 are plotted in Fig. 9.19, along with the sensitivity of the open-loop system.

## 9.7 | DISTURBANCE REJECTION

One of the uses of sensitivity analysis is to analyze the effect of disturbances on the performance of a system. The most common locations for disturbances are at the input and output of the system. We will consider both of these situations.

### 9.7.1  Disturbance at the Output

Consider the system shown in Fig. 9.20, and let

$$G = G_c G_p.$$

Suppose $G_p$ is the transfer function of a radar antenna, and $G_c$ the compensation we wish to add to improve the performance of the system to the reference input $R$. The disturbance $D$ might be the effect of the wind blowing against the antenna.

**Figure 9.20** | Disturbance at the output.

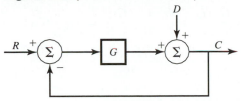

To investigate the sensitivity of the closed-loop system to the disturbance, we first note that because the system is linear we can use superposition and write

$$c(t) = c_r(t) + c_d(t),$$

where $c_r(t)$ is the response to the reference input with $d(t) = 0$ and $c_d(t)$ is the response to the disturbance with $r(t) = 0$. We then compute two transfer functions. The first is

$$\frac{C_r}{R} \triangleq T_c = \frac{G}{1 + G}.$$

This is simply the transfer function between the reference input and the output with $d(t) = 0$. The second transfer function is

$$\frac{C_d}{D} \triangleq T_d.$$

This is the transfer function between the disturbance input and the output with $r(t) = 0$. This transfer function can be found as follows. With $R = 0$,

$$C_d = D + (-GC_d),$$

which can be rewritten as

$$(1 + G)C_d = D,$$

or

$$\frac{C_d}{D} = T_d = \frac{1}{1 + G}.$$

Letting $s = j\omega$, we can then write

$$T_d(j\omega) = \frac{1}{1 + G(j\omega)}.$$

If $|G(j\omega)| \gg 1$ over the spectrum of frequencies present in $d(t)$, then

$$|T_d(j\omega)| = \frac{1}{|1 + G(j\omega)|} \approx \frac{1}{|G(j\omega)|}.$$

Thus if we can keep $|G(j\omega)|$ large over the frequencies present in $d(t)$, then we can suppress the effect of the disturbance on the position of the antenna.

The only flaw in this analysis is that there may be a significant high-frequency content to $d(t)$, as might be the case if the wind were gusting. In that case, in order to suppress the noise we may have a wider bandwidth in the forward loop than we really want.

We next consider

$$S_G^{T_c} = \frac{G}{T_c}\frac{\partial T_c}{\partial G} = \frac{G}{T_c}\frac{\partial}{\partial G}\frac{G}{1+G} = \frac{G}{T_c}\frac{\partial}{\partial G}[G(1+G)^{-1}]$$

$$= \frac{G}{T_c}\left[\frac{-G}{(1+G)^2}\frac{\partial(1+G)}{\partial G} + \frac{1}{1+G}\frac{\partial G}{\partial G}\right]$$

$$= \frac{G}{G/(1+G)} \times \frac{1}{(1+G)^2}$$

$$= \frac{1}{(1+G)}.$$

From the sensitivity analysis we see that making $G$ large also makes the closed-loop system insensitive to changes in $G$.

Now suppose we *specify* both $T_c$ and $T_d$. Then we have the two equations

$$T_c = \frac{G}{1+G} = \frac{G_cG_p}{1+G_cG_p}, \qquad \text{[9.18]}$$

$$T_d = \frac{1}{1+G} = \frac{1}{1+G_cG_p}. \qquad \text{[9.19]}$$

We see that we have two equations but only one variable, namely, $G_c$, that we can adjust. So we cannot specify both $T_c$ and $T_d$.

Next consider Fig. 9.21. In this case,

$$T_c = \frac{G}{1+GH} = \frac{G_cG_p}{1+G_cG_pH}, \qquad \text{[9.20]}$$

$$T_d = \frac{1}{1+GH} = \frac{1}{1+G_cG_pH}. \qquad \text{[9.21]}$$

**Figure 9.21 |** Nonunity feedback and disturbance at the output.

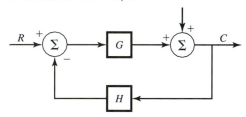

This time we have two equations and two variables, namely, $G_c$ and $H$. We can now specify *both* $T_c$ and $T_d$, and solve for $G_c$ and $H$. Dividing Eq.[9.20] by Eq.[9.21] yields

$$\frac{T_c}{T_d} = G_cG_p, \qquad \text{[9.22]}$$

or

$$G_c = \frac{T_c}{T_d} \frac{1}{G_p}.$$

Substituting Eq. [9.22] into Equation [9.21] yields

$$T_d = \frac{1}{1 + GH} = \frac{1}{1 + (T_c/T_d)H}.$$

Cross multiplying then gives

$$T_d + T_c H = 1,$$

or

$$H = (1 - T_d)\frac{1}{T_c}.$$

We illustrate this development with Example 9.7.1.

**EXAMPLE 9.7.1**

Suppose we let

$$T_c(s) = \frac{K(s+\gamma)}{s^2 + 2\zeta\omega_n s + \omega_n^2}, \qquad T_d(s) = \frac{s+b}{s+d}, \qquad G_p(s) = \frac{\delta}{s+\delta}.$$

Then

$$1 - T_d(s) = \frac{d-b}{s+d},$$

$$H(s) = \frac{[(d-b)/K](s^2 + 2\zeta\omega_n s + \omega_n^2)}{(s+\gamma)(s+d)}, \qquad [9.23]$$

and

$$G_c(s) = \frac{K_c(s+\gamma)(s+\delta)(s+d)}{(s+b)(s^2 + 2\zeta\omega_n s + \omega_n^2)}, \qquad [9.24]$$

where $K_c = K/\delta$.

Now suppose that we would like the dominant poles of $T_c$ to be $s = -3 \pm j4$. Further, suppose that the frequencies present in the disturbance are below 8 rad/s. Then our goal is to design $T_d$ so that frequencies below 8 rad/s are attenuated by 40 dB. Suppose we let $b = 20$ and $d = 2000$. Then $T_d$ is the high pass filter shown in Fig. 9.22.

We now turn our attention to the closed-loop transfer function $T_c$. We have already specified the poles, but we now need to determine $K$ and $\gamma$. The presence of the zero enables us to specify the accuracy to both a step and a ramp input. We have already chosen values for the complex poles but for the moment we will write them in symbolic form so that

$$T_c(s) = \frac{K(s+\gamma)}{(s+\sigma - j\omega_d)(s+\sigma + j\omega_d)}. \qquad [9.25]$$

**Figure 9.22** | Frequency response of $T_d(j\omega)$.

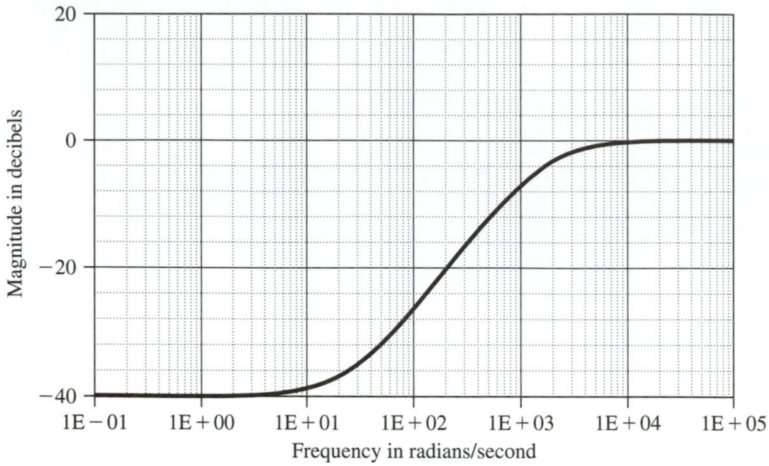

All that remains is to determine $K$ and $\delta$. Recall that for finite steady state error to a ramp input the closed-loop system must exhibit zero steady state error to a step input. That is,

$$\lim_{s \to 0} T_c(s) = 1.$$

For zero steady state error to a step input, the error to a ramp input is then

$$e_{ss}(\text{ramp}) \overset{\Delta}{=} \frac{1}{K_v} = \left[ \sum_{i=1}^{n} \frac{1}{p_i} - \sum_{i=1}^{m} \frac{1}{z_i} \right],$$

where the $p_i$ are the poles and the $z_i$ the zeros of $T_c$. Thus *zero* steady state error to a ramp input requires that

$$\sum_{i=1}^{n} \frac{1}{p_i} - \sum_{i=1}^{m} \frac{1}{z_i} = 0.$$

Note that $e_{ss}(\text{ramp})$ does not depend on $K$, only on the poles and zeros of $T_c$. Hence, we first use $\gamma$ to guarantee zero steady state error to a ramp input. Having found $\gamma$, we adjust $K$ to ensure zero steady state error to a step input.

For the $T_c$ of Eq. [9.25], the formula for zero steady state error to a ramp becomes

$$\frac{1}{\sigma + j\omega_d} + \frac{1}{\sigma - j\omega_d} - \frac{1}{\gamma} = 0,$$

which can be rewritten as

$$\frac{[\sigma - j\omega_d] + [\sigma + j\omega_d]}{\sigma^2 + \omega_d^2} - \frac{1}{\gamma} = 0,$$

and finally as

$$\gamma = \frac{\sigma^2 + \omega_d^2}{2\sigma}.$$

For the complex poles determined earlier,

$$\gamma = \frac{3^2 + 4^2}{2 \times 3} = \frac{25}{6}.$$

All that remains is to find $K$. To that end,

$$\lim_{s \to 0} T_c(s) = \frac{K(25/6)}{25} = 1,$$

or

$$K = 6.$$

Thus,

$$T_c(s) = \frac{6(s + 4.167)}{(s + 3 - j4)(s + 3 + j4)}.$$

The last task is to assemble $H$ and $G_c$. Letting $\delta = 2$, and using Eqs. [9.23] and [9.24], we have

$$H(s) = \frac{330(s + 3 - j4)(s + 3 + j4)}{(s + 4.167)(s + 2000)},$$

$$G_c(s) = \frac{3(s + 4.167)(s + 2)(s + 2000)}{(s + 20)(s + 3 - j4)(s + 3 + j4)}.$$

To implement H using analog circuitry we will need to use the biquadratic circuit presented in Chapter 3. Further, to implement $G_c$ we will need to cascade a biquad with another opamp circuit to obtain the real pole and zero. Thus, the implementation is not trivial. Further, even with a first-order plant, $G_c$ is third order. If $G_p$ is of higher order the resulting compensators are ever more complicated.

---

Example 9.7.1 used a very simple plant with one pole and no zero. We frequently encounter plant transfer functions with higher poles/zero excesses (pze's). The design procedure in this latter case requires a little more care.

Problem 1 of Section 9.10.4 is a simple exercise whose result we now restate in a more convenient form. Let

$$T_c(s) = \frac{\alpha_t(s)}{\beta_t(s)}, \qquad T_d(s) = \frac{\alpha_d(s)}{\beta_d(s)}, \qquad G_p(s) = \frac{\alpha_p(s)}{\beta_p(s)}.$$

Then for $G_c$ and $H$ to both have pze's of zero or greater we must have

$$\text{pze}(T_d) + \text{pze}(G_p) \le \text{pze}(T_c), \qquad\qquad \textbf{[9.26]}$$

and

$$\deg(\beta_d - \alpha_d) + \text{pze}(T_c) \le \deg(\beta_d), \qquad\qquad \textbf{[9.27]}$$

These equations must both be satisfied. From Eq. [9.26] we see that to keep the degree of $T_c$ as low as possible we should make $\text{pze}(T_d) = 0$. Then in Eq. [9.27], we would like to have $\deg(\beta_d - \alpha_d) = 0$ to keep the $\deg(\beta_d)$ as low as possible. We now apply these ideas to the following example.

**EXAMPLE 9.7.2**

Let

$$G_p(s) = \frac{2}{s(s+2)},$$

and suppose that the disturbance input only has frequencies below 20 rad/s. We wish to design $T_d$ so that

$$|T_d(j\omega)| \le 0.01, \qquad \omega \le 20 \text{ rad/s}.$$

Since $G_p$ has a pze of 2, we choose

$$T_c(s) = \frac{25}{(s+4-j3)(s+4+j3)},$$

and let

$$T_d(s) = \frac{s^2 + as + b}{s^2 + as + c}.$$

There is a slight difficulty here which we will have more to say about later. For the moment we note that

$$1 - T_d(s) = \frac{c - b}{s^2 + as + c},$$

so that we achieve our goal of having

$$\deg(\beta_d - \alpha_d) = 0.$$

We now have to construct a $T_d$ that meets the performance criterion stated earlier. We choose to let

$$T_d(s) = \frac{(s+\gamma)(s+\delta)}{(s+p)^2} = \frac{s^2 + (\gamma + \delta)s + \gamma\delta}{s^2 + 2ps + p^2}.$$

Then we must have

$$\gamma + \delta = 2p.$$

To achieve our goal of suppressing noise below 20 rad/s we must also have

$$\gamma\delta \ll p^2.$$

Now consider Fig. 9.23. The main feature is a line of slope 20 dB/decade that passes through −40 dB at a frequency a little above 20 rad/s. We see that to achieve our noise suppression goal, $\gamma$ will be quite small and

$$\delta \approx p.$$

We now use a convergent trial-and-error method to find $p$, $\gamma$, and $\delta$. First we choose a trial value for $p$ near where the line of slope 20 dB/decade approaches 0 dB. We next choose $\gamma$ by finding where the line of slope 20 dB/decade crosses a convenient horizontal value of gain. For instance, if we pick the horizontal value −60 dB, then $\gamma = 3$, $\delta = 3997$, and the compensator is

$$T_d(s) = \frac{s^2 + 4000s + 11{,}991}{s^2 + 4000s + 4 \times 10^6}.$$

We next check to see if $T_d(0)$ is close to $-60$ dB. We find that

$$T_d(0) = -50\,\text{dB}.$$

This is not close enough to $-60$, so our next step is to lower $\gamma$ and increase $\delta$ and repeat the process. After a few iterations we arrive at

$$T_d(s) = \frac{(s+0.3)(s+9999.7)}{s^2 + 10{,}000s + 25 \times 10^6}.$$

This transfer function is shown in Fig. 9.23 and meets the noise suppression specification. All that is left is to construct

$$H(s) = (1 - T_d)\,T_c^{-1}$$

$$= \frac{2.4997 \times 10^7}{(s+5000)^2}\,\frac{(s+4-j3)(s+4+j3)}{25}$$

$$= \frac{9.999 \times 10^5(s+4-j3)(s+4+j3)}{(s+5000)^2},$$

and

$$G_c(s) = G_p^{-1}\,\frac{T_c}{T_d}$$

$$= \frac{s(s+2)}{2}\,\frac{25(s+5000)^2}{(s+4-j3)(s+4+j3)(s+0.3)(s+9999.7)}$$

$$= \frac{12.5s(s+2)(s+5000)^2}{(s+4-j3)(s+4+j3)(s+0.3)(s+9999.7)}.$$

Once again we see that the compensation is very complex.

But there is another problem. Theoretically,

$$T_d(s) = \frac{(s+0.3)(s+9999.7)}{s^2 + 10{,}000s + 25 \times 10^6}.$$

**Figure 9.23** | Construction of $T_d(s)$.

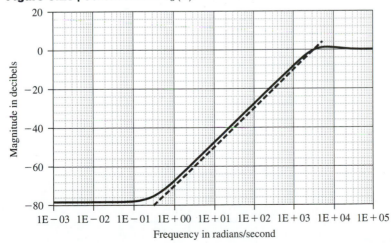

But we cannot achieve infinite precision in our implementation. Therefore,

$$1 - T_d(s) \approx \frac{K(s + \eta)}{s^2 + 10{,}000s + 25 \times 10^6}.$$

Thus, $H(s)$ has an extra zero. We can fix this problem by adding a pole to $G_c$ in the vicinity of $-\eta$, just as we found a practical PD compensator by adding a pole far to the left of the zero of the ideal PD compensator (see Problem 4 in Section 9.10.4). The greater drawback, however, is the complexity of the compensation.

---

We have invested a good deal of effort in Examples 9.7.1 and 9.7.2 to understand this algebraic approach to disturbance rejection. The time spent is not wasted, because in Chapter 12 we will return to the problem of rejecting disturbances at the output and find a much more elegant solution. We now turn our attention to disturbances at the input.

## 9.8 | DISTURBANCE AT THE INPUT

Consider first the unity feedback case, that is, let $H(s) = 1$ in Fig. 9.24. Then as before we define

$$C = C_r + C_d,$$

and find

$$T_c = \frac{G}{1 + G} = T_d.$$

Note the transfer function between the disturbance and the output is identical to the transfer function between the reference input and the output. In this case, making $|G|$ large does not help suppress the disturbance. Recalling our earlier analysis of a disturbance at the output, we see that if we have disturbances at both the input and the output, then suppression of *both* disturbances becomes very difficult.

If we next consider disturbances at the input with nonunity feedback, as shown in Fig. 9.24, we see that we have only the one equation:

$$T_c = \frac{G}{1 + GH} = \frac{G_c G_p}{1 + G_c G_p H} = T_d.$$

Thus, the two degrees of freedom provided by $G_c$ and $H$ don't do us any good, because

**Figure 9.24 |** Nonunity feedback and disturbance at the input.

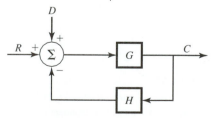

anything we do to improve the performance of $T_c$ also leads to an "improved" response to the disturbance.

Reconsidering the unity feedback case, we see that to suppress the disturbance we must have

$$|T_d| = \frac{|G_c G_p|}{|1 + G_c G_p|} \ll 1.$$

To achieve this we must have $G_c G_p \ll 1$, in which case

$$|T_d| = \frac{|G_c G_p|}{|1 + G_c G_p|} \approx |G_c G_p|.$$

This is the *opposite* of the condition we obtained for suppressing disturbances at the output, and so if we are faced with disturbances both at the input and the output, we may have great difficulty in suppressing both disturbances.

## 9.9 | REPRISE

This chapter has introduced the Bode magnitude and phase plots. Of particular interest is the asymptotic Bode magnitude plot, which is the centerpiece of Bode design, introduced in Chapter 11. The Bode magnitude plot offers great scale compression because both abscissa and ordinate are logarithmic.

In this chapter we also developed expressions related to the sensitivity of the closed-loop transfer function that can be expressed in terms of the loop transfer function. In Chapter 11 we will transfer these expressions to the Bode magnitude plot used to design our compensation.

In this text, the choice has been made to use decibels to express magnitude. This is the most common choice now, but that was not always the case. During the heyday of control in the late 1940s and the 1950s many practitioners preferred to plot simply the logarithm of the magnitude. This has the advantage that all the asymptotes have integer slopes of $0, \pm 1, \pm 2$, and so on.

The disadvantage to this approach is that the phase plot must be on a separate graph. This is not really much of a disadvantage since, as we have seen, the phase at any frequency can be derived from the magnitude plot. From a pedagogical point of view, however, it is convenient to have both the magnitude and phase plots on the same graph. This is especially true when discussing the Nyquist criterion.

Another topic addressed in the chapter was one of the most important uses of the Bode plot, namely, the identification of a plant transfer function. The key here was the ability to determine the plant response over a range of frequencies.

Two of the plant transfer functions identified were for the separately excited dc motor, introduced in Chapter 8. The transfer functions identified in this chapter were in good agreement with those found in Chapter 8 by two other identification techniques. Thus, we now have three different methods of identifying a transfer function. By combining these three methods we can generally get a very accurate model for a physical system.

With Bode analysis in hand, the next chapter could very well be Bode design. Before discussing Bode design, however, the Nyquist criterion is introduced. Strictly speaking, the Nyquist criterion is not needed for Bode design. However, the Nyquist criterion is such an elegant idea that it is worth spending some time admiring it. We will also use Nyquist analysis in Chapter 12 where we provide an elementary introduction to robust control.

# 9.10 | PROBLEMS

### 9.10.1 Drawing Asymptotic Bode Magnitude Plot

For each transfer function $G(s)$ sketch (by hand) the asymptotic Bode magnitude plot. Then compute the phase at five or six frequencies and sketch in the phase plot. Then find the accurate Bode phase and magnitude plots using MATLAB.

1. $\dfrac{10(s+1)}{s(s+10)(s+50)}$
        2. $\dfrac{1000(s+1)}{s(s+30)(s+100)}$

3. $\dfrac{50}{s(s+5)(s+50)}$
        4. $\dfrac{100(s+10)}{s(s+2)(s+50)}$

5. $\dfrac{800(s+5)}{s(s+20)^2}$
        6. $\dfrac{1000}{s[(s+1)^2+100]}$

7. $\dfrac{500}{s^2[(s+5)^2+25]}$
        8. $\dfrac{100}{s[(s+4)^2+9]}$

9. $\dfrac{10(s+5)}{s(s+0.01)(s+50)}$
        10. $\dfrac{100(s+3)}{s(s+0.5)(s+60)}$

11. $\dfrac{18}{s[(s+3)^2+9]}$
        12. $\dfrac{18(s+2)}{s[(s+3)^2+9]}$

13. $\dfrac{26}{s[(s+1)^2+25]}$
        14. $\dfrac{101}{s[(s+1)^2+100]}$

15. $\dfrac{26(s+5)}{s[(s+1)^2+25]}$
        16. $\dfrac{101(s+1)}{s[(s+1)^2+100]}$

17. $\dfrac{100[(s+1)^2+25]}{s(s+20)(s+50)}$
        18. $\dfrac{100[(s+1)^2+37]}{s(s+10)(s+400)}$

19. $\dfrac{100(s+10)}{s^2(s+50)(s+100)}$
        20. $\dfrac{100(s+20)}{s^3(s+200)}$

### 9.10.2 Transfer Function Identification

On the CD-ROM supplied with this book are data files, giving magnitude and frequency data for unknown transfer functions. In each case, identify the transfer function from the data.

1. bodeid1
        2. bodeid2
        3. bodeid3
        4. bodeid4

5. bodeid5
        6. bodeid6
        7. bodeid7
        8. bodeid8

9. bodeid9
        10. bodeid10
        11. bodeid11
        12. bodeid12

### 9.10.3 Sensitivity Analysis

For each $G(s)$, find the specified sensitivities based on the open- and-closed loop systems shown in either part (a) or part (b) of Fig. 9.25.

**Figure 9.25 |** Open- and closed-loop systems.

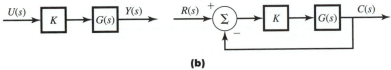

**(a)**

**(b)**

1.  $G(s) = \frac{a}{s+a}$, $S_a^G$, $S_a^{T_c}$, $S_K^G$, $S_K^{T_c}$; part (a)

2.  $G(s) = \frac{a}{s+a}$, $S_a^G$, $S_a^{T_c}$, $S_K^G$, $S_K^{T_c}$; part (b)

3.  $G(s) = \frac{a}{s(s+a)}$, $S_a^G$, $S_a^{T_c}$, $S_K^G$, $S_K^{T_c}$; part (a)

4.  $G(s) = \frac{a}{s(s+a)}$, $S_a^G$, $S_a^{T_c}$, $S_K^G$, $S_K^{T_c}$; part (b)

5.  $G(s) = \frac{ab}{(s+a)(s+b)}$, $S_a^G$, $S_a^{T_c}$, $S_K^G$, $S_K^{T_c}$; part (a)

6.  $G(s) = \frac{ab}{(s+a)(s+b)}$, $S_a^G$, $S_a^{T_c}$, $S_K^G$, $S_K^{T_c}$; part (b)

7.  $G(s) = \frac{s+a}{s(s+b)}$, $S_a^G$, $S_a^{T_c}$, $S_b^G$, $S_b^{T_c}$, $S_K^G$, $S_K^{T_c}$; part (a)

8.  $G(s) = \frac{ab}{(s+a)(s+b)}$, $S_a^G$, $S_a^{T_c}$, $S_b^G$, $S_b^{T_c}$, $S_K^G$, $S_K^{T_c}$; part (b)

9.  $G(s) = \frac{a^2}{(s+a)^2}$, $S_a^G$, $S_a^{T_c}$, $S_K^G$, $S_K^{T_c}$; part (a)

10.  $G(s) = \frac{a^2}{(s+a)^2}$, $S_a^G$, $S_a^{T_c}$, $S_K^G$, $S_K^{T_c}$; part (b)

## 9.10.4 Disturbance at the Output

1.  For the two-degree-of-freedom disturbance compensation of Example 9.7.1, let

$$T_c(s) = \frac{\alpha_t(s)}{\beta_t(s)}, \qquad T_d(s) = \frac{\alpha_d(s)}{\beta_d(s)}, \qquad G_p(s) = \frac{\alpha_p(s)}{\beta_p(s)}.$$

Show that for $H(s)$ to have a pze of zero or greater, we must have

$$\deg[\beta_d(s) - \alpha_d(s)] + \deg[\beta_t(s)] \le \deg[\beta_d(s)] + \deg[\alpha_t(s)],$$

and similarly for $G_c$ to have a pze of zero or greater, we must have

$$\deg[\alpha_t(s)] + \deg[\beta_d(s)] + \deg[\beta_p(s)] \le \deg[\alpha_d(s)] + \deg[\alpha_p(s)] + \deg[\beta_t(s)]$$

2.  For the system of Fig. 9.26, let

$$G_p(s) = \frac{2}{s(s+2)} \quad \text{and} \quad H(s) = 1.$$

**Figure 9.26 |** Unity feedback with disturbance at the output.

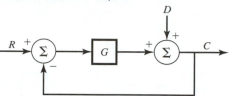

Suppose we specify the closed-loop transfer function to be

$$T_c(s) = \frac{\omega_n^2}{s^2 + 2\zeta\omega_n s + \omega_n^2},$$

with $\zeta = 0.8$ and $\omega_n = 10$.

a.  Find $G_c(s)$ and $T_d(s)$.

b.  Suppose that the disturbance at the output is sinusoidal with frequency 10 rad/s. Will $T_d$ provide good disturbance rejection? How could we improve the disturbance rejection? What price will we pay?

3.  For the system of Fig. 9.26, let

$$G_p(s) = \frac{4}{(s + 4)^2} \quad \text{and} \quad H(s) = 1.$$

Suppose we specify the closed-loop transfer function to be

$$T_c(s) = \frac{\omega_n^2}{s^2 + 2\zeta\omega_n s + \omega_n^2},$$

with $\zeta = 0.8$ and $\omega_n = 5$.

a.  Find $G_c(s)$ and $T_d(s)$.

b.  Suppose that the disturbance at the output is sinusoidal with frequency 10 rad/s. Will $T_d$ provide good disturbance rejection? How could we improve the disturbance rejection? What price will we pay?

4.  Consider again Example 9.7.2 and suppose that when implemented,

$$T_d(s) = \frac{(s + 0.25)(s + 10{,}100)}{(s + 5050)^2}.$$

a.  Make a Bode magnitude plot of $|T_d(j\omega)|$.

b.  Find $1 - T_d(s)$ and $H(s)$.

c.  Where is the zero of $1 - T_d(s)$?

d.  If we add a pole to $H(s)$ near the zero, will the modified $H(s)$ be similar to the original theoretical $H(s)$?

## 9.10.5  Additional Problems

1.  Let the closed-loop transfer function be

$$T_c(s) = \frac{K(s + \gamma)}{(s + \sigma - j\omega_d)(s + \sigma + j\omega_d)}.$$

a.  Let $\sigma = 4$ and $\omega_d = 3$. Find $\gamma$ so that the closed-loop system exhibits zero steady state error for both step and ramp inputs. Use MATLAB to plot the unit step and unit ramp responses.

b.  Repeat part (a) for $K_p = \infty$ and $K_v = 100$.

c.  Repeat part (a) for $K_p = \infty$ and $K_v = 10$.

2.  Let the closed-loop transfer function be

$$T_c(s) = \frac{K(s + \gamma)}{(s + \sigma - j\omega_d)(s + \sigma + j\omega_d)}.$$

a.  Let $\sigma = 4$ and $\omega_d = 3$. Find $\gamma$ so that the closed-loop system exhibits zero steady state error for both step and ramp inputs.

b.  Draw the root contour for the values of $K$ and $\gamma$ found in part (a) for $\gamma \in (0.1\gamma, 10\gamma)$.

c.  Repeat part (a) for $K_p = \infty$ and $K_v = 10$.

3.  We generally get our first approximation to a transfer function by laying in asymptotes on a bode magnitude plot. Once we have this first approximation, we can refine it by seeing if the phase plot of the approximation matches the actual phase data. Use this idea to verify the transfer functions in Examples 9.4.1 and 9.4.2.

4.  Plot the phase and magnitude data for the transfer functions found in Example 9.4.3 and compare with the actual data.

5.  Figure 9.27 shows a case where the disturbance occurs at the input to the plant

$$G_p(s) = \frac{1}{s(s + 1)}.$$

Consider the two compensators

$$G_{c1}(s) = \frac{K_c(s + 3)}{s + b} \quad \text{and} \quad G_{c2}(s) = \frac{K_c(s + 1.2)}{s + b}.$$

a.  For each compensator find $K_c$ and $b$ so that the dominant poles of the closed-loop system are at are at $s = -4 \pm j3$.

b.  Suppose the frequencies present in the disturbance are between 10 and 20 rad/s. For which compensator does the closed-loop system have the best noise rejection?

**Figure 9.27** | Disturbance at the plant input.

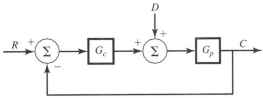

**6.** For the system of Fig. 9.27 let

$$G_p(s) = \frac{0.1}{s}.$$

Design a controller $G_c$ so that if the disturbance is a nonzero *constant* there will be zero steady state error to a unit step input.

# FURTHER READINGS

Bode, H. W. 1945. *Network Analysis and Feedback Amplifier Design.* Princeton, N.J.: D. Van Nostrand.

Chestnut, Harold, and R. W. Mayer. 1951. *Servomechanisms and Regulating Systems Design,* Vol. 1. New York: John Wiley & Sons.

D'Azzo, John J., and Constantine H. Houpis. 1988. *Linear Control System Design, Conventional and Modern.* New York: McGraw-Hill.

James, H. M., N. B. Nichols, and R. S. Phillips. 1947. *Theory of Servomechanisms.* New York: McGraw-Hill.

Ogata, K. 1970. *Modern Control Engineering.* Englewood Cliffs, N.J.: Prentice-Hall.

Saucedo, R., and E. E. Schiring, 1968. *Introduction to Continuous and Digital Control Systems.* New York: MacMillan.

# Chapter 10

# Nyquist Criterion

## 10.1 | OVERVIEW

In this chapter we introduce a method due to Nyquist for analyzing the stability of a closed-loop system. This analysis uses a a polar plot of the loop transfer function $GH$. As with the root locus analysis developed in Chapter 7, the idea is to use $GH$ to analyze the characteristic equation as

$$1 + GH = 0$$

of the *closed-loop system*. The reasons for taking this approach are the same as they were for root locus analysis, and are worth reviewing here.

For root locus analysis we recast the characteristic equation as

$$GH = -1 = 1\underline{/-180^\circ},$$

with $GH$ isolated on the left hand side of the equation. We then decomposed $GH$ into a magnitude and angle with the multiplicative gain $K$ as a scaling factor.

The Nyquist criterion is based on the evaluation of $GH$ around a closed curve, or contour, $\Omega$ in the $s$ plane that generates a second closed contour $\Gamma$ in the $GH$ plane. We then use $\Gamma$ to locate in the $s$ plane the zeros of $1 + GH$ for varying gain using a simple equation. This simple equation can be derived rigorously using complex variable theory and contour integration. It is formally known as the "principle of the arguments," but we will call it simply the Nyquist equation. By interpreting this equation we get the Nyquist criterion or test.

The development in the next sections differs somewhat from a "standard" treatment of the Nyquist criterion in that several alternatives to the standard contour in the $s$ plane are considered. The goal is to give the reader a better understanding, and appreciation, for Nyquist analysis. Additionally, some attention is given to relating Nyquist analysis to root locus analysis so that the student can see that these techniques are closely related and can be used in concert to better understand the stability of a closed-loop system.

## 10.2 | THE NYQUIST EQUATION

In this section we derive heuristically a simple equation that can be used to determine the stability of a closed-loop control system. At first glance, this equation appears to be rather trivial. However, Nyquist managed to turn it into a very powerful tool for analyzing the stability of control systems.

We begin by considering the function

$$F(s) = \frac{s - 0.5}{s(s-1)(s+4)}, \qquad \text{[10.1]}$$

where $s = \sigma + j\omega$ is a complex variable. Suppose $F$ is evaluated around the simple, circular closed contour $\Omega$ of radius 2.0 in the $s$ plane as shown in Fig. 10.1(a).

**Figure 10.1 |** (a) Curve $\Omega$ in the $s$ plane and (b) resulting curve $\Gamma$ in the $F$ plane.

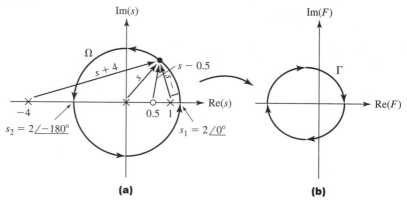

(a)                                            (b)

Evaluating $F$ at each point on $\Omega$ generates the closed contour $\Gamma$ shown in Fig. 10.1(b). The contour $\Gamma$ will be smooth because $F$ is a simple ratio of polynomials in the complex variable $s$ that is well defined along $\Omega$. Table 10.1 provides the values of $F$ at some key points along the contour $\Omega$. The closed contour $\Gamma$ could then be approximated by simply plotting and connecting these points. It is

**Table 10.1 |** Magnitude and phase of $F(s)$ along $\Omega$.

| $\theta$ | $F(2\underline{/\theta})$ |
|:---:|:---:|
| 0° | $0.125\underline{/0°}$ |
| 20° | $0.13\underline{/-20°}$ |
| 40° | $0.16\underline{/-48°}$ |
| 60° | $0.17\underline{/-81°}$ |
| 80° | $0.18\underline{/-180°}$ |
| 100° | $0.2\underline{/-138°}$ |
| 120° | $0.19\underline{/-162°}$ |
| 140° | $0.19\underline{/-175°}$ |
| 160° | $0.20\underline{/-179.7°}$ |
| 180° | $0.21\underline{/180°}$ |

worth noting that $\Gamma$ as shown in Fig. 10.1 is not drawn to scale. This is because it is the general shape of $\Gamma$ that is important, as will become clear as the discussion proceeds.

Several features in Fig. 10.1 deserve comment. First, both contours are closed. Second, the contour in the $s$ plane, where $F$ was evaluated, was traversed in the counterclockwise direction, and *encloses* the circular region in the $s$ plane. That is, the left hand of a person walking along the contour $\Omega$ in the counterclockwise direction would always point to the interior of the circular area. Further, the contour $\Gamma$ generated by the evaluation of $F$ along $\Omega$ evolves in the clockwise direction. Finally, the contour $\Gamma$ *encircles* the origin of the $F$ plane.

The distinction between enclosed and encircles would be of some import if we were to derive the Nyquist equation rigorously. As it is, we will get at the Nyquist equation through a heuristic proof and the distinction will not prove an issue. The important point is that we have to choose a direction in which to traverse $\Omega$ and that direction is important when we count the number of times $\Gamma$ encircles the orgin of the $F$ plane.

The choice of the left hand pointing to the interior of $\Omega$ is arbitrary. We could just as well have chosen to traverse $\Omega$ in the other direction keeping our right hand pointing to the interior of the closed contour.

Based on the forgoing discussion, the next goal is to determine from an examination of $\Gamma$ the number of poles and zeros of $F$ enclosed by $\Omega$. Doing this will require counting "encirclements" of the origin of the $F$ plane. To obtain the *exact* shape of $\Gamma$ requires the evaluation of $F$ at every point along $\Omega$. However, if each of the terms in $F$ is represented in polar form, as shown in Fig. 10.1(a), then the correct shape of $\Gamma$ can be obtained in seven steps with no computation.

1. As the evaluation of $F$ moves from $s_1 = 2\underline{/0^\circ}$ to $s_2 = 2\underline{/-180^\circ}$, each of the vectors *inside* $\Omega$ rotates counterclockwise through $180^\circ$.

2. During this evaluation from $s_1$ to $s_2$,
   a. The vectors $s$ and $s-1$ in the denominator of $F$ will each contribute $-180^\circ$ of phase to $F$.
   b. The vector $s-0.5$ in the numerator will contribute $180^\circ$ of phase to $F$.
   c. The vector $s+4$ in the denominator will contribute *no* net phase to $F$.

3. The net change in the phase of $F$ is $-180^\circ$ or a rotation of $180^\circ$ *clockwise*.

4. Thus the lower half of the contour $\Gamma$ in the $F$ plane is generated by evaluating $F$ along the *upper* half of $\Omega$.

5. The evaluation of $F$ from $s_2$ back to $s_1$ along the *lower* half of $\Omega$ generates the upper half of $\Gamma$. However, this portion of $\Gamma$ is simply the reflection through the real axis in the $F$ plane of the bottom half of $\Gamma$.

   This follows from the fact that the points on the bottom half of $\Omega$ are the *conjugates* of the points on the upper half of $\Omega$, and the fact that $F$ has real coefficients. Thus, $F(s^*) = F(s)^*$, and the plot $\Gamma$ is symmetric about the real axis in the $F$ plane.

   The net change in the phase of $F$ from the evaluation along the bottom half of $\Omega$ is another $-180^\circ$.

**6.**   The total net change in the phase of $F$ evaluated along $\Omega$ is $-360°$, or one encirclement of the origin of the $F$ plane.

**7.**   Along $\Omega$, all components of $F$ remain finite, and hence the contour in the $F$ plane will be finite in extent.

Having made this qualitative analysis, derived from a polar decomposition of $F$, it is possible to formulate a simple equation based on the contours $\Omega$ and $\Gamma$ that can be applied to any function $F$ expressible as a ratio of polynomials in $s$ with real coefficients. Let

**1.**   $N =$ the number of rotations or encirclements of $F$ about the origin of the $F$ plane in the direction that $\Omega$ was traversed in the $s$ plane (counterclockwise in this example).

**2.**   $Z =$ the number of zeros of $F$ *inside* the contour $\Omega$.

**3.**   $P =$ the number of poles of $F$ *inside* the contour $\Omega$.

Then

$$N = Z - P. \qquad \textbf{[10.2]}$$

In the case of the simple function being considered here, this formula yields

$$N = 1 - 2 = -1,$$

or one rotation in the direction *opposite* to that in which $\Omega$ was traversed.

This formula, which seems trivial, has great power when the contour $\Omega$ and the function $F$ are carefully chosen. In Section 10.3, we briefly discuss the Nyquist criterion, and then proceed in subsequent sections to put this test to work.

## 10.3 | THE NYQUIST CRITERION

To realize the potential of Eq. [10.2], we need to choose the right function $F$ to evaluate and the right contour $\Omega$ in the $s$ plane along which to evaluate that function. That was Nyquist's great contribution; he found the right function and the right contour. The function we will ultimately choose to evaluate is $GH$, the loop transfer function of a closed-loop system. Given this choice for $F$, and since we are interested in the stability of the closed-loop system, the natural choice for $\Omega$ will normally be a closed contour that encloses the right half of the $s$ plane, traversed in the clockwise direction. There are, however, other choices for $\Omega$.

Although the ultimate choice for $F$ will be $GH$, as a first step let

$$F(s) = 1 + GH(s).$$

Since our primary goal is stability analysis, $\Omega$ should either enclose the right half of the $s$ plane or the left half of the $s$ plane, as shown in Fig. 10.2. The traditional choice is the contour that encircles the right half plane, but both contours in the figure can, and will, be employed in our analysis.

The simple transfer function of Eq. [10.1] that we analyzed was already factored and the poles and zeros obvious. Reexamining Eq. [10.2], the next question is: what are the poles and zeros of $1 + GH$? The answer is essentially obvious, but worth

**Figure 10.2 |** Contours for evaluating the stability of $1 + GH = 0$.

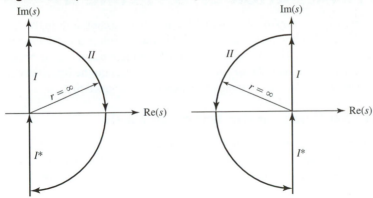

(a)                                         (b)

repeating. The zeros of $1 + GH$ are the solutions of the characteristic equation, that is, the *poles* of the closed-loop transfer function. The poles of $1 + GH$ are the poles of $GH$ because evaluating $1 + GH$ at one of the poles of $GH$ certainly makes both $GH$ and $1 + GH$ arbitrarily large.

The identification of the poles and zeros of $1 + GH$ is important because it must be understood that in the Nyquist equation $Z$ *represents the closed-loop poles*. This can be a source of some confusion, and the one way to keep it straight is to remember that $Z$ in the Nyquist equation stands for the zeros of the *characteristic equation* of the closed-loop transfer function.

To solve Eq. [10.2] it is necessary to know two of the three quantities in the equation. Because $P$ is always known, it is a matter of either knowing $N$ or $Z$. Since $Z$ represents the closed-loop poles, which change with $K$, the natural choice would seem to be $N$.

This is a viable choice because $N$ can be found by evaluating $1 + GH$ along $\Omega$. This is easy to do since $GH$ is known in factored form, with $K$ as a scaling factor. All that is required is to evaluate $GH$ along the contour $\Omega$ and add 1 to the result. Once the contour is drawn, the number of encirclements of the origin of the $1 + GH$ plane can be determined.

Finally, it seems pointless to add 1 to $GH$ at each evaluation. It is simpler to just plot $GH$ and count the encirclements of $-1$ in the $GH$ plane. To see this, suppose we generate a curve $\Gamma$, in the $1 + GH$ plane by evaluating $1 + GH$ along a closed contour $\Omega$ in the $s$ plane. If we now subtract 1 from each point on $\Gamma$ we simply translate the contour to the left by one. Then, any encirclement of the origin of the $1 + GH$ plane is an encirclement of $-1$ in the $GH$ plane. Thus, we always evaluate $GH(s)$ rather than $1 + GH(s)$. In doing so we make the polar plot completely compatible with the Bode magnitude and phase plots we analyzed in Chapter 9.

## 10.4 | EVALUATION OF *GH* ALONG $\Omega$

In this section we develop the skill of rapidly drawing the contour $\Gamma$ in the $GH$ plane. In doing so we bring into play many of the skills we developed in Chapter 9.

The evaluation of $GH$ along the contour $\Omega$ in the $s$ plane can be broken down into two cases: no poles on the imaginary axis and poles on the imaginary axis. The simpler case of no poles on the imaginary axis is investigated first.

### 10.4.1  No Poles on the Imaginary Axis

The evaluation of $GH$ necessary to complete the drawing of the contour $\Gamma$ in the $GH$ plane can, with a few exceptions, be decomposed into the evaluation of $GH$ along the three segments of the contour $\Omega$ shown in Fig. 10.2. The evaluation of $GH$ along the segment marked $I$ is simply Bode plot information. That is, the evaluation of $GH$ along segment $I$ generates the data for the Bode magnitude and phase plots of $GH$. Therefore, if the Bode magnitude and phase plots of $GH(j\omega)$ are available, then all that is required is to transfer the information to the polar plot in the $GH$ plane.

The evaluation of $GH$ along the segment of the contour marked $II$ is what might be called a "back of the envelope" calculation. Path segment $II$ is a semicircle of infinite radius. In almost all cases of interest, $GH$ has more poles than zeros. As a consequence

$$\lim_{|s| \to \infty} GH(s) = 0.$$

This means that along segment $II$, the magnitude of $GH$ almost always shrinks to zero. To get a better idea of what happens along segment $II$ of the contour, we first assume that the radius $R$ is very large, but not infinite. This case is shown in Fig. 10.3.

For $R$ very large, the evaluation of $GH$ along segment $II$ is equivalent to the evaluation of a system with $p_{ex}$ poles at the origin, where $p_{ex}$ is the pole-zero excess (pze) of $GH$. Thus, along segment $II$,

$$\underline{/GH(s)} = -p_{ex} \times \theta,$$

and as we evaluate $GH$ from $s = jR$ to $s = -jR$, the argument(angle) of $GH$ rotates

**Figure 10.3 |** Angle and magnitude contributions on segment $II$ of $\Omega$.

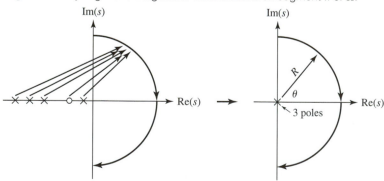

**Figure 10.4 |** Portion of contour Γ generated by evaluating *GH* along segment *II* of Ω.

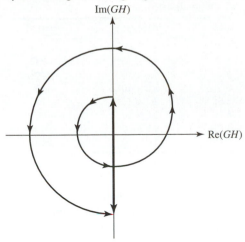

through

$$p_{ex} \times 180°,$$

in the *opposite* direction to that in which we traverse segment *II* of Ω.

Such a rotation is shown in Fig. 10.4 for a typical *GH*. In the figure, the length of *GH* has been varied to make it easier to follow the rotation. In this case the rotation is through 540°, indicating that $p_{ex} = 3$. The rotation is counterclockwise in the figure, indicating that Ω was traversed in the clockwise direction in the *s* plane.

As the radius *R* is made arbitrarily large, the magnitude of *GH* becomes arbitrarily small, and the length of the vector in Fig. 10.4 shrinks to zero. Thus, for the purposes of drawing Γ, the evaluation of *GH*(*s*) along segment *II* maps into the origin of the *GH* plane.

Finally, the portion of Γ generated by evaluating *GH* along segment *I\** is the mirror image of the portion of Γ generated by evaluating *GH* along segment *I*. As mentioned many times before, this happens because *GH* is a ratio of polynomials in *s* with *real* coefficients and hence $GH(s^*) = GH(s)^*$.

In summary, the closed contour Γ can be drawn by using Bode plot information and a simple back of the envelope calculation. The ideas just discussed are now illustrated with an example.

**EXAMPLE 10.4.1**

Let

$$GH(s) = \frac{K}{(s+1)(s+2)(s+10)}.$$

For this simple example, the portion of Γ generated by evaluating *GH* along

**Table 10.2** | Magnitude and phase of *GH* for selected frequencies, $K = 1$, for Example 10.4.1.

| $\omega$ | $|GH(j\omega)|$ | $\underline{/GH(j\omega)}$ |
|---|---|---|
| 0 | $5.0 \times 10^{-2}$ | $0^0$ |
| 1 | $3.1 \times 10^{-2}$ | $-77^0$ |
| 2 | $1.6 \times 10^{-2}$ | $-120^0$ |
| 5 | $3.3 \times 10^{-3}$ | $-173^0$ |
| 5.5 | $2.7 \times 10^{-3}$ | $-179^0$ |
| 5.7 | $2.5 \times 10^{-3}$ | $-180^0$ |
| 100 | $9.9 \times 10^{-7}$ | $-263^0$ |
| 1000 | $1.0 \times 10^{-9}$ | $-269^0$ |

segment *I* can be drawn by simply computing $GH(s)$ at a few key points as shown in Table 10.2. The data shown in the table is calculated for $K = 1$. In drawing the contour $\Gamma$, the choice of $K$ turns out to be arbitrary, since $K$ is simply a scaling factor, and thus can change the size but not the shape of the contour $\Gamma$.

The data in Table 10.2 could be extracted from the Bode magnitude and phase plots shown in Fig. 10.5. In this example, the Bode plots are not really needed, but in more complex cases they are extremely helpful in drawing the Nyquist plot.

**Figure 10.5** | Bode magnitude and phase plots for $GH(s) = \dfrac{1}{(s+1)(s+2)(s+10)}$.

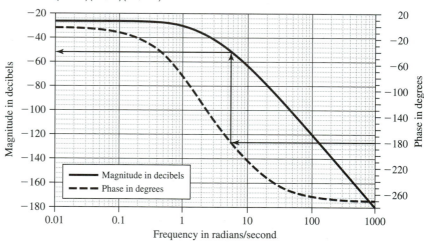

The data extracted from either the table or the Bode plots and plotted in the *GH* plane is shown in Fig. 10.6. For this simple case, an alternative approach is to use the qualitative magnitude and phase information available from Fig. 10.7. Note from

**Figure 10.6 |** Plot of $GH$ along segment I.

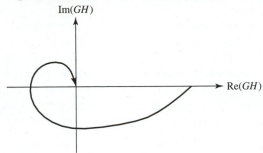

**Figure 10.7 |** Qualitative analysis of $GH$ along segment $I$ of $\Omega$.

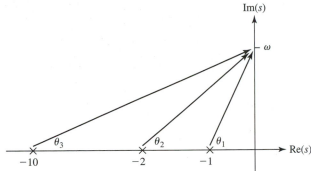

this figure that as $j\omega \rightarrow j\infty$,

$$GH(j\omega) = \frac{1}{(|s+1|\underline{/\theta_1})(|s+2|\underline{/\theta_2})(|s+10|\underline{/\theta_3})}$$

$$= \frac{1}{|s+1||s+2||s+10|\underline{/\theta_1+\theta_2+\theta_3}}$$

$$= \frac{1}{|s+1||s+2||s+10|}\underline{/-(\theta_1+\theta_2+\theta_3)}$$

$$\rightarrow 0\underline{/-270°}.$$

Thus, as we increase $\omega$ from zero toward larger and larger values along segment $I$, the vector $GH(j\omega)$ rotates clockwise through 270°, and its magnitude shrinks monotonically to zero.

The ability to make these qualitative assessments of the magnitude and phase of a transfer function from a polar decomposition of its components is very helpful in rapidly drawing the contour $\Gamma$ in the $GH$ plane.

The point of most importance on $\Gamma$ is that point where the contour crosses the negative real axis in the $GH$ plane. Here we need a precise value of the magnitude of $GH(j\omega)$. At this crossing point, $\underline{/GH} = -180°$. As we can see from table 10.2, this occurs for $s = j5.7$. This same information is available from the Bode magnitude plots.

A procedure for using the Bode magnitude and phase plots to find the point where the polar plot of $GH$ crosses the negative real axis is shown in Fig. 10.5. The first step is to find the value $-180°$ on the phase scale. Next we extend a horizontal line from $-180°$ on the phase scale until the line intersects the phase plot. Then we go vertically up to the magnitude plot and then horizontally to the left to the magnitude scale. The three arrows in the figure show the path taken. The Bode plots then yield the same information as the table, namely, that

$$GH(j5.7) = 10^{-52/20}\underline{/-180°} = 2.5 \times 10^{-3}\underline{/-180°}.$$

As we will see shortly, this point where $GH$ crosses the negative real axis is of pivotal importance.

The evaluation of $GH$ along segment $II$ is straightforward. The magnitude of $GH$ shrinks to zero and the angle of $GH$ rotates through

$$3 \times 180° = 540°$$

in the counterclockwise direction. The portion of $\Gamma$ generated by evaluating $GH$ along segment $I^*$ is simply the mirror image of $\Gamma$ from segment $I$, as shown in Fig. 10.8

**Figure 10.8 |** Completed Nyquist plot.

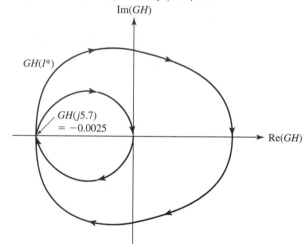

Note that for $K = 1$ the completed contour $\Gamma$ does not encircle the point $-1$ in the $GH$ plane. Thus $N = 0$. Further, all the poles of $GH$ are *outside* the contour $\Omega$ in the $s$ plane so that $P = 0$. Thus the Nyquist equation is

$$Z = N + P = 0 + 0 = 0.$$

Because $Z = 0$, for $K = 1$, there are no poles of the *closed-loop* transfer function *inside* the contour $\Omega$ in the $s$ plane. Since $\Omega$ encloses the right half of the $s$ plane, this means there are no closed-loop poles in the right half plane.

**Figure 10.9 |** Low gain root locus.

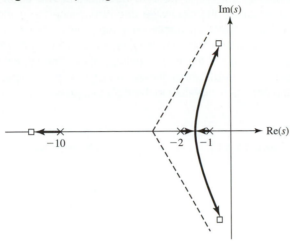

What could be called a "low-gain" root locus is shown in Fig. 10.9. As the gain increases, two of the closed-loop poles will migrate toward the asymptotes at ±60°, and for high enough gain, enter the right half plane. Thus a crucial question is: what is the gain that makes the closed-loop system unstable?

This question can be answered by noting that as $K$ increases, the contour Γ will expand in size, without changing shape, and eventually the point at which Γ crosses the negative real axis in the *GH* plane will touch, and then pass to the left of, the point −1. Once it passes the point −1, $N = 2$, as shown in Fig. 10.10.

The Nyquist equation is now

$$Z = N + P = 2 + 0 = 2.$$

**Figure 10.10 |** Nyquist plot for large gain.

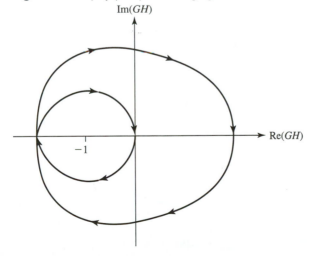

The two encirclements are called positive because, as the arrows indicate, the encirclements of −1 are in the clockwise direction. Since the contour $\Omega$ was traversed in the clockwise direction, clockwise is the *positive* direction. This indicates that there are two closed-loop poles inside $\Omega$, and thus in the right half of the $s$ plane. The *third* closed-loop pole is in the left half of the $s$ plane. This latter fact is clear from the root locus of Fig. 10.11(a), which shows one pole migrating toward $s = -\infty$ as $K \to \infty$, while the other two migrate into the right half plane.

**Figure 10.11 |** (a) Root locus and (b) Nyquist plot passes through −1 for $K = 400$.

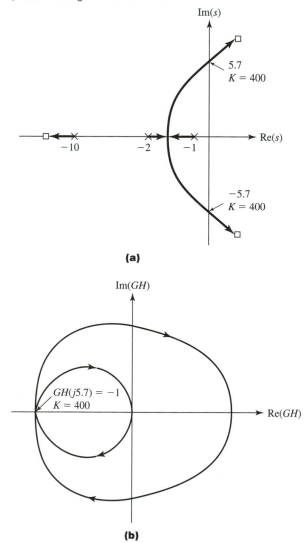

(a)

(b)

The final step is to determine the gain *K* that will cause the locus to just touch the point −1 in the *GH* plane. The value is 400, as shown in Fig. 10.11(b), and can be determined from Table 10.2. The point at which the plot of *GH* crosses the negative real axis for *K* = 1 is

$$|GH(j5.7)| = 0.0025\underline{/-180°}.$$

As *K* increases, this point on Γ moves toward −1 + *j*0 in the *GH* plane. When |*GH*(*j*5.7)| = 1, the closed-loop system has two poles on the imaginary axis and is on the brink of instability. Recall from the earlier root locus analysis that any point on the root locus satisfies the angle condition

$$\underline{/GH(s)} = -180°.$$

Hence, *s* = *j*5.7 is the point at which the root locus crosses the imaginary axis. This makes sense because this is the point at which the closed-loop system becomes unstable.

To find the gain *K* for which the closed-loop system has poles at *s* = ±*j*5.7, recall that for *K* = 1,

$$|GH(j5.7)| = 2.5 \times 10^{-3}.$$

Since *K* is simply a *scaling factor*,

$$|GH(j5.7)| = 1$$

for

$$K = \frac{1}{2.5 \times 10^{-3}} = 400.$$

We now summarize the analysis just completed.

1. For 0 < *K* < 400, the system is stable.
2. For *K* = 400, the closed-loop system has two poles on the imaginary axis.
3. For *K* > 400, the closed-loop system has two poles in the right half of the *s* plane and one pole in the left half of the *s* plane.
4. The root locus crosses the imaginary axis at *ω* = 5.7, that is, at the value of *ω* for which $\underline{/GH(j\omega)} = -180°$.

It must be said that the analysis just completed is out of step with that in most textbooks. The standard approach is to use counterclockwise as an absolute, rather than relative, positive direction, and to use a contour, traversed in the clockwise direction, that encloses the right half plane. If this is done, then the Nyquist equation must be rewritten as

$$Z = P - N, \hspace{4cm} \text{[10.3]}$$

since now, Ω is being traversed in one direction while encirclements are counted positive in the opposite direction. Thus, the encirclements are negative, and the evaluation of the Nyquist equation is

$$Z = P - N = 0 - (-2) = 2.$$

The choice of convention is really one of taste. The argument for using $Z = N + P$ is that there are a number of alternative $\Omega$ contours in the $s$ plane that can be employed. Thus, letting the direction in which $\Omega$ is traversed be the positive direction on $\Gamma$ is more flexible. As an illustration of this, the analysis is now repeated using an alternative contour.

Consider the contour in Fig. 10.2(b). It might surprise the reader to find that the Nyquist plot, namely, the contour $\Gamma$, is the same for this alternative $\Omega$. The difference is the interpretation of the Nyquist equation. In this case, $\Omega$ encloses the left half of the $s$ plane, or the region of stability, and is traversed in the counterclockwise direction. Thus, instead of being zero, $P$ is equal to three, because all three of the poles of $GH$ are enclosed by the contour $\Omega$. The encirclements of $-1$ in the $GH$ plane, however, remain clockwise.

For $k < 400$, there is no encirclement of $-1$ in the $GH$ plane, and

$$Z = N + P = 0 + 3 = 3,$$

and there are three closed-loop poles inside $\Omega$. However, since $\Omega$ encloses the left half of the $s$ plane, this means there are three closed-loop poles in the left half plane.

For $K > 400$, there are two clockwise encirclements of $-1$ in the $GH$ plane. Since $\Omega$ was traversed counterclockwise and the encirclements of $-1$ in the $GH$ plane are in the opposite direction, $N = -2$. Thus, the Nyquist equation is

$$Z = N + P = -2 + 3 = 1,$$

and there is one closed-loop pole inside $\Omega$, that is, one closed-loop pole in the left half of the $s$ plane. The other two closed-loop poles are not in the left half plane so they must be in the right half plane. As must be the case, the stability analysis yields the same answer, as long as the Nyquist equation is properly interpreted.

---

We have studied Example 10.4.1 in great detail because it contains almost all the important steps required to draw a Nyquist plot. Occasionally we encounter transfer functions that have one or two poles at the origin. This requires a slight modification to the contour we draw in the $s$ plane, as discussed next.

## 10.4.2  Poles on the Imaginary Axis

It is quite common for a transfer function to have one or two poles at $s = 0$. Poles on the imaginary axis away from the origin are a rare occurrence. Since they can be analyzed in the same way as poles at the origin, we will only consider the case of poles at the origin.

If $GH$ has poles at $s = 0$, then the contour $\Omega$ must be modified to avoid these poles, for $GH$ can not be evaluated at a point of singularity. The solution is to add a

**Figure 10.12** | Contours Ω in the *s* plane if *GH* has poles at *s* = 0.

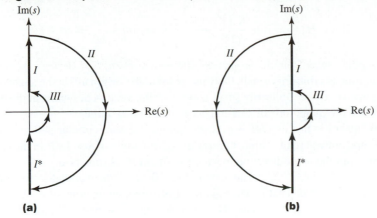

(a)   (b)

semicircular path of radius $\epsilon$, centered at $s = 0$, where $\epsilon$ is an arbitrarily small number. Two choices for Ω are shown in Fig. 10.12. Variations on these two choices could also be used.

The evaluation of *GH* along this semicircular path, labeled *III*, can best be understood by referring to Fig. 10.13. Suppose that *GH* has *k* poles at $s = 0$, then in factored form

$$GH(s) = \frac{K \prod_{i=1}^{m}(s + z_i)}{s^k \prod_{i=1}^{n-k}(s + p_i)}.$$

**Figure 10.13** | Segment *III* of Ω if *GH* has poles at *s* = 0.

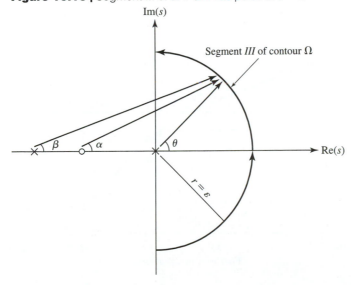

For any point on path segment *III*,

$$\lim_{\epsilon \to 0} GH(s) = \lim_{\epsilon \to 0} \frac{K \prod_{i=1}^{m}(s + z_i)}{s^k \prod_{i=1}^{n-k}(s + p_i)} = \lim_{\epsilon \to 0} \frac{1}{\epsilon \underline{/k\theta}} = \infty \underline{/-k\theta}.$$

The poles away from the origin contribute no angle to *GH* because the radius of the semicircle is arbitrarily small. Only the poles at the origin affect the angle of *GH*. At the same time, the arbitrarily small lengths of the vectors drawn from the poles at $s = 0$ cause the magnitude of *GH* to become arbitrarily large.

The upshot is that as *GH* is evaluated along the semicircular path of $\epsilon$ radius, *GH* sweeps out an arc of infinite radius through an angle of $k \times 180°$ in the *opposite* direction from the *local* direction in which segment *III* is traversed.

The word "local" is important here. In Fig. 10.12(a) the overall direction of travel along $\Omega$ is clockwise. That is, the right hand of someone walking along $\Omega$ points to the interior of the right half plane. However, *locally* on segment *III*, the direction of *rotation* is counterclockwise.

We now turn our attention to some examples as a way of illustrating these ideas.

**EXAMPLE 10.4.2**

Let

$$GH(s) = \frac{K}{s(s+4)(s+10)}.$$

The Bode magnitude and phase plots are shown in Fig. 10.14. We see that the magnitude is monotonically decreasing and the phase starts at $-90°$ and goes to $-270°$ as $\omega \to \infty$. The polar plot along segment *I* of $\Omega$ is shown in Fig. 10.15(a).

**Figure 10.14 |** Bode phase and magnitude plots for $GH(s) = \dfrac{100}{s(s+4)(s+10)}$.

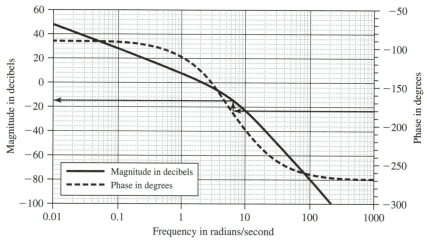

Frequency in radians/second

**Figure 10.15 |** (a) Segment *I* of Γ, (b) segments *I*, *II*, and *III* of Γ, and (c) complete contour Γ.

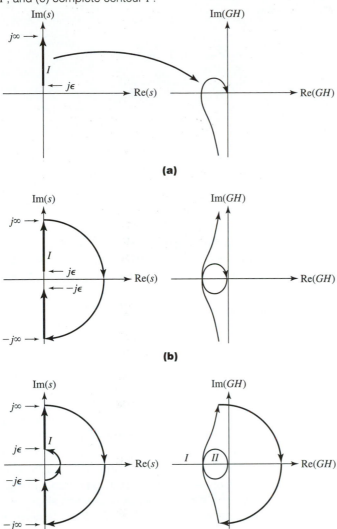

In the figure, the plot of *GH* does not touch the imaginary axis for ω close to zero. It would seem that it should since

$$\lim_{\omega \to 0} \underline{/GH(j\omega)} = -180°,$$

but the plot actually "flattens out" along an asymptote slightly to the left of the imaginary axis.

To see why, we find

$$\lim_{\omega \to 0} GH(j\omega) = \lim_{\omega \to 0} \frac{K}{(j\omega)(4 + j\omega)(10 + j\omega)}$$

$$= \lim_{\omega \to 0} \frac{K}{-14\omega^2 + j\omega(40 - \omega^2)}$$

$$= \lim_{\omega \to 0} \frac{K[-14\omega^2 - j\omega(40 - \omega^2)]}{14^2\omega^4 + \omega^2(40 - \omega^2)^2}$$

$$= \lim_{\omega \to 0} \frac{-14K\omega^2}{14^2\omega^4 + \omega^2(40 - \omega^2)^2} - \lim_{\omega \to 0} j\frac{K\omega(40 - \omega^2)}{14^2\omega^4 + \omega^2(40 - \omega^2)^2}$$

$$= -\frac{14K}{1600} - j\infty.$$

Thus, as $\omega \to 0$, the real part of $GH(j\omega)$ does not shrink to zero. However, it is still possible for

$$\lim_{\omega \to 0} GH(j\omega) = -180°,$$

since the real part is finite while the imaginary part becomes arbitrarily large.

The fact that the real part of $GH(j\omega)$ approaches a finite value as $\omega \to 0$ is of minor importance, because all we really want is the correct, overall shape of the plot of $GH$. The only point we need to know with precision is the point where $GH(j\omega)$ crosses the negative real axis. Thus, the sketch in Fig. 10.15 is designed to capture the shape of $\Gamma$ both far from the origin of the $GH$ plane, and near the origin. To accomplish this, the sketch has to be *qualitative* in nature. It's *exact* shape is not needed, as long as the overall shape is correct.

Returning to the task of drawing the complete contour $\Gamma$, we see that along segment *II*, the plot of $GH$ remains at the origin of the $GH$ plane. As we know, the mapping of $GH$ along segment *I** is the mirror image of that along segment *I*. Thus, after evaluating $GH$ along segments *I*, *II*, and *I**, $\Gamma$ has the shape shown in Fig. 10.15(b). All that remains is to evaluate $GH$ along segment *III* of $\Omega$.

$GH$ has one pole at $s = 0$. When we evaluate $GH$ along segment *III*, it will sweep out, in the $GH$ plane, an arc of infinite radius through 180° in a direction opposite to the *local* direction of rotation on segment *III* of $\Omega$. If the contour in Fig. 10.12(a) is used, then the arc will be swept out in the clockwise direction since the direction of *local* travel on segment *III* is counterclockwise. The completed Nyquist plot is shown in Fig. 10.15(c).

As discussed earlier, the point at which the contour $\Gamma$ crosses the negative real axis in the $GH$ plane is crucial. Using the Bode magnitude and phase plots, drawn for $K = 100$, we see that

$$|GH(j6.2)| = 10^{-15/20}\underline{/-180°} = 0.178\underline{/-180°}$$

Since $K$ is just a scaling factor of $GH$, if

$$K = 100 \times \frac{1}{0.178} = 562 \to 560,$$

then

$$GH(j6.2) = 1\underline{/-180°}.$$

**Table 10.3 |** Magnitude and phase of *GH* for selected frequencies.

| $\omega$ | $|GH(j\omega)|$ | $\underline{/GH(j\omega)}$ |
|---|---|---|
| 6.2 | 0.1858 | $-178.97°$ |
| 6.25 | 0.1828 | $-179.39°$ |
| 6.3 | 0.180 | $-179.8°$ |
| 6.32 | 0.1788 | $-179.96$ |
| 6.325 | 0.1785 | $-180°$ |

The values obtained from the Bode plots are approximate but still quite accurate. Table 10.3 gives the magnitude and angle of *GH* for values around 6.2 rad/s. Thus, for $K = 100$, $GH(j6.325) = 0.1785\underline{/-180°}$, whereas the Bode plots yielded $GH(j6.2) = 0.178$. The agreement is very close and the disparity of no real concern, because in practice, the actual gain of the closed-loop system will be much lower than the gain that places closed-loop poles on the imaginary axis in the *s* plane.

Note also that the frequency at which the root locus crosses the imaginary axis is very close to that from the previous example. The root loci in the two examples are very similar. The intersection of the asymptotes is nearly the same, and it is not surprising that the crossing point on the imaginary axis is close for the two examples. Indeed, for frequencies above 5 rad/s, the Nyquist plots are even similar. It is the pole at the origin that causes $\Gamma$ in this example to have infinite extent.

Returning to the current analysis, we note that for $K < 560$, and using the $\Omega$ contour of Fig. 10.12(a), the point $-1$ in the *GH* plane is in region *I*, and

$$Z = N + P = 0 + 0 = 0.$$

The system is stable because none of the closed-loop poles are inside $\Omega$, that is, in the right half of the *s* plane. For $K > 560$, the point $-1$ is in region *II*, for which $N = 2$, and

$$Z = N + P = 2 + 0 = 2,$$

so that two poles of the closed-loop system are in the right half plane.

We conclude this example with a repetition of the analysis, but using the contour of Fig. 10.12(b) for $\Omega$. As before the contour $\Gamma$ in the *GH* plane is identical to that of the previous example. However, since $\Omega$ encloses the left half of the *s* plane, the positive direction is counterclockwise. Any clockwise encirclements of $s = -1$ in the *GH* plane will be counted as negative. Thus for $K < 560$,

$$Z = N + P = 0 + 3 = 3,$$

and the system is stable because all three closed-loop poles are inside $\Omega$, that is, in the left half of the *s* plane. For $K > 560$, $N = -2$ since there are two clockwise encirclements of the point $-1$. Thus,

$$Z = N + P = -2 + 3 = 1,$$

and only one of the three closed-loop poles is inside the left half of the *s* plane. The other two, therefore, must be in the right half of the *s* plane.

Example 10.4.3 increases the number of poles of $GH$ at the origin to two. The changes in the Nyquist plot will be noted as the example unfolds.

**EXAMPLE 10.4.3**

Let

$$GH(s) = \frac{K(s+1)(s+8)}{s^2(s+10)(s+20)(s+25)}.$$

In this example there are two poles at $s = 0$, so that a contour that does not pass through $s = 0$, such as one of those in Fig. 10.12 must be used. The mapping of $GH$ along segment $I$ of $\Omega$ is shown in Fig. 10.16. Note that the sketch of $\Gamma$ in the $GH$ plane approaches but does not touch the negative real axis. Both the real and imaginary parts of $GH(j\omega)$ become arbitrarily large as $\omega \to 0$. However, the real part dominates the imaginary part, so that in the *qualitative* sketch, the contour is near but not on the real axis.

**Figure 10.16** | Contour along segment $I$.

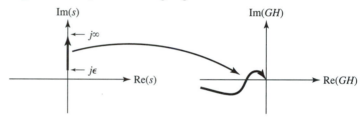

We can see this from the data in Table 10.4, which compares the magnitudes of the real and imaginary parts of $GH(j\omega)$ for very small $\omega$. As we see from table 10.2, the magnitude of the real part dominates the magnitude of the imaginary part.

**Table 10.4** | Comparison of real and imaginary parts of $GH(j\omega)$ for $K = 1$.

| $\omega$ radians/s | $1.0 \times 10^{-1}$ | $1.0 \times 10^{-2}$ | $1.0 \times 10^{-3}$ | $1.0 \times 10^{-4}$ | $1.0 \times 10^{-6}$ |
|---|---|---|---|---|---|
| Re$\{GH(j\omega)\}$ | $-1.6 \times 10^{-1}$ | $-1.6 \times 10^{1}$ | $-1.6 \times 10^{3}$ | $-1.6 \times 10^{7}$ | $-1.6 \times 10^{9}$ |
| Im$\{GH(j\omega)\}$ | $-1.5 \times 10^{-2}$ | $-1.5 \times 10^{-1}$ | $-1.5$ | $-1.5 \times 10^{1}$ | $-1.5 \times 10^{3}$ |

This means that if we plot $GH(I)$ using the same scale for both the real and imaginary axes, the contour plot would look like that shown in Fig. 10.17.

By contrast, the sketch as shown in Fig. 10.16 is drawn to capture, *qualitatively*, the *shape* of $\Gamma$ for both large $\omega$ and small $\omega$. The important features are that the contour does not touch the negative real axis as $\omega \to 0$, that the contour crosses the imaginary axis at a finite frequency, and that the contour approaches the origin at an angle of $-270°$, reflecting the fact that $GH$ has a pole-zero excess of three.

We can easily draw the portion of $\Gamma$ shown in Fig. 10.16 if we have the Bode plot of $GH$ for $K = 100$ shown in Fig. 10.18. The Bode plot is extremely useful in generating

**Figure 10.17** | *GH*( *I* ) as seen from far away.

the Nyquist plot because the scale compression provided by the logarithmic plot yields a global view of both the phase and magnitude.

**Figure 10.18** | Bode plot of $GH(s) = \dfrac{100(s+1)(s+8)}{s^2(s+10)(s+20)(s+25)}$.

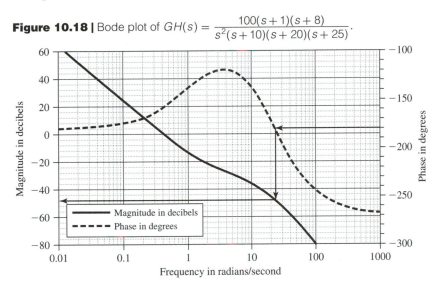

Note in the case of the magnitude plot that it drops precipitously at low frequencies, then levels off due to the presence of the two zeros, and then drops rapidly again as the final two poles begin to have an effect at higher frequencies. Values extracted from the Bode plot are shown in Table 10.5. For instance,

$$GH(j2) = -20 \text{ dB } \underline{/-126°}$$

$$= 10^{-20/20} \underline{/-126°}$$

$$= 0.1 \underline{/-126°}$$

The remaining values shown in Table 10.5 were obtained in the same way.

**Table 10.5** | Values of *GH* extracted from the Bode plot for Example 10.4.3.

| ω | 0.04 | 0.12 | 0.4 | 2 | 22 | 200 |
|---|---|---|---|---|---|---|
| $\|GH(j\omega)\|$ | 100 | 10 | 1 | 0.1 | 0.004 | $10^{-5}$ |
| $\underline{/GH(j\omega)}$ | −178° | −174° | −160° | −126° | −180° | −256° |

Of particular importance is

$$GH(j22) = 0.004 \underline{/-180°}$$

We conclude from the data that the root locus crosses the imaginary axis at $\omega = 22$ because $\underline{/GH(j22)} = -180°$.

We see from Fig. 10.18 that the frequency at which the phase equals $-180°$ can be found by extending a horizontal line from $-180°$ on the phase scale until it intersects the phase plot. It is also important to find $|GH(j22)|$. This magnitude is found by extending a vertical line upward to the magnitude plot and another line horizontally to the left to the magnitude scale. The three arrows in the figure show the path taken.

For $K = 100$, we see that

$$|GH(j22)| = 10^{-48/20} = 0.00398 \approx 0.004.$$

The gain required to place closed-loop poles at $s = \pm j22$ is the gain that makes $|GH(j22)| = 1$. Since $|GH(j22)| = 0.004$ for $K = 100$, the gain must be increased by a factor of

$$\frac{1}{0.004} = 250$$

to drive the two closed-loop poles onto the imaginary axis. Thus the gain to reach marginal stability is 25,000.

The completed Nyquist plot is shown in Fig. 10.19. The evaluation of $GH$ along the four segments of the $\Omega$ contour is shown in the figure. The mapping of most interest is that of part III. Along this portion of $\Omega$,

**Figure 10.19 |** Completed Nyquist plot, Example 10.4.3.

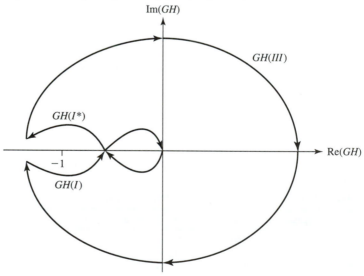

$$\lim_{\epsilon \to 0} GH(\epsilon \underline{/\theta}) = \lim_{\epsilon \to 0} \frac{8K}{(10)(20)(25)} \frac{1}{(\epsilon \underline{/\theta})(\epsilon \underline{/\theta})}$$

$$= \lim_{\epsilon \to 0} \frac{1}{(\epsilon \underline{/\theta})(\epsilon \underline{/\theta})}$$

$$= \infty \underline{/-2\theta}.$$

Thus, evaluating *GH* counterclockwise (locally) through 180° on segment *III* causes *GH* to sweep through an angle of $2 \times 180° = 360°$ in the opposite, or clockwise, direction. This rotation closes the contour $\Gamma$ in the *GH*-plane.

For $K < 25,000$, as shown in the figure, the point $-1$ in the *GH*-plane is not encircled, and

$$Z = P + N = 0 + 0 = 0,$$

indicating there are no closed-loop poles inside $\Omega$ in the *s* plane, that is, no closed-loop poles in the right half of the *s* plane, and hence the system is stable. If $K > 25,000$, then $-1$ lies inside the inner loop, and

$$Z = N + P = 2 + 0 = 2,$$

indicating there are two closed-loop poles inside $\Omega$, that is, in the right half of the *s* plane, and therefore the system is unstable.

For completeness, the Nyquist equation for the "standard" approach where counterclockwise is the absolute positive direction is included. In this approach, for $K > 25,000$,

$$Z = P - N = 0 - (-2) = 2,$$

and the result is the same. A *sketch* of the root locus, not to scale, is shown in Fig. 10.20.

**Figure 10.20** | Root locus for $GH(s) = \dfrac{K(s+1)(s+8)}{s^2(s+10)(s+20)(s+25)}$.

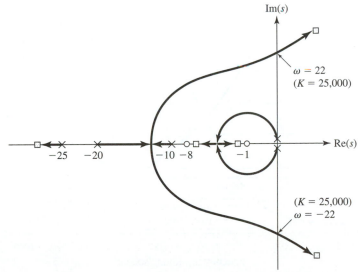

In the next example the number of poles at the origin is increased from two to three. In this case

$$\lim_{\omega \to 0} GH(j\omega) = \infty \underline{/-270°}.$$

If we let

$$\lim_{\omega \to 0} GH(j\omega)$$

be the "starting point" for drawing $GH(I)$, that portion of $\Gamma$ generated by evaluating $GH(j\omega)$ along segment $I$ of $\Omega$, then each time we add a pole at the origin to $GH$ the starting point rotates clockwise 90°. Thus, there are four possible starting positions for systems with poles at the origin, namely, $\infty\underline{/0°}$, $\infty\underline{/-90°}$, $\infty\underline{/-180°}$, and $\infty\underline{/-270°}$. It is hard to imagine a transfer function for a physical system that has more than three poles at the origin, and for that reason, only loop transfer functions with one, two, or three poles at $s = 0$ are considered in the examples of this chapter.

## EXAMPLE 10.4.4

Let

$$GH(s) = \frac{K(s+1)(s+4)}{s^3(s+20)(s+30)}.$$

The Bode magnitude and phase plots for $K = 100$ are shown in Fig. 10.21. The Nyquist plot $\Gamma$ is shown in Fig. 10.22. Because there are three poles at the origin,

$$\lim_{\epsilon \to 0} GH(j\epsilon) = \lim_{\epsilon \to 0} \frac{4K}{(20)(30)} \frac{1}{(\epsilon\underline{/90°})(\epsilon\underline{/90°})(\epsilon\underline{/90°})} = \infty \underline{/-270°}.$$

Thus, our starting point for plotting $GH(j\omega)$ along segment $I$ is $\infty\underline{/-270}$.

**Figure 10.21** | Bode plots of $GH(s) = \dfrac{100(s+1)(s+4)}{s^3(s+20)(s+30)}$.

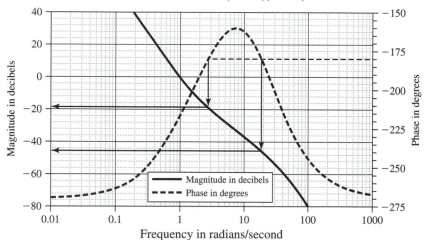

**Figure 10.22 |** Nyquist plot of $GH(s) = \dfrac{K(s+1)(s+4)}{s^3(s+20)(s+30)}$.

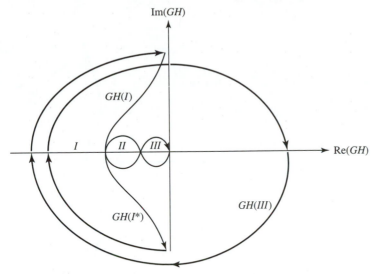

Additionally, since $p_{ex} = 3$, the plot of *GH* approaches the origin of the *GH* plane at an angle of $-270°$. That is,

$$\lim_{\omega \to \infty} GH(j\omega) = \lim_{\omega \to \infty} \frac{K}{(j\omega)^3} = \frac{K}{(\infty\underline{/90°})^3} = 0\underline{/-270°}.$$

We then add $GH(I^*)$, the mirror image of $GH(I)$ to the plot. Finally, we see that the evaluation of *GH* around part III of $\Omega$ causes the plot of *GH* to rotate through $3 \times -180° = -540°$ in the *GH* plane, thereby closing $\Gamma$.

From the Bode plot we see that $\underline{/GH(j\omega)} = -180°$ for both $\omega = 2.6$ rad/s and $\omega = 19$ rad/s. The respective values of $|GH(j\omega)|$ are 0.126 and 0.0063. Thus if the point $-1$ lies in region *II*, then

$$Z = N + P = 0 + (1 - 1) = 0.$$

In both regions 1 and 3 the Nyquist equation is

$$Z = N + P = 2 + 0 = 2$$

Thus, the system is stable if

$$\frac{100}{0.126} < K < \frac{100}{0.0063},$$

or

$$794 < K < 15{,}849.$$

Note that the closed-loop system is low gain unstable as shown in the root locus plot of Fig. 10.23.

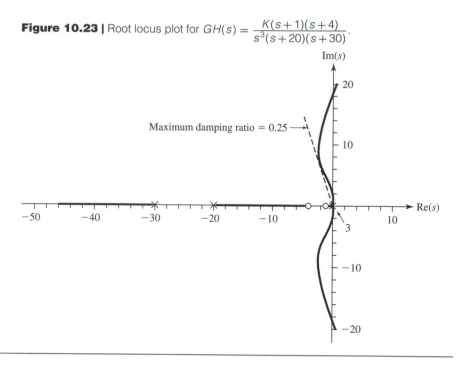

**Figure 10.23** | Root locus plot for $GH(s) = \dfrac{K(s+1)(s+4)}{s^3(s+20)(s+30)}$.

Although the system appears to be stable over a reasonably wide range of gains, roughly from $K = 800$ to $K = 15{,}000$, the root locus shows that the two complex poles that will dominate the behavior of the closed-loop system *never* have a large damping ratio. This would indicate that no matter what gain is chosen, the system response to, say a step input, will be oscillatory. The discussion in Section 10.5 will show that the same conclusion could be drawn from the Nyquist plot, or the Bode plot, without ever drawing the root locus.

## 10.5 | GAIN MARGIN AND PHASE MARGIN

The Nyquist plot yields two figures of merit that we will use with the Bode design techniques developed in Chapter 11: gain margin and phase margin. We have already encountered gain margin in an indirect way in our discussion of the Nyquist criterion. Gain margin is the factor by which the gain must be increased to make the closed-loop system marginally stable, that is, make the Nyquist plot pass through the point $-1$ in the $GH$ plane. In most cases, the larger the gain margin, the more stable the system.

However, a large gain margin by itself does not guarantee good system stability. We need to consider both gain margin and a second figure of merit called phase margin. By looking at both phase margin and gain margin we can almost always get an accurate assessment of system stability. Trying to gauge system stability from gain margin or phase margin alone often leads to the wrong conclusion about stability.

To define and understand phase margin, we begin by reconsidering Example 10.4.2. In this example, with $K = 100$,

$$GH(j6.2) = 10^{-15/20}\underline{/-180°} = 0.1785\underline{/-180°}.$$

The gain margin (GM), the amount by which we can increase the gain so that

$$|GH(j6.2)| = 1,$$

is

$$GM = \frac{1}{0.1785} = 5.6.$$

That is, we can increase the gain a factor of 5.6 before the system becomes unstable. The phase margin $\phi_m$, *for this same value of gain, namely, 100,* is shown in Fig. 10.24. It is determined by finding the frequency $\omega_m$ for which

$$|GH(j\omega_m)| = 1,$$

and then finding the angle between $GH(j\omega_m)$ and the negative real axis. This information can be found from Fig. 10.14. The magnitude plot of $GH$ crosses the 0-dB line at $\omega = 2$ rad/s. We see that

$$GH(j2) = 1\underline{/-130°}.$$

Thus,

$$\phi_m = 180° + \underline{/GH(j2)} = 180° - 130° = 50°.$$

We will find in Chapter 11 that to ensure a stable, nonoscillatory response we must normally require

$$\phi_m \geq 50°.$$

For the system of Example 10.4.2, with $K = 100$, we have both an adequate phase

**Figure 10.24 |** Definition of phase margin $\phi_m$.

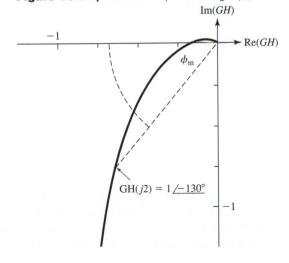

margin and a decent gain margin of 5.6. Thus, both gain margin and phase margin are telling us, that for $K = 100$ the system is stable and will not exhibit much oscillation in response to a step input.

Now consider the system from Example 10.4.4, whose Bode phase and magnitude plots are shown in Fig. 10.21. Suppose we increase the gain by 22 dB so that the system is stable and the gain margin is 20 dB. Lifting the magnitude plot up by 22 dB yields

$$GH(j4) \approx 1\underline{/-170°},$$

yielding

$$\phi_m = 180° - 170° = 10°.$$

As we will discover in Chapter 11, the system response will be very oscillatory, because we have very little phase margin. Thus, even though we have plenty of gain margin, the system will not respond well to a step input. In this case, gain margin and phase margin are not telling us the same thing. Gain margin indicates the system is very stable, but phase margin indicates that the response will be very oscillatory. For this system, phase margin is the correct indicator of system stability. In fact, further examination of Fig. 10.21 tells us that the *maximum* phase margin we can achieve is about 20°.

If we now reexamine the root locus for this system (shown in Fig. 10.23), we see that we can correlate the low *maximum* phase margin of the system with a low *maximum* damping ratio. In Chapter 11, we will see that there is a very strong correlation between the phase margin of the loop transfer function and the effective damping ratio of the dominant poles of the closed-loop system. Once again, we will have found a way to predict the time response of the closed-loop system from a figure of merit, namely, phase margin, which is obtained from the loop transfer function.

## 10.6 | THE LOG MAGNITUDE PLOT

In Chapter 11 we initiate our study of design using Bode plots. One very important advantage that the Bode plot has over the polar plot is scale compression. As we will see in Chapter 11, this scale compression is very important. This begs the question: why not a logrithmic polar plot?

Such a plot does exist and is called a log magnitude plot. On a log magnitude plot, $20 \log_{10} |GH(j\omega)|$ is plotted along the the vertical axis, and $\underline{/GH(j\omega)}$, in degrees, is plotted along the horizontal axis. Consider for example the loop transfer function

$$GH(s) = \frac{100}{s(s + 4)(s + 10)}$$

from Example 10.4.2. The log magnitude plot is shown in Fig. 10.25. Note that the plot passes under the point $(-180°, 0 \text{ dB})$, the "black dot" on the log magnitude plot that corresponds to the point $-1$ in the $GH$ plane.

One of the disadvantages of the log magnitude plot is that frequency is not shown explicitly, and the log magnitude plot by itself does not offer any advantage over the Bode phase and magnitude plots. However, we can make the log magnitude into a very useful design tool by turning it into a Nichols chart. To do so, we have to first

**Figure 10.25** | Log magnitude plot of $GH(s) = \dfrac{100}{s(s+4)(s+10)}$.

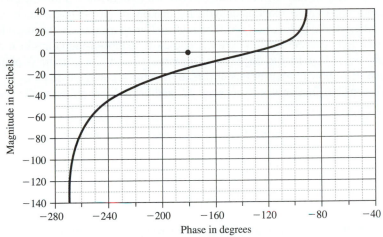

consider the so-called loci of constant $M$ and constant phase in the $GH$ plane. These loci are most useful, and also easier to understand, for the unity feedback case. The development in Sections 10.6.1, 10.6.2, and 10.6.3 assumes unity feedback.

### 10.6.1  Constant *M* Loci

We begin with a historical note and a comment about notation. Historically, the notation

$$M(s) = \frac{G(s)}{1 + G(s)}$$

has been used. We mention this because the reader may encounter this notation, especially in some of the older books on control. As we will see shortly, this usage leads to a slightly ambiguous notation. We simply point out here that

$$M(s) \equiv T_c(s).$$

Letting $s = j\omega$, we then have

$$M(j\omega) = \frac{G(j\omega)}{1 + G(j\omega)} = Me^{j\phi},$$

where

$$M = \frac{|G(j\omega)|}{|1 + G(j\omega)|} \quad \text{and} \quad \phi = \left/\frac{G(j\omega)}{1 + G(j\omega)}\right..$$

We see that the notational waters are a little muddy here because we are using $M(s)$ for the closed-loop transfer function and $M$ for the magnitude of this same function. What we really mean, of course, is that

$$T_c(j\omega) = Me^{j\phi}.$$

Having clarified the notation, to the extent that it can be clarified, we now proceed.

We are interested in plotting curves of constant magnitude $M$ and curves of constant phase $\phi$ in the $G$ plane. In other words, we want to transfer information about the closed-loop transfer function onto the log magnitude plot so that it can be used to better understand the plot of $G(j\omega)$. The information of most use is the magnitude of the closed-loop transfer function and the phase of the closed-loop transfer function. We first decide how best to display this information and plot it in the $G$ plane. We will then show how to transfer this information to the log magnitude plot.

We consider first curves of constant $M$, and begin by simplifying the notation. Let

$$G(j\omega) = \mathrm{Re}\{G(j\omega)\} + j\,\mathrm{Im}\{G(j\omega)\} = x + jy.$$

Then, for a particular $\omega$

$$M = \frac{\sqrt{x^2 + y^2}}{\sqrt{(1+x)^2 + y^2}}.$$

Squaring both sides, cross-multiplying, and rearranging, we arrive at

$$x^2 + \frac{2M^2}{M^2 - 1}x + y^2 = \frac{-M^2}{M^2 - 1}.$$

Then adding

$$\left[\frac{M^2}{(M^2 - 1)}\right]^2$$

to both sides to complete the square on $x$, yields

$$\left[x + \frac{M^2}{M^2 - 1}\right]^2 + y^2 = \frac{M^2}{(M^2 - 1)^2}. \qquad \textbf{[10.4]}$$

Equation [10.4] is the equation of a circle with center

$$\left(\frac{-M^2}{M^2 - 1},\ 0\right),$$

and radius

$$r = \left[\frac{M^2}{(M^2 - 1)^2}\right]^{1/2} = \left|\frac{M}{M^2 - 1}\right|.$$

These circles of constant $M$ are shown in Fig. 10.26.

By adding circles of constant $M$ to the polar plot of $GH(j\omega)$, we can determine the maximum value of the magnitude of $M(j\omega)$. This maximum is an accurate measure of the stability of the closed-loop system. To achieve scale compression we need to transfer the $M$ circles to the log magnitude plot. Once we have done so, we have the better part of a Nichols chart. However, a Nichols chart also shows the curves of constant phase for the closed-loop transfer function, so our next task is to find those curves.

**Figure 10.26 |** *M* circles in the *G* plane.

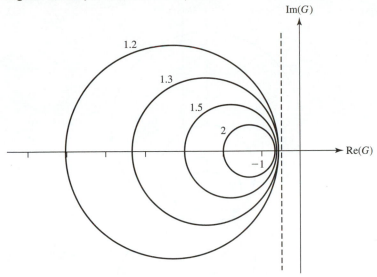

## 10.6.2  Loci of Constant Phase

The argument of $M(j\omega)$ is

$$\phi = \left/\underline{\frac{x + jy}{(1 + x) + jy}} \right. = \tan^{-1}\frac{y}{x} - \tan^{-1}\frac{y}{1 + x}.$$

Then, using the trigonometric identity

$$\tan(\alpha - \beta) = \frac{\tan\alpha - \tan\beta}{1 + \tan\alpha\tan\beta},$$

we can write

$$\tan\phi = \frac{y}{x^2 + x + y^2}.$$

Then, following tradition, we let $\tan\phi = N$, and rearrange the last equation as

$$x^2 + x + y^2 - \frac{y}{N} = 0.$$

We then complete the square on both $x$ and $y$ to obtain

$$\left(x + \frac{1}{2}\right)^2 + \left(y - \frac{1}{2N}\right)^2 = \frac{N^2 + 1}{4N^2}. \qquad\qquad \textbf{[10.5]}$$

Eq. 10.5 is the equation of a circle with center

$$\left(-\frac{1}{2}, \ \frac{1}{2N}\right),$$

**Figure 10.27 |** Constant $\phi$ circles in the $G$ plane.

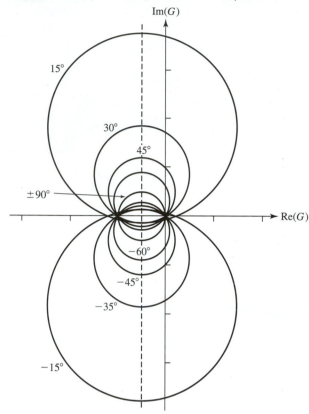

and radius

$$r = \frac{1}{2}\sqrt{1 + 1/N^2}.$$

The loci of constant phase for some representative values of $\phi$ are shown in Fig. 10.27.

### 10.6.3  The Nichols Chart

If we add the loci of constant $M$ and constant $\phi$ to the log magnitude chart, we have a Nichols chart, named for the illustrious control engineer Nathaniel "Nick" Nichols. Such a plot is shown in Fig. 10.28. By way of illustration, the loop transfer function

$$G(s) = \frac{100}{s(s + 4)(s + 10)}$$

has been added to the chart. We note that as discussed earlier, we are assuming that $H = 1$.

The reader may wonder how the loci of constant magnitude and phase are transferred to the log magnitude plot. The process is straightforward, but tedious. We

**Figure 10.28 |** Nichols chart with plot of $G(s) = \dfrac{100}{s(s+4)(s+10)}$.

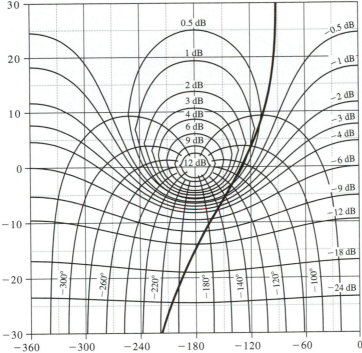

explain it for the case of circles of constant $M$. The procedure is similar for the circles of constant $\phi$.

Referring to Fig. 10.29, we see that any point $\rho e^{j\gamma}$ on a particular $M$ circle can be expressed as $re^{j\phi}$.

If we choose a specific $M$, then we know

$$r = \left| \frac{M}{M^2 - 1} \right|.$$

Given $r$, if we now choose a value of $\phi$ we can find the corresponding $\rho$ and a $\gamma$. We then plot the point $(\gamma, 20\log_{10}\rho)$ on the Nichols chart. Thus, by fixing $r$, and choosing enough values of $\phi$ between $0°$ and $-360°$, we can generate the points of the $M$ circle in terms of $20\log_{10}\rho$ and $\gamma$ and transfer them to the log magnitude plot. This is easy enough to do using MATLAB or a similar computational tool. The procedure for transferring the circles of constant phase is similar.

We will not make much use of the Nichols chart, although we will discuss it briefly via an example in Chapter 11. However, it continues to have advocates, and for that reason we have included it here.

**Figure 10.29 |** *M* circles in the *G* plane.

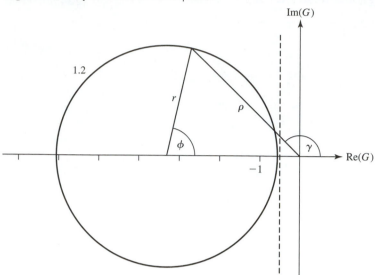

## 10.7 | REPRISE

The development of the Nyquist criterion for stability opens the way for the Bode design techniques discussed in Chapter 11. Strictly speaking, this chapter is not a necessary precursor to Bode design and could have been omitted or relegated to an appendix. This seems too harsh a fate for such an elegant idea. It is very instructive to see how Nyquist turned a seemingly trivial equation,

$$N = Z - P,$$

into an exceptionally powerful analysis tool, simply by an insightful choice of the function to evaluate and the contour on which to do the evaluation.

Another reason for pausing to discuss Nyquist theory is that it proves very useful in understanding systems of the form

$$G(s) = \frac{e^{-\tau s} K \prod_{i=1}^{m} (s + z_i)}{\prod_{i=1}^{n} (s + p_i)}.$$

The term $e^{-\tau s}$ represents a delay or "transportation lag." This term changes a system with a finite number of poles into a system with a countably infinite number of poles. The easiest way to see this is by drawing a Nyquist plot.

We will also make extensive use of the Nyquist criterion in Chapter 12 when we introduce robust control. There the geometric insight we have gained in this chapter will stand us in good stead.

Finally, the Nyquist criterion can be extended to a broader class of systems that have simple nonlinearities. It is particularly valuable for those nonlinearities that are susceptible to describing function analysis. For this reason alone, Nyquist theory deserves the attention we have given it.

# 10.8 | PROBLEMS

## 10.8.1  Nyquist Problems Standard Contour

For each loop transfer function $GH$, draw the Nyquist plot for the contour that encircles the right half of the $s$ plane in the clockwise direction (right hand points into interior of contour). Find the range of gain for which the closed-loop system is stable and draw the root locus, indicating where the locus crosses the imaginary axis.

**1.** $\dfrac{K(s+4)}{(s+2)(s-1)}$        **2.** $\dfrac{K(s+4)}{(s+2)(s-1)}$

**3.** $\dfrac{K(s+3)}{(s-1)(s-2)}$        **4.** $\dfrac{K(s+3)}{(s+1)(s-1)}$

**5.** $\dfrac{K(s+1)}{s^2(s+2)(s+3)}$        **6.** $\dfrac{K(s+2)}{s^3(s+6)}$

**7.** $\dfrac{K(s+2)(s+3)}{s^3(s+40)(s+50)}$        **8.** $\dfrac{K}{s^3(s+10)}$

**9.** $\dfrac{K(s+2)}{s^2(s+1)(s+10)}$        **10.** $\dfrac{K(s+2)}{s(s+1)(s+10)(s+40)}$

**11.** $\dfrac{K(s+1)}{s(s+4)(s+10)(s+40)}$        **12.** $\dfrac{K(s+2)}{s(s+1)(s+10)(s+40)}$

**13.** $\dfrac{K(s+4)}{s^2(s+6)(s+20)}$        **14.** $\dfrac{K(s+4)}{s^2(s+10)(s+20)}$

**15.** $\dfrac{K(s+2)}{s^2(s+5)(s+30)}$        **16.** $\dfrac{K(s+1)}{s^2(s+4)(s+20)}$

**17.** $\dfrac{100(s+3)(s+7)}{s^2(s+5)(s+8)(s+20)}$        **18.** $\dfrac{K(s+2)}{s^2(s+1)(s+20)}$

**19.** $\dfrac{K(s+2)}{s(s+4)(s+8)(s+20)}$        **20.** $\dfrac{K(s+1)}{s^2(s+2)(s+40)}$

**21.** $\dfrac{K(s+1)}{s^2(s+2)(s+10)}$        **22.** $\dfrac{K(s+2)}{[(s+1)^2+1](s+20)(s+40)}$

## 10.8.2  Nyquist Problems—Nonstandard Contour 1

For each loop transfer function $GH$, draw the Nyquist plot for the contour of Fig. 10.30(a). Find the range of gain for which the closed-loop system is stable and draw the root locus, indicating where the locus crosses the imaginary axis.

**1.** $\dfrac{K(s+4)}{(s+2)(s-1)}$        **2.** $\dfrac{K(s+4)}{(s+2)(s-1)}$

**3.** $\dfrac{K(s+3)}{(s-1)(s-2)}$        **4.** $\dfrac{K(s+3)}{(s+1)(s-1)}$

**5.** $\dfrac{K(s+1)}{s^2(s+2)(s+3)}$        **6.** $\dfrac{K(s+2)}{s^3(s+6)}$

**7.** $\dfrac{K(s+2)(s+3)}{s^3(s+40)(s+50)}$        **8.** $\dfrac{K}{s^3(s+10)}$

**Figure 10.30 |** Alternative Ω contours.

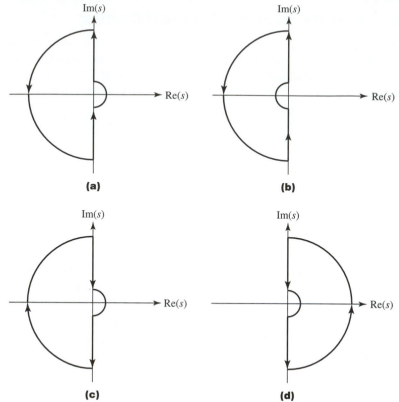

(a)

(b)

(c)

(d)

### 10.8.3   Nyquist Problems—Nonstandard Contour 2

For each of these loop transfer functions $GH$, draw the Nyquist plot for the contour of Fig. 10.30(b). Find the range of gain for which the closed-loop system is stable and draw the root locus, indicating where the locus crosses the imaginary axis.

**1.** $\dfrac{K(s+4)}{(s+2)(s-1)}$

**2.** $\dfrac{K(s+4)}{(s+2)(s-1)}$

**3.** $\dfrac{K(s+3)}{(s-1)(s-2)}$

**4.** $\dfrac{K(s+3)}{(s+1)(s-1)}$

**5.** $\dfrac{K(s+1)}{s^2(s+2)(s+3)}$

**6.** $\dfrac{K(s+2)}{s^3(s+6)}$

**7.** $\dfrac{K(s+2)(s+3)}{s^3(s+40)(s+50)}$

**8.** $\dfrac{K}{s^3(s+10)}$

### 10.8.4   Nyquist Problems—Nonstandard Contour 3

For each loop transfer function $GH$, draw the Nyquist plot for the contour of Fig. 10.30(c). Find the range of gain for which the closed-loop system is stable and draw the root locus, indicating where the locus crosses the imaginary axis.

1. $\dfrac{K(s+2)}{s^2(s+1)(s+10)}$

2. $\dfrac{K(s+2)}{s(s+1)(s+10)(s+40)}$

3. $\dfrac{K(s+1)}{s(s+4)(s+10)(s+40)}$

4. $\dfrac{K(s+2)}{s(s+1)(s+10)(s+40)}$

5. $\dfrac{K(s+4)}{s^2(s+6)(s+20)}$

6. $\dfrac{K(s+4)}{s^2(s+10)(s+20)}$

7. $\dfrac{K(s+2)}{s^2(s+5)(s+30)}$

8. $\dfrac{K(s+1)}{s^2(s+4)(s+20)}$

### 10.8.5 Nyquist Problems—Nonstandard Contour 4

For each loop transfer function $GH$, draw the Nyquist plot for the contour of Fig. 10.30(d). Find the range of gain for which the closed-loop system is stable and draw the root locus, indicating where the locus crosses the imaginary axis.

1. $\dfrac{100(s+3)(s+7)}{s^2(s+5)(s+8)(s+20)}$

2. $\dfrac{K(s+2)}{s^2(s+1)(s+20)}$

3. $\dfrac{K(s+2)}{s(s+4)(s+8)(s+20)}$

4. $\dfrac{K(s+1)}{s^2(s+2)(s+40)}$

5. $\dfrac{K(s+1)}{s^2(s+2)(s+10)}$

6. $\dfrac{K(s+2)}{(s+1+j)(s+1-j)(s+20)(s+40)}$

### 10.8.6 Phase Margin versus Gain Margin

For each loop transfer function, draw the Nyquist plot for the contour that encircles the right half of the $s$ plane in the clockwise direction (right hand points into interior of contour). Find the range of gain for which the closed-loop system is stable. Determine whether phase margin or gain margin is clearly superior as an indicator of the stability of the system, or whether both are equally good indicators.

1. $\dfrac{K(s+8)}{s^2(s+9)(s+20)}$

2. $\dfrac{K}{s(s+1)(s+5)}$

3. $\dfrac{K(s+0.5)}{s^2(s+10)}$

4. $\dfrac{K(s+5)}{s(s+0.5)(s+4)(s+10)}$

5. $\dfrac{K}{(s+1)(s+2)(s+5)}$

6. $\dfrac{K}{s(s+5)^2}$

7. $\dfrac{K(s+1)}{(s+2)^2(s+6)(s+20)}$

8. $\dfrac{K(s+10)}{(s+1)(s+2)^2(s+4)}$

### 10.8.7 Inverse Polar Plot

The characteristic equation can be rewritten as

$$1 + GH^{-1}(s) = 0.$$

It is possible, and sometimes preferable to do the Nyquist analysis using $GH^{-1}(s)$. For each loop transfer function $GH$, draw the Nyquist plot for the contour that encircles the right half of the $s$ plane in the clockwise direction (right hand points into interior of contour). Find the range of gain for which the closed-loop system is stable and draw the root locus, indicating where the locus crosses the imaginary axis.

1. $\dfrac{K(s+4)}{(s+2)(s-1)}$

2. $\dfrac{K(s+4)}{(s+2)(s-1)}$

3. $\dfrac{K(s+3)}{(s-1)(s-2)}$

4. $\dfrac{K(s+3)}{(s+1)(s-1)}$

5. $\dfrac{K(s+1)}{s^2(s+2)(s+3)}$

6. $\dfrac{K(s+2)}{s^3(s+6)}$

7. $\dfrac{K(s+2)(s+3)}{s^3(s+40)(s+50)}$

8. $\dfrac{K}{s^3(s+10)}$

9. $\dfrac{K(s+2)}{s^2(s+1)(s+10)}$

10. $\dfrac{K(s+2)}{s(s+1)(s+10)(s+40)}$

### 10.8.8   Nichols Chart

For each loop transfer function $GH$, draw the Nichols chart and find the range of gain for which the system is stable *from the Nichols chart*.

1. $\dfrac{K(s+5)}{s(s+4)(s+10)(s+40)}$

2. $\dfrac{K(s+1)}{s(s+2)(s+10)(s+40)}$

3. $\dfrac{K}{s^2(s+6)(s+20)}$

4. $\dfrac{K(s+4)}{s^2(s+15)(s+20)}$

5. $\dfrac{K(s+1)}{s^2(s+5)(s+30)}$

6. $\dfrac{K(s+10)}{s^2(s+4)(s+20)}$

7. $\dfrac{100(s+3)(s+5)}{s^2(s+10)(s+15)(s+20)}$

8. $\dfrac{K(s+8)}{s^2(s+1)(s+20)}$

9. $\dfrac{K}{s(s+4)(s+8)(s+20)}$

10. $\dfrac{K(s+10)}{s^2(s+2)(s+50)}$

11. $\dfrac{K(s+1)}{s^2(s+10)^2}$

12. $\dfrac{K(s+5)}{[(s+1)^2+1](s+20)(s+40)}$

### 10.8.9   Additional Problems

1. Use MATLAB to write a program to draw the log magnitude plot for

$$GH(s) = \frac{K(s+1)}{s(s+4)^2(s+20)}.$$

Note: this does not have to be an elaborate program. It shouldn't take more than 40 lines at most.

2. Add to the program of Problem 1 of this section so that the log magnitude plot includes the constant $M$ curve for $M = 1.2$. If you want, make the program plot a useful family of constant $M$ curves.

3. Add to the program of Problem 1 of this section so that the log magnitude plot includes the constant $\phi$ curve for $\phi = -120°$. If you want, make the program plot a useful family of constant $\phi$ curves.

4. For unity feedback let

$$G_c G_p(s) = \frac{K(s+3)}{s(s+1)(s+18)}.$$

Use Nyquist theory to find the range of gain $K$ for which the *dominant* closed-loop system poles are within the shaded region shown in Fig. 10.31.

**Figure 10.31** | Closed-loop pole in shaded region.

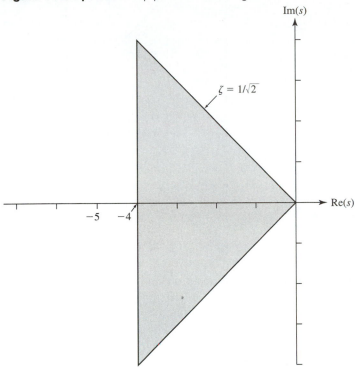

5. For unity feedback let

$$G_c G_p(s) = \frac{K(s+2)}{s(s+1)(s+10)}.$$

Use Nyquist theory to find the range of gain $K$ for which the *dominant* closed-loop system poles are within the shaded region shown in Fig. 10.32.

6. Let

$$GH(s) = \frac{K(s+2)}{s(s+1)(s+40)}.$$

Use Nyquist theory to find the range of gain $K$ for which *all* closed-loop system poles are within the shaded region shown in Fig. 10.33.

7. For each of the examples from Chapter 7 listed here, draw the Nichols chart. Then find (a) the ratio of the peak value of the time response to the steady state

**Figure 10.32 |** Closed-loop pole in shaded region.

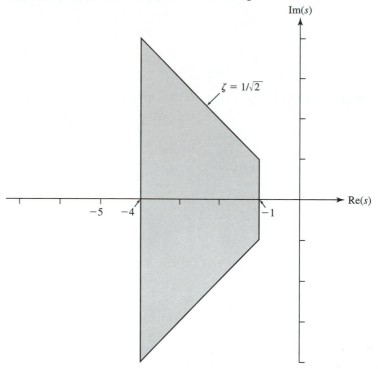

**Figure 10.33 |** Closed-loop pole in shaded region.

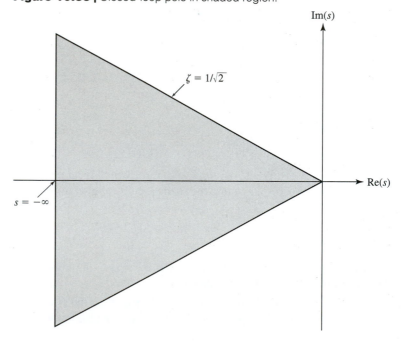

value of the time response and (b) the ratio of the peak value of $|M(j\omega)|$ to $|M(j0)|$. How do these ratios compare?

   a.  Example 7.3.1    b.  Example 7.3.2

   c.  Example 7.3.3    d.  Example 7.4.1

**8.** Show that the distance from the point $-1$ in the $GH$ plane to the polar plot of $GH$ is $1 + GH$. Describe how this fact can be used to find graphically the maximum magnitude of the closed-loop transfer function.

# FURTHER READINGS

Bode, H. W. 1945. *Network Analysis and Feedback Amplifier Design.* Princeton, N.J.: D. Van Nostrand.

Chestnut, Harold, and R. W. Mayer. 1951. *Servomechanisms and Regulating Systems Design,* Vol. 1. New York: John Wiley & Sons.

D'Azzo, John J., and Constantine H. Houpis. 1988. *Linear Control System Design: Conventional and Modern.* New York: McGraw-Hill.

James, H. M., N. B. Nichols, and R. S. Phillips. 1947. *Theory of Servomechanisms.* New York: McGraw-Hill.

Nyquist, H. Regeneration theory. *Bell Systems Technical Journal,* 11:126–147.

Ogata, K. 1970. *Modern Control Engineering.* Englewood Cliffs, N.J.: Prentice-Hall.

Saucedo, R., and E. E. Schiring. 1968. *Introduction to Continuous and Digital Control Systems.* New York: MacMillan.

# 11 Chapter

# Bode Design

## 11.1 | OVERVIEW

The Bode design technique developed in this chapter are among the best for designing compensation for continuous systems. The Bode magnitude plot offers excellent scale compression, and there are many figures of merit that can be measured on this plot that can be used by the designer to get a useful estimate of the time response of the closed-loop system.

The compensation technique considered in this chapter will be exclusively cascade compensation with unity feedback, as depicted in Fig. 11.1. Systems with nonunity feedback can be transformed to an equivalent unity feedback form. Thus, very little is lost by limiting the discussion to the unity feedback case.

The first order of business will be to determine figures of merit for the *closed-loop system* that can be represented on the Bode magnitude plot of $G_c G_p(j\omega)$. As usual, the design technique will use the loop transfer function. Since $H = 1$, the loop transfer function becomes the forward loop transfer function $G_c G_p$.

Once suitable figures of merit are determined, lag, PI, lead, lead/lag, and lead/PI compensators can all be designed using the techniques presented in this chapter. For most of the design examples, the root locus and step response of the compensated system are included so that they can be correlated to the final Bode plot.

## 11.2 | FIGURES OF MERIT

There is a large amount of information on the Bode plot of $G_c G_p$ that can help the designer predict the time domain behavior of the closed-loop system. Some of these figures of merit have been introduced previously. An informal "catalog" of the information readily available from the Bode plot that helps predict the time domain response of the closed-loop system is now given.

1. **Gain margin,** as defined and discussed in Chapter 10, is a measure of system stability. As shown in Chapter 10, it is very easy to extract the gain margin from the Bode magnitude and phase plots of the loop transfer function.

**Figure 11.1** | Cascade compensation with unity feedback.

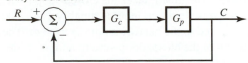

2.  **Phase margin** also measures the stability of the system. It also correlates quite well with another measure of stability, namely, percent overshoot. Through the course of numerous design examples in this chapter it will become clear that a phase margin of 50° or more is needed to keep the overshoot down to an acceptable level.

    A useful, qualitative assessment of phase margin can be obtained by looking at the slope of $G_c G_p$ at the point where it crosses the 0-dB line. Generally, if the slope is $-20$ dB/decade for a sufficient distance on both sides of this crossover point, the phase margin will be more than adequate.

3.  **The slope of the low-frequency asymptote** determines the system type. In factored form

$$G_c G_p(s) = \frac{K' \prod_{i=1}^{m}(s + z_i)}{\prod_{i=1}^{n}(s + p_i)}.$$

We will find it convenient to rewrite $G_c G_p$ in what we called in Chapter 9 the "time constant" form

$$G_c G_p(s) = \frac{K \prod_{i=1}^{m}(1 + s/z_i)}{\prod_{i=1}^{n}(1 + s/p_i)}.$$

Then, if all the poles and zeros of $G_c G_p$ are strictly in the left half plane, at low frequency the plot of $|G_c G_p(j\omega)|$ approaches the dc gain $K$. That is, $|G_c G_p(j\omega)|$ approaches a straight line of slope 0 dB/decade.

By contrast, if

$$G_c G_p = \frac{K \prod_{i=1}^{m}(1 + s/z_i)}{s^\ell \prod_{i=1}^{n-\ell}(1 + s/p_i)},$$

then as $\omega$ tends to zero, $|G_c G_p(j\omega)|$ tends to the sum of the dc gain and the term

$$\frac{1}{|j\omega|^\ell} = \frac{1}{\omega^\ell}.$$

On a Bode plot, this latter term is a line of slope $-20 \times \ell$ dB/decade, passing through the 0-dB line at $\omega = 1$. Thus, for low frequency,

$$20 \log_{10} |G_c G_p(j\omega)| = 20 \log_{10} K - 20 \times \ell \log_{10}(\omega).$$

As discussed in Chapter 10 this is a line of slope $-20 \times \ell$ dB/decade whose intersection with the 0-dB line will depend on $K$. Thus, a type 1 system has a low-frequency asymptote with slope $-20$ dB/decade, while for a type 2 system the slope is $-40$ dB/decade, and so on.

4.   **The crossover frequency** $\omega_c$ is the frequency at which the plot of $|G_cG_p(j\omega)|$ crosses the 0-dB line. The time it takes the closed-loop system to rise to 63% of its final value in response to a step input is roughly $1/\omega_c$. Thus, the crossover frequency is also related to the bandwidth of the system. The larger $\omega_c$, the wider the bandwidth of the closed-loop system and the faster its response.

Besides the figures of merit just discussed, we can add additional measures of performance to the Bode magnitude plot of $G_cG_p(j\omega)$. Most of these additional measures of performance were discussed in Chapter 9 under the topic of sensitivity. Since these performance measures were developed in terms of the performance of the *closed-loop* system, our discussion here will center on transferring these performance measures to the Bode magnitude plot of $G_cG_p$. In doing so we will use our usual ploy of trying to predict the time domain performance of the closed system by analyzing the loop transfer function in the frequency domain.

Consider first

$$\left|\frac{E(j\omega)}{R(j\omega)}\right| = \frac{|E(j\omega)|}{|R(j\omega)|}.$$     [11.1]

This ratio is a measure of the *closed-loop* system's ability to pass sinusoidal frequencies. If the ratio of $|E(j\omega)|$ to $|R(j\omega)|$ is small, then sinusoidal inputs of frequency $\omega$ pass through the system essentially unattenuated. This ratio is thus a measure of the closed-loop system's bandwidth, and this bandwidth affects the speed of the transient response of the closed-loop system. That is, the wider the bandwidth, the faster the transient response.

The next task is to find a figure of merit related to Eq. [11.1] that can be transferred to the Bode magnitude plot of $G_cG_p$. This figure of merit is determined by noting that for unity feedback we have previously established that

$$E(s) = R(s)\left[\frac{1}{1 + G_cG_p(s)}\right].$$     [11.2]

It is worth recalling from Chapter 9 that

$$\frac{E(s)}{R(s)} = \frac{1}{1 + G_cG_p(s)} = T_d(s),$$

where $T_d$ is the transfer function between the output of the closed-loop system and a disturbance at the output. Thus, to suppress a disturbance at the output, we need to make $|G_cG_p(j\omega)|$ large for those frequencies present in the disturbance signal, that is, widen the bandwidth beyond these frequencies. The range of frequencies present in the disturbance signal then becomes a consideration in choosing the bandwidth for the closed-loop system.

Returning to Eq. [11.1], suppose we want

$$\frac{|E(j\omega)|}{|R(j\omega)|} = \frac{1}{|1 + G_cG_p(j\omega)|} \leq \epsilon,$$     [11.3]

where $\epsilon$ is assumed to be a small number, normally on the order of 0.01. If $\epsilon$ is small, then for the inequality to hold $|G_c G_p(j\omega)|$ must be large *relative* to 1.0. Hence

$$\frac{1}{|1 + G_c G_p(j\omega)|} \approx \frac{1}{|G_c G_p(j\omega)|}. \qquad [11.4]$$

This means that

$$\left| \frac{E(j\omega)}{R(j\omega)} \right| \leq \epsilon,$$

a condition imposed on the *closed-loop* system, can be represented on the Bode plot of $|G_c G_p(j\omega)|$ by

$$|G_c G_p(j\omega)| > \frac{1}{\epsilon}. \qquad [11.5]$$

This last inequality is particularly useful because the Bode magnitude plot of $|G_c G_p(j\omega)|$ is, for the most part, monotonically decreasing with increasing frequency. Sometimes the presence of a zero will "flatten" the magnitude plot over a limited range of frequencies, but by and large the magnitude plot sinks constantly as the frequency increases. Thus, if inequality 11.5 holds for some $\omega_\ell$, it will hold for all $\omega < \omega_\ell$. This turns out to be very useful as we will see shortly.

Another performance measure of importance is that related to a disturbance at the input of the closed-loop system as shown in Fig. 11.2. The most common use of this disturbance is to model noise on the feedback signal. The reference input is generally an uncorrupted or "clean" signal. The feedback signal, however, can be noisy. This noise is often introduced by a transducer that converts the output signal to a form in which it can be subtracted from the reference input.

**Figure 11.2 |** Cascade compensation with a disturbance at the input.

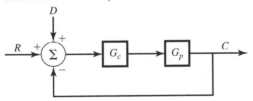

We have already seen an illustration of this type of sensor noise, namely, the output of the "tach generator" in Chapter 8 that measured the speed of the dc motor shaft. Even though the signal from the tach generator is linear with speed, it can also be quite noisy due to commutator contact bounce.

The noise makes the feedback signal "fuzzy." That is, the signal bounces about some mean value very rapidly, as shown in Fig. 11.3. The solid dark line in the figure represents the mean value of the signal. It is this mean value that the system should respond to, not the high-frequency chatter about the mean.

**Figure 11.3 |** Noisy feedback signal.

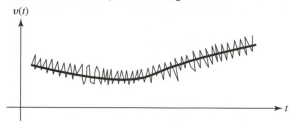

The feedback signal can be thought of as the sum of the true error signal and unwanted noise. In many instances, this additive noise is not a serious problem because the plant acts as a low-pass filter and the noise is automatically filtered out. This is especially true of many electromechanical systems. However, if the bandwidth of the closed-loop system is too large, the noise could impact performance. It is therefore worthwhile to develop a strategy for mitigating the effect of the noise.

The general idea, as discussed in Chapter 9, is to make the bandwidth of the closed-loop system large enough to get the desired performance, but, at the same time, small enough to suppress any input noise. As discussed in Chapter 9, for linear time invariant systems we can invoke superposition and write

$$c(t) = c_r(t) + c_d(t),$$

where $c_r(t)$ is the response with the disturbance input set to zero and $c_d(t)$ is the response with the reference input set to zero. As discussed in Chapter 9, we then can show that

$$\frac{C_r(s)}{R(s)} = \frac{C_d(s)}{D(s)} = \frac{G_c(s)G_p(s)}{1 + G_c(s)G_p(s)}. \qquad \textbf{[11.6]}$$

One means of suppressing the noise at the input is to make $C_d(j\omega)$ small for all frequencies *above* some threshold frequency $\omega_h$. The idea is that noise has substantial high-frequency content, and if this high-frequency content can be filtered out, the effects of the noise will be mitigated without seriously affecting the performance of the system.

One way to accomplish this is to make

$$\left| \frac{C_d(j\omega)}{D(j\omega)} \right| \le \epsilon, \quad \text{for } \omega > \omega_h. \qquad \textbf{[11.7]}$$

Here, $\epsilon$ is a small quantity, again on the order of 0.01. But Inequality [11.7] is equivalent to

$$\left| \frac{G_c G_p(j\omega)}{1 + G_c G_p(j\omega)} \right| \le \epsilon, \quad \text{for } \omega > \omega_h. \qquad \textbf{[11.8]}$$

Now, for the quantity on the left-hand side of this last inequality to be small, $|G_c G_p(j\omega)|$ must be small *relative* to 1. If this is the case, then

$$\left| \frac{G_c G_p(j\omega)}{1 + G_c G_p(j\omega)} \right| \approx |G_c G_p(j\omega)|.$$

Thus, an inequality equivalent to [11.8] that we can put on the Bode plot of $|G_c G_p(j\omega)|$ is

$$|G_c G_p(j\omega)| \leq \epsilon, \quad \text{for } \omega \geq \omega_h. \qquad \text{[11.9]}$$

If Inequality [11.9] holds for $\omega_h$, it is usually satisfied for all higher frequencies because, as discussed earlier, the Bode magnitude plot, by and large, decreases monotonically with increasing frequency.

It probably has not escaped the notice of the alert reader that the performance measure for suppression of noise at the input is the inverse of the performance measure for system bandwidth. This sets up the classic tug of war between performance and stability. We want to keep the bandwidth as wide as possible to ensure good performance, but we don't want it any wider than necessary because we do not want to let in unwanted noise at the input.

At this juncture we have defined a set of figures of merit that quantify the three important characteristics of the time response that we have discussed many times before, namely, transient speed of response, stability, and steady state accuracy. With these figures of merit in hand, the next order of business is to develop techniques for designing lag, lead, and lag/lead compensators that meet a set of specifications based on these figures of merit.

# 11.3 | LAG COMPENSATOR DESIGN

A methodology for designing lag compensation was introduced in Chapter 7. In one of the approaches discussed there, a pole and zero were placed close to the origin of the $s$ plane to improve steady state accuracy. The same approach is used here, as described in Example 11.3.1.

**EXAMPLE 11.3.1**

For the system of Fig. 11.1, let

$$G_p(s) = \frac{4}{(s+2)(s+4)}.$$

The specifications are

1. $K_p \geq 100$.
2. $t_p \leq 1$ s.
3. $\phi_m \geq 50°$.
4. PO $\leq 10\%$.

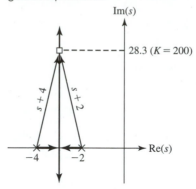

**Figure 11.4 |** Root locus for simple gain compensation.

An ongoing theme in this chapter will be the relationship between root locus design and Bode design. With that in mind, we first draw the root locus for simple gain adjustment of the system, as shown in Fig. 11.4.

Now,

$$K_p = \lim_{s \to 0} \frac{4K}{(s+2)(s+4)} = \frac{K}{2}.$$

Thus, for $K_p = 100$, $K$ must be 200.

We can see from Fig. 11.4, that

$$4K = |s+2| \times |s+4| = |s+2|^2.$$

Hence, the imaginary part of the closed-loop pole is

$$w = \sqrt{|s+2|^2 - 1^2} = \sqrt{4K - 1} = 28.3.$$

Meeting the accuracy specification requires that the closed-loop poles be at

$$s = -3 \pm j28.3.$$

The angle these poles make with the negative real axis is

$$\theta = \tan^{-1} \frac{28.3}{3} = 83.9°,$$

yielding a damping ratio of

$$\zeta = \cos \theta = \cos 83.9° = 0.11.$$

This is an unacceptably low damping ratio that will result in a very oscillatory response to a step input.

The poor stability of the gain-compensated system can be determined from the Bode plot shown in Fig. 11.5 where the plant gain has been adjusted to achieve the desired steady state accuracy of $K_p = 100$. The gain adjusted plant crosses the 0-dB

**Figure 11.5 |** Bode asymptotic magnitude plot for Example 11.3.1.

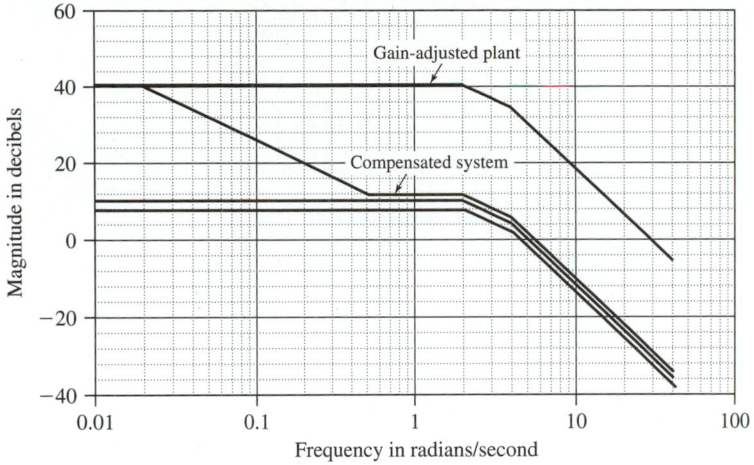

line at $\omega_c = 30$ rad/s. The phase of the gain adjusted system at crossover is

$$\underline{/K\,G_p(\,j30)} = -\tan^{-1}\frac{30}{2} - \tan^{-1}\frac{30}{4} = -168.6°,$$

so that

$$\phi_m = 180° + \underline{/K\,G_p(\,j30)} = 11.4°.$$

This very small phase margin is the frequency domain figure of merit that indicates the system has very low damping. Generally, it is desirable to have

$$\phi_m \geq 50°.$$

At this point, it is worth noting that the low-phase margin can be quickly predicted from the Bode magnitude plot of the gain compensated system because its slope is $-40$ dB/decade for more than a decade before it crosses the 0-dB line.

Since the phase of $G_cG_p(\,j\omega)$ at crossover is mainly determined by the slope of the magnitude plot from a decade below to a decade above $\omega_c$, the phase at crossover, as predicted by the slope of the magnitude plot, should be nearly $-180°$. This conclusion is in very good agreement with the computed value of $\phi_m$.

The ability to *quickly* get a good estimate of the phase of $G_cG_p(\,j\omega)$ from the slope of the magnitude plot is a valuable design skill, and one of the goals of this chapter is to hone that skill.

The first step in the lag compensator design is to obtain an acceptable phase margin by reducing the gain. This may seem counterproductive, since the system now no longer meets the steady state accuracy condition. It is not, however, because once the phase margin is correctly adjusted the steady state accuracy can be restored via a lag compensator. Remember it is the height of the low-frequency asymptote that determines steady state accuracy.

Figure 11.5 actually shows three designs. The first crosses the 0-dB line at

$$\omega_c = 4.5 \text{ rad/s}.$$

The phase margin for this design is

$$\phi_m = 180° + \underline{/KG_p(j4.5)}$$
$$= 180° - \tan^{-1}\frac{4.5}{2} - \tan^{-1}\frac{4.5}{4}$$
$$= 180° - 66° - 48.4°$$
$$= 65.6°.$$

This is more phase margin than required, so the gain is adjusted upward, increasing the crossover frequency. Two successive calculations show that for $\omega_c = 5.0$ and 5.5 rad/s, the phase margins are 60° and 56°, respectively.

The last value is about 6° more than required by the specification. This excess phase margin is necessary, however, because the next step is to add a lag compensator that will reduce the phase margin by five or six degrees. Thus, choosing $\omega_c = 5.5$ rad/s will enable us to meet the design specification on phase margin when the lag compensator is added.

This example seems to contradict the earlier statement that the magnitude plot should cross the 0-dB line with a slope of −20 dB/decade, because the slope at crossover is clearly −40 dB/decade. However, there is a significant amount of slope of 0 dB/decade in the decade below crossover, enough, in fact, to allow the magnitude plot to cross at −40 dB/decade and still yield a satisfactory phase margin.

The lag compensator is constructed as follows. A frequency about 1 decade below $\omega_c$ is chosen for the location of the zero of the lag. A line of slope −20 dB/decade is layed in through the location of the zero and extended upward and to the *left* until in intersects the low-frequency asymptote that we set earlier to meet the specification on $K_p$. This point of intersection defines the pole of the lag compensator. It is important to emphasize again that the low-frequency asymptote, a straight line at height 40 dB, was set to ensure the specified steady state accuracy, namely, $K_p = 100$.

The overall system is now

$$G_c(s)G_p(s) = \frac{100(1 + s/0.5)}{(1 + s/0.02)(1 + s/2)(1 + s/4)}.$$

Since

$$G_p(s) = \frac{0.5}{(1 + s/2)(1 + s/4)},$$

the compensator is

$$G_c(s) = \frac{200(1 + s/0.5)}{1 + s/0.02} = \frac{8(s + 0.5)}{s + 0.02}.$$

The net change to the phase margin due to the addition of the lag compensator is

$$\gamma = \tan^{-1}\frac{5.5}{0.5} - \tan^{-1}\frac{5.5}{0.02} = 84.8° - 89.8° = -5°.$$

Thus, with the lag compensator added, the phase margin is

$$\phi_m = 56° + \gamma = 56° - 5° = 51°,$$

which just meets the specification of 50°.

The next step is to put the system back into the form used to draw the root locus. We thus write

$$G_cG_p(s) = \frac{8(s+0.5)}{(s+0.02)}\frac{4}{(s+2)(s+4)}$$

$$= \frac{32(s+0.5)}{(s+0.02)(s+2)(s+4)}.$$

The root locus for this system is shown in Fig. 11.6(a).

For $K = 32$, the dominant complex poles of the closed-loop system are at $s = -2.8 \pm j5.47$. This translates to a damping ratio of

$$\zeta = \cos\left(\tan^{-1}\frac{5.47}{2.8}\right) = \cos 62.9° = 0.46.$$

The time response is shown in Fig. 11.6(b). As we can see, the system reaches a peak at about 0.75 s. However, the value at this peak is the steady state value of 1.0. Also the settling time, although not a specification, is not very good because the system "creeps" toward steady state. A redesign might lower the damping ratio to try

**Figure 11.6 |** (a) Root locus and (b) step response for lag design of Example 11.3.1.

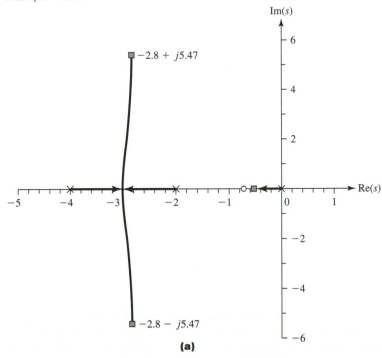

**(a)**

**Figure 11.6 |** Continued

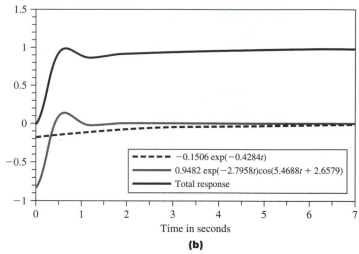

to make the system response overshoot a bit and thereby eliminate, at least partially, the creeping effect (see Problem 1 in Section 11.9.2).

Based on example 11.3.1 we can now state a four-step design procedure for lag compensation.

1. Gain adjust $G_p$ until the phase margin is about 6° greater than the desired phase margin.
2. Determine the location of the low-frequency asymptote of $G_cG_p$, using the steady state accuracy specification.
3. Place the zero of the lag compensator about one decade below the crossover frequency $\omega_c$ determined in step 1.
4. Lay in a line of slope $-20$ dB/decade through the location of the zero of the lag and project it upward to the left until it intersects the low-frequency asymptote. This intersection determines the pole of the lag compensator.

If the zero of the lag compensator is a decade below crossover then it should decrease the phase margin by no more than 5° or 6°. Based on our prior analysis, which showed

$$\frac{|E(j\omega)|}{|R(j\omega)|} \approx \frac{1}{|G_cG_p(j\omega)|},$$

we also conclude that the lag compensator reduces the bandwidth of the closed-loop system rather severely. Thus, the improvement in steady state accuracy and stability has been purchased at the price of reduced performance, as witnessed by the way the step response creeps toward steady state.

# 11.4 | LEAD COMPENSATOR DESIGN

The primary purpose of lead compensation, as discussed in Chapter 7, is to improve the transient response. In terms of frequency domain analysis, the figures of merit that measure speed of response are crossover frequency and bandwidth. Both of these figures of merit will come into play in Example 11.4.1.

**EXAMPLE 11.4.1**

Consider the system of Fig. 11.1 and let

$$G_p(s) = \frac{1}{s(s+1)}.$$

We wish to design a lead compensator:

$$G_c(s) = \frac{K_c(s+z_1)}{s+p_1}$$

that meets the following specifications:

1. $K_v \geq 100$.

2. Phase margin $\phi_m \geq 50°$.

3. $\dfrac{|E(j\omega)|}{|R(j\omega)|} \leq 0.02$ for $\omega \leq 1$ rad/s.

4. $\dfrac{|C(j\omega)|}{|R(j\omega)|} \leq 0.1$ for $\omega \geq 100$ rad/s.

   We begin by outlining in a general way the procedures we will follow throughout the rest of the chapter. We will first transfer the specifications to the Bode magnitude chart. We will then examine the specifications to see if they make sense and if it will be possible to meet the specifications. With some experience, this can be done almost at a glance.

   If the specifications seem reasonable, we then fit the magnitude plot of the *overall* forward loop transfer function $G_cG_p$ onto the Bode plot in such a way that the specifications are met. We work in terms of the *overall* forward loop transfer function $G_cG_p$. Our final step will be to determine the compensator. We now proceed with the design, pointing our the essential steps as we proceed. This process of fitting $G_cG_p(j\omega)$ to the specifications is often called "loop shaping."

   Normally, our first step is to put $G_p(s)$ in "time constant" form. However, in this instance,

$$G_p(s) = \frac{1}{s(1+s)}$$

is already in time constant form, so we proceed.

   The next step is to determine the gain necessary to make $K_v \geq 100$. With the overall system, plant and compensator, in time constant form we find

$$K_v = \lim_{s \to 0} s G_c G_p(s)$$

$$= \lim_{s \to 0} K \frac{s(1+s/z_1)}{(1+s/p_1)} \frac{1}{s(1+s)}$$

$$= K.$$

**Figure 11.7 |** Three-lead designs for Example 11.4.1.

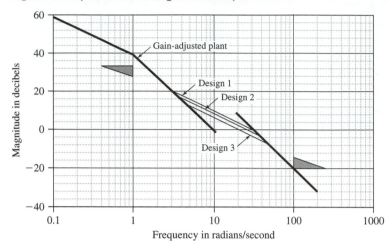

Thus, $K = K_v = 100$. A little thought should convince the reader that with $G_c G_p$ in time constant form the gain $K$ will always be the *appropriate* error constant.

The gain adjusted plant is shown in Fig. 11.7. It is probably worth reviewing the placement of the low-frequency asymptote at this juncture. If $G_c G_p(j\omega)$ is in time constant form, then as $\omega$ tends to zero the magnitude contributions of all poles and zeros away from the origin go to 0 dB.

Thus, in this example, at very low frequency the only two terms contributing to the magnitude plot are the gain $K_v$ and the term $1/s$. The term $1/s$ is a line of slope $-20$ dB/decade that passes through 0 dB at a frequency of 1 rad/s. If we add up the contributions of the gain and the term $1/s$ we get the low-frequency portion of the asymptotic Bode magnitude plot.

Since $K_v = 40$ dB, if we add 40 dB to the plot of $1/s$ we find that the low-frequency asymptote passes through the point (1 rad/s, 40 dB) on the Bode plot. The low-frequency asymptote can be established by drawing a straight line of slope $-20$ dB/decade through the point (1 rad/s, 40 dB).

We now see that with $K_v = 100$, the gain adjusted plant has almost no phase margin because the slope of the magnitude plot is $-40$ dB for a decade before crossover at $\omega_c = 10$ rad/s, making the phase at crossover nearly $-180°$. We will see shortly how the lead compensator improves the phase margin.

The next step is to add the *closed-loop* specification

$$\frac{|E(j1)|}{|R(j1)|} \approx \frac{1}{|G_c G_p(j1)|} \le 0.02,$$

to the Bode plot. The approximate equivalent condition that can be put on the Bode plot is

$$|G_c G_p(j1)| \ge \frac{1}{0.02} = 50 = 34 \text{ dB} \quad \text{for } \omega \le 1 \text{ rad/s.} \qquad \textbf{[11.10]}$$

It is clear that the gain-adjusted plot of the plant decreases monotonically with increasing frequency. The addition of the lead compensator will not change that. Thus, if Eq. [11.10] holds for $\omega = 1$ rad/s, it will hold for $0 < \omega \leq 1$ rad/s, as we discussed earlier.

To meet the specification on bandwidth that we have just added to the Bode plot, the magnitude plot of $G_c G_p$ must pass over the point (1 rad/s, 34 dB). This point is marked on the Bode plot by the upper right corner of the shaded triangle in Fig. 11.7.

Three lead compensators designs are shown in Fig. 11.7. We will have more to say about those designs shortly, but an important point to note at this juncture is that for all three designs, the zero of the compensator breaks in after the pole of the plant at $s = -1$. Thus the low-frequency portion of the magnitude plot of $G_c G_p$ is just the gain-adjusted plant.

As can be seen from the figure, the magnitude plot of $G_c G_p$ clears the bandwidth specification with room to spare. Thus the design does not fully exploit this specification. However, a subsequent lead/lag design will.

The next step is to transfer the specification

$$\frac{|C(j100)|}{|R(j100)|} \approx |G_c G_p(j100)| \leq 0.1 = -20 \text{ dB}, \quad \text{for } \omega \geq 100 \text{ rad/s}. \qquad \textbf{[11.11]}$$

to the Bode plot. Since $|G_c G_p(j\omega)|$ decreases monotonically as the frequency increases, Eq. [11.11] holds for all $\omega \geq 100$ rad/s. Thus the composite Bode magnitude plot of $G_c G_p(j\omega)$ must pass under the point (100 rad/s, −20 dB). This point is marked by the lower left corner of the shaded triangle, as shown in Fig. 11.7.

An asymptote of slope −40 dB/decade is now constructed that passes through the point (100 rad/s, −20 dB). This is the high-frequency asymptote of $G_c G_p(j\omega)$. It has the same slope as the high-frequency asymptote of $G_p(j\omega)$ because $G_c G_p$ and $G_p$ have the same pole-zero excess.

The necessary groundwork has now been laid, and we can complete the compensator design in rather short order. As shown in Fig. 11.7, several lines of slope −20 dB/decade connect the two asymptotes of slope −40 dB/decade. All that remains is to see which of the proposed designs best meets the given specifications.

We want the Bode magnitude plot of $G_c G_p(j\omega)$ to pass through the 0-dB line at a slope of −20 dB/decade to achieve the specified phase margin. As we have said before, and will say again, it is the slope of the magnitude plot in the decade below and the decade above $\omega_c$ that primarily determines the phase of $G_c G_p(j\omega_c)$ and hence determines the phase margin.

If the slope were −20 dB/decade for a decade above and below $\omega_c$, then the phase of $G_c G_p(j\omega_c)$ would be approximately −90°. As we can see from the Bode plot, this is not the case. For all three designs, the slope is −20 dB/decade on both sides of $\omega_c$ but there is also some slope of −40 dB/decade in the decade below and the decade above crossover. As a consequence, the phase of $G_c G_p(j\omega)$ will be between −90° and −180°. What we hope is that for one of the designs shown

$$\underline{/G_cG_p(j\omega_c)} \leq -130°,$$

yielding $\phi_m \geq 50°$.

The next step is to investigate the phase margin of the three designs shown. This is a simple task given the power of modern calculators because all we need to do is evaluate less than a dozen arctangents.

For design 1, the crossover frequency is 30 rad/s, and

$$G_cG_p(s) = \frac{100(1 + s/3)}{s(1 + s/1)(1 + s/30)},$$

$$\underline{/G_cG_p(j30)} = \tan^{-1}\frac{30}{3} - 90° - \tan^{-1}30 - \tan^{-1}\frac{30}{30}$$

$$= 84.3° - 90° - 89.1° - 45°$$

$$= -139°.$$

The phase margin is then

$$\phi_m = 180° - 139° = 41°.$$

The phase margin is too small, but it can be increased by lowering the crossover frequency.

For instance, design 3 has a crossover frequency of 20 rad/s, with

$$G_cG_p(s) = \frac{100(1 + s/5)}{s(1 + s)(1 + s/50)},$$

and

$$\underline{/G_cG_p(j20)} = \tan^{-1}\frac{20}{5} - 90° - \tan^{-1}20 - \tan^{-1}\frac{20}{50}$$

$$= 76° - 90° - 87.1° - 21.8°$$

$$= -123°,$$

yielding a phase margin of 57°. This is more phase margin than specified. Note, however, that designs 1 and 3 "bracket" the designs that will best meet the specifications. Thus, the next step is to raise the crossover frequency slightly.

Design 2 has a crossover frequency of 25 rad/s and

$$G_cG_p(s) = \frac{100(1 + s/4)}{s(1 + s)(1 + s/40)}.$$

Then,

$$\underline{/G_cG_p(j25)} = \tan^{-1}\frac{25}{4} - 90° - \tan^{-1}25 - \tan^{-1}\frac{25}{40}$$

$$= 80.9° - 90° - 87.7° - 32°$$

$$= -129°,$$

yielding a phase margin of 51°. This is close to the design specification, and since

$\phi_m$ is obtained from the asymptotic Bode magnitude plot, the *actual* crossover and phase margin may vary by a small amount, and could be slightly lower. Thus, Design 2 looks like a good choice.

At this point a few comments are worth making. Note that once we put the figures of merit on the Bode plot and placed the high-frequency asymptote we established a "design corridor." The design corridor is the space between the two asymptotes of slope −40 dB/decade. It is the *width* of the design corridor that determines the maximum phase margin we can achieve.

Phase margin turns out to be a very good measure of percent overshoot and percent overshoot, as we know, is a good indicator of stability. Thus, we are able to use phase margin, a figure of merit on the Bode plot, to gauge percent overshoot, a figure of merit of stability in the *time domain*.

Also note that once the design corridor is established we can very rapidly evaluate our design options by simply calculating a few arctangents, an easy matter with a modern calculator. Thus, the whole design can be done on a single Bode magnitude plot in a matter of a few minutes. If we then wish to turn to the computer to refine our design we can. If we do so we will already have a very clear picture of what the design limitations are. In other words, we have been able to use simple, fundamental principles to see clearly the design trade-offs. Plato, and Socrates, would be proud of us. We have crawled out of the cave. Well, at least we're in the tunnel on our way out of the cave.

To reinforce these ideas, we include the root locus and step response for two of the designs just completed. To draw the root locus we put $G_cG_p(s)$ in the form used for drawing the root locus. For design 2, we have

$$G_cG_p(s) = \frac{100(1 + s/4)}{s(1 + s)(1 + s/40)} = \frac{1000(s + 4)}{s(s + 1)(s + 40)}.$$

The root locus is shown in Fig. 11.8(a). Note that the dominant complex poles are at $s = -18.2 \pm j23.3$. The damping ratio of these poles is $\zeta = 0.62$. The unit step response of the system, as shown in Fig. 11.8(b), has a percent overshoot of 20%. This correlates reasonably well with the percent overshoot predicted by the formula for $T_{N2}$.

If a smaller percent overshoot is desired, design 3 could be chosen. The root locus and time response for design 3 are shown in Figs. 11.9(a) and 11.9(b). The root root locus is not dramatically different in overall shape, but the complex conjugate poles have a damping ratio of $\zeta \approx 0.8$. This decreases the overshoot slightly from 20% to 18%.

The decrease in percent overshoot is considerably less than one might expect from the change in damping ratio. Part of the reason is the term $0.48e^{-6.61t}$ in the step response. Because the coefficient of $e^{-6.61t}$ is quite large, the term does not die out very quickly. Since the size of these coefficients cannot be predicted in advance, it may take several iterations to refine an initial design to a final choice. This is a good point at which to use a software package like MATLAB to refine the design.

**Figure 11.8 |** (a) Root locus and (b) step response for design 2 of Example 11.4.1.

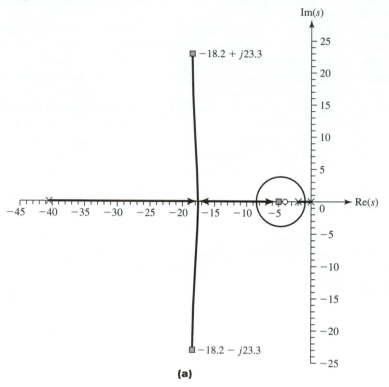

**(a)**

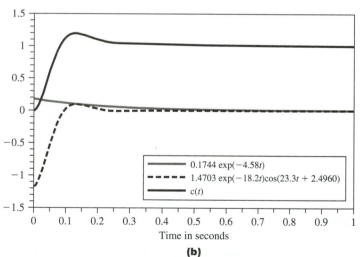

**(b)**

**Figure 11.9 |** (a) Root locus and (b) step response for design 3 of Example 11.4.1.

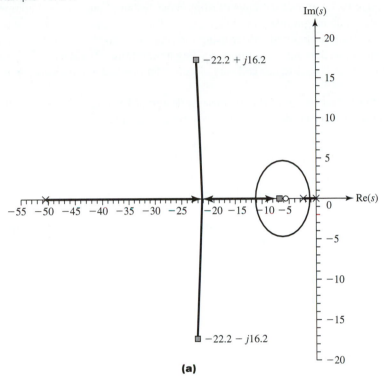

**(a)**

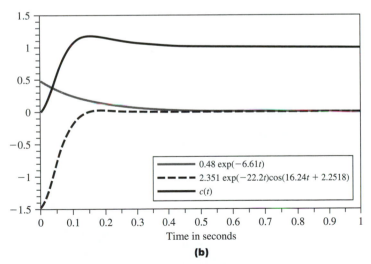

**(b)**

## 11.5 | LEAD/LAG DESIGN PROCEDURE

Examples 11.3.1 and 11.4.1 have illustrated the design of lag and lead compensators using the Bode magnitude plot of $G_c G_p(j\omega)$. These designs are very close to the lag and lead designs obtained earlier using the root locus approach. In this section, we develop a procedure for obtaining a lead/lag design from a Bode plot of $|G_c G_p(j\omega)|$. The procedure is easy to use and very effective for plants that have two, three, or four poles.

Consider again the lead compensator design of Example 11.4.1. Recall that we noted earlier that the specification on bandwidth, namely,

$$\frac{|E(j\omega)|}{|R(j\omega)|} \leq 0.02 \quad \text{for } \omega < 1 \text{ rad/s},$$

was exceeded. That is, the asymptote of slope $-40$ dB/decade that breaks in at $\omega = 1$ passed well above the upper right corner of the shaded triangle that represents this specification on the Bode plot.

Suppose this asymptote is moved over so that it just touches the upper right corner of the triangle, as shown in Fig. 11.10. Two things happen. First, the pole of the plant at $s = -1$ is canceled. This has to be the case because the slope of the magnitude plot does not change at $\omega = 1$.

Second, the design corridor between the two asymptotes with slope $-40$ dB/ decade has widened. Widening this corridor means that there will be more slope of $-20$ dB/decade on both sides of $\omega_c$, which, in turn, means that the phase margin will increase. The price paid for the increased phase margin is that the compensator will no longer be a first order lead, but a second order lead/lag.

The overall system shown in Fig. 11.10 is

$$G_c G_p(s) = \frac{100(1 + s/2.5)}{s(1 + s/0.5)(1 + s/50)} = \left[ \frac{100(1 + s)(1 + s/2.5)}{(1 + s/0.5)(1 + s/50)} \right] \left[ \frac{1}{s(1 + s)} \right].$$

**Figure 11.10 |** Bode plot with asymptote moved to the left.

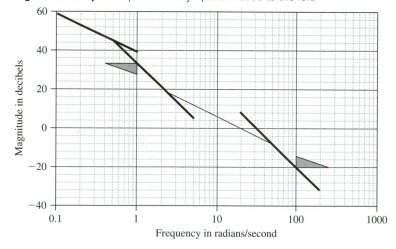

Thus, the compensator is

$$G_c = \frac{100(1+s)(1+s/2.5)}{(1+s/0.5)(1+s/50)} = \frac{1000(s+1)(s+2.5)}{(s+0.5)(s+50)}.$$

This is a second-order lead/lag compensator with lead portion

$$\frac{1000(s+2.5)}{(s+50)}$$

and lag portion

$$\frac{(s+1)}{(s+0.5)}.$$

We see that the lag portion provides a very modest doubling of the steady state accuracy to a ramp input, and the lead portion is only slightly different from the lead compensator of Example 11.4.1.

The phase margin is larger, however. The crossover is at 20 rad/s, so that

$$\underline{/G_cG_p\,(j20)} = \tan^{-1}\frac{20}{2.5} - 90° - \tan^{-1}\frac{20}{0.5} - \tan^{-1}\frac{20}{50}$$

$$= 82.9° - 90° - 88.6° - 21.8°$$

$$= -118°.$$

Thus $\phi_m = 62°$. Recall that design 3 of Example 11.4.1 had the same crossover frequency and a phase margin of 57°. Thus, moving the asymptote to the left has increased the gain margin by 5° without reducing the crossover frequency.

The alert reader may question putting the asymptote that defines the left side of the design corridor right at the point (34 dB, 1 rad/s). Actually, at a frequency half a decade above the break frequency of $\omega = 0.5$ rad/s the asymptotic plot is indistinguishable from the actual plot. It would a different matter if we were to break the asymptotic plot down another 20 dB/decade right at the point (34 dB, 1 rad/s). If we did so, we would have to place the corner of the asymptotic plot 3 dB above the upper right corner of the triangle to exactly meet our bandwidth specification.

Examples 11.3.1 and 11.4.1 reveal most of the significant features of a general Bode design methodology. All that remains is to formalize that methodology and then demonstrate it through some examples.

# 11.6 | GENERAL DESIGN PROCEDURE

Examples 11.3.1 and 11.4.1 lead to a general six step design algorithm.

1. Plot the low-frequency asymptote adjusted to meet the steady state accuracy specification.

2. Determine the "over/under" points. That is, the points that satisfy

$$\frac{|E(j\omega_1)|}{|R(j\omega_1)|} \le \epsilon_1, \quad \text{for } \omega < \omega_\ell \quad \text{and} \quad \frac{|C(j\omega_2)|}{|R(j\omega_2)|} \le \epsilon_2, \quad \text{for } \omega > \omega_h,$$

and mark them on the Bode plot.

3. Establish an asymptote at −40 dB/decade through through the "under" point determined by

$$\frac{|C(j\omega_2)|}{|R(j\omega_2)|} \le \epsilon_2.$$

For a compensator with an equal number of poles and zeros, the high-frequency asymptote will have the same slope as the high-frequency asymptote of $|G_p(j\omega)|$.

If the high-frequency asymptote has a slope steeper than −40 dB/decade, then the additional poles will have to break off the asymptote of slope −40 dB/decade that forms the right side of the design corridor. These additional break points generally create extra poles in the compensator unless they correspond to poles of the plant.

For most of the examples considered in this chapter, the pole-zero excess of the plant will be two, and the high-frequency asymptote will have slope −40 dB/decade. However, Example 11.6.2 considers a plant with a pole-zero excess of three, causing the high-frequency asymptote of $|G_cG_p(j\omega)|$ to be −60 dB/decade. In this case, a decision will have to be made as to where the additional break point should be.

For systems with a pole-zero excess of four or more, the situation becomes more difficult. However, it is rare for a system to have more than three poles in the design corridor. Thus, in many cases, the additional break points lie outside the design corridor and don't have that much impact on the design.

4. Establish an asymptote at −40 dB/decade through the "over" point determined by

$$\frac{|E(j\omega_1)|}{|R(j\omega_1)|} \le \epsilon_1.$$

Extend this asymptote until it meets the low-frequency asymptote.

5. Connect the two asymptotes of slope −40 dB/decade that define the "design corridor" by an asymptote of slope −20 dB/decade so that the magnitude plot of $G_cG_p(j\omega)$ crosses the 0-dB line with sufficient phase margin.

6. Determine

$$G_c(s) = \frac{G_c(s)G_p(s)}{G_p(s)}.$$

The design methodology is now illustrated with some examples. The first example treats a type 0 system. In this case the Bode design procedure will cancel *both* the plant poles. The result is a third-order compensator.

**EXAMPLE 11.6.1**

Consider the system of Fig. 11.1 and let

$$G_p(s) = \frac{4}{(s+2)(s+4)}.$$

We wish to design a lead/lag compensator

$$G_c(s) = \frac{K_c(s+z_1)(s+z_2)}{(s+p_1)(s+p_2)}$$

that meets these specifications:

1. $K_p \geq 100$.
2. Phase margin $\phi_m \geq 50°$.
3. $\left| \dfrac{E(j\omega_1)}{R(j\omega_1)} \right| \leq 0.02$ for $\omega \leq 1$ rad/s.
4. $\left| \dfrac{C(j\omega_2)}{R(j\omega_2)} \right| \leq 0.1$ for $\omega \geq 100$ rad/s.

The specifications are the same as in Example 11.4.1, the plant is the same as in Example 11.3.1.

As always, the first step is to put $G_c G_p$ in the "time constant" form

$$G_c G_p(s) = \frac{K_p \prod_{i=1}^{3}(1 + s/z_i)}{\prod_{i=1}^{3}(1 + s/p_i)} \frac{1}{(1 + s/2)(1 + s/4)}.$$

The next step is to set the low-frequency asymptote. The system is type 0 with

$$K_p = 100 \quad (40\,\text{dB}).$$

The low-frequency asymptote is thus a horizontal line at 40 dB.

The asymptotic Bode plots of five trial designs are shown in Fig. 11.11. Note how compact the design procedure is. We put all five trial designs on the same Bode magnitude plot where we can easily compare them. We also show enough of the gain-adjusted plant to indicate that it has a very poor phase margin.

We next mark on the Bode plot the points that correspond to satisfaction of the bandwidth specification and the noise suppression specification. These points are (1 rad/s, 34 dB) and (100 rad/s, −20 dB), respectively.

We establish the left-hand side of the design corridor by passing an asymptote of slope −20 dB/decade through the point (1 rad/s, 37 dB) and connecting it to the low-frequency asymptote. This creates a pole at $s = -0.7$. We then increase the slope to −40 dB/decade at $\omega = 1$. This means that we have added a second pole to

**Figure 11.11 |** Five lead/lag designs for Example 11.6.1.

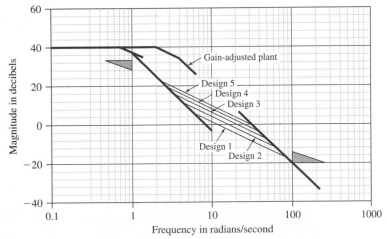

$G_cG_p$ at $s = -1$. Since $\omega = 1$ is a break frequency, we have placed the corner 3 dB above the point (1 rad/s, 34 dB).

An alternative approach would be to extend the asymptote of slope $-40$ dB/decade through the point (1 rad/s, 34 dB) until it meets the low-frequency asymptote. This would create a double pole at $s = -0.7$. Instead, we have chosen two distinct poles, one at $s = -0.5$ and one at $s = -1$. In this particular case, the choice is moot.

The high-frequency asymptote again has slope of $-40$ dB/decade because the plant has two poles and no zeros. The design corridor between the two asymptotes of slope $-40$ dB/decade is sufficiently wide to meet the design specifications.

The specifications contain an implicit optimization problem. They call for $\phi_m \geq 50°$. Since the rise time is roughly equal to the inverse of the crossover frequency, by making the crossover frequency as large as possible, while still meeting the other design specifications we can optimize the performance in terms of speed of response. This is very easy to do. As shown in Fig. 11.11, we simply lay in a series of slopes of $-20$ dB/decade between the two sides of the design corridor and compute the phase margin in each case. In the process we will also find the maximum available phase margin.

For design 1,

$$G_cG_p(s) = \frac{100(1 + s/6)}{(1 + s/0.7)(1 + s/1)(1 + s/85)}. \qquad [11.12]$$

The crossover frequency is $\omega_c = 11$ rad/s. The phase at crossover is

$$\begin{aligned}
\underline{/G_cG_p(j11)} &= \tan^{-1}\frac{11}{6} - \tan^{-1}\frac{11}{0.7} - \tan^{-1}\frac{11}{1} - \tan\frac{11}{85} \\
&= 61.4° - 86.4° - 84.8° - 7.4° \\
&= -117°,
\end{aligned}$$

yielding a phase margin of 63°.

For design 2,

$$G_cG_p(s) = \frac{100(1 + s/4.5)}{(1 + s/0.7)(1 + s/1)(1 + s/60)}, \qquad [11.13]$$

with a crossover frequency of $\omega_c = 15$ rad/s. The phase at crossover is

$$\begin{aligned}
\underline{/G_cG_p(j15)} &= \tan^{-1}\frac{15}{4.5} - \tan^{-1}\frac{15}{0.7} - \tan^{-1}\frac{15}{1} - \tan\frac{15}{60} \\
&= 73.3° - 89.7° - 88.2° - 14° \\
&= -116°,
\end{aligned}$$

and the phase margin is 64°.

For design 3,

$$G_cG_p(s) = \frac{100(1 + s/3.3)}{(1 + s/0.7)(1 + s/1)(1 + s/50)}, \qquad [11.14]$$

with a crossover frequency of $\omega_c = 20$ rad/s. The phase at crossover is

$$\underline{/G_cG_p(j20)} = \tan^{-1}\frac{20}{3.2} - \tan^{-1}\frac{20}{0.7} - \tan^{-1}\frac{20}{1} - \tan\frac{20}{60}$$

$$= 80.9° - 89.8° - 87.1° - 18.4°$$

$$= -114°,$$

with the phase margin increasing slightly to 66°.

For design 4,

$$G_cG_p(s) = \frac{100(1 + s/2.7)}{(1 + s/0.7)(1 + s)(1 + s/40)},$$ [11.15]

with a crossover frequency of $\omega_c = 25$ rad/s. The phase at crossover is

$$\underline{/G_cG_p(j25)} = \tan^{-1}\frac{25}{2.7} - \tan^{-1}\frac{25}{0.7} - \tan^{-1}\frac{25}{1} - \tan^{-1}\frac{25}{40}$$

$$= 83.8° - 89.8° - 87.7° - 32°$$

$$= -126°,$$

and the phase margin has now decreased to 54°.

Finally, for design 5,

$$G_cG_p(s) = \frac{100(1 + s/2.3)}{(1 + s/0.7)(1 + s)(1 + s/30)},$$ [11.16]

with crossover at $\omega_c = 30$ rad/s. The phase at crossover is

$$\underline{/G_cG_p(j30)} = \tan^{-1}\frac{30}{2.3} - \tan^{-1}\frac{30}{0.7} - \tan^{-1}\frac{30}{1} - \tan^{-1}\frac{30}{30}$$

$$= 85.6° - 89.9° - 88.1° - 45°$$

$$= -137°,$$

with the phase margin now down to 43°.

There are several observations worth making here. First, moving from design 1 to design 5, the phase margin first increases and then decreases again. The maximum phase margin will occur when the crossover frequency is near the center of the design corridor. In other words, the phase margin is maximized when there is approximately the same amount of slope of $-20$ dB/decade on both sides of the crossover frequency, as is the case for designs 2 and 3. Thus the maximum phase margin obtainable is around 66°.

A second important observation is that the angle contributions due to the poles at $s = -0.5$ and $s = -1$ change by only a degree or so from design to design. This is because both poles are a decade or more below the crossover frequency and hence their angle contributions are nearly at the maximum of $-90°$. Thus, the changes in the phase margin from design to design depend almost entirely on the pole and zero of $G_cG_p$ created by laying in the asymptote at $-20$ dB/decade across the design corridor.

A third and final observation is that with these five designs we have achieved two simple optimizations. That is, we could choose the system that maximizes the phase margin. Alternatively, we could choose to maximize the crossover frequency while maintaining a minimum phase margin of say 50°. Thus, the proposed graphical design technique is simple to use and leads rapidly to a solution, while easily accomodating simple optimization schemes.

Given the specifications, a good choice in this particular case might be design 4, for which

$$
G_c(s) = \frac{G_c(s)G_p(s)}{G_p(s)}
$$

$$
= \frac{\dfrac{100(1 + s/2.7)}{(1 + s/0.7)(1 + s)(1 + s/40)}}{\dfrac{(1/2)}{(1 + s/2)(1 + s/4)}}
$$

$$
= \frac{100(1/2.7)(1/2)(1/4)(s + 2)(s + 2.7)(s + 4)}{(1/2)(1/0.7)(1/40)(s + 0.7)(s + 1)(s + 40)}
$$

$$
= \frac{130(s + 2)(s + 2.7)(s + 4)}{(s + 0.7)(s + 1)(s + 40)}.
$$

The compensator turns out to be third order. This happens because both plant poles have been canceled. This is certainly not a big liability, but from the standpoint of an analog implementation, it would be better if a second-order compensator with about the same performance could be found. As it turns out, the design just completed can be used as a guide in reducing the order of $G_c$.

If the order of the compensator is to be reduced to two, then one of the poles of the plant must remain uncanceled. The following designs are based on allowing the pole at $s = -2$ to break in. This is an example of letting the plant work for us whenever possible.

Three designs are shown in Fig. 11.12. Letting the plant pole at $s = -2$ break in narrows the "design corridor." However, the corridor is still wide enough to find a design that meets the specifications. With a little experience, one glance at the width of the design corridor is usually enough to tell whether the design specifications can be met. Table 11.1 summarizes the three designs shown in Fig. 11.12.

We now have to choose between design 2 and design 3. Design 2 meets the specifications and has a slightly higher crossover frequency than design 3. Design 3, on the other hand, has a better phase margin and will exhibit less overshoot. For design 2,

$$
G_c(s) = \frac{200(s + 4)(s + 5)}{(s + 0.5)(s + 40)}.
$$

The root locus and step response for design 2 are shown in Fig. 11.13.

**Table 11.1 |** Summary of three lead/lag designs for Example 11.6.1.

| $G_cG_p(s)$ | $\omega_c$ (rad/s) | $\phi_m$ |
|---|---|---|
| $\dfrac{100(1 + s/4)}{(1 + s/0.5)(1 + s/2)(1 + s/35)}$ | 30 | 46.6° |
| $\dfrac{100(1 + s/5)}{(1 + s/0.5)(1 + s/2)(1 + s/40)}$ | 25 | 52.4° |
| $\dfrac{100(1 + s/6)}{(1 + s/0.5)(1 + s/2)(1 + s/50)}$ | 20 | 58.6° |

**Figure 11.12 |** Three second-order lead/lag compensators, Example 11.6.1.

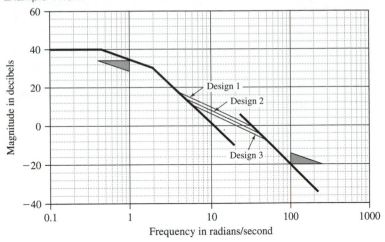

**Figure 11.13 |** (a) Root locus and (b) step response redesign 2, Example 11.6.1.

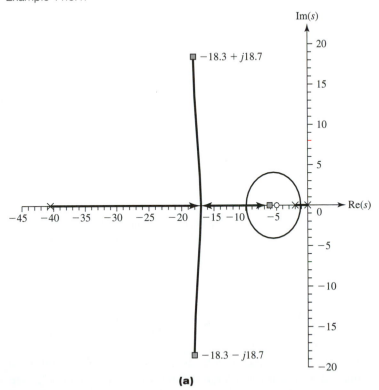

(a)

**Figure 11.13** | Continued

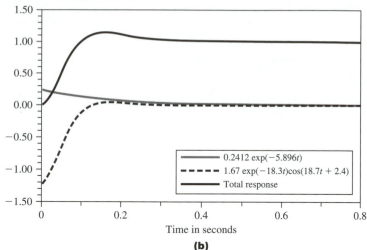

**(b)**

Before leaving this example, we state a rule of thumb for finding the crossover frequency for which the phase margin is maximized. As we have already discussed, maximum phase margin occurs when the slope of −20 dB/decade is equally balanced on both sides of the crossover frequency, or when

$$\log_{10} \omega_c = \frac{\log_{10} \omega_h + \log_{10} \omega_\ell}{2},$$  **[11.17]**

where $\omega_\ell$ and $\omega_h$ are the frequencies for which the asymptotes of slope −40 dB/decade that define the design corridor cross the 0-dB line. Equation [11.17] is equivalent to

$$\omega_c = \sqrt{\omega_\ell \omega_h},$$

the so-called geometric mean of the line segment on the 0-dB line determined by the design corridor. For the example under consideration, we obtain

$$\omega_c = \sqrt{10 \times 30} = 17.3 \text{ rad/s.}$$

We can either compute the geometric mean or simply find the midpoint of the line segment on the Bode plot. This provides a good starting point for finding the crossover frequency that yields the maximum phase margin.

---

The examples considered so far have been of low order, two poles and no zeros. We might well ask what happens if the plant has a larger number of poles, plus some zeros. The answer is that the techniques presented so far have to be modified somewhat, but not a great deal.

The main effect of additional poles is that the compensator will be of higher order. Further, if a system has a large number of poles, certain poles are usually more important than others and dominate the behavior of the system. Generally, these additional poles and zeros will be far enough away from the crossover frequency that they will have minimal effect on the phase margin. There are, of course, exceptions. The intent in this chapter is to treat the predominate case where a few poles dominate the behavior of a system.

To partially answer the question of how the design methodology works for more complicated systems, the next example considers a system with a pole-zero excess of three. The modifications to the design technique needed to treat this case will prove to be minimal.

**EXAMPLE 11.6.2**

Consider the plant

$$G_p(s) = \frac{100}{s(s+1)(s+10)}$$

This system has three poles that are within the design corridor. The goal is to design a *second-order* compensator

$$G_c(s) = \frac{K_c(s+z_1)(s+z_2)}{(s+p_1)(s+100)}$$

that will meet these specifications:

1. $K_v \geq 100$.

2. $\dfrac{|E(j\omega)|}{|R(j\omega)|} \leq 0.02$ for $\omega \leq 1$ rad/s.

3. $\dfrac{C(j\omega)}{R(j\omega)} \leq 0.1$ for $\omega \geq 100$ rad/s.

4. Phase margin: $45° \leq \phi_m \leq 50°$.

5. Crossover frequency $\omega_c$ maximized consistent with specifications 1 to 4.

The asymptotic Bode magnitude plot is shown in Fig. 11.14. Setting the low-frequency asymptote and placing the bandwidth and noise suppression specifications on the Bode magnitude plot are by now routine steps in the design process and will not be discussed.

Since the system has a pole-zero excess of three, the high-frequency asymptote must have a slope of −60 dB/decade. In the figure the design corridor defined by two asymptotes of slope −40 dB/decade still exists. A pole has been added at $s = -100$ to make the high-frequency asymptote have the required slope of −60 dB/decade.

The placement of the pole at $s = -100$ is somewhat arbitrary. In this case, we have placed it far enough above the intended crossover frequency that it should have minimal impact on the phase margin. There are, of course, other choices. One is to give the high-frequency asymptote a slope of −60 dB/decade. This will lead to a double pole when the slope of −20 dB/decade intersects the slope of −60 dB/decade.

The main difference between these strategies will be the amount of compensator gain required. In many cases, the available gain is limited. If we add a gain limitation to the specifications, then we may have to investigate more design options to find the most suitable compensation.

**Figure 11.14** | Three lead/lag designs for Example 11.6.2.

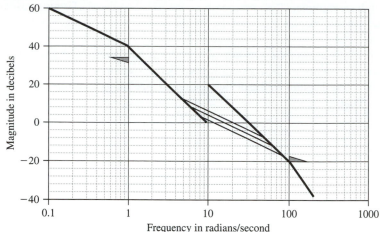

The first of three designs we consider is

$$G_c(s)G_p(s) = \frac{100(1 + s/8)}{s(1 + s)(1 + s/80)(1 + s/100)}.$$

For this design, $\omega_c = 12$ rad/s. Then the phase at crossover is

$$\underline{/G_cG_p(j12)} = \tan^{-1}\frac{12}{8} - 90° - \tan^{-1}12 - \tan^{-1}\frac{12}{80} - \tan^{-1}\frac{12}{100}$$

$$= 56.3° - 90° - 85.2° - 8.5° - 6.8°$$

$$= -134°.$$

This resulting phase margin is 46°.

This is at the lower end of the specified interval for phase margin. By increasing the crossover frequency slightly, it should be possible to improve the phase margin by better balancing the amount of slope of −20 dB/decade on either side of the crossover frequency.

To that end, we consider design 2 for which

$$G_c(s)G_p(s) = \frac{100(1 + s/6)}{s(1 + s)(1 + s/60)(1 + s/100)}.$$

For this design $\omega_c = 15$ rad/s, and the phase at crossover is

$$\underline{/G_cG_p(j15)} = \tan^{-1}\frac{15}{6} - 90° - \tan^{-1}15 - \tan^{-1}\frac{15}{60} - \tan^{-1}\frac{15}{100}$$

$$= 68.2° - 90° - 86.2° - 14° - 8.5°$$

$$= -131°,$$

improving the phase margin slightly to 49°. Since the greater the phase margin, the smaller the overshoot and the stabler the response, the general rule is to make the phase margin as large as is reasonably possible. In this case, 49° is probably right at the maximum attainable phase margin.

To check this suspicion, we consider a third design:

$$G_c(s)G_p(s) = \frac{100(1 + s/5)}{s(1 + s)(1 + s/50)(1 + s/100)}.$$

In this case, $\omega_c = 20$ rad/s, and the phase at crossover is

$$\underline{/G_cG_p(j20)} = \tan^{-1}\frac{20}{5} - 90° - \tan^{-1}20 - \tan^{-1}\frac{20}{50} - \tan^{-1}\frac{20}{100}$$

$$= 76° - 90° - 87° - 22° - 11.31°$$

$$= -134°.$$

The phase margin has decreased to 46°. As suspected, the maximum phase margin is about 50°. We can check this by finding the geometric mean frequency

$$\omega = \sqrt{10 \times 30} = 17 \text{ rad/s}.$$

Given the small range of variation in phase margin, design 3 has the maximum crossover frequency obtainable while still meeting the other specifications. If we choose design 3, then

$$G_c(s) = \frac{1000(s + 5)(s + 10)}{(s + 50)(s + 100)}.$$

Accurate Bode magnitude and phase plots for the compensated system are shown in Fig. 11.15. Note that the actual phase margin and crossover frequency are almost exactly those predicted from the *asymptotic* Bode plot.

The root locus and time response are shown in Figs. 11.16(a) and 11.16(b), respectively. Because the phase margin is on the low side, the percent overshoot is 28%. The system is not, however, very oscillatory. This leads us to an interesting

**Figure 11.15 |** Bode phase and magnitude plots for system 3.

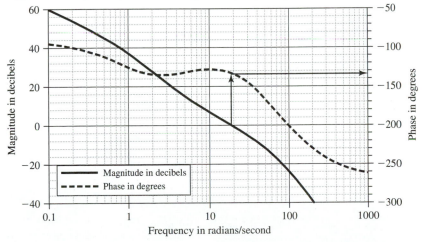

**Figure 11.16 |** (a) Root locus and (b) step response for design 3 of Example 11.6.2.

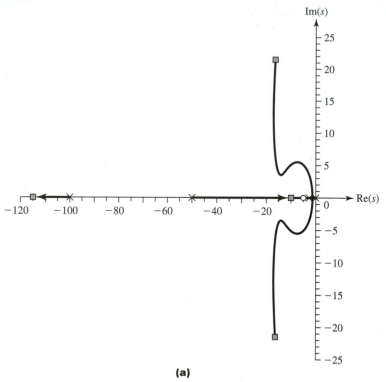

**(a)**

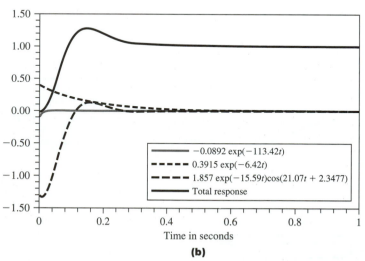

**(b)**

observation. If we can keep the overshoot down around 20%, then the step response seldom oscillates. It simply overshoots and then sinks back to steady state. Thus, the settling time is usually a function of how fast the response approaches steady state following the overshoot.

Our purpose in Example 11.6.2 was to show that a system with a pole-zero excess greater than two can be successfully analyzed using the design techniques presented in this chapter. Indeed, the methodology outlined here is merely a set of guidelines. As we grow more comfortable with Bode design these guidelines can be adjusted and modified to suit the problem.

Example 11.6.3 reconsiders an earlier design, that of Example 7.3.2 in Chapter 7. This provides another opportunity to compare root locus design and Bode design.

**EXAMPLE 11.6.3**

The approach taken in Example 7.3.2 was to make the closed-loop transfer function look as much like $T_{N2}$ as possible. In Example 7.3.2, the plant was

$$G_p(s) = \frac{10}{s(s+1)},$$

and the compensator, for the case of near, but not exact, cancellation was

$$G_c(s) = \frac{1.87(s+1.1)}{s+6.15}.$$

The Bode magnitude and phase plots for

$$G_c G_p(s) = \frac{18.7(s+1.1)}{s(s+1)(s+6.15)}$$

are shown in Fig. 11.17. Note that the crossover frequency is a decade below that of any of the Examples in this chapter, and that $K_v = 3.2$. These are not very stringent specifications compared to those set out in this chapter.

**Figure 11.17 |** Bode phase and magnitude plots for Example 7.3.2.

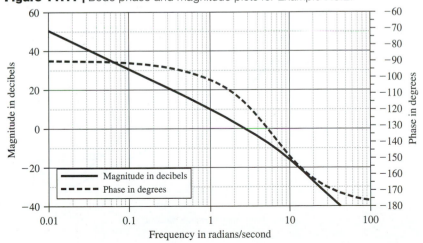

By way of comparison, a Bode design is now presented based on these more stringent specifications:

1.  $K_v \geq 100$.

2.  $\dfrac{|E(j\omega_1)|}{|R(j\omega_1)|} \leq 0.01$ for $\omega_1 \leq 0.2$ rad/s.

3.  $\dfrac{|C(j\omega_2)|}{|R(j\omega_2)|} \leq 0.1$ for $\omega_2 \geq 100$ rad/s.

4.  $\omega_c$ in the neighborhood of 3 rad/s.

5.  $\phi_m$ large enough to keep the percent overshoot under 10%.

The specifications are chosen so that the Bode design will yield performance similar to the original root locus design.

Only one design is shown in Fig. 11.18, namely,

$$G_c G_p(s) = \frac{100(1 + s/1.1)}{s(1 + s/0.04)(1 + s/300)}.$$

The crossover frequency is $\omega_c = 3.5$ rad/s, so that the phase of the system at crossover is

$$\underline{/G_c G_p(j3.5)} = \tan^{-1}\frac{3.5}{1.1} - 90° - \tan^{-1}\frac{3.5}{0.04} - \tan^{-1}\frac{3.5}{300}$$

$$= 72.6° - 90° - 89.4° - 0.7°$$

$$= -108°.$$

The phase margin is then 72°, and

$$G_c = \frac{109(s+1)(s+1.1)}{(s+0.04)(s+300)}.$$

The root locus and step response for this design are shown in Figs. 11.19(a) and 11.19(b), respectively. The root locus does not show the closed-loop pole at $s = -296$.

**Figure 11.18 |** Lead/lag design for Example 11.6.3.

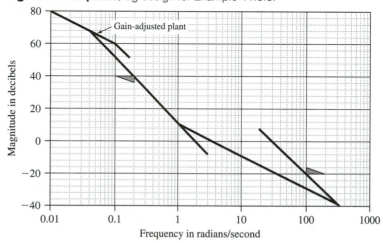

**Figure 11.19** | (a) Root locus and (b) step response for
Example 11.6.3.

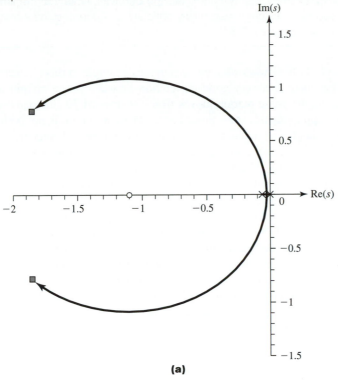

**(a)**

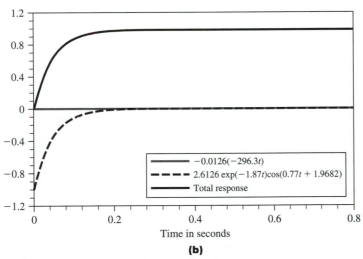

**(b)**

It is not expected that this pole will have much impact on the time response. It is the two complex poles that will dominate the behavior. Note that the time response of the closed-loop system is essentially critically damped and more than meets the specifications of Example 7.3.2.

---

Example 11.6.3 shows what every previous example in this chapter has shown, namely, that there is a very good correlation between phase margin and percent overshoot. As the phase margin moves from 50° toward 70° the percent overshoot drops from approximately 20% toward zero. The correlation is not perfect, and the percent overshoot corresponding to a given phase margin will vary from problem to problem. The correlation is strong enough, however, to give the experienced designer a very good idea of the percent overshoot that the time response will exhibit.

The compensator of Example 11.6.3 meets more stringent specifications than the compensator of Example 7.3.2. The price paid for this improved importance is roughly a 50-fold increase in gain. Moreover, increasing the gain almost always increases the cost of the control effort. If the amplification is done electronically the increased cost and weight may not be that significant. The situation may be quite different if the amplification is done mechanically or hydraulically, for instance.

In engineering there is always a trade-off between cost and performance that dictates the design choice. In the present case, it may turn out that it is preferable to relax the specifications and choose the original root locus design if the cost is significantly less. On the other hand, if accurate tracking of ramp, or ramp-like, inputs is necessary, then the Bode design will probably be the choice.

## 11.7 | CLOSED-LOOP ANALYSIS

In this section, we take a very brief look at design using the closed-loop system. The primary tool for this type of analysis is the Nichols chart. We introduced the Nichols chart at the end of Chapter 10, noting that it was a semi-logarithmic polar plot of $G(j\omega)$ augmented with circles of constant magnitude and constant phase for the *closed-loop* system.

From the 1940s to 1960, the Nichols chart was in wide use. Some very good designers of that era preferred it to the Bode plot as a design tool. Our preference has already been made clear, but to give the reader a feel for this design tool, Fig. 11.20 shows two designs from this chapter plotted on a Nichols chart.

For the design we chose in Example 11.6.2, $G_c G_p(j\omega)$ had a phase margin of 45°. The closed-loop system had a percent overshoot of 28% for a unit step input. By contrast, for the design we chose in Example 11.6.3, $G_c G_p(j\omega)$ had a phase margin of 72° and the percent overshoot was under 5%. We now would like to see if we can deduce the percent overshoot of the time responses of each of these systems from the plot of its loop transfer function on the Nichols chart.

We see that the plot for the system of Example 11.6.2 just touches the 2 dB $M$ circle. That means that if we plot $M(j\omega)$ [remember that $M(j\omega) \equiv T_c(j\omega)$], then the maximum value of the magnitude will be 125% of $M(0)$. Note that this

**Figure 11.20 |** Nichols chart plot of $G_c G_p(j\omega)$ for designs of Examples 11.6.2 and 11.6.3.

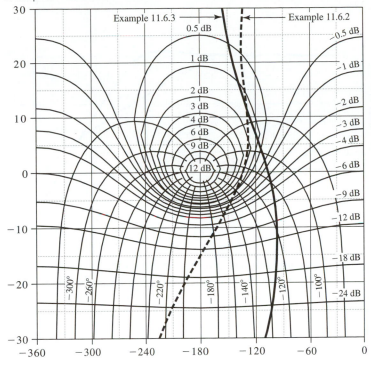

corresponds pretty well with the percent overshoot of 28%. For the system of Example 11.6.3, we have to interpolate a bit. If we guess that the nearest approach is to the 1.5 dB $M$ circle, then the maximum value of $M(j\omega)$ would be about 105% of the value $M(0)$. Again, this agrees quite well with the percent overshoot of the step response.

Instead of a Nichols chart, some designers prefer to simply use the Bode magnitude and phase plots of the closed-loop system. The advantage here is that the frequency information is more readily available. In Fig. 11.21, we show the magnitude plots of the closed-loop transfer functions that resulted from our designs in the two examples. What a designer familiar with this technique looks for is a nice "flat" frequency response out to the hump. If the response is flat out to the hump, then the designer can take the ratio of the hump to the dc value of the closed-loop system (normally 1.0) and make a very good estimate of the percent overshoot to a step input. If the plot is wavy before the hump, then chances are that the step response is not going to behave well.

This is the extent of our discussion of the Nichols chart and design using the closed-loop transfer function. Use of Nichols charts has declined, but many designers still use it. As with most things in life, everybody has their own favorite flavor of ice cream. It is worth noting that control system craftsmen like "Nick" Nichols and

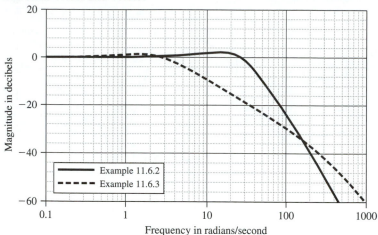

**Figure 11.21 |** Bode magnitude plots of $T_c(j\omega)$ for designs of Exercises 11.6.2 and 11.6.3.

George Axelby were truly artists at shaping the plot of the loop transfer function on the Nichols chart. They then could predict with great accuracy the performance of the closed-loop system.

## 11.8 | REPRISE

In this chapter, the Bode design method was introduced and then refined through a series of examples. The key properties of this design technique revealed by these examples are enumerated here.

1. It is possible to predict the behavior of the closed-loop system from a Bode magnitude plot of the open-loop transfer function $G_c G_p(s)$. Gain margin, phase margin, the height of the low-frequency asymptote, and the crossover frequency $\omega_c$ all give reliable information about the closed-loop performance in the time domain.

2. It is possible to transfer specifications couched in terms of the closed-loop system to the asymptotic Bode magnitude plot of $G_c G_p(j\omega)$. Two such specifications introduced in this chapter were those on the bandwidth and noise suppression characteristics of the *closed-loop* system.

3. There is a very strong correlation between phase margin and percent overshoot. This particular figure of merit is extremely useful to the experienced designer.

4. The asymptotic Bode magnitude plot provides excellent scale compression.

5. The ability to estimate the phase margin from the Bode magnitude plot is an invaluable aid to the experienced designer. With the exception of Example 11.6.3, all the other asymptotic Bode plots in the chapter are drawn to exactly the same scale. This enables the width of the design corridor to be compared from example to example.

With experience, a designer can predict quite accurately the maximum phase margin available by merely looking at the width of the design corridor between the two asymptotes of slope $-40$ dB/decade. As a consequence, usually only two or three design iterations are required to achieve a final design. In the process, it may be necessary to compute the arctangent of about a dozen angles, but this is not a great inconvenience with a modern calculator or MATLAB.

6.  It is possible to easily do some simple optimization. Since the phase margin tends to peak when the crossover frequency is near the middle of the design corridor, we can maximize phase margin, or, alternatively, maximize $\omega_c$, while simultaneously keeping $\phi_m$ above some minimum value. Many variations are possible, including varying the specifications on bandwidth and noise suppression to meet phase margin and crossover frequency constraints. Indeed, the Bode design method is the genesis of the current interest in robust control, a topic we will discuss in Chapter 12.

7.  The techniques presented in this chapter can be easily modified for application to higher-order systems. The simple, low-order plants used in the examples of this chapter were chosen to help reveal the essential features of Bode design. Once mastered, these techniques work equally well on more complicated systems.

Bode design is without question the best method to use for the design of cascade compensation for linear time-invariant systems. However, the root locus approach can be helpful in seeing what the Bode design is accomplishing. As the reader can verify by reviewing the examples of this chapter, Bode design is a pole cancellation technique. In many cases, the resulting overall system closely approximates an old friend, namely the normalized, second-order transfer function $T_{N2}$. The root locus plots included with each example corroborate this statement. The fact that the Bode design approach can in many cases yield a closed-loop system that approximates $T_{N2}$ accounts in large part for its power.

# 11.9 | PROBLEMS

## 11.9.1 Bode Design

For each problem, using the unity feedback configuration of Fig. 11.22, design a compensator that meets the stated specifications.

1.  $G_p(s) = \dfrac{10}{(s+1)(s+3)}$.

    Design the lowest-order compensator that will meet these specifications:

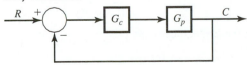

**Figure 11.22 |** Cascade compensation with unity feedback.

a.  $K_p \geq 100$.

b.  $\left| \dfrac{E(j\omega)}{R(j\omega)} \right| \leq 0.01$ for $\omega \leq 1$ rad/s.

c.  $\left| \dfrac{C(j\omega)}{R(j\omega)} \right| \leq 0.1$ for $\omega \geq 200$ rad/s.

d.  Phase margin $\phi_m$ of at least $50°$.

e.  Crossover frequency $\omega_c$ maximized, consistent with specifications a–d.

2.  $G_p(s) = \dfrac{10}{(s+1)(s+3)}$.

Design the lowest order compensator that will meet these specifications:

a.  $K_p \geq 100$.

b.  $\left| \dfrac{E(j\omega)}{R(j\omega)} \right| \leq 0.02$ for $\omega \leq 1$ rad/s.

c.  $\left| \dfrac{C(j\omega)}{R(j\omega)} \right| \leq 0.1$ for $\omega \geq 100$ rad/s.

d.  Phase margin $\phi_m$ of at least $60°$.

e.  Crossover frequency $\omega_c$ maximized consistent with specifications a–d.

3.  $G_p(s) = \dfrac{10}{(s+1)(s+3)}$.

Design the lowest order compensator that will meet these specifications:

a.  $K_p \geq 100$.

b.  $\left| \dfrac{E(j\omega)}{R(j\omega)} \right| \leq 0.02$ for $\omega \leq 1$ rad/s.

c.  $\left| \dfrac{C(j\omega)}{R(j\omega)} \right| \leq 0.05$ for $\omega \geq 300$ rad/s.

d.  Phase margin $\phi_m$ of at least $55°$.

e.  Crossover frequency $\omega_c$ maximized consistent with specifications a–d.

4.  $G_p(s) = \dfrac{10}{(s+1)(s+3)}$.

Design the lowest order compensator that will meet these specifications:

a.  $K_p \geq 100$.

b.  $\left| \dfrac{E(j\omega)}{R(j\omega)} \right| \leq 0.02$ for $\omega \leq 1$ rad/s.

c.  $\left| \dfrac{C(j\omega)}{R(j\omega)} \right| \leq 0.05$ for $\omega \geq 150$ rad/s.

d.  Phase margin $\phi_m$ of at least $60°$.

e.  Crossover frequency $\omega_c$ maximized consistent with specifications a–d.

5.  $G_p(s) = \dfrac{40}{(s+2)(s+20)}$.

Design a compensator

$$G_c(s) = \frac{K_c(s+z_1)(s+z_2)}{(s+p_1)(s+p_2)}$$

that will meet these specifications:

a.  $K_p \geq 100$.

b. $\left|\dfrac{E(j\omega)}{R(j\omega)}\right| \leq 0.02$ for $\omega \leq 1$ rad/s.

c. $\left|\dfrac{C(j\omega)}{R(j\omega)}\right| \leq 0.05$ for $\omega \geq 100$ rad/s.

d. Phase margin: $45° \leq \phi_m \leq 50°$.

e. Crossover frequency $\omega_c$ maximized consistent with specifications a–d.

6. $G_p(s) = \dfrac{40}{(s+2)(s+20)}$.

Design a compensator

$$G_c(s) = \dfrac{K_c(s+z_1)(s+z_2)}{(s+p_1)(s+p_2)}$$

that will meet these specifications:

a. $K_p \geq 100$.

b. $\left|\dfrac{E(j\omega)}{R(j\omega)}\right| \leq 0.02$ for $\omega \leq 1$ rad/s.

c. $\left|\dfrac{C(j\omega)}{R(j\omega)}\right| \leq 0.1$ for $\omega \geq 100$ rad/s.

d. Phase margin: $\phi_m \geq 55°$.

e. Crossover frequency $\omega_c$ maximized consistent with specifications a–d.

7. $G_p(s) = \dfrac{40}{(s+2)(s+20)}$.

Design a compensator

$$G_c(s) = \dfrac{K_c(s+z_1)(s+z_2)}{(s+p_1)(s+p_2)}$$

that will meet these specifications:

a. $K_p \geq 100$.

b. $\left|\dfrac{E(j\omega)}{R(j\omega)}\right| \leq 0.02$ for $\omega \leq 1$ rad/s.

c. $\left|\dfrac{C(j\omega)}{R(j\omega)}\right| \leq 0.1$ for $\omega \geq 200$ rad/s.

d. Crossover frequency $\omega_c \geq 20$ rad/s.

e. Phase margin $\phi_m$ maximized consistent with specifications a–d.

8. $G_p(s) = \dfrac{10}{s(s+5)}$.

Design a compensator

$$G_c(s) = \dfrac{K_c(s+z_1)(s+z_2)}{(s+p_1)(s+p_2)}$$

that will meet these specifications:

a. $K_v \geq 100$.

b. $\left|\dfrac{E(j\omega)}{R(j\omega)}\right| \leq 0.02$ for $\omega \leq 1$ rad/s.

c. $\left|\dfrac{C(j\omega)}{R(j\omega)}\right| \leq 0.05$ for $\omega \geq 150$ rad/s.

   d.   Phase margin $\phi_m \geq 60°$.
   e.   Crossover frequency $\omega_c$ maximized consistent with specifications a–d.

9.   $G_p(s) = \dfrac{10}{s(s+5)}$.

Design a compensator

$$G_c(s) = \frac{K_c(s+z_1)(s+z_2)}{(s+p_1)(s+p_2)}$$

that will meet these specifications:
   a.   $K_v \geq 100$.
   b.   $\left|\dfrac{E(j\omega)}{R(j\omega)}\right| \leq 0.02$ for $\omega \leq 1$ rad/s.
   c.   $\left|\dfrac{C(j\omega)}{R(j\omega)}\right| \leq 0.1$ for $\omega \geq 100$ rad/s.
   d.   Crossover frequency, $\omega_c \geq 15$ rad/s.
   e.   Phase margin $\phi_m$ maximized consistent with specifications a–d.

10.   $G_p(s) = \dfrac{100}{s(s+1)(s+10)}$.

Design a compensator

$$G_c(s) = \frac{K_c(s+z_1)(s+z_2)}{(s+p_1)(s+100)}$$

that will meet these specifications:
   a.   $K_v \geq 100$.
   b.   $\left|\dfrac{E(j\omega)}{R(j\omega)}\right| \leq 0.02$ for $\omega \leq 1$ rad/s.
   c.   $\left|\dfrac{C(j\omega)}{R(j\omega)}\right| \leq 0.1$ for $\omega \geq 100$ rad/s.
   d.   Phase margin: $45° \leq \phi_m \leq 50°$.
   e.   Crossover frequency $\omega_c$ maximized consistent with specifications a–d.

11.   $G_p(s) = \dfrac{300}{s(s+3)(s+50)}$.

Design a compensator

$$G_c(s) = \frac{K_c(s+z_1)(s+z_2)}{(s+p_1)(s+100)}$$

that will meet these specifications:
   a.   $K_v \geq 100$.
   b.   $\left|\dfrac{E(j\omega)}{R(j\omega)}\right| \leq 0.02$ for $\omega \leq 1$ rad/s.
   c.   $\left|\dfrac{C(j\omega)}{R(j\omega)}\right| \leq 0.1$ for $\omega \geq 100$ rad/s.
   d.   Phase margin: $\phi_m \geq 50°$.
   e.   Crossover frequency $\omega_c$ maximized consistent with specifications a–d.

12. $G_p(s) = \dfrac{50}{s(s+10)(s+50)}$.

Design a compensator

$$G_c(s) = \dfrac{K_c(s+z_1)(s+z_2)}{(s+p_1)(1+s/100)}$$

that will meet these specifications:

a. $K_v \geq 100$.

b. $\left|\dfrac{E(j\omega)}{R(j\omega)}\right| \leq 0.02$ for $\omega \leq 1$ rad/s.

c. $\left|\dfrac{C(j\omega)}{R(j\omega)}\right| \leq 0.1$ for $\omega \geq 100$ rad/s.

d. Phase margin: $50° \leq \phi_m \leq 60°$.

e. Crossover frequency $\omega_c$ maximized consistent with specifications a–d.

13. $G_p(s) = \dfrac{50}{s(s+50)}$.

Design the lowest-order compensator that will meet these specifications:

a. $K_v \geq 100$.

b. $\left|\dfrac{E(j\omega)}{R(j\omega)}\right| \leq 0.02$ for $\omega \leq 1$ rad/s.

c. $\left|\dfrac{C(j\omega)}{R(j\omega)}\right| \leq 0.1$ for $\omega \geq 100$ rad/s.

d. Crossover frequency $\omega_c \geq 10$ rad/s.

e. Phase margin $\phi_m$ maximized consistent with specifications a–d.

14. $G_p(s) = \dfrac{60}{(s+2)(s+30)}$.

Design a compensator

$$G_c(s) = \dfrac{K_c(s+z_1)(s+z_2)}{(s+p_1)(s+p_2)}$$

that will meet these specifications:

a. $K_p \geq 100$.

b. $\left|\dfrac{E(j\omega)}{R(j\omega)}\right| \leq 0.02$ for $\omega \leq 1$ rad/s.

c. $\left|\dfrac{C(j\omega)}{R(j\omega)}\right| \leq 0.05$ for $\omega \geq 100$ rad/s.

d. Phase margin: $45° \leq \phi_m \leq 50°$.

e. Crossover frequency $\omega_c$ maximized consistent with specifications a–d.

15. $G_p(s) = \dfrac{60}{(s+2)(s+30)}$.

Design a compensator

$$G_c(s) = \dfrac{K_c(s+z_1)(s+z_2)}{(s+p_1)(s+p_2)}$$

that will meet these specifications:

a.   $K_p \geq 100$.

b.   $\left| \dfrac{E(j\omega)}{R(j\omega)} \right| \leq 0.02$ for $\omega \leq 1$ rad/s.

c.   $\left| \dfrac{C(j\omega)}{R(j\omega)} \right| \leq 0.1$ for $\omega \geq 100$ rad/s.

d.   Phase margin: $50° \leq \phi_m \leq 60°$.

e.   Crossover frequency $\omega_c$ maximized consistent with specifications a–d.

16.   $G_p(s) = \dfrac{100}{s(s + 2)(s + 30)}$.

Design a compensator

$$G_c(s) = \frac{K_c(s + z_1)(s + z_2)}{(s + p_1)(s + p_2)}$$

that will meet these specifications:

a.   $K_v \geq 100$.

b.   $\left| \dfrac{E(j\omega)}{R(j\omega)} \right| \leq 0.02$ for $\omega \leq 1$ rad/s.

c.   $\left| \dfrac{C(j\omega)}{R(j\omega)} \right| \leq 0.05$ for $\omega \geq 100$ rad/s.

d.   Phase margin: $\phi_m \geq 50°$.

e.   Crossover frequency $\omega_c$ maximized consistent with specifications a–d.

17.   $G_p(s) = \dfrac{100}{s(s + 2)(s + 30)}$.

Design a compensator

$$G_c(s) = \frac{K_c(s + z_1)(s + z_2)}{(s + p_1)(s + p_2)}$$

that will meet these specifications:

a.   $K_v \geq 100$.

b.   $\dfrac{|E(j\omega)|}{|R(j\omega)|} \leq 0.02$ for $\omega \leq 1$ rad/s.

c.   $\dfrac{|C(j\omega)|}{|R(j\omega)|} \leq 0.1$ for $\omega \geq 300$ rad/s.

d.   Phase margin: $\phi_m \geq 50°$.

e.   Crossover frequency $\omega_c$ maximized consistent with specifications a–d.

18.   $G_p(s) = \dfrac{5}{s(s + 0.5)}$.

Design a compensator

$$G_c(s) = \frac{K_c(s + z_1)(s + z_2)}{(s + p_1)(s + p_2)}$$

that will meet these specifications:

a.   $K_v \geq 100$.

b.   $\dfrac{|E(j\omega)|}{|R(j\omega)|} \leq 0.01$ for $\omega \leq 0.1$ rad/s.

c. $\dfrac{|C(j\omega)|}{|R(j\omega)|} \le 0.05$ for $\omega \ge 30$ rad/s.

d. Phase margin $\phi_m$ maximized.

For your final design, estimate the percent overshoot from these categories:

a. PO < 10%.

b. 10% < PO < 30%.

c. PO > 30%.

19. $G_p(s) = \dfrac{10}{s^2}$.

Design a compensator

$$G_c(s) = \dfrac{K_c \prod_{i=1}^{n}(s + z_i)}{\prod_{i=1}^{n}(s + p_i)}$$

that will meet these specifications:

a. $K_a \ge 100$.

b. $\left|\dfrac{E(j\omega)}{R(j\omega)}\right| \le 0.02$ for $\omega \le 1$ rad/s.

c. $\left|\dfrac{C(j\omega)}{R(j\omega)}\right| \le 0.1$ for $\omega \ge 200$ rad/s.

d. Phase margin: $\phi_m \ge 55°$.

e. Crossover frequency $\omega_c$ as large as possible consistent with specifications a–d.

f. Order of compensator as low as possible.

20. $G_p(s) = \dfrac{10}{s^2}$.

Design a compensator

$$G_c(s) = \dfrac{K_c \prod_{i=1}^{n}(s + z_i)}{\prod_{i=1}^{n}(s + p_i)}$$

that will meet these specifications:

a. $K_a \ge 100$.

b. $\left|\dfrac{E(j\omega)}{R(j\omega)}\right| \le 0.01$ for $\omega \le 1$ rad/s.

c. $\left|\dfrac{C(j\omega)}{R(j\omega)}\right| \le 0.1$ for $\omega \ge 200$ rad/s.

d. Phase margin: $\phi_m \ge 60°$.

e. Crossover frequency $\omega_c$ as large as possible consistent with specifications a–d.

f. Order of compensator as low as possible.

21. $G_p(s) = \dfrac{20}{s^2(s + 4)}$.

Design a compensator

$$G_c(s) = \dfrac{K_c(s + z_1)(s + z_2)}{(s + p_1)(s + p_2)}$$

that will meet these specifications:

    a.   $K_a \geq 10$.

    b.   $\left|\dfrac{E(j\omega)}{R(j\omega)}\right| \leq 0.01$ for $\omega \leq 0.1$ rad/s.

    c.   $\left|\dfrac{C(j\omega)}{R(j\omega)}\right| \leq 0.1$ for $\omega \geq 60$ rad/s.

    d.   Phase margin: $\phi_m \geq 55°$.

    e.   Crossover frequency: $\omega_c \geq 10$ rad/s.

**22.**   $G_p(s) = \dfrac{10}{s^2(s+2)}$.

Design a compensator

$$G_c(s) = \frac{K_c(s+z_1)(s+z_2)}{(s+p_1)(s+p_2)}$$

that will meet these specifications:

    a.   $K_a \geq 10$.

    b.   $\left|\dfrac{E(j\omega)}{R(j\omega)}\right| \leq 0.01$ for $\omega \leq 0.1$ rad/s.

    c.   $\left|\dfrac{C(j\omega)}{R(j\omega)}\right| \leq 0.1$ for $\omega \geq 60$ rad/s.

    d.   Phase margin: $\phi_m \geq 55°$.

    e.   Crossover frequency: $\omega_c \geq 10$ rad/s.

**23.**   $G_p(s) = \dfrac{100(s+6)}{s^2(s+20)}$.

Design a compensator

$$G_c(s) = \frac{K_c\prod_{i=1}^{n}(s+z_i)}{\prod_{i=1}^{n}(s+p_i)}$$

that will meet these specifications:

    a.   $K_a \geq 100$.

    b.   $\left|\dfrac{E(j\omega)}{R(j\omega)}\right| \leq 0.02$ for $\omega \leq 1$ rad/s.

    c.   $\left|\dfrac{C(j\omega)}{R(j\omega)}\right| \leq 0.1$ for $\omega \geq 100$ rad/s.

    d.   Phase margin: $\phi_m \geq 50°$.

    e.   Crossover frequency $\omega_c > 15$ rad/s.

    f.   Order of compensator as low as possible.

**24.**   $G_p(s) = \dfrac{100(s+6)}{s^2(s+20)}$.

Design a compensator

$$G_c(s) = \frac{K_c\prod_{i=1}^{n}(s+z_i)}{\prod_{i=1}^{n}(s+p_i)}$$

that will meet these specifications:

    a.   $K_a \geq 100$.

b.   $\left|\dfrac{E(j\omega)}{R(j\omega)}\right| \leq 0.02$ for $\omega \leq 1$ rad/s.

c.   $\left|\dfrac{C(j\omega)}{R(j\omega)}\right| \leq 0.05$ for $\omega \geq 200$ rad/s.

d.   Phase margin: $\phi_m \geq 50°$.

e.   Crossover frequency $\omega_c > 20$ rad/s.

f.   Order of compensator as low as possible.

25.   $G_p(s) = \dfrac{300}{s(s+5)(s+60)}$.

Design a compensator

$$G_c(s) = \frac{K_c(s+z_1)(s+z_2)}{(s+p_1)(s+p_2)}$$

that will meet these specifications:

a.   $K_v \geq 100$.

b.   $\left|\dfrac{E(j\omega)}{R(j\omega)}\right| \leq 0.02$ for $\omega \leq 1$ rad/s.

c.   $\left|\dfrac{C(j\omega)}{R(j\omega)}\right| \leq 0.05$ for $\omega \geq 200$ rad/s.

d.   Phase margin: $\phi_m \geq 50°$.

e.   $\omega_c \geq 20$ rad/s.

f.   $|p_1| \times |p_2|$ minimized consistent with specifications a–e.

26.   $G_p(s) = \dfrac{300}{s(s+5)(s+60)}$.

Design a compensator

$$G_c(s) = \frac{K_c(s+z_1)(s+z_2)}{(s+p_1)(s+p_2)}$$

that will meet these specifications:

a.   $K_v \geq 100$.

b.   $\left|\dfrac{E(j\omega)}{R(j\omega)}\right| \leq 0.01$ for $\omega \leq 1$ rad/s.

c.   $\left|\dfrac{C(j\omega)}{R(j\omega)}\right| \leq 0.1$ for $\omega \geq 200$ rad/s.

d.   Phase margin: $\phi_m \geq 55°$.

e.   $\omega_c \geq 30$ rad/s.

f.   $|p_1| \times |p_2|$ minimized consistent with specifications a–e.

27.   $G_p(s) = \dfrac{40(s+2)}{s(s+60)}$.

Design a compensator

$$G_c(s) = \frac{K_c(s+z_1)}{(s+p_1)}$$

that will meet these specifications:

a.   $K_v \geq 100$.

b.  $\left|\dfrac{E(j\omega)}{R(j\omega)}\right| \leq 0.01$ for $\omega \leq 1$ rad/s.

c.  $\left|\dfrac{C(j\omega)}{R(j\omega)}\right| \leq 0.1$ for $\omega > \omega_h$, $100 \leq \omega_h \leq 200$ rad/s.

d.  $\omega_c \geq 20$ rad/s.

e.  Phase margin: $\phi_m \geq 50°$.

f.  $\omega_h$ *minimized* consistent with the other specifications.

**28.**  $G_p(s) = \dfrac{40(s+2)}{s(s+60)}$.

Design a compensator

$$G_c(s) = \frac{K_c(s+z_1)}{(s+p_1)}$$

that will meet these specifications:

a.  $K_v \geq 100$.

b.  $\left|\dfrac{E(j\omega)}{R(j\omega)}\right| \leq 0.01$ for $\omega \leq 1$ rad/s.

c.  $\left|\dfrac{C(j\omega)}{R(j\omega)}\right| \leq 0.1$ for $\omega > \omega_h$, $100 \leq \omega_h \leq 200$ rad/s.

d.  $\omega_c \geq 20$ rad/s.

e.  Phase margin: $\phi_m \geq 50°$.

f.  $\omega_h$ *minimized* consistent with the other specifications.

**29.**  $G_p(s) = \dfrac{20}{s(s+5)}$.

Design a compensator

$$G_c(s) = \frac{K_c(s+z_1)(s+z_2)}{(s+p_1)(s+p_2)}$$

that will meet these specifications:

a.  $K_v \geq 100$.

b.  $\left|\dfrac{E(j\omega)}{R(j\omega)}\right| \leq 0.02$ for $\omega \leq 0.1$ rad/s.

c.  $\left|\dfrac{C(j\omega)}{R(j\omega)}\right| \leq 0.1$ for $\omega \geq 30$ rad/s.

d.  Phase margin $\phi_m$ maximized.

**30.**  $G_p(s) = \dfrac{(s+10)}{s(s+2)(s+50)}$.

Design the lowest order compensator

$$G_c(s) = \frac{K_c \prod_{i=1}^{n}(s+z_i)}{\prod_{1=1}^{n}(s+p_i)}$$

that will meet these specifications:

a.  $K_v \geq 100$.

b.  $\left|\dfrac{E(j\omega)}{R(j\omega)}\right| \leq 0.01$ for $\omega \leq 1$ rad/s.

c. $\left|\dfrac{C(j\omega)}{R(j\omega)}\right| \le 0.1$ for $\omega > 200$ rad/s.

d. Phase margin: $\phi_m \ge 60°$.

e. $\omega_c$ maximized consistent with the other specifications.

**31.** $G_p(s) = \dfrac{10}{(s+1)(s+2)}$.

Design the lowest-order compensator that will meet these specifications:

a. $K_p \ge 100$.

b. $\left|\dfrac{E(j\omega)}{R(j\omega)}\right| \le 0.01$ for $\omega \le 1$ rad/s.

c. $\left|\dfrac{C(j\omega)}{R(j\omega)}\right| \le 0.1$ for $\omega \ge 200$ rad/s.

d. Phase margin $\phi_m$ of at least $55°$.

e. Crossover frequency $\omega_c$ maximized consistent with specifications a–d.

**32.** $G_p(s) = \dfrac{10}{s(s+10)}$.

Design the lowest-order compensator that will meet these specifications:

a. $K_p \ge 100$.

b. $\left|\dfrac{E(j\omega)}{R(j\omega)}\right| \le 0.02$ for $\omega \le 1$ rad/s.

c. $\left|\dfrac{C(j\omega)}{R(j\omega)}\right| \le 0.1$ for $\omega \ge 200$ rad/s.

d. Crossover frequency $\omega_c \ge 10$ rad/s.

e. Phase margin $\phi_m$ maximized consistent with specifications a–d.

**33.** $G_p(s) = \dfrac{60}{(s+2)(s+30)}$.

Design a compensator

$$G_c(s) = \dfrac{K_c(s+z_1)(s+z_2)}{(s+p_1)(s+p_2)}$$

that will meet these specifications:

a. $K_p \ge 100$.

b. $\left|\dfrac{E(j\omega)}{R(j\omega)}\right| \le 0.02$ for $\omega \le 1$ rad/s.

c. $\left|\dfrac{C(j\omega)}{R(j\omega)}\right| \le 0.05$ for $\omega \ge 100$ rad/s.

d. Phase margin: $45° \le \phi_m \le 50°$.

e. Crossover frequency $\omega_c$ maximized consistent with specifications a–d.

**34.** $G_p(s) = \dfrac{10}{s(s+1)}$.

Design a compensator

$$G_c(s) = \dfrac{K_c(s+z_1)(s+z_2)}{(s+p_1)(s+p_2)}$$

that will meet these specifications:

a. $K_v \geq 100$.

b. $\left| \dfrac{E(j\omega)}{R(j\omega)} \right| \leq 0.02$ for $\omega \leq 1$ rad/s.

c. $\left| \dfrac{C(j\omega)}{R(j\omega)} \right| \leq 0.05$ for $\omega \geq 200$ rad/s.

d. Phase margin: $\phi_m$ maximized.

**35.** $G_p(s) = \dfrac{20}{s(s+20)}$.

Design a compensator

$$G_c(s) = \frac{K_c(s+z_1)(s+z_2)}{(s+p_1)(s+p_2)}$$

that will meet these specifications:

a. $K_v \geq 100$.

b. $\left| \dfrac{E(j\omega)}{R(j\omega)} \right| \leq 0.02$ for $\omega \leq 1$ rad/s.

c. $\left| \dfrac{C(j\omega)}{R(j\omega)} \right| \leq 0.05$ for $\omega \geq 200$ rad/s.

d. Phase margin $\phi_m$ maximized.

**36.** $G_p(s) = \dfrac{40(s+2)}{s(s+1)(s+20)}$.

Design a compensator

$$G_c(s) = \frac{K_c(s+z_1)(s+z_2)}{(s+p_1)(s+p_2)}$$

that will meet these specifications:

a. $K_v \geq 100$.

b. $\left| \dfrac{E(j\omega)}{R(j\omega)} \right| \leq 0.02$ for $\omega \leq 1$ rad/s.

c. $\left| \dfrac{C(j\omega)}{R(j\omega)} \right| \leq 0.1$ for $\omega \geq 100$ rad/s.

d. $\omega_c \geq 20$ rad/s.

e. Phase margin: $\phi_m \geq 50°$.

**37.** $G_p(s) = \dfrac{20}{s(s+5)}$.

Design a compensator

$$G_c(s) = \frac{K_c(s+z_1)(s+z_2)}{(s+p_1)(s+p_2)}$$

that will meet these specifications:

a. $K_v \geq 100$.

b. $\left| \dfrac{E(j\omega)}{R(j\omega)} \right| \leq 0.02$ for $\omega \leq 0.1$ rad/s.

c. $\left| \dfrac{C(j\omega)}{R(j\omega)} \right| \leq 0.1$ for $\omega \geq 30$ rad/s.

d. Phase margin $\phi_m$ maximized.

38. $G_p(s) = \dfrac{40(s+2)}{s(s+60)}$.

    Design a compensator

    $$G_c(s) = \frac{K_c(s+z_1)}{(s+p_1)}$$

    that will meet these specifications:
    a. $K_v \geq 100$.
    b. $\left|\dfrac{E(j\omega)}{R(j\omega)}\right| \leq 0.01$ for $\omega \leq 1$ rad/s.
    c. $\left|\dfrac{C(j\omega)}{R(j\omega)}\right| \leq 0.1$ for $\omega > \omega_h$, $100 \leq \omega_h \leq 200$ rad/s.
    d. $\omega_c \geq 20$ rad/s.
    e. Phase margin: $\phi_m \geq 50°$.
    f. $\omega_h$ *minimized* consistent with the other specifications.

39. $G_p(s) = \dfrac{16}{s(s+8)}$.

    Design a compensator

    $$G_c(s) = \frac{K_c(s+z_1)(s+z_2)}{(s+p_1)(s+p_2)}$$

    that will meet these specifications:
    a. $K_v \geq 100$.
    b. $\left|\dfrac{E(j\omega)}{R(j\omega)}\right| \leq 0.02$ for $\omega \leq 0.1$ rad/s.
    c. $\left|\dfrac{C(j\omega)}{R(j\omega)}\right| \leq 0.05$ for $\omega \geq 40$ rad/s.
    d. Phase margin $\phi_m$ maximized.

40. $G_p(s) = \dfrac{120(s+2)}{s(s+10)(s+60)}$.

    Design a compensator

    $$G_c(s) = \frac{K_c(s+z_1)}{s+p_1}$$

    that will meet these specifications:
    a. $K_v \geq 100$.
    b. $\left|\dfrac{E(j\omega)}{R(j\omega)}\right| \leq 0.01$ for $\omega \leq 1$ rad/s.
    c. $\left|\dfrac{C(j\omega)}{R(j\omega)}\right| \leq 0.1$ for $\omega > \omega_h$, $100 \leq \omega_h \leq 200$ rad/s.
    d. $\omega_c \geq 20$ rad/s.
    e. Phase margin: $\phi_m \geq 50°$.
    f. $\omega_h$ *minimized* consistent with the other specifications.

**41.** $G_p(s) = \dfrac{50}{s(s+1)}$.

Design the lowest-order compensator that meets these specifications:

a.   $K_v \geq 100$.

b.   $\dfrac{|E(j\omega)|}{|R(j\omega)|} \leq 0.02$ for $\omega \leq 1$ rad/s.

c.   $\dfrac{|Y(j\omega)|}{|R(j\omega)|} \leq 0.1$ for $\omega \geq 100$ rad/s.

d.   $\phi_m \geq 50°$.

e.   Crossover frequency $\omega_c$ maximized consistent with the other specifications.

## 11.9.2   Additional Problems

1.   Redesign the lag compensator of Example 11.3.1 so that the phase margin is 45°. Draw the root locus and plot the time response to a unit step input.

2.   For each of the Bode designs in this chapter, make a table similar to that shown here that compares the actual rise time to 63% of final value to the rise time predicted by $t_r \approx 1/\omega_c$.

|            | Ex. 1 | Ex. 2 | ... |
|------------|-------|-------|-----|
| Actual $t_r$ |       |       |     |
| $1/\omega_c$ |       |       |     |

3.   For each of the Bode designs in this chapter, make a table similar to that shown here that compares percent overshoot to phase margin and the damping ratio of the dominant closed-loop poles.

|             | Ex. 1 | Ex. 2 | ... |
|-------------|-------|-------|-----|
| % Overshoot |       |       |     |
| $\phi_m$    |       |       |     |
| $\zeta$     |       |       |     |

4.   Sketch the root locus for Example 11.6.3, including the third closed-loop pole near the pole of $G_c G_p(s)$ at $s = -300$. Verify that the third *closed-loop* pole is at $s \approx -296$.

5.   Reconsider the "smart" missile control problem from Chapter 7, as shown in Fig. 11.23. The missile has a TV camera in its nose that relays a picture to the pilot. The pilot then directs the missile by centering the target on a display in the cockpit with a joystick. The signal from the pilot then causes the guidance system of the missile to move toward the target. Let the dynamics of the missile and its control system be

$$G_p(s) = \frac{200}{s(s+5)(s+15)}.$$

For the unity feedback, cascade compensation configuration used in this chapter, design the compensator $G_c$ to these specifications:

a. $K_v \geq 100$.

b. $\left|\dfrac{E(j\omega)}{R(j\omega)}\right| \leq 0.01$ for $\omega \leq 1$ rad/s.

c. $\left|\dfrac{C(j\omega)}{R(j\omega)}\right| \leq 0.1$ for $\omega \geq 100$ rad/s.

d. $\phi_m \geq 60°$.

e. $\omega_c$ as large as possible.

**Figure 11.23 |** Smartbomb system.

Target

6. Redo Problem 5, using these specifications:

a. $K_v \geq 100$.

b. $\left|\dfrac{E(j\omega)}{R(j\omega)}\right| \leq 0.05$ for $\omega \leq 1$ rad/s.

c. $\left|\dfrac{C(j\omega)}{R(j\omega)}\right| \leq 0.05$ for $\omega \geq 300$ rad/s.

d. $\phi_m \geq 45°$.

e. $\omega_c$ as large as possible.

7. Figure 11.24 shows a block diagram of a speed controller for an automobile that we considered in Chapter 7, where

$$G_{\text{spdc}}(s) = \frac{10}{(s+3)(s+3.2)} \qquad G_{\text{car}}(s) = \frac{1}{s+2.5}.$$

Design a controller $G_c$ that meets these specifications:

a. $K_p \geq 20$.

b. $\phi_m \geq 50°$.

c. $G_c$ first order (one pole and one zero).

**Figure 11.24 |** Block diagram of automobile speed control.

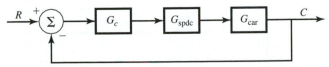

8. Consider again the system shown in Fig. 11.25, first considered in Chapter 7, where the plant has a feedback loop. Let

$$G_1(s) = \frac{1}{s^2} \qquad G_2(s) = \frac{120s + 100}{s^2 + 12s + 72}.$$

Use the Bode design methods of this chapter to design a controller $G_c$ to meet these specifications:

a. $K_v \geq 100$.

b. $\left| \dfrac{E(j\omega)}{R(j\omega)} \right| \leq 0.02$ for $\omega \leq 1$ rad/s.

c. $\left| \dfrac{C(j\omega)}{R(j\omega)} \right| \leq 0.1$ for $\omega \geq 100$ rad/s.

d. $\phi_m$ as large as possible.

**Figure 11.25 |** Multiloop control.

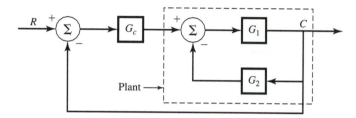

9. Figure 11.26 shows a unity feedback loop for the pitch control of an aircraft, first considered in Chapter 7, where

$$G_{\text{flap}}(s) = \frac{4000}{(s + 8)} \qquad G_p(s) = \frac{(s + 6)(s + 15)}{s(s + 3 - j12)(s + 3 + j12)}.$$

Design a compensator to meet these specifications:

a. $K_v \geq 100$.

b. $\left| \dfrac{E(j\omega)}{R(j\omega)} \right| \leq 0.1$ for $\omega \leq 1$ rad/s.

**Figure 11.26 |** Pitch control of aircraft.

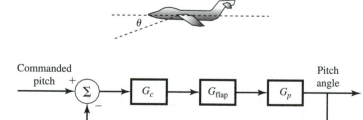

c.  $\left|\dfrac{C(j\omega)}{R(j\omega)}\right| \leq 0.05$ for $\omega \geq 300$ rad/s.

d.  $\phi_m$ as large as possible.

10.  In Chapter 7 we considered the the roll characteristics of a missile about its longitudinal axis, as shown in Fig. 11.27. The dynamics about the longitudinal axis are given by

$$G_m(s) = \frac{1}{s(s+15)}.$$

Redesign the the compensator $G_c$ using the methods of this chapter to meet these specifications:

a.  $K_v \geq 100$.

b.  $\left|\dfrac{E(j\omega)}{R(j\omega)}\right| \leq 0.02$ for $\omega \leq 1$ rad/s.

c.  $\left|\dfrac{C(j\omega)}{R(j\omega)}\right| \leq 0.1$ for $\omega \geq 100$ rad/s.

d.  $\phi_m \geq 55°$.

e.  $\omega_c$ as large as possible.

**Figure 11.27 |** Roll control of missile.

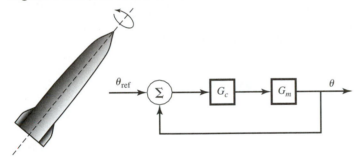

11.  Figure 11.28 shows a high-speed magnetic levitation train. On curves it is

**Figure 11.28 |** Roll control of maglev train.

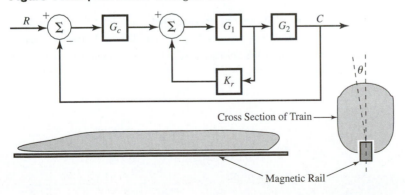

necessary to bank the train to match the bank of the rail. The block diagram shows how this might be accomplished with a rate gyro. $R$ is a bank command in degrees and $C$ is the actual amount of bank, also in degrees. Since the train is floating, its dynamics have been modeled as

$$G_{\text{maglev}}(s) = \frac{1}{Js^2}.$$

In the figure, the transfer function has been broken down into

$$G_1(s) = \frac{1}{Js} \quad \text{and} \quad G_2(s) = \frac{1}{s}.$$

We do not need to know $J$. We simply assume the ratio

$$\frac{K_r}{J}$$

is known. Design the compensator $G_c$ to meet these specifications:

a.  $K_v \geq 500$.
b.  $\left| \dfrac{E(j\omega)}{R(j\omega)} \right| \leq 0.02$ for $\omega \leq 1$ rad/s.
c.  $\left| \dfrac{C(j\omega)}{R(j\omega)} \right| \leq 0.1$ for $\omega \geq 300$ rad/s.
d.  $\phi_m \geq 70°$.
e.  PO $\leq 10\%$.
f.  Rise time to 90% of final value $\leq 0.2$ s.

# FURTHER READINGS

Bode, H. W. 1945. *Network Analysis and Feedback Amplifier Design,* Princeton, N.J.: D. Van Nostrand.

Chestnut, Harold, and R. W. Mayer. 1951. *Servomechanisms and Regulating Systems Design,* Vol. 1. New York: John Wiley & Sons.

D'Azzo, John J., and Constantine H. Houpis. 1988. *Linear Control System Design: Conventional and Modern.* New York: McGraw-Hill.

James, H. M., N. B. Nichols, and R. S. Phillips. 1947. *Theory of Servomechanisms.* New York: McGraw Hill.

Nise, Norman S. 2000. *Control System Engineering.* New York: John Wiley & Sons.

Ogata, K. 1970. *Modern Control Engineering.* Englewood Cliffs, N.J.: Prentice-Hall.

Saucedo, R., and E. E. Schiring. 1968. *Introduction to Continuous and Digital Control Systems.* New York: MacMillan.

# Chapter 12

# Robust Control

## 12.1 | OVERVIEW

At a farm below the front range of the Peruvian Andes, a backpacker can get a night's rest and an early breakfast. Four hours of hard walking will bring the backpacker to a crest from which he can see the spine of the Andes, an endless chain of peaks rising to 21,000 feet. The backpacker now has a difficult choice. He can look at this marvelous panorama for an hour or so and then return to the farm for dinner. Or, he can continue on.

If he continues on, another five hours of strenuous hiking will bring him into a canyon that ends in a sheer wall rising thousands of feet overhead. A half hour later as he nears the head wall, he realizes there is another canyon to his right and looking up it he sees Salcantay, a magnificent towering peak sacred to the Incas, shining in the fading late afternoon light.

After a sleepless night in the thin air admiring the glories of the Milky Way from eleven degrees south latitude, he awakes to begin the climb to the pass below Salcantay. The going is slow and the air thin. The backpacker crunches over the hard snow of avalanche paths that spill down from above like the tongues of angry Inca gods. He chews the cocoa leaves given him by his Peruvian indian guide, who, with lungs that reach his kneecaps, strolls leisurely along up ahead.

In the late afternoon the backpacker reaches the pass at 15,000 feet. Directly above him is the glacier of Salcantay, and below it, boulders the size of five-story buildings cracked off from the mountain by the relentless glacier. Towering over the glacier is the mountain itself. The backpacker recalls that the remains of ancient Incas have been found near the tops of several of these 21,000-foot peaks.

The backpacker sleeps that night in the pass, awakened intermittently by the cracking roar of the avalanches that serenade him through the night. In the morning he starts down. Below him lies the jungle thrusting upward against the mountain. He stops for a swim in the frigid water of a stream running down off the great mountain. And then the most glorious sight of all: where the jungle meets the mountain, the great trees that form the jungle canopy are covered with snow from the night before, glistening monarchs as noble as the mountain above.

In this chapter, we face the mathematical equivalent of the backpacker's dilemma: to fully understand the ramifications of modern robust control would take us on a lengthy mathematical journey. The rewards would be great, just as the backpacker's reward was great. Unfortunately, that journey is too long and hard. We will have to content ourselves with the four hour hike to the crest of the front range. We will take in the panorama and then move on.

Although we do not have the mathematical tools to understand robust control completely, we can understand its intent and relate it to the design techniques of previous chapters. This is a worthwhile exercise that will at least give us an appreciation of the implications of robust control.

Robust control seeks to quantify uncertainties in the modeling of physical systems to ensure that the compensated system in always stable. It goes without saying that this has obviously always been a goal of control system designers. The recent advances are more mathematically rigorous than the work done during the 1940s and 1950s. From one point of view, the work on robust control over the last decade or so serves to illuminate and corroborate the techniques that have been developed over the last half century for single-input, single-output (SISO) systems.

In addition to increasing our knowledge of single-input, single-output systems, robust control control also has provided new advances. It has, for instance, been used effectively in the control of multi-input, multi-output (MIMO) systems. MIMO systems are outside the purview of this book, so we will content ourselves with an introductory look at how robust control relates to the control strategies for SISO systems developed in Chapter 11.

To reach this more limited goal we will have to spend a little time extending our understanding of the idea of a norm. In doing so, we will keep the mathematics on a short leash, and just try to get an intuitive feel for the norms used in robust control, particularly the so-called infinity norm. Once we have a clear understanding of norms, at least in an elementary, intuitive way, we can proceed with the discussion of robust control. What we will find is that the design techniques we developed in Chapter 11 are completely coincident with the tenets of robust control theory.

## 12.2 | NORMS WITHOUT TEARS

Our goal in this section is to motivate a particular measure of distance between mathematical objects called the infinity norm. The infinity norm is put to great use in robust control theory. We will not tarry long here, because our goal is simply to get an intuitive feel for this norm.

The reader is familiar with the idea of a norm in two-dimensional and three-dimensional spaces where each of the coordinate axes is the real line. The usual norm in a two-dimensional space is the so-called Euclidean norm defined by

$$\|\mathbf{x}\| = [\mathbf{x}^T \mathbf{x}]^{1/2}$$

$$= \left[ [x_1 \quad x_2] \begin{bmatrix} x_1 \\ x_2 \end{bmatrix} \right]^{1/2}$$

$$= [x_1^2 + x_2^2]^{1/2}.$$

Using this norm the distance between two vectors

$$\mathbf{x} = \begin{bmatrix} x_1 \\ x_2 \end{bmatrix} \quad \text{and} \quad \mathbf{y} = \begin{bmatrix} y_1 \\ y_2 \end{bmatrix}$$

can be measured in a meaningful and useful way. That is,

$$\|\mathbf{x} - \mathbf{y}\| = [(\mathbf{x} - \mathbf{y})^T (\mathbf{x} - \mathbf{y})]^{1/2}$$
$$= [(x_1 - y_1)^2 + (x_2 - y_2)^2]^{1/2}.$$

The Euclidean norm is very familiar, and because of this familiarity very "plausible." We can build on this plausibility to find the essential qualities of a norm. Having done so, we will then move on to find that we can measure the distance between functions in much the same way that we measure the distance between two points.

Our next step is to ferret out the intrinsic properties of a norm. We do so in terms of the familiar Euclidean norm. Consider Fig. 12.1. Euclidean geometry tells us that

$$\|\mathbf{x} + \mathbf{y}\|^2 \leq \|\mathbf{x}\|^2 + \|\mathbf{y}\|^2.$$

In fact, we know from Pythagoras that the only time we have

$$\|\mathbf{x}\|^2 + \|\mathbf{y}\|^2 = \|\mathbf{x} + \mathbf{y}\|^2$$

is when $\mathbf{x}$ and $\mathbf{y}$ are orthogonal to each other. This so-called triangle inequality is the key property of a norm.

Besides the crucial triangle inequality property, the Euclidean norm has two other distinguishing characteristics. One is that

$$\|\mathbf{x}\| = \left[x_1^2 + x_2^2\right]^{1/2} > 0,$$

unless $\mathbf{x} = 0$, in which case $\|\mathbf{x}\| = 0$. This norm also has the property that if $a$ is a real number, then

$$\|a\mathbf{x}\| = [(ax_1)^2 + (ax_2)^2]^{1/2}$$
$$= |a| \left[ax_1^2 + ax_2^2\right]^{1/2}$$
$$= |a| \|\mathbf{x}\|.$$

**Figure 12.1 |** Illustration of the triangle inequality.

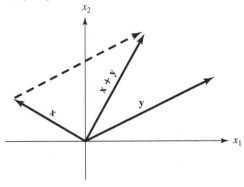

Having made these observations, we are now in position to formally define a norm.

---

**Definition 12.2.1 (Norm)**

Given a linear space, a scalar valued function that operates on the vectors (objects) **x** that belong to the space, and denoted by $\|\mathbf{x}\|$, is called a norm if the function has these properties:

1.   $\|\mathbf{x}\| \geq 0$ and $\|\mathbf{x}\| = 0$ if and only if $\mathbf{x} = \mathbf{0}$.
2.   $\|\mathbf{x} + \mathbf{y}\| \leq \|\mathbf{x}\| + \|\mathbf{y}\|$.
3.   $\|\lambda\mathbf{x}\| = |\lambda|\|\mathbf{x}\|$, where $\lambda$ is a scalar multiplier of **x**.

---

As it turns out, there are a lot of functions that fit this definition for what are called linear spaces. The attentive reader will note that the idea of a linear space has not yet been defined, even though it appears in Definition 12.2.1. The reason for that is that most of the spaces that we are familiar with are linear. For the sake of completeness, however, we give a formal definition.

---

**Definition 12.2.2 (Linear Space)**

Let $X$ denote a set of "objects." These objects constitute a linear space if addition and scalar multiplication are defined on $X$ and:

1.   $\mathbf{x} + \mathbf{y} = \mathbf{y} + \mathbf{x}$ for any **x** and **y** that belong to $X$.
2.   $(\mathbf{x} + \mathbf{y}) + \mathbf{z} = \mathbf{x} + (\mathbf{y} + \mathbf{z})$ for any **x**, **y**, **z** that belong to $X$.
3.   There exists and element **0** that belongs to $X$ such that $\mathbf{0} + \mathbf{x} = \mathbf{x}$ for any **x** (including **0**) that belongs to $X$.
4.   For any **x** that belongs $X$, there exists a **y** that belongs to $X$ such that $\mathbf{x} + \mathbf{y} = \mathbf{0}$. The object **y** is called the additive inverse of **x**.
5.   $1 \times \mathbf{x} = \mathbf{x}$ for any **x** that belongs to $X$.
6.   If $\alpha$ and $\beta$ are arbitrary scalars then $\alpha(\beta\mathbf{x}) = (\alpha\beta)\mathbf{x}$ for any **x** that belongs to $X$.
7.   If $\alpha$ and $\beta$ are arbitrary scalars then $(\alpha + \beta)\mathbf{x} = \alpha\mathbf{x} + \beta\mathbf{x}$ for any **x** that belongs to $X$.
8.   If $\alpha$ is an arbitrary scalar then $\alpha(\mathbf{x} + \mathbf{y}) = \alpha\mathbf{x} + \beta\mathbf{y}$ for any **x** and **y** that belong to $X$.

---

In the course of defining a linear space, we introduce other words whose definitions are not very well defined like "scalar" and "belonging to." In point of fact, it is impossible to be completely consistent with this process, so we simply rely on familiar mathematical structures to understand the terms. The two-dimensional vectors that we can draw on a set of Cartesian coordinates constitute a linear space. The scalars that we normally use with these vectors are real and complex numbers. Clearly the scalars are different from the objects (vectors) that belong to the space.

**Figure 12.2 |** Norm of a continuous function.

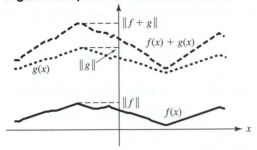

We come now to the infinity norm. Consider Fig. 12.2. As it happens, we can take well-behaved functions of a variable $x$ defined on some common domain and use the maximum absolute value of a function on this common domain as a norm. That is let

$$\gamma(x) = \sup_{x \in \mathcal{D}} |f(x)|,$$

where

$$\sup_{x \in \mathcal{D}}$$

means the least upper bound of the function over the domain of the function. In a casual way, we can see from Fig. 12.2 that $\gamma$ satisfies the triangle inequality. Without much more difficulty, we can show that $\gamma$ also satisfies the other two requirements of a norm.

We have to pick a name for this norm. The name that has been chosen by the researchers in robust control is the "infinity" norm. To understand the origins of this name would require us spending more time than we really need to talking about norms, so we will just accept the name and write

$$\|f(x)\|_\infty \overset{\Delta}{=} \sup_{x \in \mathcal{D}} |f(x)|. \qquad\qquad \textbf{[12.1]}$$

We now proceed to a discussion of robust control.

# 12.3 | NORMS FOR ROBUST CONTROL

## 12.3.1  Overview

The interest in robust control over the last decade or so is largely due to John Doyle and Bruce Francis. From the viewpoint of single-input, single-output systems, the contributions of robust control are primarily an extension of Bode's work on sensitivity analysis plus a sounder theoretical basis for the loop-shaping techniques that had been in use for 60 years.

Doyle et al. (1992) considered three norms, and one normlike quantity. Of the three norms two are the familiar "one norm" and "two norm" defined for a function $u(t)$ by

$$\|u(t)\|_1 = \int_{-\infty}^{\infty} |u(t)| \, dt \quad \text{and} \quad \|u(t)\|_2 = \left[ \int_{-\infty}^{\infty} u(t)^2 \, dt \right]^{1/2}.$$

The third norm, the so-called infinity norm, which we discussed earlier, is defined by

$$\|u(t)\|_{\infty} = \sup_{t} |u(t)|, \quad t \in \mathcal{D}.$$

As discussed earlier, by "sup" we mean the least upper bound or supremum of $u(t)$ over all $t \in \mathcal{D}$. The functions to which we will apply the infinity norm are very well behaved, and we can replace the sup with the maximum value of $|u(t)|$.

The normlike quantity investigated by Doyle et al. is the power function defined by

$$\text{pow}(u) = \left[ \lim_{T \to \infty} \frac{1}{2T} \int_{-T}^{T} u(t)^2 \, dt \right]^{1/2}.$$

The power function has all the characteristics of a norm except that $\text{pow}(u)$ can equal zero when $u(t)$ is not identically zero.

These same norms can be applied to transfer functions in the Laplace variable $s$. If $G(s)$ is a transfer function, then

$$\|G(j\omega)\|_1 = \int_{-\infty}^{\infty} |G(j\omega)| \, d\omega,$$

$$\|G(j\omega)\|_2 = \left[ \int_{-\infty}^{\infty} |G(j\omega)|^2 \, dt \right]^{1/2},$$

$$\|G(j\omega)\|_{\infty} = \max_{\omega} |G(j\omega)|, \quad \forall \omega.$$

Of all these norms, the one with the most utility turns out to be the infinity norm. Not only is it easy to compute, but it also is one of the best estimates of the gain of a system. Thus, the infinity norm will be the norm of choice as we next revisit the sensitivity analysis we began in Chapter 9.

## 12.4 | SENSITIVITY FUNCTIONS

In Chapter 9 we considered the sensitivity of a closed-loop system to disturbances at the input and output. For disturbances at the output we found that the transfer function between the output $C(s)$ and a disturbance $D(s)$ was

$$\frac{C(s)}{D(s)} \triangleq T_d(s) = \frac{1}{1 + G(s)H(s)}.$$

The function $T_d$ is generally called $S$ in the robust control literature, and we will adopt that name. We note in passing that the notation of robust control is by no means uniform. We will make some attempt to stay in reasonable conformity with this notation, but we will make exceptions. For instance, in the literature on robust control, the loop transfer function is normally signified by $L(j\omega)$. We will use, instead $GH(j\omega)$, the notation we have used in previous chapters. However, we will let

$$S(s) \equiv T_d(s),$$

and call $S$ the sensitivity function, in keeping with the notation of robust stability.

In Chapter 9, we also considered disturbances at the input for the unity feedback case and found the transfer function between the output $C(s)$ and the disturbance $D(s)$ to be

$$T_c(s) = \frac{G(s)}{1 + G(s)},$$

where $G(s)$ was the overall transfer function in the forward loop. We noted in Chapter 9 that a disturbance at the input in many cases was a result of sensor noise. In that vein, we now wish to extend this idea to the nonunity feedback case, as shown in Fig. 12.3.

It is easy enough to show that with $R = 0$,

$$\frac{C(s)}{N(s)} \triangleq S_c(s) = \frac{G(s)H(s)}{1 + G(s)H(s)}.$$

We will call $S_c$ the complementary sensitivity function. The name arises from the fact that

$$S_c(s) = 1 - S(s).$$

We mention that Doyle [Doyle, et al., 1992]. use the symbol $T$ for the complimentary sensitivity function.

The infinity norms associated with these two functions are defined by

$$\|S\|_\infty \triangleq \max_\omega |S(j\omega)| \quad \text{and} \quad \|S_c\|_\infty \triangleq \max_\omega |S_c(j\omega)|, \quad \forall \omega.$$

As noted, we have eschewed the "sup" in favor of the more familiar "max."

With these definitions we are now positioned to consider margins of stability. We will be interested in three types of uncertainty: disturbances at the input, disturbances at the output, and unmodeled dynamics in the transfer function. We will first consider the three types of uncertainty individually and then examine what happens if they are all present.

**Figure 12.3 |** Disturbance (sensor noise) in a feedback loop.

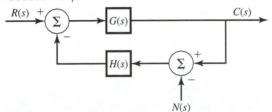

## 12.5 | ROBUST STABILITY MARGINS

For the nonunity feedback case, let

$$GH(s) = \frac{1000(s+2)}{s(s+0.5)(s+40)}. \qquad \textbf{[12.2]}$$

This is a slight modification of Example 11.4.1 in Chapter 11. It is chosen because it yields a phase margin on the order of 50°, which is the nominal *minimum* phase margin specification used in Chapter 11.

An accurate polar plot of $GH(j\omega)$ is shown in Fig. 12.4. The radius $r$ of the circle in the figure defines the point of nearest approach of $GH(j\omega)$ to the point $-1$ in the $GH$ plane. Note further that

$$r = 1 + GH(j\omega). \qquad \textbf{[12.3]}$$

Now, since

$$S(j\omega) = \frac{1}{1 + GH(j\omega)},$$

if $r$ represents the *minimum* length of $1 + GH(j\omega)$ over all $\omega$ then $r$ must represent the *inverse* of

$$\|S\|_\infty \overset{\Delta}{=} \max_\omega |S(j\omega)|, \ \forall \omega.$$

**Figure 12.4 |** Nyquist plot for $GH(s) = \frac{1000(s+2)}{s(s+0.5)(s+40)}$.

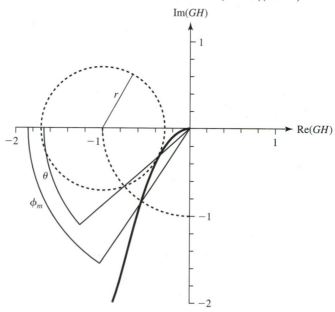

That is

$$r = \|S\|_\infty^{-1} \overset{\Delta}{=} \min_\omega |S(j\omega)|, \ \forall \omega.$$

It is suggested by Wolovich (1994) that a useful lower bound on the phase margin $\phi_m$ is

$$\theta = 2 \sin^{-1} \frac{r}{2}.$$

This is easy enough to see since $\theta$ is the apex angle of an isosceles triangle with base $r$. If we now choose a value for $\theta$, we can get a reasonable idea of what $r = \|S\|_\infty^{-1}$ should be.

We know from Chapter 11 that to keep the percent overshoot under 20%, we want $\phi_m \geq 50°$. However, $\theta$ is a lower bound on $\phi_m$, and potentially a *conservative* lower bound. If we pick $\theta = 40°$,

$$\|S\|_\infty^{-1} = 2 \sin 20° = 0.684,$$

or

$$\|S\|_\infty = 1.46 \ (3 \ \text{dB}).$$

A if we choose $\theta = 30°$, then

$$\|S\|_\infty = 1.93 \ (6 \ \text{dB}).$$

Our choice of $\theta$ will depend on how conservative we think this bound is for a particular problem. We will make use of this bound later when we relate robust control to the design techniques of Chapter 11. However, our immediate goal is to see how we can make a system robust against disturbances at the output.

## 12.6 | DISTURBANCE REJECTION

Recall that in Chapter 9 we established that the transfer function between $C$ and a disturbance $D$ at the output is

$$\frac{C(s)}{D(s)} = \frac{1}{1 + GH(s)} \overset{\Delta}{=} S(s).$$

Now suppose that $d(t)$ is bandlimited, consisting mainly of lower frequencies. Then for any frequency $\omega$ within the spectrum of $d$, we can write.

$$\frac{|C(j\omega)|}{|D(j\omega)|} = \frac{1}{|1 + GH(j\omega)|} \ll 1. \qquad\qquad \textbf{[12.4]}$$

Since we are assuming linearity, the total output will be that due to the disturbance added to that due to the reference input. If Inequality [12.4] holds, then the portion of the output due to the noise will be suppressed. The alert reader will remember that we started with similar inequalities in Chapter 11. More about that later.

Now let

$$\|D\|_\infty \overset{\Delta}{=} \max_\omega |D(j\omega)|.$$

Since disturbances are generally regarded as having primarily low-frequency content, $|D(j\omega)|$ will be large for low frequencies and grow progressively smaller as $\omega$ increases. That being the case, at low frequencies we should have

$$\frac{1}{|D(j\omega)|} \ll 1.$$

Thus, at least at low frequencies, disturbance rejection could be formulated as

$$\frac{1}{|1 + GH(j\omega)|} < \frac{1}{|D(j\omega)|}. \qquad \textbf{[12.5]}$$

This is, as we shall see, a very appealing formulation, but it begs the question of how to formulate disturbance rejection at higher frequencies where $|D(j\omega)|$ may not be large. Actually, at higher frequencies, where $|D(j\omega)|$ is small, disturbance rejection is not much of an issue. At higher frequencies, the problem is noise at the input and unmodeled dynamics. For that reason, but also because Inequality [12.5] is so simple and easy to work with, we adopt the noise rejection criterion

$$\left| \frac{D(j\omega)}{1 + GH(j\omega)} \right| < 1 \quad \forall \omega, \qquad \textbf{[12.6]}$$

or equivalently

$$|D(j\omega)| < |1 + GH(j\omega)| \quad \forall \omega. \qquad \textbf{[12.7]}$$

We now do the following thought experiment. We walk along a plot of $GH(j\omega)$ in the $GH$ plane. At each point $GH(j\omega)$ along the plot, we hold out a rod of length $|D(j\omega)|$ and rotate through $360°$. If Inequality [12.7] holds, we can repeat this test at every point along the plot of $GH$, and the rod will never touch the point $-1$ in the $GH$ plane. At each point on the plot of $GH$, we also record the point of nearest approach to the point $-1$ in the $GH$ plane, as shown in Fig. 12.5(a).

By connecting the points of nearest approach for each frequency we can generate a line of nearest approach that is a measure of how good our disturbance rejection is. The farther the points of this line are from $-1$ the better our disturbance rejection. Also, once we get close to the origin of the $GH$ plane, the plot of $GH(j\omega)$ should be to the right of, or below, this line of nearest approach.

This a very appealing idea because it formulates disturbance rejection in the same manner that we formulated relative stability when we introduced the Nyquist criterion. In the case of both disturbance rejection and stability, the farther we are from $-1$, the better off we are. The fact that we have been able to formulate disturbance rejection in a manner similar to that for stability will pay big dividends shortly.

Since

$$S(j\omega) = \frac{1}{1 + GH(j\omega)},$$

we can now rephrase Eq. [12.6] as

$$|D(j\omega)S(j\omega)| < 1, \quad \forall \omega. \qquad \textbf{[12.8]}$$

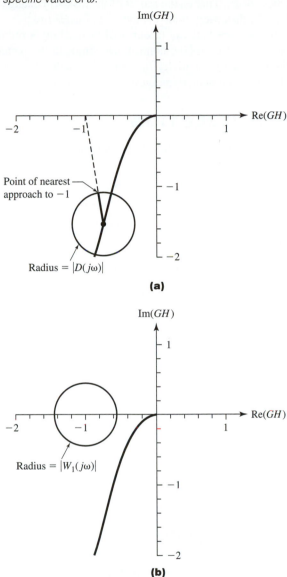

**Figure 12.5** | Point of nearest approach to −1 for a *specific* value of $\omega$.

(a)

(b)

Using the infinity norm we could also write Eq. [12.8] as

$$\| W_1(j\omega)S(j\omega) \|_\infty < 1, \qquad\qquad [12.9]$$

where $W_1(j\omega) \equiv D(j\omega)$, thereby putting the inequality into the notation used by Doyle. An alternative graphical interpretation of Eq. [12.9] is shown in Fig. 12.5(b). At *each* frequency $\omega$, we construct a disk centered at −1 in the $GH$ plane with radius $|W_1(j\omega)|$. If Inequality [12.9] holds, then the plot of $GH(j\omega)$ will never intersect any of these disks. That is, the radius of the disk will change with $\omega$, but for no value of $\omega$ does the disk every intersect the plot of $GH(j\omega)$.

At this juncture, we are halfway to our goal of reaching a rudimentary understanding of what is meant by robust control. To complete the picture, we need to consider the complementary sensitivity function. This will enable us to investigate sensor noise and unmodeled plant dynamics.

## 12.7 | NOISE REJECTION

Recall that the transfer function between the noise input in the feedback loop and the output, as shown in Fig. 12.3, is

$$\frac{C(s)}{N(s)} = \frac{G(s)H(s)}{1 + G(s)H(s)}.$$

Our analysis follows the same lines as that in the previous section. Assume the noise has a frequency response

$$N(j\omega) \equiv W_n(j\omega).$$

Using the notation $W_n(j\omega)$ moves us (incrementally) closer to the notation of robust control.

Noise is generally assumed to be high frequency in nature. Therefore, we would expect $|W_n(j\omega)|$ to be large at high frequencies but small at lower frequencies. The exact form of $|W_n(j\omega)|$ is something the theorists always leave to the practitioners. However, using arguments similar to those we used for disturbance rejection, we can say that at high frequencies we want

$$\frac{|G(s)H(s)|}{|1 + G(s)H(s)|} \ll 1,$$

and since at high frequencies,

$$\frac{1}{|W_n(j\omega)|} \ll 1,$$

an appealing noise rejection criterion, at least at higher frequencies, is

$$\frac{|GH(j\omega)|}{|1 + GH(j\omega)|} < \frac{1}{|W_n(j\omega)|}. \tag{12.10}$$

We assume that $|W_n(j\omega)|$ is small at low frequencies. Thus we can argue that at low frequencies our real concern is to satisfy Inequality [12.9] rather than Inequality [12.10]. As a consequence, we decide that a good criterion for noise rejection is

$$\left| \frac{GH(j\omega)W_n(j\omega)}{1 + GH(j\omega)} \right| < 1, \quad \forall \omega, \tag{12.11}$$

or equivalently

$$|GH(j\omega)W_n(j\omega)| < |1 + GH(j\omega)|, \quad \forall \omega. \tag{12.12}$$

**Figure 12.6 |** Line of closest approach to −1 for sensor noise.

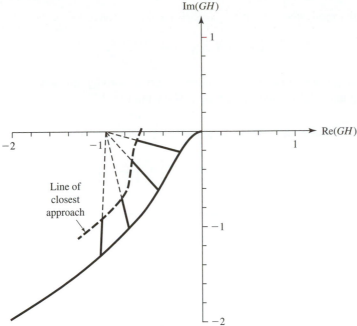

Inequality [12.12] can be used to perform the same thought experiment that we did for the case of disturbance rejection. We walk along the plot of $GH(j\omega)$ and at each $GH(j\omega)$ construct a rod of length $|GH(j\omega)W_n(j\omega)|$. If Inequality [12.12] holds then at every point along the plot of $GH(j\omega)$ the rod will be too short to touch the point −1 in the $GH$ plane As before, we can find the nearest approach to the point −1 for each point on the plot of $GH$. All this is shown in Fig. 12.6. The only difference between Fig. 12.5 and Fig. 12.6 is the length of the rod we use to find the point of nearest approach to −1.

At this juncture, we have established a new formulation for noise and disturbance rejection, topics that we first addressed in Chapter 9. We see that this new formulation is very nearly coincident with the Nyquist stability criterion of Chapter 10.

In Section 12.8 we extend our analysis to a new problem, namely, unmodeled dynamics. We already know from Chapter 8 that the transfer function we use to represent a physical system is only an approximation of the actual system. It is well known that most physical systems have high-frequency dynamics that are hard to identify and model. Thus, our approach in Section 12.8 will be to find a bound that ensures that the unmodeled dynamics do not cause instability.

We will be able to find such a bound, and, remarkably, this bound *will have the same form* as those we have already established for disturbance rejection and noise rejection. The fact that all these bounds have the same *form,* leads to a compact, unified, mathematically simple set of bounds presented in Section 12.9.

# 12.8 | UNMODELED PLANT DYNAMICS

We initially motivated the complementary sensitivity function

$$S_c(s) = 1 - S(s) = \frac{GH(s)}{1 + GH(s)}$$

by considering sensor noise. The complementary sensitivity function is also useful in analyzing unmodeled plant dynamics, as shown in Fig. 12.7.

**Figure 12.7** | Block diagram of plant with unmodeled dynamics.

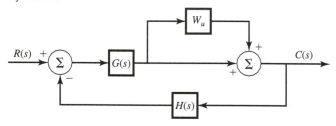

In the figure the closed-loop transfer function between $R$ and $C$ is

$$\frac{C(s)}{R(s)} = \frac{G(s)[1 + W_u(s)]}{1 + G(s)H(s)[1 + W_u(s)]},$$

where $W_u(s)$ represents the unknown dynamics of the plant.

The stability of the system now rests on the stability of the characteristic equation

$$1 + GH(s)[1 + W_u(s)]. \qquad \textbf{[12.13]}$$

If we assume that all the poles and zeros of both $GH$ and $W_u$ are in the left half of the $s$ plane then stability means that a plot of

$$GH(j\omega)[1 + W_u(j\omega)]$$

does not encircle the point $-1$ in the $s$ plane.

Now note that Eq. [12.13] can be written

$$1 + GH(s) + GH(s)W_u(s). \qquad \textbf{[12.14]}$$

Equation [12.14] suggests the following way of checking stability. First we make a plot of $GH(j\omega)$. Then at each point $GH(j\omega)$ take a rod of length $|GH(j\omega)W_u(j\omega)|$ and rotate through 360° holding out the rod. If we cannot reach the point $-1$ with the rod, then the system is stable. Further, if at each point along the polar plot of $GH(j\omega)$ we record the nearest approach to $-1$ we can generate a line of nearest approach that tells us the relative stability of the system. Thus, our criterion for stability is

$$|GH(j\omega)W_u(j\omega)| < |1 + GH(j\omega)|, \quad \forall \omega, \qquad \textbf{[12.15]}$$

or, equivalently,

$$\frac{|GH(j\omega)W_u(j\omega)|}{|1+GH(j\omega)|} < 1, \quad \forall\omega. \qquad \textbf{[12.16]}$$

We can rewrite Inequality [12.16] as

$$\frac{|GH(j\omega)W_u(j\omega)|}{|1+GH(j\omega)|} = \frac{|GH(j\omega)||W_u(j\omega)|}{|1+GH(j\omega)|} = |S_c(j\omega)W_u(j\omega)| < 1, \quad \forall\omega. \qquad$$
$$\textbf{[12.17]}$$

Inequality [12.17] means than a sufficient condition for stability against sensor noise and unmodeled dynamics is

$$\|S_c W_u\|_\infty < 1. \qquad \textbf{[12.18]}$$

Before proceeding, we note that the notation $W_u(s)$ is not that usually found in the literature on robust control. We have used it to this point in the discussion to keep the equations as uncluttered as possible. The more standard notation for $W_u(s)$ is

$$\Delta(s)W_2(s),$$

where $W_2(s)$ is a fixed transfer function and $\Delta(s)$ is a scaling transfer function with the property that

$$|\Delta(j\omega)| \le 1, \quad \forall\omega.$$

Given the magnitude constraint on $\Delta$, we could restate Eq. [12.18] as

$$\|S_c W_2\|_\infty < 1.$$

The introduction of $\Delta(s)$ is a convenience. It enables us to pick a fixed function $W_2$ and then modulate it with $\Delta$. For our elementary treatment of robust control, we will not make any real use of $\Delta$.

## 12.9 | COMBINING UNCERTAINTIES

In Sections 12.6 through 12.8, we have looked at including disturbances at the output and sensor noise and model uncertainty in the stability analysis. We have seen that all three lead to the same uncertainty formulation. Because in each case we formulate robustness using an inequality of the same form, we can easily combine these robustness criteria.

The first step in this process is to accout for unmodeled dynamics in our inequalities for noise and disturbance rejection. Considering disturbance rejection first, we replace

$$\frac{1}{1+GH(s)}$$

by

$$\frac{1}{1+[1+\Delta(s)W_2(s)]GH(s)} \triangleq \tilde{S}.$$

But

$$\tilde{S} = \frac{1/[1 + GH(s)]}{1 + \{[\Delta(s)W_2(s)]GH(s)]/[1 + GH(s)]\}}$$
$$= \frac{S(s)}{1 + \Delta(s)W_2(s)S_c(s)}.$$

Thus our new disturbance rejection condition is

$$|W_1(j\omega)\tilde{S}(j\omega| < 1, \quad \forall\omega,$$

which we can also write as

$$\|W_1\tilde{S}\|_\infty < 1.$$

If we combine this with the stability conditions for model uncertainty and noise rejection, we have

$$|W_1(j\omega)||\tilde{S}(j\omega| < 1 \quad \text{and} \quad \frac{|W_2(j\omega)GH(j\omega)|}{|1 + GH(j\omega)|} < 1, \quad \forall\omega, \qquad \textbf{[12.19]}$$

or alternatively

$$\|W_1\tilde{S}\|_\infty < 1 \quad \text{and} \quad \|W_2 S_c\|_\infty < 1.$$

The reason we need only the two functions $W_1$ and $W_2$ follows from the fact that both noise rejection and unmodeled dynamics are high-frequency phenomena. Thus, we can combine $W_n(j\omega)$ and $W_u(j\omega)$ into a single function $W_2(j\omega)$. To that end, Doyle [Doyle, et al., 1992] proves the following theorem.

> **Theorem 12.9.1**
>
> A necessary and sufficient condition for robust performance is
>
> $$\|W_1 S\|_\infty + \|W_2 S_c\|_\infty < 1.$$

Note that the theorem is stated in terms of $S$ and *not* $\tilde{S}$.

This theorem requires only a slight modification to the thought problem we have considered twice already. The modification is simply the length of the rod we use when we stand on the plot of $GH(j\omega)$ for a particular $\omega$. In this case, the rod is of length

$$|W_1(j\omega)| + |W_2(j\omega)GH(j\omega)|.$$

If the inequality of Theorem 12.9.1 is satisfied, the rod will not reach the point $-1$ in the $GH$ plane. In Fig. 12.8(a), we show the "rod" stretched out toward, but not reaching the point $-1$ in the $GH$ plane.

Another interpretation given by Doyle [Doyle, et al., 1992] is shown in Fig. 12.8(b). Here the idea is that for each frequency we construct two circles one of radius $|W_1(j\omega)|$ centered at $-1$ in the $GH$ plane and second of radius $|W_2(j\omega)GH(j\omega)|$ centered at $GH(j\omega)$. We have to construct such a pair of circles for each frequency. If the theorem holds, no pair of circles will intersect.

Yet another way to interpret this result is shown in Fig. 12.9. Using rods of length $|W_1(j\omega)|$ and $|W_2(j\omega)GH(j\omega)|$, we define the lines of nearest approach for both

**Figure 12.8 |** Two interpretations of robustness.

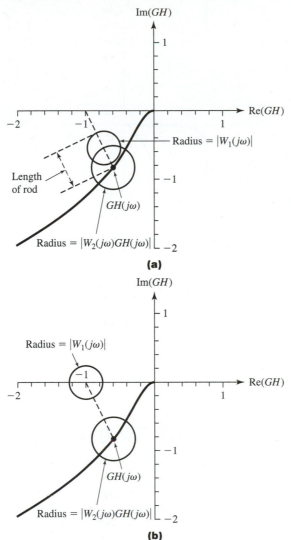

**(a)**

**(b)**

disturbance rejection and noise rejection/unmodeled dynamics. Since disturbances are basically low-frequency phenomena, and unmodeled dynamics and noise rejection high-frequency phenomena, we can combine these two lines of nearest approach into a single "net" line of nearest approach, as shown in the figure.

Our design goal will be to keep the polar plot of $GH(j\omega)$ below this net line of nearest approach, in the *vicinity* of $-1$. Figure 12.9 helps clarify what we mean by "in the vicinity." From the figure, we see that in *most cases* if

$$-1 < \text{Re}(GH)(j\omega) < 0 \quad \text{and} \quad -1 < \text{Im}(GH) < 0,$$

**Figure 12.9** | Net line of nearest approach in the vicinity of −1.

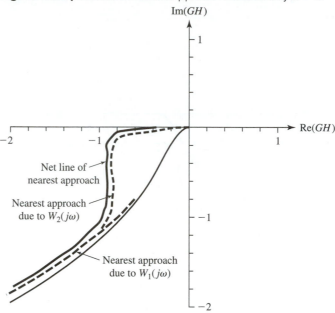

then the plot $GH(j\omega)$ will be below the net line of nearest approach. The use of the idea of net line of nearest approch is clearly problem-dependent. However, this does not keep it from being a useful design tool, as the example we consider in Section 12.10 shows.

## 12.10 | CONNECTIONS TO THE PAST

In Chapter 11 we designed to five main specifications, namely, steady state accuracy, midfrequency gain, crossover frequency, high-frequency noise rejection, and phase margin. Our next goal is to relate the design techniques of Chapter 11 to the robust performance criteria of this chapter. The three specifications of Chapter 11 that can be related to robust stability are midfrequency gain, crossover frequency, and high-frequency noise rejection.

Considering midfrequency gain first, we recall that in Chapter 11, we expressed the bandwidth of the closed-loop system by the inequality

$$\frac{|E(j\omega)|}{|R(j\omega)|} = \frac{1}{|1 + G(j\omega)|} \le \epsilon \ll 1, \quad \forall \omega \le \omega_\ell.$$

We also pointed out that the midfrequency gain requirement was identical to the disturbance rejection inequality

$$\frac{|D(j\omega)|}{|R(j\omega)|} = \frac{1}{|1 + G(j\omega)|} = \epsilon \ll 1.$$

We note that this is exactly the *form* of the robust stability performance measure for a disturbance at the output, namely,

$$\frac{1}{|1 + GH(j\omega)|} < \frac{1}{|W_1(j\omega)|}, \quad \forall \omega.$$

Since these performance measures are identical in form, we now seek to connect them.

In Chapter 11 our strategy was to note that for $\epsilon$ small,

$$|1 + G(j\omega)| \approx |G(j\omega)|,$$

and hence we had

$$|G(j\omega)| \geq \frac{1}{\epsilon}, \quad \forall \omega \leq \omega_\ell.$$

In the case of robust stability, a basic assumption is that the frequency spectrum of the disturbance consists primarily of low frequencies. Thus, $|W_1(j\omega)|$ will be large for low frequencies and small for middle and higher frequencies. Then, for $|W_1(j\omega)| \gg 1$,

$$\frac{1}{|1 + GH(j\omega)|} \approx \frac{1}{|GH(j\omega)|} < \frac{1}{|W_1(j\omega)|} \ll 1,$$

and one way to guarantee good disturbance rejection is to require that

$$|GH(j\omega)| > |W_1(j\omega)|, \quad \forall \omega. \tag{12.20}$$

Since

$$|W_1(j\omega)| \gg 1, \quad \forall \omega \leq \omega_\ell,$$

we have a condition very similar to the midfrequency gain specification of Chapter 11.

Now consider the robust stability requirement that

$$\|S\|_\infty^{-1} \geq 0.5,$$

suggested by Wolovich [Wolovich, 1994], and recall that that requirement was derived by finding a lower bound on the phase margin of the system. Thus, the robust stability requirement on midfrequency gain corresponds to the specification on minimum acceptable phase margin used in Chapter 11. In other words, $\|W_1\|_\infty^{-1}$ plays the role of phase margin.

Finally, consider the robust stability requirement on noise rejection and/or unmodeled dynamics:

$$|W_2(j\omega)GH(j\omega)| < |1 + GH(j\omega)|, \quad \forall \omega. \tag{12.21}$$

Now $|W_2(j\omega)|$ is small for low frequencies and gets progressively larger as $\omega$ increases, while $|GH(j\omega)|$ tends to zero for high frequencies. Thus, at higher frequencies where $|GH(j\omega)|$ is small

$$|1 + GH(j\omega)| \approx 1.$$

Using this result in Inequality [12.21] yields

$$|W_2(j\omega)GH(j\omega)| < 1.$$

Now, since

$$|W_2(j\omega)GH(j\omega)| \leq |W_2(j\omega)||GH(j\omega)|,$$

if we require the stronger condition

$$|W_2(j\omega)||GH(j\omega)| < 1,$$

we arrive at

$$|GH(j\omega)| < |W_2(j\omega)|^{-1} \ll 1.$$

For unity feedback, this is precisely the inequality that we specified in Chapter 9 for the suppression of high-frequency noise. Based on the results in this chapter this same inequality would work against unmodeled dynamics.

We now see that the connections between the design techniques in Chapter 11 and robust control are very strong. To solidify our understanding of the connections between the old and the new, consider Example 12.10.1.

---

**EXAMPLE 12.10.1**

Let

$$G_p(s) = \frac{10}{s(s+2)}.$$

We wish to design a compensator

$$G_c(s) = \frac{K_c(s+z_1)(s+z_2)}{(s+p_1)(s+p_2)},$$

that meets these specifications:

1. $K_v \geq 100$.
2. $\phi_m \geq 55°$.
3. Bode magnitude plot of $G_cG_p(j\omega)$ above plot of $|W_1(j\omega)|$.
4. Bode magnitude plot of $G_cG_p(j\omega)$ below plot of $|W_2(j\omega)|$.

Our specifications look very much like those of Chapter 11. The only difference is that instead of requiring the plot of $G_cG_p(j\omega)$ to pass above a single point and below a single point, we now have to be keep $G_cG_p(j\omega)$ between two curves. Thus, we can use the loop-shaping techniques we developed in Chapter 11 without modification.

Three designs are shown in Fig. 12.10, and summarized in Table 12.1. In this example, $W_1(j\omega)$ and $W_2(j\omega)$ were obtained from transfer functions. In practice, one might first make some measurements of $W_1(j\omega)$ and $W_2(j\omega)$ to get an idea of their frequency responses, and then find a transfer function that approximates the actual responses. Alternatively, the actual frequency responses of $W_1$ and $W_2$, if known, could simply be put on the Bode magnitude plot. We are rarely that lucky, however.

**Table 12.1** | Three designs.

| $G_cG_p(j\omega)$ | $\omega_c$ (rad/s) | $\phi_m$ |
|---|---|---|
| $\dfrac{100(1+s)}{s(1+s/0.18)(1+s/60)}$ | 16 | 72° |
| $\dfrac{100(1+s/0.7)}{s(1+s/0.18)(1+s/40)}$ | 25 | 57° |
| $\dfrac{100(1+s/0.55)}{s(1+s/0.18)(1+s/35)}$ | 30 | 49° |

**Figure 12.10** | Asymptotic Bode magnitude plot for Example 12.10.1.

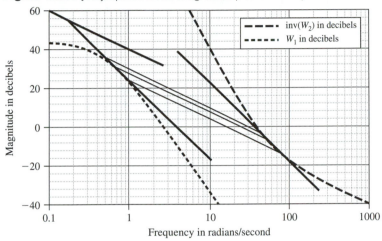

If we choose

$$G_cG_p(s) = \frac{100(1+s/0.7)}{s(1+s/0.18)(1+s/40)},$$

then

$$G_c(s) = \frac{103(s+0.7)(s+2)}{(s+0.18)(s+40)}.$$

A polar of $G_cG_p(j\omega)$, plus the lines of nearest approach due to $W_1(j\omega)$ and $W_2(j\omega)$ are shown in Fig. 12.11. Note that in the vicinity of $-1$ in the $G_cG_p$ plane the line of nearest approach due to $W_1(j\omega)$ is essentially coincident with the plot of $G_cG_p(j\omega)$. This makes sense because the particular $W_1(j\omega)$ used in the example is clearly dominated at high frequencies by $GH(j\omega)$.

However, examining the line of nearest approach due to $W_2(j\omega)$, we immediately see a problem. The line is very close to the point $-1$ in the $G_cG_p$ plane. If $W_2(j\omega)$ represents unmodeled dynamics, then the system verges on instability.

To correct this problem we redesign the compensator as shown in Fig. 12.12. The new overall transfer function is

$$G_cG_p(s) = \frac{720(s+1)}{s(s+0.18)(s+40)},$$

**Figure 12.11 |** Polar plots of $G_cG_p(j\omega)$ and lines of nearest approach for Example 12.10.1.

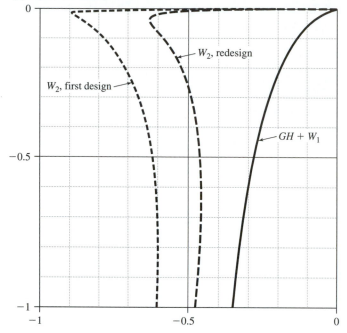

**Figure 12.12 |** Redesign for Example 12.10.1.

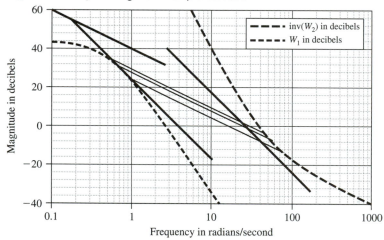

with resulting compensator

$$G_c(s) = \frac{72(s+1)(s+2)}{(s+0.18)(s+40)}.$$

The retest of robustness is also shown in Fig. 12.11. As can be seen, the stability is greatly improved. Whether the redesign is robust enough, however, is a decision for the designer.

# 12.11 | REPRISE

In this chapter we put forward the basic tenets of robust control. We have certainly not exhausted the subject, but that was not our goal. Our goal was to provide the reader with the background to investigate the literature on robust control, and there is certainly plenty to read.

One of the important features of robust control is that we can formulate criteria for disturbance rejection, noise rejection and stability in the face of unmodeled system dynamics using inequalities that all have the same form. This is important because it leads to very simple constraints for guaranteeing robustness that are easy to manipulate mathematically. This simplicity is one of the great strengths of robust control.

In Section 12.10 we showed that the design techniques of Chapter 11 are coincident with the developments of this chapter, for the case of SISO systems. The fathers of modern control theory, Bode, Chestnut, Nichols, Axelby, and many others knew full well the dangers of building control systems with wide bandwidths. To paraphrase Harold Chestnut: "the bandwidth should be sufficient to meet performance requirements, but no wider."

Designers like Axelby and Nichols were expert "loop shapers." They understood intuitively many of the results given more rigorous mathematical form by Doyle and others. This last statement is not meant to denigrate in any way the recent work in robust control, but rather to point out that recent developments, at least for SISO systems, are the fruit of half a century of work by many talented control engineers. In fairness, it should be noted that robust control has been applied with success to multi-input, multi-output (MIMO) systems.

If robust control has a shortcoming, it is that the bounds proposed tend to be conservative. That means that in some cases, higher performance could be obtained with no real loss in stability. However, those who pilot space shuttles and lunar landers would undoubtedly opt for a little less performance and more stability, and the conservativeness is probably a small price to pay for the workability of the theory.

# 12.12 | PROBLEMS

## 12.12.1 Compensator Design

The CD-ROM that comes with this book contains frequency responses for a set of functions $W_1(j\omega)$ and $W_2(j\omega)$ for the frequency range 0.001 to 1000 rad/s. For each problem, design the compensator $G_c$ using the specified responses for $W_1(j\omega)$ and $W_2(j\omega)$.

1.  Let

$$G_p(s) = \frac{10}{s(s+10)} \quad \text{and} \quad G_c(s) = \frac{K_c(s+z_1)(s+z_2)}{(s+p_1)(s+p_2)}.$$

Use files w1.a and w2.q and these specifications:
a.  $K_v \geq 100$.
b.  $\phi_m \geq 50°$.

    c.   $\omega_c$ maximized.
    d.   $|G_cG_p(j\omega)| \geq |W_1(j\omega)|, \ \forall\omega.$
    e.   $|G_cG_p(j\omega)| \leq |W_2(j\omega)|^{-1}, \ \forall\omega.$

**2.**   Let

$$G_p(s) = \frac{10}{s(s+5)} \quad \text{and} \quad G_c(s) = \frac{K_c(s+z_1)}{(s+p_1)}.$$

Use files w1.a and w2.q and these specifications:
    a.   $K_v \geq 100.$
    b.   $\phi_m \geq 50°.$
    c.   $\omega_c$ maximized.
    d.   $|G_cG_p(j\omega)| \geq |W_1(j\omega)|, \ \forall\omega.$
    e.   $|G_cG_p(j\omega)| \leq |W_2(j\omega)|^{-1}, \ \forall\omega.$

**3.**   Let

$$G_p(s) = \frac{10}{s(s+0.5)} \quad \text{and} \quad G_c(s) = \frac{K_c(s+z_1)}{(s+p_1)}.$$

Use files w1.q and w2.r and these specifications:
    a.   $K_v \geq 100.$
    b.   $\phi_m \geq 55°.$
    c.   $\omega_c$ maximized.
    d.   $|G_cG_p(j\omega)| \geq |W_1(j\omega)|, \ \forall\omega.$
    e.   $|G_cG_p(j\omega)| \leq |W_2(j\omega)|^{-1}, \ \forall\omega.$

**4.**   Let

$$G_p(s) = \frac{10}{s(s+0.5)} \quad \text{and} \quad G_c(s) = \frac{K_c(s+z_1)(s+z_2)}{(s+p_1)(s+p_2)}.$$

Use files w1.q and w2.r and these specifications:
    a.   $K_v \geq 100.$
    b.   $\phi_m \geq 55°.$
    c.   $\omega_c$ maximized.
    d.   $|G_cG_p(j\omega)| \geq |W_1(j\omega)|, \ \forall\omega.$
    e.   $|G_cG_p(j\omega)| \leq |W_2(j\omega)|^{-1}, \ \forall\omega.$

**5.**   Let

$$G_p(s) = \frac{30}{s(s+3)} \quad \text{and} \quad G_c(s) = \frac{K_c(s+z_1)(s+z_2)}{(s+p_1)(s+p_2)}.$$

Use files w1c and w2c and these specifications:
    a.   $K_p \geq 100.$
    b.   $\phi_m \geq 50°.$
    c.   $\omega_c$ maximized.
    d.   $|G_cG_p(j\omega)| \geq |W_1(j\omega)|, \ \forall\omega.$
    e.   $|G_cG_p(j\omega)| \leq |W_2(j\omega)|^{-1}, \ \forall\omega.$

**6.**   Let

$$G_p(s) = \frac{10}{(s+2)(s+5)} \quad \text{and} \quad G_c(s) = \frac{K_c(s+z_1)(s+z_2)}{(s+p_1)(s+p_2)}.$$

Use files w1.a and w2.s and these specifications:

a. $K_p \geq 100$.

b. $\phi_m \geq 50°$.

c. $\omega_c$ maximized.

d. $|G_c G_p(j\omega)| \geq |W_1(j\omega)|$, $\forall \omega$.

e. $|G_c G_p(j\omega)| \leq |W_2(j\omega)|^{-1}$, $\forall \omega$.

7. Let

$$G_p(s) = \frac{40}{s(s+20)} \quad \text{and} \quad G_c(s) = \frac{K_c(s+z_1)(s+z_2)}{(s+p_1)(s+p_2)}.$$

Use files w1.b and w2.b and these specifications:

a. $K_v \geq 100$.

b. $\phi_m \geq 55°$.

c. $\omega_c$ maximized.

d. $|G_c G_p(j\omega)| \geq |W_1(j\omega)|$, $\forall \omega$.

e. $|G_c G_p(j\omega)| \leq |W_2(j\omega)|^{-1}$, $\forall \omega$.

8. Let

$$G_p(s) = \frac{5}{s^2} \quad \text{and} \quad G_c(s) = \frac{K_c(s+z_1)(s+z_2)}{(s+p_1)(s+p_2)}.$$

Use files w1.c and w2.c and these specifications:

a. $K_a \geq 1$.

b. $\phi_m \geq 55°$.

c. $\omega_c$ maximized.

d. $|G_c G_p(j\omega)| \geq |W_1(j\omega)|$, $\forall \omega$.

e. $|G_c G_p(j\omega)| \leq |W_2(j\omega)|^{-1}$, $\forall \omega$.

9. Let

$$G_p(s) = \frac{5}{s^2} \quad \text{and} \quad G_c(s) = \frac{K_c(s+z_1)(s+z_2)}{(s+p_1)(s+p_2)}.$$

Use files w1.d and w2.d and these specifications:

a. $K_a \geq 10$.

b. $\phi_m \geq 45°$.

c. $\omega_c \geq 4$ rad/s.

d. $|G_c G_p(j\omega)| \geq |W_1(j\omega)|$, $\forall \omega$.

e. $|G_c G_p(j\omega)| \leq |W_2(j\omega)|^{-1}$, $\forall \omega$.

10. Let

$$G_p(s) = \frac{5}{s(s+10)} \quad \text{and} \quad G_c(s) = \frac{K_c(s+z_1)(s+z_2)}{(s+p_1)(s+p_2)}.$$

Use files w1.e and w2.e and these specifications:

a. $K_v > 10$.

b. $\phi_m \geq 50°$.

c. $\omega_c$ maximized.

d. $|G_c G_p(j\omega)| \geq |W_1(j\omega)|$, $\forall \omega$.

e. $|G_c G_p(j\omega)| \leq |W_2(j\omega)|^{-1}$, $\forall \omega$.

11. Let

$$G_p(s) = \frac{5}{s(s+10)} \quad \text{and} \quad G_c(s) = \frac{K_c(s+z_1)(s+z_2)}{(s+p_1)(s+p_2)}.$$

Use files w1.f and w2.f and these specifications:
a. $K_v > 100$.
b. $\phi_m$ maximized.
c. $|G_c G_p(j\omega)| \geq |W_1(j\omega)|$, $\forall\omega$.
d. $|G_c G_p(j\omega)| \leq |W_2(j\omega)|^{-1}$, $\forall\omega$.

12. Let

$$G_p(s) = \frac{100}{s(s+2)(s+20)} \quad \text{and} \quad G_c(s) = \frac{K_c(s+z_1)(s+z_2)}{(s+p_1)(s+p_2)}.$$

Use files w1.g and w2.g and these specifications:
a. $K_v > 500$.
b. $\phi_m \geq 55°$.
c. $|G_c G_p(j\omega)| \geq |W_1(j\omega)|$, $\forall\omega$.
d. $|G_c G_p(j\omega)| \leq |W_2(j\omega)|^{-1}$, $\forall\omega$.
e. $\omega_c$ maximized.

13. Let

$$G_p(s) = \frac{100}{s(s+4)(s+8)} \quad \text{and} \quad G_c(s) = \frac{K_c(s+z_1)(s+z_2)}{(s+p_1)(s+p_2)}.$$

Use files w1.h and w2.h and these specifications:
a. $K_v > 500$.
b. $\phi_m \geq 50°$.
c. $\omega_c$ maximized.
d. $|G_c G_p(j\omega)| \geq |W_1(j\omega)|$, $\forall\omega$.
e. $|G_c G_p(j\omega)| \leq |W_2(j\omega)|^{-1}$, $\forall\omega$.

14. Let

$$G_p(s) = \frac{100}{s(s+2)(s+8)} \quad \text{and} \quad G_c(s) = \frac{K_c(s+z_1)(s+z_2)}{(s+p_1)(s+p_2)}.$$

Use files w1.i and w2.i and these specifications:
a. $K_v > 100$.
b. $\phi_m \geq 50°$.
c. $\omega_c$ maximized.
d. $|G_c G_p(j\omega)| \geq |W_1(j\omega)|$, $\forall\omega$.
e. $|G_c G_p(j\omega)| \leq |W_2(j\omega)|^{-1}$, $\forall\omega$.

15. Let

$$G_p(s) = \frac{240}{(s+6)(s+20)} \quad \text{and} \quad G_c(s) = \frac{K_c(s+z_1)(s+z_2)}{(s+p_1)(s+p_2)}.$$

Use files w1.j and w2.j and these specifications:
a. $K_p > 100$.
b. $\phi_m$ maximized.

c. $\omega_c$ maximized.

d. $|G_c G_p(j\omega)| \geq |W_1(j\omega)|$, $\forall \omega$.

e. $|G_c G_p(j\omega)| \leq |W_2(j\omega)|^{-1}$, $\forall \omega$.

16. Let

$$G_p(s) = \frac{10}{s(s+1)} \quad \text{and} \quad G_c(s) = \frac{K_c(s+z_1)}{(s+p_1)}.$$

Use files w1.k and w2.k and these specifications:

a. $K_v > 100$.

b. $\phi_m$ maximized.

c. $|G_c G_p(j\omega)| \geq |W_1(j\omega)|$, $\forall \omega$.

d. $|G_c G_p(j\omega)| \leq |W_2(j\omega)|^{-1}$, $\forall \omega$.

17. Let

$$G_p(s) = \frac{60}{s(s+60)} \quad \text{and} \quad G_c(s) = \frac{K_c(s+z_1)(s+z_2)}{(s+p_1)(s+p_2)}.$$

Use files w1.l and w2.l and these specifications:

a. $K_v > 100$.

b. $\phi_m \geq 50°$.

c. $\omega_c$ maximized.

d. $|G_c G_p(j\omega)| \geq |W_1(j\omega)|$, $\forall \omega$.

e. $|G_c G_p(j\omega)| \leq |W_2(j\omega)|^{-1}$, $\forall \omega$.

18. Let

$$G_p(s) = \frac{10}{(s+1)(s+2)} \quad \text{and} \quad G_c(s) = \frac{K_c(s+z_1)(s+z_2)}{(s+p_1)(s+p_2)}.$$

Use files w1.m and w2.m and these specifications:

a. $K_p > 100$.

b. $\phi_m \geq 50°$.

c. $\omega_c$ maximized.

d. $|G_c G_p(j\omega)| \geq |W_1(j\omega)|$, $\forall \omega$.

e. $|G_c G_p(j\omega)| \leq |W_2(j\omega)|^{-1}$, $\forall \omega$.

19. Let

$$G_p(s) = \frac{10}{s(s+10)} \quad \text{and} \quad G_c(s) = \frac{K_c(s+z_1)(s+z_2)}{(s+p_1)(s+p_2)}.$$

Use files w1.n and w2.n and these specifications:

a. $K_v > 500$.

b. $\phi_m \geq 50°$.

c. $\omega_c$ maximized.

d. $|G_c G_p(j\omega)| \geq |W_1(j\omega)|$, $\forall \omega$.

e. $|G_c G_p(j\omega)| \leq |W_2(j\omega)|^{-1}$, $\forall \omega$.

20. Let

$$G_p(s) = \frac{10}{(s+0.5)(s+2)(s+60)} \quad \text{and} \quad G_c(s) = \frac{K_c(s+z_1)(s+z_2)}{(s+p_1)(s+p_2)}.$$

Use files w1.o and w2.o and these specifications:

a.   $K_v > 100$.

b.   $\phi_m$ maximized.

c.   $\omega_c \geq 10$ rad/s.

d.   $|G_c G_p(j\omega)| \geq |W_1(j\omega)|$, $\forall \omega$.

e.   $|G_c G_p(j\omega)| \leq |W_2(j\omega)|^{-1}$, $\forall \omega$.

**21.**   Let

$$G_p(s) = \frac{30}{s(s+3)} \quad \text{and} \quad G_c(s) = \frac{K_c(s+z_1)(s+z_2)}{(s+p_1)(s+p_2)}.$$

Use files w1.p and w2.p and these specifications:

a.   $K_v > 100$.

b.   $\phi_m \geq 50°$.

c.   $\omega_c$ maximized.

d.   $|G_c G_p(j\omega)| \geq |W_1(j\omega)|$, $\forall \omega$.

e.   $|G_c G_p(j\omega)| \leq |W_2(j\omega)|^{-1}$, $\forall \omega$.

## 12.12.2   Additional Problems

**1.**   Give an example of a function $u$ that is not identically zero and yet $\text{pow}(u) = 0$.

**2.**   Write a MATLAB program to make a polar plot of $GH(j\omega)$, and the lines of nearest approach due to $W_1(j\omega)$ and $W_2(j\omega)$. Use it to test the robustness of your designs in Section 12.12.1.

**3.**   Compare the lower bound on the phase margin as suggested by Wolovich and illustrated in Fig. 12.7 to the estimate (not always a bound) $\phi_m \approx \sin^{-1} r$, for the following $GH(s)$.

a.   $\dfrac{K}{s(s+10)(s+50)}$    b.   $\dfrac{K}{(s+1)(s+10)(s+50)}$

c.   $\dfrac{K(s+5)}{s^2(s+10)(s+50)}$    d.   $\dfrac{K(s+1)}{s^3(s+50)}$

**4.**   Inside the "box" in the $GH$ plane defined by the points $(0, 0)$, $(0, -j)$, $(-1, -j)$, and $(0, -1)$, the lines of nearest approach are always to the left of and above the polar plot of $GH$. This is is not the case farther from the origin. Find some examples to illustrate this.

**5.**   Using the program written in Problem 2 draw the polar plot of $G_c G_p(j\omega)$ and the lines of nearest approach for the other two designs in Fig. 12.10. The data files you need are w1.a and w2.a on the CD-ROM that comes with the book.

**6.**   Using the program written in Problem 2 draw the polar plot of $G_c G_p(j\omega)$ and the lines of nearest approach for the other two designs in Fig. 12.12. The data files you need are w1.a and w2.a on the CD-ROM that comes with the book.

**7.**   The line of slope $-40$ dB/decade that forms the left-hand side of the design corridor in Fig. 12.10 touches the plot of $|W_1(j\omega)|$. Using the program written in Problem 2, draw the polar plot of the line of nearest approach due to $W_1$ for $0.2 \le \omega \le 0.5$. What can you conclude? The data files you need are w1.a and w2.a on the CD-ROM that comes with the book.

8. Discuss whether Inequality [12.19] or the inequality given in Theorem 12.9.1 is the most conservative condition for guaranteeing robustness.

9. Reconsider the "smart" missile control problem from Chapter 11, as shown in Fig. 12.13. The missile has a T.V. camera in its nose that relays a picture to the pilot. The pilot then directs the missile by centering the target on a display in the cockpit with a joystick. The signal from the pilot then causes the guidance system of the missile to move toward the target. Let the dynamics of the the missile and its control system be

$$G_p(s) = \frac{200}{s(s+5)(s+15)}.$$

Assume that the missile has potential unmodeled dynamics at high speed in turns. Also assume that there is low-frequency disturbance at launch and at lower speeds. For the unity feedback, cascade compensation configuration used in this chapter, design the compensator $G_c$. Use w1.g and w2.a and these specifications:

a. $K_v > 10$.
b. $\phi_m \ge 50°$.
c. $\omega_c$ as large as possible.
d. Compensator of as low an order as possible.

**Figure 12.13 |** Smartbomb system.

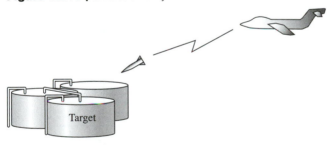

10. Use w1.h and w2.h and redo Problem 5, using these specifications:
a. $K_v > 20$.
b. $\phi_m \ge 55°$.
c. $\omega_c$ as large as possible.
d. Compensator of as low an order as possible.

11. Figure 12.14 shows a block diagram of a speed controller for an automobile that we first considered in Chapter 7, where

$$G_{\text{spdc}}(s) = \frac{10}{(s+3)(s+3.2)} \qquad G_{\text{car}}(s) = \frac{1}{s+2.5}.$$

**Figure 12.14 |** Block diagram of automobile speed control.

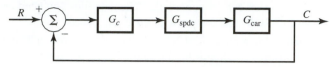

Assume sensor noise and intermittent wind buffeting disturbances at the output (speed of car). Use w1.c and w2.i. Design a controller $G_c$ that meets these specifications:

a.   $K_p \geq 10$.
b.   $\phi_m \geq 55°$.
c.   $\omega_c$ as large as possible.
d.   Compensator of as low an order as possible.

12.   Consider again the system shown in Fig. 12.15, first considered in Chapter 7, where the plant has a feedback loop. Let

$$G_1(s) = \frac{1}{s^2} \qquad G_2(s) = \frac{120s + 100}{s^2 + 12s + 72}.$$

Use w1.j and w2.j. Design a controller $G_c$ to meet these specifications:

a.   $K_v \geq 50$.
b.   $\phi_m \geq 50°$.
c.   $\omega_c$ as large as possible.
d.   Compensator of as low an order as possible.

**Figure 12.15 |** Multiloop control.

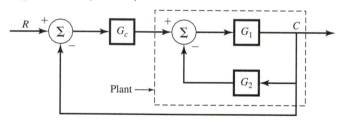

13.   Figure 12.16 shows a unity feedback loop for the pitch control of an aircraft, first considered in Chapter 7, where

$$G_{flap}(s) = \frac{4000}{(s + 8)} \qquad G_p(s) = \frac{(s + 6)(s + 15)}{s(s + 3 - j12)(s + 3 + j12)}.$$

Assume unmodeled dynamics and wind buffeting at the output (pitch of aircraft). Use w1.l and w2.l. Design a compensator to meet these specifications:

a.   $K_v \geq 50$.
b.   $\phi_m \geq 50°$.

**Figure 12.16 |** Pitch control of aircraft.

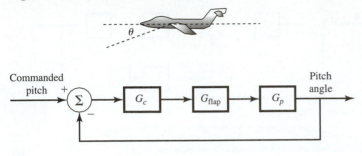

c.   $\omega_c > 10$ rad/s.

d.   Compensator of the lowest order possible.

14.   In Chapter 7 we first considered the the roll characteristics of a missile about its longitudinal axis, as shown in Fig. 12.17. The missile roll dynamics are given by

$$G_m(s) = \frac{1}{s(s+15)}.$$

Assume unmodeled dynamics in some rolls and wind buffeting at the output (roll). Use W1.m and W2.m. Redesign the compensator $G_c$ using the methods of this chapter to meet these specifications:

a.   $K_v \geq 100$.

b.   $\phi_m \geq 50°$.

c.   $\omega_c$ as large as possible.

**Figure 12.17 |** Roll control of missile.

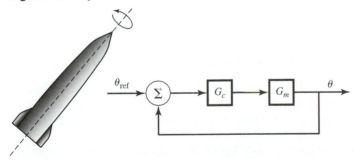

15.   Consider again the high-speed magnetic levitation train of Fig. 12.18, first considered in Chapter 7. On curves, it is necessary to bank the train to match the bank of the turn. The block diagram shows how this might be accompished with a rate gyro. $R$ is a bank command in degrees and $C$ is the actual amount of bank in degrees. Since the train is floating its dynamics have been modeled as

$$G_{\mathrm{maglev}}(s) = \frac{1}{Js^2}.$$

**Figure 12.18 |** Roll control of a maglev train.

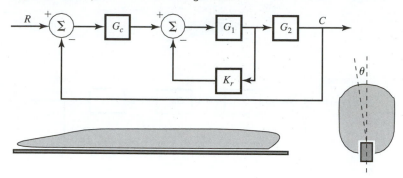

where $J$ is the moment of inertia of the train. In the figure these dynamics are broken down into

$$G_1(s) = \frac{1}{Js} \quad \text{and} \quad G_2(s) = \frac{1}{s}.$$

We do not need to know the value of $J$. Simply assume that the ratio

$$\frac{K_r}{J}.$$

Assume wind buffeting at the output and unmodeled dynamics in high-speed turns. Use w1.o and w2.o. Redesign the control system $G_c$ using the methods of this chapter to these specifications:

a.   $K_v \geq 500$.
b.   $\phi_m \geq 70°$.
c.   PO $\leq 10\%$.
d.   Rise time to 90% of final value $\leq 0.2$ s.

# FURTHER READINGS

Bode, H. W. 1945. *Network Analysis and Feedback Amplifier Design.* Princeton, N.J.: D. Van Nostrand.

Chestnut, Harold, and R. W. Mayer. 1951. *Servomechanisms and Regulating Systems Design,* Vol. 1. New York: John Wiley & Sons.

Doyle, John C., Bruce A. Francis, and Allen R. Tannenbaum. 1992. *Feedback Control Theory.* New York: MacMillan.

James, H. M., N. B. Nichols, and R. S. Phillips. 1947. *Theory of Servomechanisms.* New York: McGraw-Hill.

Wolovich, William A. 1994. *Automatic Control Systems—Basic Analysis and Design.* New York: Harcourt Brace.

# Chapter 13

# Position Control
## *A Case Study*

## 13.1 | OVERVIEW

In this chapter we will again do a complete design, starting with the identification of the transfer function of a physical system, a circular positioning table, and ending with the implementation of a design that meets a simple set of performance specifications.

The physical system to be controlled is shown in Fig 13.1. It consists of a dc motor connected to a turntable on one shaft end and to a heliopot on the other shaft end. It is, in fact, an actual version of the simple robot "arm" of Fig. 1.7.

The heliopot is a voltage divider with the resistance coil shaped like a circle. The wiper, or movable contact, moves along the resistance coil, as shown in Fig. 13.2. If a voltage is applied across the resistance coil, between contacts CW and CCW, then the wiper will give the angular position of the table as a voltage. In what follows $+10$ V will be applied to one end of the resistance coil and $-10$ V to the other end. Thus, the position of the table will be a voltage between these two limits. Note that the position is modulo $360°$.

Our first goal is to identify the transfer function of the system. The system is nothing more than a dc motor connected at one shaft end to an inertial load, the load in this case being the table. The model for the dc motor, given by Eq. [3.21], and repeated here for convenience, is

$$G_\theta(s) = \frac{K_m}{[s^2 + (B/J)s + K_r/J](s + R_q/L_q) + K_v K_m s}. \qquad [13.1]$$

If we assume, as we have done before, that the shaft connecting the motor to the table is perfectly rigid, the term $K_r/J$ can be removed because there will be no torque component due to the twisting of the shaft. The model of the system is then

$$\frac{K_m}{s[s^2 + (B/J + R_q/L_q)s + (BR_q/JL_q) + K_v K_m)]},$$

**413**

**Figure 13.1 |** Positioning table.

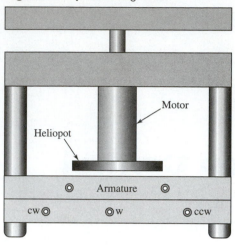

**Figure 13.2 |** Internal configuration of heliopot.

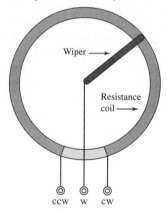

or more generally

$$G_\theta(s) = \frac{K_m}{s(s + p_1)(s + p_2)}. \qquad \text{[13.2]}$$

The motor used to power the table is a 100 oz-in. permanent magnet, dc motor. The expectation is that

$$p_2 \gg p_1,$$

so that a simplified, but useful, model for the system is

$$G_\theta(s) = \frac{K}{s(s + p)}, \qquad \text{[13.3]}$$

with $K = K_m/p_2$. The rationale for expecting the wide separation between $p_1$ and $p_2$

is a matter of experience. We expect $p_1$ to be determined primarily by the mechanical characteristics of the system, while $p_2$ will be largely a function of the electrical dynamics of the armature winding. The electrical dynamics are much faster, so the time constant of the pole at $s = -p_2$ should be much smaller.

We note before proceeding that the identification phase of the design cycle is invariably difficult. In the present case, we have a system that is not perfectly linear for which we are trying to derive a linear model. Further, we expect the pole at $s = -p_2$ to be widely separated from the other two poles. None of this makes the identification process any easier. We simply have to buckle down and scratch out a solution to this problem. As we will see in what follows, we can finally arrive at a reasonably good model of this system.

## 13.2 | MODEL IDENTIFICATION

### 13.2.1 Frequency Analysis Identification

We will first attempt to identify the parameters of the transfer function by using frequency domain analysis. That analysis will shed some light on the transfer function but will not be totally satisfying. We will then explore an alternative approach and finally arrive at a reasonable model for the positioning table.

A block diagram of the laboratory setup to collect the frequency response data for the positioning table is shown in Fig. 13.3. The function generator produces a sinusoidal signal that is amplified by the power amplifier. The power amplifier is connected to the armature winding of the dc motor. The armature voltage is also sent to one channel of the oscilloscope. The other channel of the oscilloscope receives the voltage from the heliopot that is attached to the other end of the shaft of the dc motor. The heliopot voltage measures the position of the table.

As the armature voltage is varied sinusoidally, the shaft of the motor oscillates back and forth sinusoidally at the same frequency as the armature voltage. The heliopot voltage also varies sinusoidally at the same frequency, thereby recording the oscillations of the motor shaft.

By comparing the magnitude of the armature voltage to that of the heliopot, we can find the magnitude of the motor's frequency response at a given frequency. The time shift between the armature voltage and the heliopot voltage, as recorded on the oscilloscope, provides the means of measuring the phase of the motor's frequency

**Figure 13.3 |** Block diagram of setup for identifying transfer function.

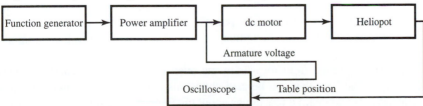

**Figure 13.4** | Laboratory setup for identifying transfer function.

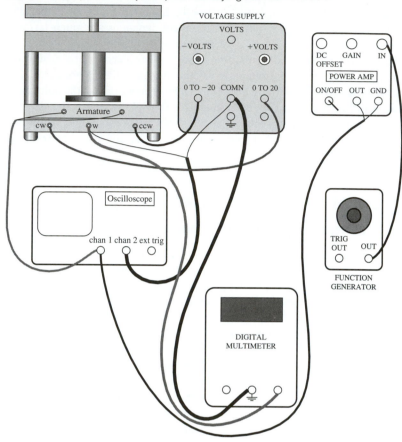

response at a given frequency. By making magnitude and time shift measurements over a range of frequencies, we can find the Bode magnitude and phase plots of the motor.

In Fig. 13.4 we see the actual laboratory setup for finding the frequency response of the transfer function of the motor. The function generator, connected to the input of the power amplifier, supplies a sinusoidal signal to the armature winding of the dc motor. The output of the power amplifier is connected to the armature windings of the motor via channel 1 of the oscilloscope. This is accomplished by a T-connector at the input to channel 1 of the oscilloscope. The dual voltage supply provides $\pm 10$ V to the inputs CW and CCW of the heliopot. The wiper of the heliopot is connected to channel 2 of the oscilloscope. Note that this signal is referenced to the common of the dual voltage supply.

The data obtained from measurements over a range of frequencies is shown in Fig. 13.5. The best that can be said about this data is that it is not very good. Nonetheless, we can learn a few things about the transfer function from this data.

**Figure 13.5** | Measured Bode magnitude and phase data for positioning table.

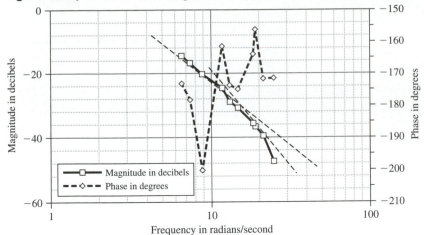

The frequency data, such as it is, indicates that the phase is very close to $-180°$ for very low frequencies. This is not unexpected, and indicates that the transfer function has two poles at or near $s = 0$. We can also discern a slope of $-40$ dB/decade. There may even be a third pole somewhere out beyond 15 rad/s, but since the magnitude data is only slightly better in quality than the frequency data, we can't really be very sure where the third pole is.

From the magnitude data we can make a first guess that the transfer function is

$$G(s) = \frac{K}{s(s + p_1)(s + p_2)},$$

with $0 < p_1 < 4$ rad/s and $p_2$ unknown.

If we let $p_1 = 4$, then we have the *very preliminary* model

$$G(s) = \frac{K}{s(s + 4)(s + p_2)}.$$

This may not seem like much, but we have made real progress. For one thing we know that the mathematical model that we assumed at the outset is probably correct. We are also reasonably confident of the locations of two of the three poles.

In an effort to refine this model we now investigate an alternative identification procedure, namely, applying a pulse to the system when it is at rest. The first step in this process is to do some analysis of the ideal impulse response of a simple system, and then extend the analysis to a finite width pulse.

## 13.2.2  Ideal Impulse Identification

For this analysis, we neglect the third pole and assume a model of the form

$$G(s) = \frac{K}{s(s + p)}.$$

**Figure 13.6 |** Ideal impulse response.

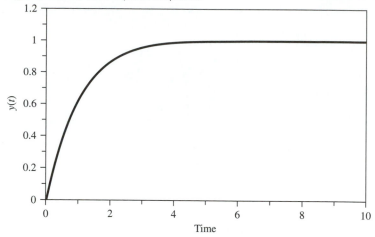

The rationale for this is that we expect that the third pole of our model is widely separated from the other two. We are relying on our knowledge of the physics of electric motors in making this assumption. More specifically, we expect the pole at $s = -p_2$ to depend primarily on the electrical time constant of the armature winding of the dc motor and to have a very small time constant. Thus, for this analysis, we don't lose much by neglecting the pole at $s = -p_2$.

For this simplified model, the ideal impulse response in the Laplace domain is

$$Y(s) = G(s) = \frac{A}{s} + \frac{B}{s + p},$$

where

$$A = sG(s)\big|_{s=0} = \frac{K}{p},$$

$$B = (s + p)G(s)\big|_{s=-p} = -\frac{K}{p} = -A.$$

Thus,

$$y(t) = A[1 - e^{-pt}].$$

The response for $A = 1$, $p = 1$ is shown in Fig. 13.6. The constant $A$ is $y_{ss}$, the steady state value of the response. We see that we can easily find the time constant of the pole at $s = -p$ by measuring the rate of decay as the response nears steady state.

### 13.2.3   Finite Width Pulse Identification

In the laboratory, we will have to use a pulse of finite width, actually about 60 ms in width, to move the turntable sufficiently to make useful measurements. Before we can proceed, we need to analyze the response to a finite-width pulse.

Analytically, we can form the pulse by subtracting a delayed unit step from the unit step; that is,

$$u_{\text{pulse}}(t) = [\mathbf{1}(t) - \mathbf{1}(t - T)].$$

Again letting

$$G_p(s) = \frac{K}{s(s + p)},$$

we have

$$Y_{\text{step}}(s) = \frac{K}{s^2(s + p)}.$$

The partial fraction expansion of is

$$Y_{\text{step}}(s) = \frac{A}{s} + \frac{B}{s^2} + \frac{C}{s + p},$$

with

$$A = \frac{d}{ds}[s^2 Y(s)]\Big|_{s=0} = \frac{-K}{p^2},$$

$$B = [s^2 Y(s)]\Big|_{s=0} = \frac{K}{p},$$

$$C = [(s + p)Y(s)]\Big|_{s=-p} = \frac{K}{p^2}.$$

We note for future reference that $A < 0$, $B > 0$, $C > 0$, and $C = -A$.
We now have

$$y(t) = [A + Bt + Ce^{-pt}]\mathbf{1}(t) - \left[A + B(t - T) + Ce^{-p(t-T)}\right]\mathbf{1}(t - T).$$

The decomposition of $y(t)$ into components is shown in Fig. 13.7(a). For $0 < t < T$, the response is

$$[A + Bt + Ce^{-pt}]\mathbf{1}(t).$$

For $t > T$, the step portion is cancelled and the ramp becomes a steady offset of value $BT$. That is,

$$y(t) = A - A + Bt - (Bt - BT) + Ce^{-pt} - Ce^{-(pt-pT)}$$

$$= BT + Ce^{-pt} - Ce^{-pt}e^{pT}$$

$$= BT - C[e^{pT} - 1]e^{-pt}.$$

**Figure 13.7 |** (a) Components of pulse response and (b) total pulse response.

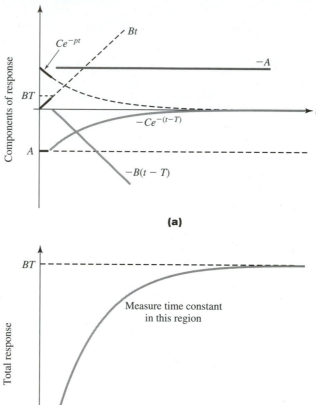

(a)

(b)

Since $e^{pT} > 1$, the term

$$C[e^{pT} - 1]e^{-pt}$$

is positive. We see from the last expression that the response is very similar to that for an ideal impulse. Indeed, in the laboratory the response reaches steady state in several seconds, while the pulse only lasts 60 ms. Consequently, the finite-width pulse response turns out to be a pretty good approximation to the response to an ideal, zero-width pulse.

Our next goal is to measure the pulse response and apply the analysis just completed to see if it will help us refine our estimate of the pole we suspect is in the vicinity of $s = -4$.

# 13.3 | PULSE IDENTIFICATION OF A TRANSFER FUNCTION

## 13.3.1 Turntable Data Analysis

Figure 13.8 shows in block diagram form how the response of the turntable motor is collected. The pulse is generated by a software routine and sent to a digital-to-analog converter (DAC) housed in an ouput slot of the computer. The output of the DAC is connected to the input of a power amplifier. The output of the power amplifier, in turn, is connected to the armature winding of the dc motor that turns the positioning table. The power amplifier is necessary to give the step input signal applied to the armature winding of the dc motor sufficient power to move the table through an angle of about 90°. The signal applied to the armature winding, along with the signal from the heliopot, are then sent to two channels of the oscilloscope.

**Figure 13.8 |** Block diagram of setup for measuring the pulse response of a positioning table.

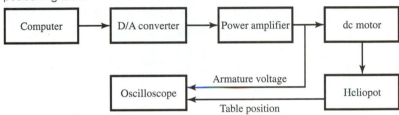

Figure 13.9 shows the actual laboratory setup for measuring the response of the positioning table to the pulse. The pulse generated by the computer program and delivered to the DAC is brought out from the DAC to the panel shown in the figure. As discussed in Chapter 8, the panel simply makes it more convenient to connect the signal from the DAC to the power amplifier. The dual voltage supply provides ±10 V to the CW and CCW terminals of the heliopot.

The wiper of the heliopot is connected to the oscilloscope. Note that the ground of the oscilloscope and the ground of the dual supply are connected. This is not very obvious in the figure because a shielded cable is used to connect the signal to the ocilloscope and the ground of the oscilloscope is not shown, explicitly.

The multimeter is used to help zero the table. That is, the table is turned manually until the voltage from the wiper is zero. It just turns out to be more convenient to do this with a mulitmeter than with the oscilloscope.

The response to a 60-ms pulse is shown in Fig. 13.10. We can get an estimate of the pole location from both Fig. 13.10 and the plot of

$$x(t) = \ln[y_{ss} - y(t)],$$

shown in Fig. 13.11. We know from the discussions in Chapter 3 and in this chapter that the value of $p$ is just the negative of the slope of the graph in Fig. 13.11. The changes in slope are clearly visible in the figure. We make our measurements at larger values of $t$, that is near steady state. Here the slope is nearly constant and from the

**Figure 13.9 |** Setup for measuring pulse response of a positioning table.

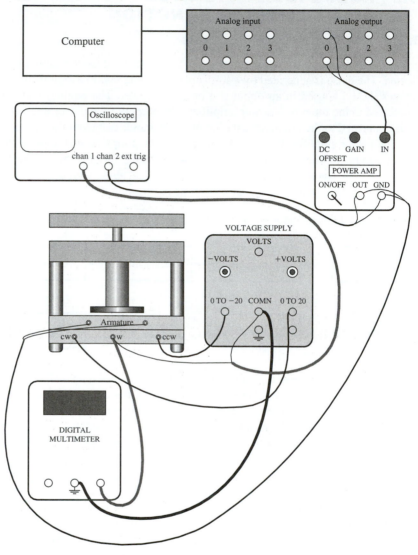

two figures we see that

$$4.2 < p < 4.4.$$

Thus, our original guess of the pole location is reasonably close. We could "refine" our estimate of $p$ to say 4.3, but that hardly seems reasonable, given the accuracy of the measurement we have just made. So, assuming $p = 4$ and noting that the final value is

$$y_{ss} = 4.55 = BT = \frac{KT}{p},$$

**Figure 13.10 |** Response to a 60-ms pulse.

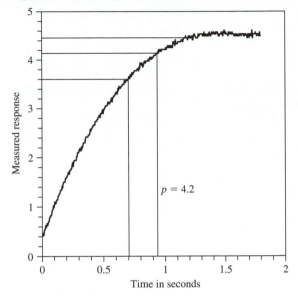

**Figure 13.11 |** Plot of $\ln[y_{ss} - y(t)]$ versus time.

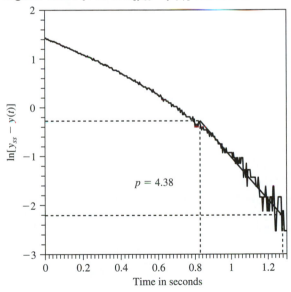

we can find

$$K = \frac{4.55 \times 4}{0.06} = 303.$$

Recall that the derivation of the response to the finite width pulse assumed the pulse was of unit height. In the laboratory, the voltage applied to the motor for 60 ms was around 30 V. This means $K$ is too large by a factor of 30. Thus, ignoring for the moment the pole at $s = -p_2$, and adjusting the gain by a factor of 30, we have the approximate model

$$G_p(s) = \frac{10}{s(s+4)}.$$

If we wish, we can get a sanity check on the gain by using the frequency response data (see Problem 14 in Section 13.6).

The finite-width pulse identification has proved very useful, because it corroborates our initial estimate of the location of the pole at $s = -p_1$. Our next task is to try to find the third pole at $s = -p_2$. In doing so we should also be able to refine our estimate of the gain.

## 13.3.2  Finding the Third Pole

At this juncture, our model for the positioning table is

$$G(s) = \frac{K}{s(s+4)(s+p_2)}.$$

We have made some real headway, because we are now confident of the location of two of the poles. If we can find the remaining pole, then we can find the gain. So our next task is clearly to find the location of the third pole at $s = -p_2$.

Before proceeding to that task, we mention that there is another method that we could have employed to find the pole that we have decided is around $s = -4$. We leave the task of determining that alternative method as an exercise (see Problem 5 in Section 13.6).

We now identify the location of the third pole. What we really want to know is whether this other pole will have a significant impact on our design. To that end, we present a method of determining that third pole. We forewarn the reader that the analysis is lengthy and tedious, but we encourage the reader to perservere and follow the analysis presented. This analysis is fairly representative of that required in any identification effort. Put another way, identification almost always involves a good deal of thrashing around.

To find the third pole we first consider what happens if we add unity feedback and forward gain to our system. If we do so, the root locus is that shown in Fig 13.12.

Note that for large enough gain, the closed-loop system will have the form

$$T_c(s) = \frac{\bar{K}\omega_n^2}{(s+p)\left(s^2 + 2\zeta s + \omega_n^2\right)}. \qquad \text{[13.4]}$$

The overall gain $K$ has been written as the product $\bar{K}\omega_n^2$, because this proves convenient a little later in the analysis.

We know that for the normalized second-order system

$$T_{N2}(s) = \frac{\omega_n^2}{s^2 + 2\zeta\omega_n s + \omega_n^2},$$

**Figure 13.12 |** Root locus for transfer function with unity gain.

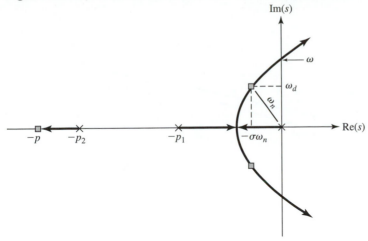

the damping ratio can be obtained from the formula for the percent overshoot, namely,

$$PO = e^{-\zeta\pi/(\sqrt{1-\zeta^2})}.$$

We now derive a similar formula for the system of Eq. [13.4].

Applying a step input to the transfer function of Eq. [13.4] we obtain

$$C(s) = \frac{1}{s} \frac{\bar{K}\omega_n^2}{(s+p)(s^2 + 2\zeta s + \omega_n^2)}$$

$$= \frac{1}{s} + \frac{A}{s+p} + \frac{|M|e^{j\phi}}{s+\sigma - j\omega_d} + \frac{|M|e^{j\phi}}{s+\sigma - j\omega_d}.$$

Then

$$A = (s+p)\left[\frac{\bar{K}\omega_n^2}{s(s+p)(s^2 + 2\zeta s + \omega_n^2)}\right]\bigg|_{s=-p}$$

$$= \left[\frac{\bar{K}\omega_n^2}{s(s+\sigma - j\omega_d)(s+\sigma + j\omega_d)}\right]\bigg|_{s=-p}$$

$$= \frac{\bar{K}\omega_n^2}{(-p)[(\sigma - p) - j\omega_d][(\sigma - p) + j\omega_d]}$$

$$= \frac{\bar{K}\omega_n^2}{(-p)[(\sigma - p)^2 + \omega_d^2]}$$

$$= \frac{-\bar{K}\omega_n^2}{pV_p^2},$$

where $V_p$ is the magnitude of the vector drawn from the real closed-loop pole at $s = -p$ to the complex closed-loop pole at $s = -\sigma + j\omega_d$, as shown in Fig. 13.13.

**Figure 13.13** | Calculation of gain to place complex poles.

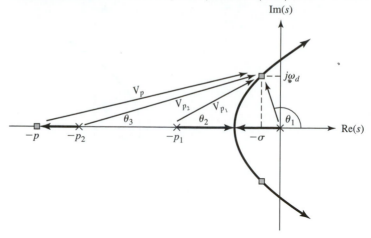

The overall gain $K = \bar{K}\omega_n$ required to place a closed-loop pole at $s = -\sigma + j\omega_d$ is

$$\bar{K}\omega_n^2 = \left\{\left[(p_2 - \sigma)^2 + \omega_d^2\right]\left[(p_1 - \sigma)^2 + \omega_d^2\right]\left[\sigma^2 + \omega_d^2\right]\right\}^{1/2}$$
$$= \left\{\left[(p_2 - \sigma)^2 + \omega_d^2\right]\left[(p_1 - \sigma)^2 + \omega_d^2\right]\right\}^{1/2}\omega_n$$
$$= V_{p_1} V_{p_2}\omega_n.$$

Then,

$$|A| = \frac{V_{p_1} V_{p_2}\omega_n}{p V_p^2}.$$

From Fig. 13.13 we can see that

$$V_p^2 > V_{p_1} V_{p_2} \quad \text{and} \quad p > \omega_n.$$

Thus

$$|A| < 1.$$

**Figure 13.14** | Angles $\phi_1$ and $\phi_2$ from partial fraction expansion.

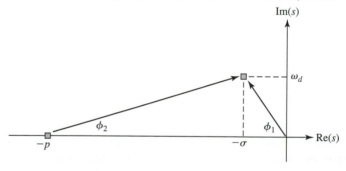

In a similar fashion, referring to Fig. 13.14, we find

$$|M|e^{j\gamma} = (s + \sigma - j\omega_d)\left[\frac{\bar{K}\omega_n^2}{s(s + p)(s + \sigma - j\omega_d)(s + \sigma + j\omega_d)}\right]\Bigg|_{s=-\sigma+j\omega_d}$$

$$= \left[\frac{\bar{K}\omega_n^2}{s(s + p)(s + \sigma + j\omega_d)}\right]\Bigg|_{s=-\sigma+j\omega_d}$$

$$= \frac{\bar{K}\omega_n^2}{[-\sigma + j\omega_d][(p - \sigma) + j\omega_d][j2\omega_d]}$$

$$= \frac{\bar{K}\omega_n^2}{\left[\sqrt{\sigma^2 + \omega_d^2}\,\underline{/\pi - \phi_1}\right]\left[\sqrt{(p - \sigma)^2 + \omega_d^2}\,\underline{/\phi_2}\right][2\omega_d\,\underline{/\pi/2}]}$$

$$= \frac{\bar{K}\omega_n^2}{2\omega_d\sqrt{\sigma^2 + \omega_d^2}\sqrt{(p - \sigma)^2 + \omega_d^2}}\,\underline{/\frac{\pi}{2} + \phi_1 - \phi_2}$$

$$= \frac{\bar{K}\omega_n^2}{2\omega_n\sqrt{1 - \zeta^2}\,\omega_n\sqrt{(p - \sigma)^2 + \omega_d^2}}\,\underline{/\frac{\pi}{2} + \phi_1 - \phi_2}$$

$$= \frac{\bar{K}}{2\sqrt{1 - \zeta^2}\sqrt{(p - \sigma)^2 + \omega_d^2}}\,\underline{/\frac{\pi}{2} + \phi_1 - \phi_2},$$

where

$$|M| = \frac{\bar{K}}{2\sqrt{1 - \zeta^2}\sqrt{(p - \sigma)^2 + \omega_d^2}} \quad \text{and} \quad \gamma = \underline{/\frac{\pi}{2} + \phi_1 - \phi_2},$$

and $\phi_1$ and $\phi_2$ are shown in Fig. 13.14.

Then,

$$c(t) = \left[1 + 2|M|e^{-\sigma t}\cos\left(\omega_d t + \frac{\pi}{2} + \phi_1 - \phi_2\right) + Ae^{-pt}\right]1(t).$$

Noting that

$$\cos\left(\alpha + \frac{\pi}{2}\right) = \cos\alpha\cos\frac{\pi}{2} - \sin\alpha\sin\frac{\pi}{2} = -\sin\alpha,$$

we can also write

$$c(t) = [1 - 2|M|e^{-\sigma t}\sin(\omega_d t + \phi_1 - \phi_2) + Ae^{-pt}]1(t).$$

We next find the time $t$ at which the response reaches its maximum. To that end, we first decide whether we have to consider the term $Ae^{-pt}$. One consideration is the size of $A$. We already know $|A| < 1$. The other consideration is the relative rate of decay of $e^{-pt}$. If we assume that

$$\frac{p}{\sigma} > 10, \qquad\qquad [13.5]$$

then, given that $|A| < 1$, we can pretty much ignore the term $Ae^{-pt}$, because we expect this term to decay much faster than the envelope of the dominant complex poles. As discussed earlier, some engineering knowledge and judgment comes into play here. As we have discussed, we expect the pole at $s = -p_2$ to have a time constant that depends mainly on the electrical time constant of the armature winding and we expect that time constant to be small.

Assuming that Inequality [13.5] holds, we can then write

$$c(t) \approx 1 - 2|M|e^{-\sigma t} \sin(\omega_d t + \phi_1 - \phi_2),$$

and

$$\frac{d}{dt}c(t) = -2|M|\frac{d}{dt}[e^{-\sigma t}\sin(\omega_d t + \phi_1 - \phi_2)]$$

$$= -2|M|[(-\sigma)e^{-\sigma t}\sin(\omega_d t + \phi_1 - \phi_2) + \omega_d e^{-\sigma t}\cos(\omega_d t + \phi_1 - \phi_2)].$$

Equating this last expression to zero yields

$$(-\sigma)\sin(\omega_d t + \phi_1 - \phi_2) + \omega_d\cos(\omega_d t + \phi_1 - \phi_2) = 0,$$

or

$$\frac{\sin(\omega_d t + \phi_1 - \phi_2)}{\cos(\omega_d t + \phi_1 - \phi_2)} = \frac{\omega_d}{\sigma} = \frac{\omega_n\sqrt{1 - \zeta^2}}{\zeta\omega_n} = \frac{\sqrt{1 - \zeta^2}}{\zeta},$$

where $\zeta = \cos\phi_1$. Thus we have maxima and minima at

$$\tan(\omega_d t + \phi_1 - \phi_2) = \frac{\sqrt{1 - \zeta^2}}{\zeta}.$$

But, from Fig. 13.14,

$$\tan\phi_1 = \frac{\sqrt{1 - \zeta^2}}{\zeta},$$

so that we can write

$$\tan(\omega_d t + \phi_1 - \phi_2) = \tan\phi_1.$$

Now, since the tangent function repeats every $\pi$ radians, we must have minima and maxima when

$$\omega_d t - \phi_2 = k\pi, \qquad k = 1, 2, \ldots,$$

or

$$t = \frac{k\pi + \phi_2}{\omega_d}.$$

The global maximum occurs for $k = 1$, or

$$t_p = \frac{\pi + \phi_2}{\omega_d}.$$

We next compute

$$-\sigma t_p = -\zeta \omega_n \left( \frac{\pi + \phi_2}{\omega_n \sqrt{1 - \zeta^2}} \right) = \frac{\zeta(\pi + \phi_2)}{\sqrt{1 - \zeta^2}}$$

and

$$\sin(\omega_d t + \phi_1 - \phi_2) = \sin \left[ \left( \omega_d \frac{\pi + \phi_2}{\omega_d} \right) + \phi_1 - \phi_2 \right]$$

$$= \sin(\phi_1 + \pi)$$

$$= -\sin(\phi_1)$$

$$= -\sqrt{1 - \zeta^2}.$$

Thus,

$$c(t_p) = 1 + 2|M|e^{[-\zeta(\pi + \phi_2)/\sqrt{1 - \zeta^2}]} \sin \phi_1$$

$$= 1 + 2|M|e^{[-\zeta(\pi + \phi_2)/\sqrt{1 - \zeta^2}]} \sqrt{1 - \zeta^2}$$

$$= 1 + 2 \frac{\bar{K}}{2\sqrt{1 - \zeta^2}\sqrt{(p - \sigma)^2 + \omega_d^2}} \sqrt{1 - \zeta^2} e^{[-\zeta(\pi + \phi_2)/\sqrt{1 - \zeta^2}]}$$

$$= 1 + \frac{\bar{K}}{\sqrt{(p - \sigma)^2 + \omega_d^2}} e^{[-\zeta(\pi + \phi_2)/\sqrt{1 - \zeta^2}]}.$$

Since the steady state value for a unit step input is 1.0, we have

$$\text{PO} = \frac{\bar{K}}{\sqrt{(p - \sigma)^2 + \omega_d^2}} e^{[-\zeta(\pi + \phi_2)/\sqrt{1 - \zeta^2}]} \times 100.$$

Recall that for $T_{N2}(s)$

$$\text{PO} = e^{[-\zeta\pi/\sqrt{1 - \zeta^2}]} \times 100.$$

In the latter case $\zeta$ could be determined from the percent overshoot. For the case where a third pole is present, this is not possible since the percent overshoot depends on $p$, $\sigma$, $\omega_n$, $\phi_2$, and $\zeta$. Although we cannot determine $\zeta$ from the percent overshoot, we have another alternative and that is to measure the time constant of the exponential envelope of the response.

Figure 13.15 shows in block diagram form the laboratory setup to apply unity feedback and cascade compensation to the positioning table. The feedback and compensator box (FAC), which we first introduced in Chapter 3 and used again in Chapter 8, subtracts the table position in volts supplied by the heliopot from the reference input, also in volts, which is supplied by the FAC. The error signal is fed forward through a gain stage and through the two inverting opamp stages. The output of the FAC then goes to the input of the power amplifier. The output of the power amplifier is connected to the armature windings of the dc motor that moves the table.

Figure 13.16 shows the actual laboratory setup for applying unity feedback and cascade compensation to the positioning table. The setup is similar to that used in Chapter 8, except we will initiate the step from the FAC, using a toggle switch. We

**Figure 13.15 |** Block diagram of laboratory setup for applying unity feedback and cascade compensation to a positioning table.

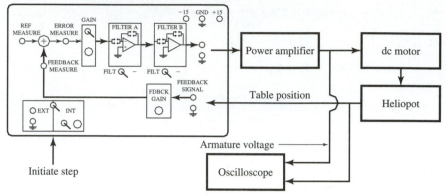

set both the toggle switches in the forward path to "$-1$" so that we have simple gain compensation with unity feedback. Later we will use this same setup to implement a lead compensator, but for now we simply want gain compensation.

With the gain of the power amplifier at maximum we get the response shown in Fig. 13.17. The fact that we cannot drive the dominant poles to the imaginary axis with the power amplifier at full gain is an indication that the pole at $s = -p_2$ is far to the left of the origin in the $s$ plane.

From the figure we can see that one time constant of decay in the envelope is about 1.65 s. Thus,

$$\sigma = \frac{1}{1.65} = 0.606.$$

Further, the damped frequency $\omega_d$ is 2.283 Hz.

At this point we know both $\sigma$ and $\omega_d$. Then, since

$$\frac{\sigma}{\omega_d} = \frac{\zeta\omega_n}{\omega_n\sqrt{1-\zeta^2}} = \frac{\zeta}{\sqrt{1-\zeta^2}},$$

we can square both sides to obtain

$$\left(\frac{\sigma}{\omega_d}\right)^2 = \frac{\zeta^2}{1-\zeta^2}.$$

This last expression can be rearranged as

$$\left(\frac{\sigma}{\omega_d}\right)^2 = \zeta^2\left[1 - \left(\frac{\sigma}{\omega_d}\right)^2\right].$$

**Figure 13.16 |** Actual laboratory setup for applying unity feedback and lead compensation to a positioning table.

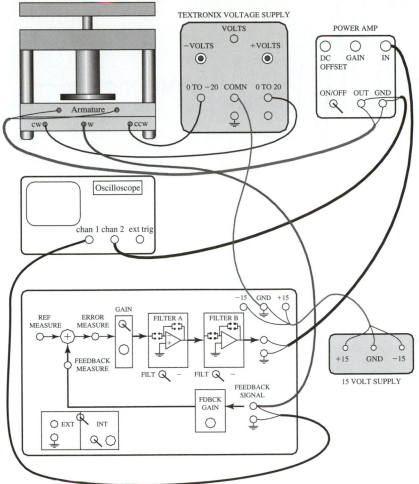

Finally, letting

$$\rho = \frac{\sigma}{\omega_d},$$

we have

$$\zeta = \frac{\rho}{\sqrt{1 - \rho^2}}.$$

In the present case,

$$\rho = \frac{0.606}{14.345} = 0.0422,$$

**Figure 13.17 |** Sample response under feedback.

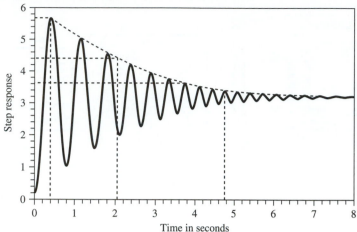

and

$$\zeta = \frac{0.0422}{\sqrt{1 - 0.0422^2}} = 0.0422.$$

We now have been able to determine both $\zeta$ and $\omega_d$, and consequently we can find

$$\omega_n = \frac{\omega_d}{\sqrt{1 - \zeta^2}} = \frac{14.345}{\sqrt{1 - 0.0422^2}} = 14.36 \text{ rad/s}.$$

It is now possible to plot the location of the complex poles shown in Fig. 13.13.

Having found the complex poles, and knowing that $p_1 \approx 4$, we can compute $p_2$ from the angle condition of the root locus. That is,

$$-\theta_1 - \theta_2 - \theta_3 = -180°.$$

Since $\theta_1$ and $\theta_2$ are known quite accurately, we can rewrite this equation as

$$
\begin{aligned}
\theta_3 &= 180° - \theta_1 - \theta_2 \\
&= 180° - \left(90° + \tan^{-1}\frac{\sigma}{\omega_d}\right) - \tan^{-1}\frac{\omega_d}{p_1 - \sigma} \\
&= 90° - \tan^{-1}\frac{\sigma}{\omega_d} - \tan^{-1}\frac{\omega_d}{p_1 - \sigma},
\end{aligned}
$$

where $\sigma$ is the *magnitude* of the real part of the complex poles.

Then, having found $\theta_3$, we can compute

$$p_2 = \sigma + \frac{\omega_d}{\tan\theta_3}.$$

**Figure 13.18 |** Comparison of measured and simulated responses $p_1 = 4$.

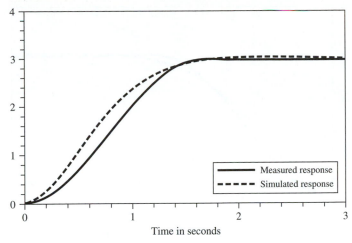

Time in seconds

Measured response
Simulated response

Thus,

$$\theta_3 = 90° - \tan^{-1}\frac{0.606}{14.36} - \tan^{-1}\frac{14.36}{4 - 0.606}$$

$$= 90° - 2.416° - 76.7°$$

$$= 10.88°,$$

and

$$p_2 = \sigma + \frac{14.36}{\tan 10.88°}$$

$$= 75.$$

At this juncture we have the model

$$G(s) = \frac{K}{s(s + 4)(s + 75)}.\qquad\qquad \textbf{[13.6]}$$

We now try to validate this model by measuring the critically damped response of the system and comparing it to the critically damped response determined using the transfer function given in Eq. [13.6]. Finding the critically damped response of the real system is just a trial-and-error process. We simply keep adjusting the gain until the overshoot just disappears. The result of this comparison is shown in Fig. 13.18. If anything, $p_1 < 4$. If we try $p_1 = 3.5$ and recompute $p_2$, we obtain

$$G(s) = \frac{K}{s(s + 3.5)(s + 92)}.\qquad\qquad \textbf{[13.7]}$$

Figure 13.19 shows the simulated versus the measured response for this revised model. What is evident is that *no* linear model is going to fit exactly because of nonlinear effects in the dc motor. Thus, we settle for the transfer function of Eq. [13.7]. As we

**Figure 13.19 |** Comparison of measured and simulated responses $p_1 = 3.5$.

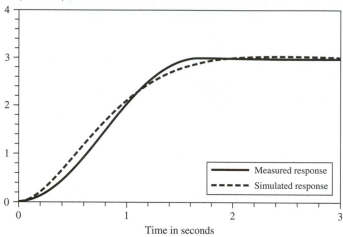

Time in seconds

shall see shortly, it will not matter much whether we use this transfer function or that given by Eq. [13.6].

We can now make a final estimate of the gain using the frequency response data for $\omega = 6.572$ rad/s. That is,

$$|G(j6.572)| = \left| \frac{K}{s(s+3.5)(s+92)} \right|\Big|_{s=j6.572} = 10^{-14.498/20} = 0.188,$$

and we can then solve for

$$K = 6.572 \times \sqrt{6.572^2 + 3.5^2} \times \sqrt{6.572^2 + 92^2} \times 0.188 = 849.$$

Thus, our final model is

$$G_p(s) = \frac{849}{s(s+3.5)(s+92)}. \qquad\qquad \textbf{[13.8]}$$

As we will see in the design in Section 13.4, a precise value for the gain is not needed.

## 13.4 | LEAD COMPENSATION

We now design a lead compensator based on the model of Eq. [13.8]. Our design specifications are simple:

1.  PO < 10 %.
2.  Rise time to 63% of final value less than 0.3 s.

The compensator we will use is

$$G_c = \frac{K_c(s+4)}{s+50}.$$

The full root locus is shown in Fig. 13.20. In Fig. 13.21, we have focused on the root locus to the right of $s = -60$. Notice that the system is essentially critically damped until the break out at $s = -20$. The gain required to reach the break-out point

**Figure 13.20 |** Full root locus with lead compensation.

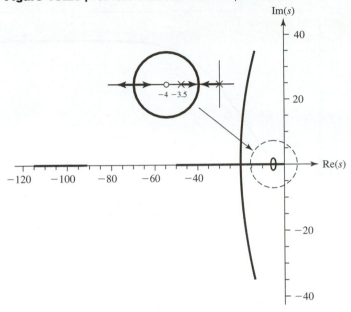

**Figure 13.21 |** Root locus to right of $s = -60$.

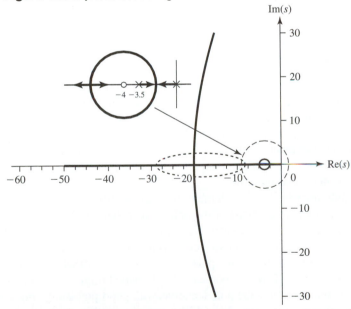

is $K = 4.5 \times 10^4$. The power amplifier in the laboratory cannot produce that much gain. So the dominant closed-loop poles are in the region enclosed by the ellipse.

We now test our design using the laboratory setup of Fig. 13.16 with the lead compensator implemented on one of the inverting opamp stages of the FAC. The measured step response with the power amplifier at full gain is shown in Fig. 13.22.

**Figure 13.22 |** Measured step response with lead compensator.

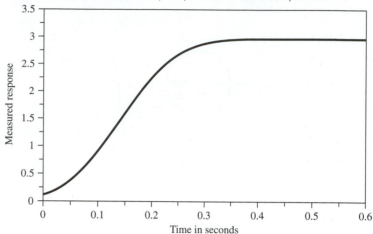

The response is very good, and consistent with all the analysis we have done leading up to the design. The design is also very robust in the sense that any reasonable variation in the gain will have very little effect on the response.

## 13.5 | REPRISE

In this chapter, we have added to our bag of system identification tricks as we sought a reasonably accurate model of a positioning table. Our efforts were rewarded and we were able to find a very simple yet very robust compensator. Most of our effort went into identifying the parameters of the transfer function of the positioning table. Once we had the transfer function, the compensation was routine. This is not always the case, but it certainly is of great importance to determine the model of the physical system as accurately as possible.

Although we expended considerable effort in trying to get the best possible model, in the end the *relative* locations of the poles rather than the exact locations was of the most importance. Once we knew that there was a pole near $s = -4$ and a second pole far to the left near $s = -100$, we could decide on a compensation strategy. Given the relative locations of these two poles it was easy to see that we could get a fast overdamped response. This was borne out by the actual implementation.

The fact that we knew the pole locations with good precision simply made the design process go a lot faster. Indeed, we met our specifications in one iteration. If our knowledge of the pole locations had been less precise, we would probably have had to try several designs but eventually we would have found a good design.

# 13.6 | PROBLEMS

1.  The pulse responses of six positioning tables similar to the one used in this chapter are on the CD-ROM that comes with the text. The armature voltage response is also included. The file name includes the width, in milliseconds, of the pulse. For instance, the filename pt1i30 is the response of positioning table 1 to a 30-ms pulse. The file pt1i30av is the armature voltage response to the same pulse. For each set of data files identify the transfer function.

    a.  pt1i30 and pti30av          b.  pt2i50 and pt2i50av

    c.  pt3i40 and pt3i40av          d.  pt4i30 and pt4i30av

    e.  pt5i50 and pt5i50av          f.  pt6i30 and pt6i30av

2.  Suppose on the oscilloscope the corresponding peak values of the sine waves representing the armature voltage and the heliopot voltage are separated by 0.4 s, with the peak of the heliopot voltage to the right of the armature voltage peak. The frequency of the two sine waves is 1 Hz. What is the phase of the motor transfer function at this frequency?

3.  For a frequency of 2 Hz, the peak-to-peak voltage of the armature voltage is 20 V, while that of the heliopot is 0.5 V. What is the magnitude of the motor transfer function at this frequency?

4.  The frequency responses of six positioning tables similar to the one used in this chapter are on the CD-ROM that comes with the text. The files on the CD-ROM are

    a.  pt1fid          b.  pt2fid

    c.  pt3fid          d.  pt4fid

    e.  pt5fid          f.  pt6fid

    Use frequency response identification methods to try to identify the two poles away from the origin. Note: you should first do Problems 2 and 3.

5.  Can you think of a way to use the identification technique introduced in Chapter 8 to identify the pole that we ultimately decided was at $s = -3.5$?

6.  Consider the lead compensator used in Section 13.4. The forward loop transfer function is

$$G_c G_p(s) = \frac{K(s + 4)}{s(s + 3.5)(s + 50)(s + 92)}.$$

    Using MATLAB, find the closed loop responses for a series of gains and try to match the response of the simulation to the actual response in Section 13.4.

7.  Repeat Problem 6 using

$$G_c G_p(s) = \frac{K(s + 4)}{s(s + 3.5)(s + 50)}.$$

8.  Apply an impulse of height 30 and width 60 ms to the transfer function

$$G_p(s)\frac{849}{s(s + 3.5)(s + 92)}.$$

How does this response compare with the measured impulse response? Note that this is a problem for using MATLAB.

9.  Repeat Problem 8 for an input $30\delta(t)$.

10. Apply an impulse of height 30 and width 60 ms to the transfer function

$$G_p(s)\frac{849}{s(s+3.5)(s+92)}.$$

Then use identification technique presented in Chapter 8 to identify the poles at $s = -3.5$ and $s = -92$. Note that you should look at Problem 5 first to make sure you know how to proceed.

11. Repeat Problem 10 for $30\delta(t)$.

12. Apply an impulse of height 30 and width 30 ms to the transfer function

$$G_p(s)\frac{849}{s(s+3.5)(s+92)}.$$

The use identification technique presented in Chapter 8 to identify the poles at $s = -3.5$ and $s = -92$. Note that you should look at Problem 5 first to make sure you know how to proceed.

13. Suppose we know that $-4 < p_1 < -2$. From the standpoint of robustness, should we choose $p_1 = 2$ or $p_1 = 4$?

14. Assuming that the model of the motor is

$$G_{\text{motor}}(s) = \frac{10}{s(s+4)},$$

use the frequency response data in Fig. 13.5 to see if the gain of 10 is reasonable.

15. Using the table of resistor and capacitor values in Chapter 3, design the lead compensator used in Section 13.4. Draw a picture showing where the components are placed on one of the inverting opamp stages of the FAC.

16. Discuss why we do not need to find the plant gain to simulate the critically damped responses of our model, as shown in Figs. 13.18 and 13.19.

## FURTHER READINGS

Eykhoff, P. 1974. *System Identification*. London: John Wiley.

Graupe, D. 1972. *Identification of Systems*. New York: Van Nostrand-Reinholt.

Rake, H. 1981. *Step Response and Frequency Response Methods,* IFAC System Identification Tutorial. Oxford: Pergamon Press.

# Discrete Systems

## 14.1 | OVERVIEW

In this chapter we develop the mathematical machinery to design compensators that are implemented using a microprocessor. The compensator will be a computer program that computes the control at regular intervals of time. To do this we need to introduce the $\mathcal{Z}$ transform. This transform will enable us to preserve, in large part, the frequency domain techniques developed in the previous chapters.

Although the compensation will be done digitally, the plant, or physical system to be controlled, will be continuous. We then have what is commonly called a "sampled data system." We will have to do some work to arrive at a useful mathematical model for sampled data systems.

Once we have that model, however, we will be able to bring to bear all the analytical techniques that we developed for continuous systems. As we will see the $\mathcal{Z}$ transform plays the key role in this development.

There are basically two ways to approach the $\mathcal{Z}$ transform. One way is to think in terms of systems that are intrinsically discrete, and can be represented by a difference equation of the form

$$a_m y(kT + mT) + a_{m-1} y[kT + (m-1)T] + \cdots + a_0 y(kT)$$
$$= b_\ell u(kT + \ell T) + b_{\ell-1} u[kT + (\ell - 1)T] + \cdots + b_0 u(kT). \quad \textbf{[14.1]}$$

Such systems arise in a number of ways. A model of the U.S. economy, for instance, is usually modeled by a difference equation because most economic data is still reported monthly and quarterly. A model of the growth of a cancer is discrete because the cancer cells divide at distinct points in time.

An alternative approach to the $\mathcal{Z}$ transform is to sample a continuous signal. This is the approach we will adopt because it best fits the problem we are trying to solve, namely, the control of a continuous system by a discrete controller. We will, however, also discuss intrinsically discrete systems.

## 14.2 | THE IDEAL SAMPLER

Figure 14.1 is a representation of the so-called ideal sampler. It consists of a switch that closes and reopens instantaneously every $T$ units of time. For our purposes time will be in seconds, although this is not always the case. In chemical processes, for instance, the unit of time could very well be minutes or even hours.

**Figure 14.1 |** Ideal sampler.

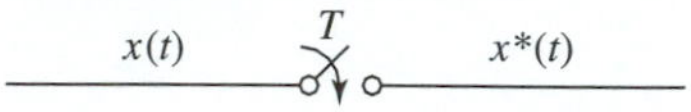

$$x(t) \qquad \overset{T}{\diagup}\!\!\!\diagdown \qquad x^*(t)$$

Of course, no switch opens and closes instantaneously, but the modern analog-to-digital (A/D) converter comes very close. A/D converters with a conversion rate of 100 kHz are fairly inexpensive, and conversion rates in the megaherz range are available.

In control applications, the sampling rate is usually less than 100 Hz. If the conversion rate is 100 kHz, the conversion is completed in less than one one-thousandth of the typical sample period. Thus, the conversion rate of the A/D converter is close enough to instantaneous to enable us to use the following mathematical model of the sampling process. Let

$$x^*(t) = \delta_T(t)x(t),$$

where

$$\delta_T(t) \overset{\triangle}{=} \sum_{k=0}^{\infty} \delta(t - kT). \qquad \text{[14.2]}$$

The function $\delta_T$ represents a half "picket fence" of delta functions, as shown in Fig. 14.2. This definition of $x^*$ is in keeping with the one-sided Laplace transform used to analyze continuous control systems.

The function used in signal processing and communications is

$$\text{III}_T(t) \overset{\triangle}{=} \sum_{k=-\infty}^{\infty} \delta(t - kT). \qquad \text{[14.3]}$$

This second function is more in keeping with the Fourier transform, where the time function is integrated from $t = -\infty$ to $t = +\infty$. We will not have occasion to use this latter function.

**Figure 14.2 |** The function $\delta_T(t)$.

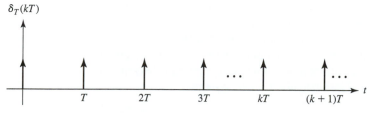

# 14.3 | THE LAPLACE TRANSFORM OF $x^*(t)$

As the reader is probably well aware, the Dirac delta function is not a function in the normal sense. P. A. M. Dirac, who introduced the delta function, called it an "improper function." This idea was later refined by a mathematician named Schwarz into the concept of the "generalized" function.

We will eliminate the delta function by simply taking the Laplace transform of $x^*(t)$ to obtain

$$\mathcal{L}\{x^*(t)\} \triangleq X^*(s)$$

$$= \sum_{k=0}^{\infty} \int_0^{\infty} x(t)e^{-st}\delta(t - kT)\,dt$$

$$= \sum_{k=0}^{\infty} x(kT)e^{-kTs}. \qquad\qquad [14.4]$$

This last expression for $X^*(s)$ represents a Laplace transform, but it is not a transform that is easy to use, because the complex variable $s$ occurs in the exponent of the transcendental function $e$. By contrast, the Laplace transforms that we have used previously have been ratios of polynomials in the Laplace variable $s$ with real coefficients. These latter transforms are easy to manipulate and interpret, as we have seen in preceding chapters.

Ultimately, we will be able to achieve these same ratios of polynomials in a new variable $z$ by transforming $X^*(s)$ to reach what we will call the $z$ plane. Before doing so, we tarry long enough in the new domain to make a few observations that will be useful later.

First, we note that the functions to which we apply the sampling process will almost invariably be continuous. The only exceptions will be functions that are piecewise continuous, by which we mean that the functions can have a countably infinite number of *finite* jumps. The most notable example will be the unit step function. These exceptional cases will be discussed as they arise.

Second, we see that by applying the Laplace transform to $x^*(t)$, we have sifted out the values $x(0), x(T), x(2T), \ldots, x(kT), \ldots$. These are simply the instantaneous values of $x(t)$ at the successive closures of the ideal switch. These values serve as weighting coefficients for the complex functions $e^{-kTs}$. They are exactly the set of values that we would wish to "collect" by sampling $x(t)$ every $T$ units of time.

We also note that $X^*(s)$ is periodic. To see this note that for $m = 0, 1, 2, \ldots,$

$$X^*\left(\frac{s \pm j2m\pi}{T}\right) = \sum_{k=0}^{\infty} x(kT)e^{-kT(s \pm j2m\pi/T)}$$

$$= \sum_{k=0}^{\infty} x(kT)e^{-kTs}e^{\pm j2m\pi}$$

$$= \sum_{k=0}^{\infty} x(kT)e^{-kTs}$$

$$= X^*(s).$$

Thus, if we pass a vertical line through any point $s$ in the complex plane, the value of $X^*(s)$ is repeated at intervals of $2\pi/T$ along the line. In particular, any pole or zero of $X^*(s)$ will be repeated every $2\pi/T$. We will have more to say about this periodicity later when we discuss aliasing.

We have discussed $X^*(s)$ as if its poles were in the $s$ plane, the same plane where we normally plot the poles and zeros of $X(s)$, the Laplace transform of the unsampled function. Another approach sometimes taken in the literature is to distinguish the complex plane where we plot the poles and zeros of the conventional Laplace transform of a continuous function $x$ from the complex plane where we plot the poles and zeros of the Laplace transform of $x^*(t)$. One way to distinguish the two planes is to use two different dummy variables such as $s$ and $p$.

Since the notation $X^*(s)$ is used almost universally, we will take the first approach and plot the poles and zeros of the starred transform in the same plane where we plot the poles and zeros of the conventional, or unstarred, transform. This is the most compact approach, and, as we will see in Section 14.4, the most intuitive choice.

## 14.4 | THE $\mathcal{Z}$ TRANSFORM OF $x(t)$

We now transform $X^*(s)$ by substituting for $s$ in our expression for $X^*(s)$. That is, we write

$$X(z) = X^*(s)|_{s=\ln z/T}$$

$$= \sum_{k=0}^{\infty} x(kT)e^{-kT(\ln z/T)}$$

$$= \sum_{k=0}^{\infty} x(kT)(e^{\ln z})^{-k}$$

$$= \sum_{k=0}^{\infty} x(kT)z^{-k}.$$

The expression

$$X(z) \overset{\triangle}{=} \sum_{k=0}^{\infty} x(kT)z^{-k} \qquad\qquad \textbf{[14.5]}$$

is often used as the definition of the $\mathcal{Z}$ transform, if the starting point is intrinsically discrete systems, rather than the sampling of continuous signals. In the case of an intrinsically discrete system, all we have are the values of the time function every $T$ units of time. In the case of the continuous time function $x$ that we started out with, we have established a transform for what might be called the "natural" discretization of $x(t)$. That is, if we have a closed form expression for $x(t)$, then $x(t)$ is discretized by simply substituting $kT$ for $t$ in this expression. The $\mathcal{Z}$ transform is then obtained by simply using the values of $x(t)$ at the discrete points in time $0, T, 2T, \ldots$ to weight the terms $z^{-k}$ in the infinite series.

We now see that we have a direct connection between the continuous time function $x$ and the $\mathcal{Z}$ transform of $x(kT)$ that seems to obviate the need for the intermediate starred functions $x^*(t)$ and $X^*(s)$. Nonetheless, we will find the intermediate functions $x^*(t)$ and $X^*(s)$ very useful in subsequent discussions.

Before proceeding, it is worth making sure that the nature of the substitution of variables

$$X(z) = X^*(s)|_{s=\ln z/T} \qquad\qquad \textbf{[14.6]}$$

is fully understood. Equation [14.6] relates a transform in the $z$ plane to one in the $s$ plane. The mapping that relates these two transforms defines $s$ in terms of $z$ and is thus a mapping from the $z$ plane back to the $s$ plane. This may seem backward, but in fact if we are to turn $X^*(s)$ into $X(z)$, then we need an explicit formula for $s$ in terms of the $z$ that is it related to.

If we want to know what this point $z$ is, then we use the inverse mapping $z = e^{sT}$. Using the inverse mapping, and substituting $s \pm j2n\pi/T$, $n = 0, 1, 2, \ldots$, we have

$$z = e^{(s \pm j2n\pi/T)T} = e^{sT} e^{j2n\pi} = e^{sT}.$$

Thus, the inverse image of each point in the $z$ plane is a countably infinite number of points in the $s$ plane. This can also be seen from our earlier result, which showed that $X^*(s)$ is periodic with period $2\pi/T$.

This means that all of the poles of $X^*(s)$ that lie along a vertical line in the $s$ plane map to the same point in the $z$ plane. Thus, multiple poles of $X^*(s)$ in the $s$ plane become a single pole of $X(z)$ in the $z$ plane. It also means that strips of the $s$ plane of vertical width $2\pi/T$ are mapped on top of each other in the $z$ plane. We will have more to say about this later in the chapter.

At this juncture, we have accomplished part of our goal. We now have a transform $X(z)$ defined in terms of a complex variable $z$. However, our expression for $X(z)$ is an infinite sum in the complex variable $z$. What we would like to achieve is something of the form

$$X(z) = \frac{K \prod_{i=1}^{m}(z - a_i)}{\prod_{i=0}^{n}(z - b_i)}, \qquad\qquad \textbf{[14.7]}$$

where the $a_i$ and $b_i$ are either real or complex conjugate pairs. Under these conditions, we can write

$$X(z) = \frac{K(z^m + \alpha_{m-1}z^{m-1} + \cdots + \alpha_1 z + \alpha_0)}{z^n + \beta_{n-1}z^{n-1} + \cdots + \beta_1 z + \beta_0}, \qquad\qquad \textbf{[14.8]}$$

where all the $\alpha_i$ and $\beta_i$ are *real*.

Actually, we are not very far from this goal. We will now show that we can find closed-form expressions for the $\mathcal{Z}$ transforms of all the functions that we will need to study the control of discrete and sampled data systems.

# 14.5 | $\mathcal{Z}$ TRANSFORMS USEFUL IN CONTROL

In this section our goal is to quickly find the $\mathcal{Z}$ transforms of the functions we will subsequently need for our analysis of control systems. These are the same functions for which we found the Laplace transforms in Chapter 2. We will try to accomplish this goal with as few words as possible.

## 14.5.1 The Discrete Delta Function

The counterpart in the $z$ domain of the continuous delta function is

$$\delta_0(kT) = \begin{cases} 1 & k = 0 \\ 0 & \text{otherwise.} \end{cases} \qquad \textbf{[14.9]}$$

Unlike its continuous counterpart, $\delta_0$ is a well-defined function. The $\mathcal{Z}$ transform is

$$\mathcal{Z}\{\delta_0(kT)\} = \sum_{k=0}^{\infty} \delta_0(kT)z^{-k} = z^0 = 1.$$

Recall that the Laplace transform of $\delta(t)$ is also 1. Thus, the discrete delta function, like its continuous counterpart, represents the instantaneous injection of "energy" into a system.

## 14.5.2 The Discrete Step Function

We consider next the discrete step function

$$\mathbf{1}(kT) = \begin{cases} 1 & k \geq 0 \\ 0 & k < 0. \end{cases} \qquad \textbf{[14.10]}$$

The $\mathcal{Z}$ transform of the unit step is

$$\mathcal{Z}\{\mathbf{1}(kT)\} \triangleq \mathbf{1}(z) = \sum_{k=0}^{\infty} z^{-k}.$$

Multiplying both sides of this last equation by $z$ results in

$$z\mathbf{1}(z) = z + \sum_{k=0}^{\infty} z^{-k} = z + \mathbf{1}(z).$$

A little rearrangement then yields

$$\mathbf{1}(z) = \frac{z}{z - 1}. \qquad \textbf{[14.11]}$$

Note that Eq. [14.11] holds if the infinite sum converges, that is, if $|z| > 1$. Thus, the region of convergence is the area outside the unit circle in the $z$ plane. This region of convergence for an infinite sum is completely analogous to the region of convergence we determined for the Laplace transform of a continuous function. In the latter case, the region of convergence was an infinite half-plane to the right of a vertical line. Here the region of convergence turns out to be an infinite region outside of a disk.

This correspondence will make more sense very shortly when we show how the $s$ plane maps into the $z$ plane under $z = e^{sT}$. More specifically, we will show that the left half of the $s$ plane maps into the interior of the unit circle in the $z$ plane, the imaginary axis into the unit circle, and the right half of the $s$ plane into the region exterior to the unit circle.

We also note that in defining the discrete step function we have set

$$\lim_{t \to 0} \mathbf{1}(t) = \lim_{t \to 0^+} \mathbf{1}(t) = 1.$$

That is, we have taken the limit from the right rather than the left. This choice is consistent with our derivation of the Laplace transform of the unit step. The impact of this choice is easier to understand if we find

$$\mathcal{L}\{\mathbf{1}^*(t)\} = \sum_{k=0}^{\infty} \int_0^{\infty} e^{-st} \delta(t - kT) \, dt.$$

For $k > 0$, we have

$$\int_0^{\infty} e^{-st} \delta(t - kT) \, dt = e^{-kTs},$$

since for $k > 0$, $\delta(t - kT)$ is in the interval $(0, \infty)$.

However, for $k = 0$ we have

$$\int_0^{\infty} \delta(t) \, dt,$$

and the delta function is evaluated at the lower limit of the interval of integration. Thus, we have to decide what the value of this integral should be. Our "choice," consistent with our treatment of the continuous delta and step functions, is to let the integral have value 1.

## 14.5.3 Discrete Form of $e^{-at}$

Let

$$x(kT) = \begin{cases} e^{-akT} & k \geq 0 \\ 0 & k < 0. \end{cases}$$

Then

$$X(z) = \sum_{k=0}^{\infty} e^{-akT} z^{-k}$$

$$= \sum_{k=0}^{\infty} (e^{aT} z)^{-k}$$

$$= \sum_{k=0}^{\infty} w^{-k}, \quad w = e^{aT} z$$

$$= \frac{w}{w - 1}$$

$$= \frac{e^{aT} z}{e^{aT} z - 1}$$

$$= \frac{z}{z - e^{-aT}}, \quad |z| > e^{-aT}.$$

### 14.5.4  Discrete Form of $x(t) = t1(t)$

Let

$$x(kT) = \begin{cases} kT & k \geq 0 \\ 0 & k < 0 \end{cases},$$

then

$$X(z) = \sum_{k=0}^{\infty} kTz^{-k}.$$    [14.12]

We next note that

$$-Tz\frac{d}{dz}\frac{z}{z-1} = -Tz\frac{d}{dz}\sum_{k=0}^{\infty}z^{-k}$$

$$= -Tz\sum_{k=0}^{\infty}-kz^{-(k+1)}$$

$$= \sum_{k=0}^{\infty}kTz^{-k}$$

$$= X(z), \qquad |z| > 1.$$

Thus

$$X(z) = -Tz\frac{d}{dz}\frac{z}{z-1}$$

$$= -Tz\left[\frac{-z}{(z-1)^2} + \frac{1}{z-1}\right]$$

$$= \frac{Tz}{(z-1)^2}, \qquad |z| > 1.$$

### 14.5.5  Discrete Form of $x(t) = A\cos(\omega t + \phi)$

Let

$$x(kT) = \begin{cases} A\cos(\omega kT + \phi) & n \geq 0 \\ 0 & n < 0 \end{cases},$$

The first step is choose the alternative representation

$$x(kT) = A\left(\frac{e^{j(\omega kT + \phi)} + e^{-(j\omega kT + \phi)}}{2}\right).$$

**Table 14.1 |** Some additional transforms.

| $x(kT)$    $k \geq 0$ | $X(z)$ |
|---|---|
| 1 | $\dfrac{z}{z-1}$ |
| $kT$ | $\dfrac{Tz}{(z-1)^2}$ |
| $(kT)^2$ | $\dfrac{T^2z(z+1)}{(z-1)^3}$ |
| $(kT)^3$ | $\dfrac{T^3z(z^2+4z+1)}{(z-1)^4}$ |
| $e^{-akT}$ | $\dfrac{z}{z-e^{-aT}}$ |
| $kTe^{-akT}$ | $\dfrac{Tz(e^{-at})}{(z-e^{-aT})^2}$ |
| $(kT)^2e^{-akT}$ | $\dfrac{T^2e^{-aT}z(z+e^{-aT})}{(z-e^{-aT})^3}$ |
| $\sin \omega kT$ | $\dfrac{z\sin \omega T}{s^2-2z\cos \omega T+1}$ |
| $\cos \omega kT$ | $\dfrac{z(z-\cos \omega T)}{z^2-2z\cos \omega T+1}$ |
| $2|M|e^{\sigma kT}\cos(\omega kT+\phi)$ | $\dfrac{z|M|e^{j\phi}}{z-e^{\sigma T}e^{j\omega T}}+\dfrac{z|M|e^{-j\phi}}{z-e^{\sigma T}e^{-j\omega T}}$ |

Then,

$$X(z) = \frac{A}{2}\sum_{k=0}^{\infty}e^{j\phi}e^{j\omega kT}z^{-k} + \frac{A}{2}\sum_{k=0}^{\infty}e^{-j\phi}e^{-j\omega kT}z^{-k}$$

$$= \frac{A}{2}\frac{ze^{j\phi}}{z-e^{-j\omega T}} + \frac{A}{2}\frac{ze^{-j\phi}}{z-e^{j\omega T}}$$

$$= \frac{Az\left[\dfrac{z(e^{j\phi}+e^{-j\phi})}{2} - \dfrac{e^{j(\omega T+\phi)}+e^{-j(\omega T+\phi)}}{2}\right]}{z^2 - 2\left(\dfrac{e^{j\omega T}+e^{-j\omega T}}{2}\right)z + 1}$$

$$= \frac{Az[z\cos\phi - \cos(\omega T+\phi)]}{z^2-2z\cos\omega T+1}, \quad |z| > 1.$$

We summarize the $z$ transforms we have derived to this point, plus some additional transforms, in Table 14.1.

# 14.6 | ALTERNATIVE REPRESENTATION

The $\mathcal{Z}$ transforms we have considered to this point arise naturally from our initial approach of sampling a continuous signal. In this approach, the sampling interval $T$ is explicitly present. This development is important to the understanding of sampled data systems. For systems that are intrinsically discrete, we can derive an alternative representation of the transforms in Table 14.1.

**Table 14.2 |** Table of $\mathcal{Z}$ transforms for intrinsically discrete functions.

| $x(k)$   $k \geq 0$ | $X(z)$ |
|---|---|
| 1 | $\dfrac{z}{z-1}$ |
| $k$ | $\dfrac{z}{(z-1)^2}$ |
| $k^2$ | $\dfrac{z(z+1)}{(z-1)^3}$ |
| $k^3$ | $\dfrac{z(z^2+4z+1)}{(z-1)^4}$ |
| $a^k$ | $\dfrac{z}{z-a}$ |
| $ka^k$ | $\dfrac{az}{(z-a)^2}$ |
| $k^2 a^k$ | $\dfrac{az(z+a)}{(z-a)^3}$ |
| $2|M|(\sqrt{\alpha^2+\beta^2})^k \cos(\omega k + \phi)$ | $\dfrac{z|M|e^{j\phi}}{z-\alpha-j\beta} + \dfrac{z|M|e^{-j\phi}}{z-\alpha+j\beta}$ |
| $\omega = \tan^{-1}\frac{\beta}{\alpha}$ | |

Suppose in our earlier derivation of the $\mathcal{Z}$ transform of $x(kT) = e^{-akT}$, we let $\alpha = e^{-aT}$, then

$$x(k) = \begin{cases} \alpha^k & k \geq 0 \\ 0 & k < 0 \end{cases},$$  [14.13]

and

$$X(z) = \frac{z}{z-\alpha}.$$

In this form, the sampling interval $T$ is "hidden" in the definition of $\alpha$.

The $\mathcal{Z}$ transform we have just derived has its own natural setting, namely, that of systems that are intrinsically discrete. For instance, in the modeling of cell division, where the cells divide at regular intervals, this alternative form has some appeal.

Table 14.2. gives the alternative transform representations for a subset of the functions in Table 14.1 that prove useful when analyzing systems that are instrinsically discrete.

## 14.7 | IMPORTANT THEOREMS

When we introduced the Laplace transform in Chapter 2, we did not offer a complete development, but instead considered only those properties germane to the study of control systems. We do the same here for the $\mathcal{Z}$ transform. The treatment should be sufficient as a review. Many of the theorems are discrete analogs of those for the Laplace transform.

## 14.7.1 Linearity

> **Theorem 14.7.1**
> Suppose that $f(kT)$ and $g(kT)$ have $\mathcal{Z}$ transforms $F(z)$ and $G(z)$, respectively. If $y(kT) = af(kT) + bg(kT)$, then
>
> $$\mathcal{Z}\{y(kT)\} = aF(z) + bG(z).$$

*Proof*

$$\mathcal{Z}\{y(kT)\} = \sum_{k=0}^{\infty} [af(kT) + bg(kT)]z^{-k}$$

$$= \sum_{k=0}^{\infty} af(kT)z^{-k} + \sum_{k=0}^{\infty} bg(kT)z^{-k}$$

$$= aF(z) + bG(z).$$

■

## 14.7.2 Right Shifting Property

> **Theorem 14.7.2**
> Given $f(kT)$ with $\mathcal{Z}$ transform $F(z)$, let $y(kT) = f(kT - mT)$. Then,
>
> $$Y(z) = z^{-m}F(z) + \sum_{i=0}^{m-1} f(iT - mT)z^{-i}.$$

*Proof*

$$Y(z) = \sum_{k=0}^{\infty} y(kT)z^{-k}$$

$$= \sum_{k=0}^{\infty} f(kT - mT)z^{-k}$$

$$= f(-mT)z^{0} + f(T - mT)z^{-1} + \cdots + f((m-1)T - mT)z^{-(m-1)}$$

$$\quad + f(0)z^{-m} + f(T)z^{-(m+1)} + \cdots$$

$$= z^{-m} \sum_{k=0}^{\infty} f(kT)z^{-k} + \sum_{i=0}^{m-1} f(iT - mT)z^{-i}$$

$$= z^{-m} F(z) + \sum_{i=0}^{m-1} f(iT - mT)z^{-i}.$$

■

If $f(kT) = 0$ for $k < 0$, then the right shifting theorem simplifies to

$$Y(z) = z^{-m} F(z).$$

### 14.7.3   Left Shifting Property

**Theorem 14.7.3**

Suppose $f(kT)$ has $\mathcal{Z}$ transform $F(z)$, and let

$$y(kT) = f(kT + mT).$$

Then,

$$Y(z) = z^m F(z) - \sum_{i=0}^{m-1} f(iT)z^{m-i}.$$

*Proof*

$$Y(z) = \sum_{k=0}^{\infty} f(kT + mT)z^{-k}$$

We make the substitution of variables $i = k + m$ to obtain

$$Y(z) = \sum_{i=m}^{\infty} f(iT)z^{-(i-m)}$$

$$= z^m \sum_{i=m}^{\infty} f(iT)z^{-i}$$

$$= z^m \sum_{i=0}^{m-1} f(iT)z^{-i} + z^m \sum_{i=m}^{\infty} f(iT)z^{-i}$$

$$- z^m \sum_{i=0}^{m-1} f(iT)z^{-i}$$

$$= z^m \sum_{i=0}^{\infty} f(iT)z^{-i} - z^m \sum_{i=0}^{m-1} f(iT)z^{-i}$$

$$= z^m F(z) - \sum_{i=0}^{m-1} f(iT)z^{m-i},$$

where the region of convergence of $Y(z)$ will be the same as that of $F(z)$.    ∎

The left shifting property will be very useful in solving difference equations. If the "initial conditions" are all zero, that is $f(iT) = 0, i = 0, 1, \ldots, m - 1$, then

$$\mathcal{Z}\{y(kT + mT)\} = z^m Y(z). \qquad \textbf{[14.14]}$$

## 14.7.4 Final Value Theorem

**Theorem 14.7.4**

Suppose $f(kT)$ has $\mathcal{Z}$ transform $F(z)$. Then,

$$\lim_{k \to \infty} f(kT) = \lim_{z \to 1} (1 - z^{-1}) F(z).$$

***Proof*** First note that we can write

$$\lim_{z \to 1} \sum_{k=0}^{\infty} [f(kT) - f((k-1)T)] z^{-k} = f(\infty).$$

We can also write

$$\sum_{k=0}^{\infty} [f(kT) - f((k-1)T)] z^{-k} = \sum_{k=0}^{\infty} f(kT) z^{-k} - \sum_{k=0}^{\infty} f(kT - T) z^{-k}$$

$$= (1 - z^{-1}) F(z).$$

Hence,

$$\lim_{z \to 1} (1 - z^{-1}) F(z) = f(\infty).$$

∎

The theorem is valid if the poles of $(1 - z^{-1}) F(z)$ are inside the unit circle or at $z = 1$. If $(1 - z^{-1}) F(z)$ has poles outside the unit circle or on the unit circle away from $z = 1$, the theorem is not valid.

# 14.8 | TRANSFER FUNCTION IN THE $z$ PLANE

Consider Eq. [14.1]. We wish to find the transfer function representation of this difference equation. When we find a transfer function we always set the initial conditions to zero so we can get at the intrinsic chracteristics of the equation. Thus, applying the $\mathcal{Z}$ transform to both sides of Eq. [14.1] and using Eq. [14.14], we have

$$a_m z^m Y(z) + a_{m-1} z^{m-1} Y(z) + \cdots + a_1 z Y(z) + a_0 Y(z)$$

$$= b_\ell z^\ell U(z) + b_{\ell-1} z^{\ell-1} U(z) + \cdots + b_1 z U(z) + b_0 U(z).$$

This equation can be rearranged as

$$\frac{Y(z)}{U(z)} = \frac{\sum_{i=0}^{\ell} b_i z^i}{\sum_{i=0}^{m} a_i z^i} \triangleq G(z). \qquad \textbf{[14.15]}$$

Equation [14.15] is a transfer function relationship of exactly the same form that we obtained when we applied the Laplace transform to a *differential* equation with the initial conditions set to zero. Equation [14.15] can be represented by the block

**Figure 14.3 |** Block diagram representation of transfer function.

diagram shown in Fig. 14.3. Of great importance is the fact that we can write

$$Y(z) = U(z)G(z).$$

What we have shown in an indirect way is that convolution in the time domain corresponds to multiplication in the $z$ domain. This is completely analogous to the result we obtained in the continuous case with the Laplace transform. We will have occasion to show this result more formally later in the chapter.

## 14.9 | THE INVERSE $\mathcal{Z}$ TRANSFORM

We will obtain the inverse $\mathcal{Z}$ transform in exactly the same way that we obtained the inverse Laplace transform, namely, by partial fraction expansion. The reason that the partial fraction expansion method works so well can be found in the form of Eq. [14.15]. The transfer function between the input $U$ and the output $Y$ is a ratio of polynomials in $z$ with *real* coefficients.

The fact that the coefficients are real is crucial because it guarantees that the roots of the numerator and denominator of the transfer function $G(z)$ and the output $Y(z)$ will be either real or complex conjugate pairs. This, in turn, means that the individual terms in the partial fraction expansion of $Y(z)$ or $G(z)$ will be simple in form and we will be able to do the inverse transformation by inspection.

Almost without exception, the transform pairs encountered using the partial fraction expansion technique will be those found in the Tables 14.1 and 14.2. The partial fraction method for $\mathcal{Z}$ transforms is very straightforward and similar in most respects to the partial fraction expansion for Laplace transforms. We first illustrate the method with some examples from which we can then abstract some general guidelines.

**EXAMPLE 14.9.1**

Suppose

$$Y(z) = \frac{1}{(z-1)(z-0.5)}.$$

Then the partial fraction expansion is

$$\frac{1}{(z-1)(z-0.5)} = A + \frac{Bz}{z-1} + \frac{Cz}{z-0.5}.$$

The constant $A$ is needed because each of the partial fraction expansion terms has a $z$ in the numerator. This is different than the Laplace partial fraction expansions where there was only a constant in the numerator. If $A \neq 0$, when we do the inverse transformation we will have a term $A\delta_0(kT)$. This is not a problem, however, since $\delta_0$ is a well-defined function.

Returning to the problem under consideration, we find $A$ by setting $z = 0$, yielding

$$A = Y(z)\big|_{z=0} = \frac{1}{(-1)(-0.5)} = 2,$$

We see that if $Y(z)$ had a multiplicative factor $z^k$, $k \geq 1$, in the numerator, then the constant term would be zero. There are a number of ways to find $B$ and $C$. One way is to put the partial fraction expansion over a common denominator to obtain:

$$\frac{1}{(z-1)(z-0.5)} = \frac{(A+B+C)z^2 + (-1.5A - 0.5B - C)z + 0.5A}{(z-1)(z-0.5)}.$$

Equating coefficients in the numerators on both sides of the equation yields the three linear equations

$$A + B + C = 0,$$

$$-1.5A - 0.5B - C = 0,$$

$$0.5A = 1.$$

The last equation verifies that $A = 2$. The remaining two equations then become

$$B + C = -2,$$

$$-0.5B - C = 3,$$

yielding

$$B = 2 \quad \text{and} \quad C = -4.$$

It is worth noting at this point that if $A$ is not included in the partial fraction expansion, then, placing the terms over a common denominator yields

$$\frac{1}{(z-1)(z-0.5)} = \frac{(B+C)z^2 - (0.5B+C)z}{(z-1)(z-0.5)}.$$

When we try to equate the numerator on both sides of the equation, we end up with

$$1 = (B+C)z^2 - (0.5B+C)z,$$

which doesn't work. Without $A$ we have no constant term to equate to 1.

---

Now that we have some understanding of the differences between the partial fraction expansions of continuous and discrete transfer functions, we demonstrate a much better method for finding the constants, or residues, in the expansion.

**EXAMPLE 14.9.2**

Using the transfer function from Example 14.9.1, we write

$$\bar{Y}(z) = \frac{Y(z)}{z} = \frac{1}{z(z-1)(z-0.5)}$$

$$= \frac{A}{z} + \frac{B}{z-1} + \frac{C}{z-0.5}.$$

Several things are worth pointing out. First, by dividing $Y(z)$ by $z$ we get a partial fraction that looks just like that for a continuous transfer function. Second, we automatically get the residue $A$. Third, once we find the three residues, we can get the partial fraction expansion of $Y(z)$ by multiplying through by $z$. We can then take the inverse transform and find $y(k)$.

We now proceed just as we would for a continuous system. Thus,

$$A = z\bar{Y}(z)|_{z=0}$$

$$= \left[\frac{z}{z(z-1)(z-0.5)}\right]\bigg|_{z=0}$$

$$= 2,$$

$$B = (z-1)\bar{Y}(z)|_{z=1}$$

$$= \left[\frac{z-1}{z(z-1)(z-0.5)}\right]\bigg|_{z=1}$$

$$= 2,$$

$$C = (z-0.5)\bar{Y}(z)|_{z=0.5}$$

$$= \left[\frac{z-0.5}{z(z-1)(z-0.5)}\right]\bigg|_{z=0.5}$$

$$= -4.$$

Then,

$$\frac{Y(z)}{z} = \frac{2}{z} + \frac{2}{z-1} - \frac{4}{z-0.5},$$

and

$$Y(z) = \frac{2z}{z} + \frac{2z}{z-1} - \frac{4z}{z-0.5}.$$

Applying the inverse $\mathcal{Z}$ transform to both side of this last equation then yields the same result as before, namely,

$$y(k) = [2\delta_0(k) + 2 - 4(0.5)^k]\mathbf{1}(k),$$

Before departing this example, we put the intersample period $T$ into the solution as follows. The point $z = 0.5$ corresponds to the point

$$s = \ln\frac{z}{T} = \ln\frac{0.5}{T},$$

in the $s$ plane. Thus, we could write the solution as

$$y(kT) = [2\delta_0(KT) + 2 - 4e^{\alpha kT}]\mathbf{1}(kT),$$

where

$$\alpha = \ln\frac{0.5}{T}.$$

If we know $T$, then we can evaluate $\alpha$.

The next example shows how to evaluate the residues when there are complex roots.

**EXAMPLE 14.9.3**

Let

$$Y(z) = \frac{0.2z}{(z-1)(z-0.6-j0.2)(z-0.6+j0.2)}.$$

The multiplicative factor $z$ in the numerator means there will be no constant term in the partial fraction expansion, which can be written as

$$\frac{Y(z)}{z} = \frac{A}{z-1} + \frac{Me^{j\phi}}{z-0.6-j0.2} + \frac{Me^{-j\phi}}{z-0.6+j0.2}.$$

The evaluation now proceeds just as it would for a Laplace transform:

$$A = (z-1)\left[\frac{Y(z)}{z}\right]\bigg|_{z=1}$$

$$= \frac{0.2}{(z-0.6-j0.2)(z-0.6+j0.2)}\bigg|_{z=1}$$

$$= 1.$$

The evaluation of $Me^{j\phi}$ proceeds in the same way:

$$Me^{j\phi} = (z-0.6-j0.2)\left[\frac{Y(z)}{z}\right]\bigg|_{z=0.6+j0.2}$$

$$= \frac{0.2}{(z-1)(z-0.6+j0.2)}\bigg|_{z=0.6+j0.2}$$

$$= \frac{0.2}{(-0.08-j0.16)}$$

$$= 1.12e^{j2.03}.$$

Then

$$y(k) = \mathcal{Z}^{-1}\left\{\frac{z}{z-1}\right\} + \mathcal{Z}^{-1}\left\{\frac{1.12e^{j2.03}}{z-0.6-j0.2} + \frac{1.12e^{-j2.03}}{z-0.6-j0.2}\right\}$$

$$= [1 + 2.24(\sqrt{0.2^2 + 0.6^2})^k \cos(1.25k + 2.03)]\mathbf{1}(k),$$

where the damped frequency is

$$\omega = \tan^{-1}\frac{0.2}{0.6} = 1.25.$$

We can also obtain $y(kT)$ with a little work. We note that

$$0.6 + j0.2 = re^{j\omega} = e^{(\ln r/T)T}e^{(j\omega/T)T},$$

where

$$r = \sqrt{0.6^2 + 0.2^2}.$$

Then, letting

$$\sigma = \ln \frac{r}{T}, \quad \bar{\omega} = \frac{\omega}{T}, \quad M = 1.12, \quad \text{and} \quad \phi = 2.03,$$

we can write

$$y(kT) = \mathcal{Z}^{-1}\left\{\frac{z}{z-1}\right\} + \mathcal{Z}^{-1}\left\{\frac{Me^{j\phi}}{z - e^{\sigma T}e^{j\bar{\omega}T}} + \frac{Me^{-j\phi}}{z - e^{\sigma T}e^{-j\bar{\omega}T}}\right\}$$
$$= [1 + 2Me^{\sigma T}\cos(\bar{\omega}T + \phi)]\mathbf{1}(kT),$$

where the final result is obtained using the last transform pair in Table 14.1. Then subsituting the values for $M$ and $\phi$, we have

$$y(kT) = [1 + 2.24e^{\sigma kT}\cos(\bar{\omega}kT + 2.03)]\mathbf{1}(t),$$

with

$$\sigma = \ln \frac{\sqrt{0.2^2 + 0.6^2}}{T} \quad \text{and} \quad \bar{\omega} = \frac{\omega}{T} = \frac{1.25}{T}.$$

Note that all we have done is find the equivalent poles in the $s$ plane and then substitute $kT$ for $t$.

## 14.10 | THE SOLUTION OF DIFFERENCE EQUATIONS

The solution of difference equations with initial conditions using the $\mathcal{Z}$ transform is completely analogous to the solution of differential equations with initial conditions using the Laplace transform. The analogy is clearest if we set the problem up to be solved using the left shifting property, as illustrated by Example 14.10.1.

**EXAMPLE 14.10.1**

Consider the difference equation

$$y(kT + 2T) - 5y(kT + T) + 6y(kT) = u(kT), \qquad \text{[14.16]}$$

with $y(0) = 1$ and $y(T) = 0$ and $u(kT)$ the discrete impulse function. Most often we suppress the $T$ and write:

$$y(k+2) - 5y(k+1) + 6y(k) = u(k), \qquad \text{[14.17]}$$

with $y(0) = 1$ and $y(1) = 0$. Applying the $\mathcal{Z}$ transform to either representation yields

$$z^2 Y(z) - \sum_{i=0}^{1} y(iT)z^{2-i} - 5[zY(z) - \sum_{i=0}^{0} y(iT)z^{1-i}] + 6Y(z) = U(z). \qquad \text{[14.18]}$$

Equation [14.18] can be rearranged as

$$[z^2 - 5z + 6]Y(z) = z^2 y(0) + zy(1) - 5zy(0) + U(z),$$

or finally

$$Y(z) = \frac{z^2 y(0) + [y(1) - 5y(0)]z}{z^2 - 5z + 6} + \frac{U(z)}{z^2 - 5z + 6}.$$    **[14.19]**

Substituting the initial conditions and letting $u(kT) = \delta_0(kT)$ then yields

$$Y(z) = \frac{z^2 - 5z}{z^2 - 5z + 6} + \frac{1}{z^2 - 5z + 6} = \frac{z^2 - 5z + 1}{z^2 - 5z + 6}.$$

We can now find $Y(z)$ by partial fraction expansion. That is,

$$\frac{Y(z)}{z} = \frac{z^2 - 5z + 1}{z(z-2)(z-3)} = \frac{A}{z} + \frac{B}{z-2} + \frac{C}{z-3},$$

and

$$A = \left[ z \frac{Y(z)}{z} \right]\Big|_{z=0} = \left[ \frac{z^2 - 5z + 1}{(z-2)(z-3)} \right]\Big|_{z=0} = \frac{1}{6},$$

$$B = \left[ (z-2)\frac{Y(z)}{z} \right]\Big|_{z=2} = \left[ \frac{z^2 - 5z + 1}{z(z-3)} \right]\Big|_{z=2} = \frac{5}{2},$$

$$C = \left[ (z-3)\frac{Y(z)}{z} \right]\Big|_{z=3} = \left[ \frac{z^2 - 5z + 1}{z(z-2)} \right]\Big|_{z=3} = -\frac{5}{3}.$$

Finally,

$$Y(z) = \frac{1}{6} + \frac{z(5/2)}{z-2} - \frac{z(5/3)}{z-3},$$

and

$$y(k) = \left[ \frac{1}{6}\delta_0(k) + \frac{5}{2}(2)^k - \frac{5}{3}(3)^k \right] 1(k).$$

The result can also be expressed in terms of $kT$. We have merely to solve the expression

$$e^{\alpha T} = a,$$

for $\alpha$ using $a = 2$ and $a = 3$. That is,

$$\alpha_1 = \frac{\ln 2}{T} \quad \text{and} \quad \alpha_2 = \frac{\ln 3}{T},$$

yielding

$$y(kT) = \left[ \frac{1}{6}\delta_0(kT) + \frac{5}{2}(e^{\alpha_1 T})^k - \frac{5}{3}(e^{\alpha_2 T})^k \right] 1(kT)$$

$$= \left[ \frac{1}{6}\delta_0(kT) + \frac{5}{2}(e^{\alpha_1 kT}) - \frac{5}{3}(e^{\alpha_2 kT}) \right] 1(kT).$$

## 14.11 | CONVOLUTION VERSUS MULTIPLICATION

In this section we verify a result we obtained indirectly earlier, namely, that the convolution of two time functions corresponds to the multiplication of their respective $\mathcal{Z}$ transforms in the frequency domain.

Figure 14.3 shows the block diagram relationship between input and output in the $z$ domain. For linear, time-invariant systems we know that we can write

$$y(kT) = \sum_{i=0}^{\infty} g(kT - iT)u(iT). \qquad \textbf{[14.20]}$$

This is the convolution summation expression for $y(kT)$, the discrete equivalent of the convolution integral for continuous linear, time-invariant systems. If $g(kT)$ is the impulse response of a causal system, then $g$ is zero for negative time and we can write

$$y(kT) = \sum_{i=0}^{k} g(kT - iT)u(iT). \qquad \textbf{[14.21]}$$

The block diagram in the time domain is shown in Fig. 14.4.

**Figure 14.4 |** Signal diagram in the time domain.

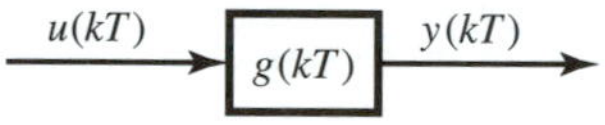

To verify that this expression is consistent with our $z$ domain relationships we simply find the $\mathcal{Z}$ transform of $y(kT)$, which is

$$Y(z) = \sum_{k=0}^{\infty} \left\{ \sum_{i=0}^{\infty} g(kT - iT)u(iT) \right\} z^{-k}. \qquad \textbf{[14.22]}$$

We now make the substitution of variable $\ell = k - i$, noting that when $k = 0, \ell = -i$. Then,

$$Y(z) = \sum_{\ell=-i}^{\infty} \left\{ \sum_{i=0}^{\infty} g(\ell T)u(iT) \right\} z^{-(\ell+i)}$$

$$= \left\{ \sum_{\ell=-i}^{\infty} g(\ell T)z^{-\ell} \right\} \left\{ \sum_{i=0}^{\infty} u(iT)z^{-i} \right\}.$$

If $g(\ell T)$ is causal, then $g(\ell T)$ must be zero for negative time, that is, for $\ell < 0$. Thus we can change the lower limit on the first summation from $\ell = -i$ to $\ell = 0$, obtaining

$$Y(z) = \left\{ \sum_{\ell=0}^{\infty} g(\ell T)z^{-\ell} \right\} \left\{ \sum_{i=0}^{\infty} u(iT)z^{-i} \right\}$$

$$= G(z)U(z). \qquad \textbf{[14.23]}$$

Equation [14.23] is exactly the relationship between $R$ and $Y$ in the $z$ plane that we derived earlier. Thus, we have verified the basic rule that multiplication in the $z$ domain corresponds to convolution in the time domain. The converse is also true. We will not have any occasion to use the convolution approach. Indeed, for linear time-invariant systems, the $z$ domain is the simplest place to carry out both analysis and design.

## 14.12 | FREQUENCY RESPONSE

Using the Laplace transform, we were able to show that if we applied the input $A\cos(\omega t)$ to a linear time-invariant system with transfer function $G(s)$, the steady state output $y_{ss}$ was of the form

$$y_{ss} = \lim_{t\to\infty} y(t) = A|G(j\omega)|\cos(\omega t + \phi), \qquad [14.24]$$

where $\phi = \underline{/G(j\omega)}$. A similar result can be obtained for discrete systems. Let $G(z)$ be the $\mathcal{Z}$ transform of a discrete LTI system, and let the input to this system be $u(kt) = A\cos(\omega kT)$, with $T$ the sampling period. Then

$$\mathcal{Z}\{u(kT)\} = \frac{Az(z - \cos\omega T)}{z^2 - 2z\cos\omega T + 1}$$

$$= \frac{Az(z - \cos\omega T)}{(z - e^{j\omega T})(z - e^{-j\omega T})}.$$

Suppose

$$G(z) = \frac{K\prod_{i=1}^{m}(z - b_i)}{\prod_{i=1}^{n}(z - p_i)}.$$

For simplicity we assume no repeated poles, which is the case for almost all systems. The special case of repeated poles simply complicates the notation without changing the outcome. Then

$$Y(z) = U(z)G(z)$$

can be expressed as

$$Y(z) = \frac{Mz}{z - e^{j\omega T}} + \frac{M^*z}{z - e^{-j\omega T}} + \sum_{i=1}^{n}\frac{C_i z}{z - p_i}. \qquad [14.25]$$

If $|p_i| < 1, i = 1, 2, \ldots n$, then, as we shall see shortly, the steady state response will only depend upon the first two terms on the right-hand side of Eq. [14.25]. Consequently, we will only evaluate the two constants, $M$ and $M^*$.

Now

$$M = (z - e^{j\omega T})\frac{A(z - \cos\omega T)}{(z - e^{j\omega T})(z - e^{-j\omega T})}G(z)\Bigg|_{z=e^{j\omega T}}$$

$$= \frac{A[e^{j\omega T} - 0.5(e^{j\omega T} + e^{-j\omega T})]}{e^{j\omega T} - e^{-j\omega T}}G(e^{j\omega T})$$

$$= \frac{A(e^{j\omega T} - e^{-j\omega T})}{2(e^{j\omega T} - e^{-j\omega T})}G(e^{j\omega T})$$

$$= \frac{A}{2}G(e^{j\omega T}).$$

The other residue is the complex conjugate of $M$. As in the continuous case, this results from the fact that $G(z)$ is the ratio of polynomials in $z$ with *real* coefficients.

Having found $M$, we can now write

$$Y(z) = \frac{Mz}{z - e^{j\omega T}} + \frac{M^*z}{z - e^{-j\omega T}} + \sum_{i=1}^{n}\frac{C_i z}{z - p_i}.$$

If we now take the inverse transform of $Y(z)$, we obtain

$$y(kT) = Me^{j\omega kT} + M^*e^{-j\omega kT} + \sum_{i=1}^{n}C_i p_i^k. \qquad \textbf{[14.26]}$$

If $|p_i| < 1$ for $i = 1, 2, \ldots, n$, then

$$\lim_{k\to\infty}\sum_{i=1}^{n}C_i p_i^k = 0.$$

Thus,

$$y_{ss} \triangleq \lim_{k\to\infty} y(kT) = Me^{j\omega kT} + M^*e^{-j\omega kT}.$$

Now let

$$M = |M|e^{j\theta}.$$

Then

$$Me^{j\omega kT} + M^*e^{-j\omega kT} = \frac{2|M|\left[e^{j(\omega kT+\theta)} + e^{-j(\omega kT+\theta)}\right]}{2}$$

$$= 2|M|\cos(\omega kT + \theta).$$

Recalling that $M = (A/2)G(e^{j\omega T})$, we can finally write

$$y_{ss} = A|G(e^{j\omega T})|\cos(\omega kT + \theta). \qquad \textbf{[14.27]}$$

We have obtained a result that is analogous to that for continuous systems. For a sinusoidal input, the steady state output is also sinusoidal, scaled by the gain factor $|G(e^{j\omega T})|$ and shifted in phase by $\theta = \underline{/G(e^{j\omega T})}$. An important difference is that in the continuous case we have $|G(j\omega)|$, while in the discrete case we have $|G(e^{j\omega T})|$. The reason for this is discussed in Section 14.13.

# 14.13 | THE MAPPING $e^{sT}$

In this section, we investigate in more detail the mapping $z = e^{sT}$ that we used to transform $X^*(s)$ into $X(z)$. We begin by letting $x(t) = e^{-at}\mathbf{1}(t)$, $a > 0$. The Laplace transform of this function is

$$X(s) = \frac{1}{s+a}.$$  [14.28]

By contrast, the starred transformation is

$$X^*(s) = \sum_{k=0}^{\infty} e^{-akT} e^{-kTs} = \frac{e^{sT}}{e^{sT} - e^{-aT}}.$$  [14.29]

Recalling that $X^*(s)$ is periodic in $s$ we note that $X^*(s)$ will have poles at $s = -a \pm j2n\pi/T, n = 1, 2, \ldots$, as shown in Fig. 14.5. Thus, $X^*(s)$ has a countably infinite number of poles, one of which is the pole of $X(s)$ at $s = -a$. We see that the poles of $X^*(s)$ consist of the pole of $X(s)$ and copies of this pole, repeated at intervals of $2\pi/T$. The same would be true for any other function whose Laplace transform exists. Remember, for the linear time-invariant systems we are considering, the poles will be either real or complex conjugate pairs. Thus, the example under consideration, while simple, is representative of all the time functions and transforms discussed in this book.

We can see from Fig. 14.5 that the pole of the Laplace transform $X(s)$ will lie in a strip of width $2\pi/T$ centered on the real axis of the $s$ plane. This strip is called the primary strip. This pole is then repeated in the secondary strips above and below the primary strip.

**Figure 14.5** | Poles of $X^*(s) = \dfrac{e^{sT}}{e^{sT} - e^{-aT}}$.

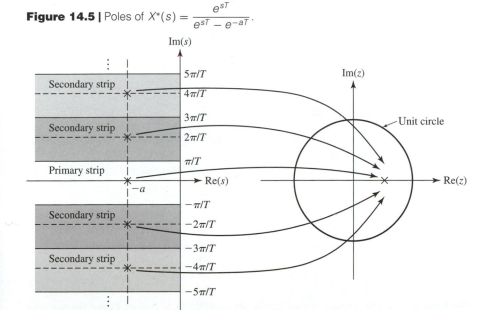

Under the mapping $s = \ln z / T$, $X^*(s)$ is mapped into the $\mathcal{Z}$ transform

$$X(z) = \frac{z}{z - e^{-aT}}.$$

Several points are worth noting at this juncture. First, *all* the poles of $X^*(s)$ map to the *same location* in the $z$ plane, as shown in Fig. 14.5. We know that every pole of $X(s)$, generates an infinite number of poles in $X^*(s)$.

Second, to obtain $X(z)$ from $X^*(s)$ we had to substitute an expression in $z$ for $s$, namely, $s = \ln z / T$. The inverse mapping from the $s$ plane to the $z$ plane is $z = e^{sT}$. As we have seen, the mapping is one-to-one on strips of the $s$ plane of width $2\pi / T$. Thus, if we wish to know where a specific point in the $s$ plane maps in the $z$ plane we use $z = e^{sT}$.

In particular, if we know the locations of the poles of $X^*(s)$ in the $s$ plane we find the points in the $z$ plane using $z = e^{sT}$. Since the poles of $X^*(s)$ are simply the poles of $X(s)$, plus the copies of these poles that appear along vertical lines at intervals of $2\pi / T$, we conclude that the poles of $X(z)$ are simply the poles of $X(s)$ mapped under $z = e^{sT}$.

Third, since our $s$ domain transfer functions are ratios of polynomials in $s$ with real coefficients, they can be expanded by partial fractions into terms that correspond to the entries in the tables of $\mathcal{Z}$ transforms presented earlier. Thus, for the class of time functions we are considering, we can say unequivocally that if a continuous time function $x(t)$ has Laplace transform $X(s)$ with a pole at $s = -a$, then the discrete equivalent of this function, when $\mathcal{Z}$ transformed, will have a pole at $z = e^{-aT}$.

Fourth, we note from the tables of $\mathcal{Z}$ transforms that the same cannot be said for zeros. In fact, the tables show examples of continuous time functions whose Laplace transforms have no zeros but whose $\mathcal{Z}$ transform equivalents do have zeros. In other cases neither the Laplace or $\mathcal{Z}$ transforms have zeros. Thus, there is no convenient mapping of zeros. While this result might seem to be "half a loaf," it is the important half of the loaf because, as in the $s$ plane, the $z$ plane poles determine the time functions, or modes, that appear in the time response.

## 14.14 | THE PRIMARY STRIP

In this section we explore further the fact that multiple points in the $s$ plane map under $z = e^{sT}$ to a single point in the $z$ plane.

Suppose we map the primary strip of the $s$ plane into the $z$ plane. We begin by mapping the points of a vertical line

$$s = \sigma + j\omega,$$

where $\sigma < 0$ is fixed. Under the mapping $z = e^{sT}$, a point on this line maps to

$$z = e^{(\sigma + j\omega)T} = e^{\sigma T} e^{j\omega T}.$$

The term $e^{\sigma T}$ is a real number that can be thought of as a scaling factor for the unit phasor $e^{j\omega T}$.

**Figure 14.6 |** Mapping primary strip to the $z$ plane.

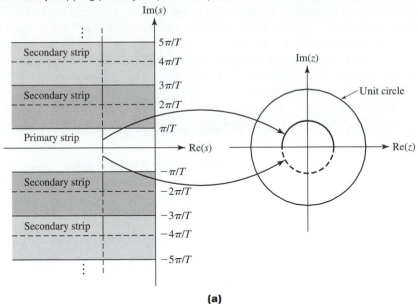

**(a)**

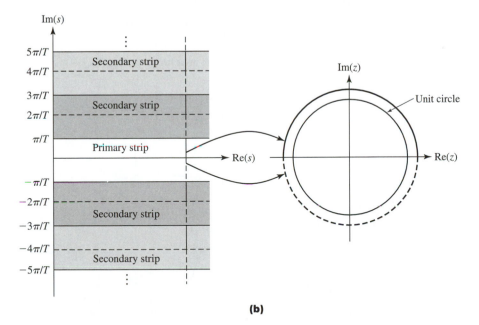

**(b)**

If $-\pi/T \leq \omega \leq \pi/T$, and $\sigma$ is fixed, with $\sigma < 0$, then the mapping of this portion of the vertical line in the $s$ plane to the $z$ plane is a circle with radius $e^{-aT} < 1$, as shown in Fig. 14.6(a). If $\sigma > 0$, the line segment maps to a circle with radius greater than one, as shown in Fig. 14.6(b). If $\sigma = 0$, the line segment maps onto the unit circle.

In the $s$ plane, the region of stable poles is the left half plane. Thus, we see that the region of stability in the $z$ plane is the interior of the unit circle. For clarity, the line segments in the primary and secondary strips of Fig. 14.6(a) and 14.6(b) have been divided into dashed and solid portions, the solid portions correspond to $0 \le \omega \le \pi/T$, and map onto the upper half of the circle in the $z$ plane. The dashed portions of the line segments correspond to $-\pi/T \le \omega \le 0$ and map onto the bottom half of the circle in the $z$ plane.

In summary,

1.  The left half of the primary strip in the $s$ plane maps onto the interior of the unit circle.

2.  The imaginary axis between $-j\pi/T$ and $j\pi/T$ in the $s$ plane maps onto the unit circle in the $z$ plane.

3.  The right half of the primary strip maps onto the region exterior to the unit circle.

4.  The same pattern holds for each of the secondary strips.

Now consider

$$x(t) = \cos(\omega t).$$

The corresponding $\mathcal{Z}$ transform is

$$X(z) = \frac{z(z - \cos \omega T)}{z^2 - 2z \cos \omega T + 1} = \frac{z(z - \cos \omega T)}{(z - e^{j\omega T})(z - e^{-j\omega T})}.$$

The poles of $X(z)$, and the related poles of $X^*(s)$, are shown in Fig. 14.7. To keep the

**Figure 14.7 |** Poles of $X^*(s)$ and $X(z)$ for $x(t) = \cos \omega T$.

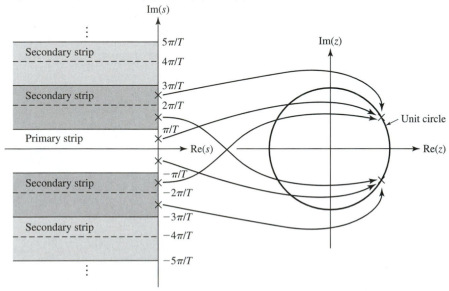

figure uncluttered, we have shown only the mappings from the primary strip and the two adjacent secondary strips. From this figure, we see that once the poles of $X^*(s)$ are mapped to the $z$ plane we cannot distinguish the poles in the primary strip from the poles in the secondary strips. Thus, the largest frequency we can distinguish is $\omega = \pi/T$, which is half the sampling frequency of $2\pi/T$. This is what might be called a "back door" approach to the Nyquist rate. The "front door" approach is discrete Fourier analysis.

**EXAMPLE 14.14.1**

Suppose the sampling rate is 10 Hz, so that $T = 0.1$ s, and we try to sample a 6-Hz sine wave. Then the sine function has poles at $z = e^{\pm j6(2\pi)}$. Consider the mapping of the poles as the frequency increases from 0 to 6 Hz. The paths followed as the frequency increases are shown in Fig. 14.8.

Note that at a frequency of 5 Hz, the two paths meet at $z = -1$. The pole migrating to 6 Hz then continues on, ending up at a point that corresponds to $-4$ Hz. The pole migrating to $-6$ Hz, does the same thing, ending up at a point on the unit circle that corresponds to 4 Hz. Thus the 6-Hz sine wave will appear to be a 4-Hz sine wave.

Note that as the poles continue to migrate toward 10 Hz ($2\pi/T$ rad/s) and $-10$ Hz ($-2\pi/T$ rad/s) the aliased frequency will continued to decrease.

**Figure 14.8** | Poles of $X^*(s)$ and $X(z)$ for $x(t) = \cos\omega T$.

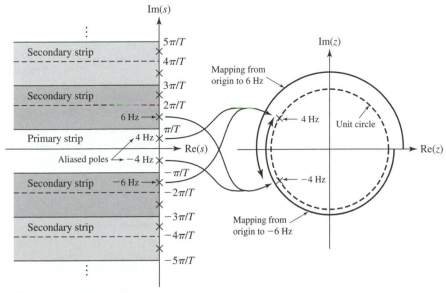

## 14.15 | THE STARRING RULE

We now develop a rule for manipulating block diagrams that will be needed to obtain the final formulation of the sampled data control problem. First recall that

$$G(z) = G^*(s)|_{s=\ln z/T}.$$  **[14.30]**

Then, if we have

$$Y(z) = G(z)R(z),$$  **[14.31]**

and we restrict the mapping to the primary strip, we certainly have

$$Y^*(s) = G^*(s)R^*(s).$$  **[14.32]**

Now consider Fig. 14.9. The output of $Y(s)$ is the Laplace transform of a continuous function $y(t)$. We can write

$$Y(s) = R^*(s)G(s).$$

**Figure 14.9 |** Sampling a continuous system.

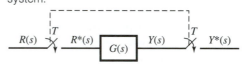

Now suppose we wish to sample the output to obtain $Y^*(s)$. We can write

$$Y^*(s) = \{R^*(s)G(s)\}^*.$$  **[14.33]**

However, by equating the right-hand sides of Eqs. [14.32] and [14.33] we see that we have

$$\{R^*(s)G(s)\}^* = R^*(s)G^*(s).$$  **[14.34]**

Equation [14.34] is very useful for the analysis of sampled data systems. To see why, consider Fig. 14.10, which shows the transformations previously discussed plus two that are new. We have already analyzed the route across the top of the chart. Of the two new paths, one is the Laplace transform of the continuous time function $x(t)$. This path is familiar. However, the other new path is not. It charts a passage from

**Figure 14.10 |** Chart of various sampling transformations.

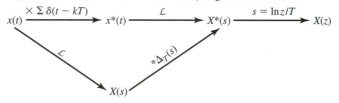

$X(s)$ directly to $X^*(s)$. The operation is shown symbolically as

$$X(s) * \Delta_T(s),$$

where $\Delta_T(s) = \mathcal{L}\{\delta_T(t)\}$, and the $*$ stands for *convolution* of the two Laplace transforms in the $s$ plane. This is a standard result from complex variable theory, namely,

$$\mathcal{L}[x(t)y(t)] = X(s) * Y(s).$$

Although we do not presume a background in complex variable theory, the operation can still be understood qualitatively, which is all that is needed. The convolution of the two functions merely defines a mapping from one function $X(s)$ to a second function $X^*(s)$. The domain and range of the mapping are the same, namely, the $s$ plane. Thus the "starring" operation that we defined earlier is just this mapping of one Laplace transform into another. We will make use of this operation to find the proper mathematical setting for studying sampled data systems.

## 14.16 | SAMPLED DATA SYSTEMS

Figure 14.11 is a block diagram of a sampled data system. The plant $g_p(t)$ is continuous. The output $c(t)$ is fed back and subtracted from the reference input $r(t)$. This subtraction is represented by an analog operation in the diagram, and the difference $e(t)$ is sampled at regular intervals by an A/D converter.

**Figure 14.11 |** Block diagram of sampled data system.

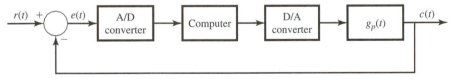

The function of the computer is to implement a control strategy. As we will see shortly, that control strategy will ultimately be represented as a transfer function in the $z$ plane. The transfer function, in turn, will be translated into a difference equation that the computer will evaluate to produce the control signal.

The difference equation is driven by the sampled error signal $e(t)$. The output of the difference equation is fed to a digital to analog (D/A) converter, which turns the digital control signal into a *piecewise continuous* analog control signal, which drives the plant. Our real interest is to design the difference equation that controls the performance of the system. To do so we need a precise mathematical model of the overall system. We accomplish this by defining mathematical structures for the A/D converter, the D/A converter, and the computer.

Figure 14.12(a) shows how the block diagram can be modified to reflect these mathematical structures. Note that this representation is in the $s$ domain. We replace the A/D converter with an ideal sampler and its related mathematical structure $\delta_T$. This is a very reasonable choice for the A/D converter given the conversion speeds we have previously discussed. The time between samples is $T$, and the two samplers

**Figure 14.12 |** (a) First and (b) second modifications of the sampled data block diagram.

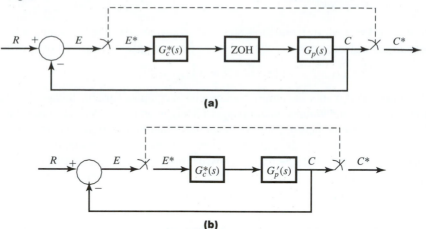

**(a)**

**(b)**

shown in Fig. 14.12(a) are synchronized so that they open and close at the same time. This synchronization is represented by the dashed line that connects the two samplers.

We next replace the D/A converter with a zero-order hold (ZOH), also as shown in Fig. 14.12(a). The impulse response of the zero-order hold is shown in Fig. 14.13. We see that if a unit impulse is applied to the zero-order hold at $t = 0$, the hold immediately puts out a value of one and holds it for $T$ units of time. No physical device behaves exactly like this, but a modern D/A converter can convert a digital input to an analog output in roughly $10^{-5}$ s. This is nearly the ideal behavior shown in the figure.

**Figure 14.13 |** Impulse response of zero-order hold.

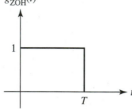

In actual operation, the computer outputs can be thought of as impulses of weight $u(kT)$, delivered to the D/A converter every $T$ units of time. Between inputs from the computer the zero-order hold keeps its output at the last value received from the computer. Over time, the output looks like that shown in Fig. 14.14.

We represent the computer algorithm by $G_c^*(s)$. This may seem a little strange, but we know that $G_c^*(s)$ becomes $G_c(z)$ if we make the substitution $s = \ln z / T$ in $G_c^*(s)$. $G_c(z)$, in turn, defines a difference equation that relates $e(kT)$, the output of

**Figure 14.14** | Output of zero-order hold.

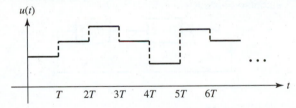

the D/A converter to $u(kT)$, the control applied to the zero-order hold. The reason we represent the computer algorithm initially as $G_c^*(s)$ is that we will have to apply the starring algorithm to achieve our final mathematical representation.

We now derive the Laplace transform of the zero-order hold. Note that

$$g_{ZOH}(t) = \mathbf{1}(t) - \mathbf{1}(t - T).$$

Thus

$$\mathcal{L}\{g_{ZOH}\} = \mathcal{L}\{\mathbf{1}(t)\} - \mathcal{L}\{\mathbf{1}(t - T)\} = \frac{1}{s} - \frac{e^{-Ts}}{s} = \frac{1 - e^{-Ts}}{s}.$$

Having found $G_{ZOH}(s)$, we next define

$$G'_p(s) \triangleq G_{ZOH}(s)G_p(s).$$

That is, we sweep the D/A converter in with the plant transfer function. This leads to the second modification of our block diagram, as shown in Fig. 14.12(b)

Using Fig. 14.12(b), we are now in a position to build the mathematical model we need to design compensators in the digital domain. From Fig. 14.12(b), we see that we can write

$$C(s) = E^*(s)G_c^*(s)G'_p(s). \qquad [14.35]$$

We can also write

$$E^*(s) = [R(s) - C(s)]^*$$
$$= R^*(s) - C^*(s). \qquad [14.36]$$

Substituting Eq. [14.36] into Eq. [14.35] yields

$$C(s) = [R^*(s) - C^*(s)]G_c^*(s)G'_p(s)$$
$$= [R^*(s)G_c^*(s)G'_p(s)] - [C^*(s)G_c^*(s)G'_p(s)]. \qquad [14.37]$$

If we now apply the starring operation to both sides of Eq. [14.37] we obtain

$$C^*(s) = [R^*(s)G_c^*(s)G'_p(s)]^* - [C^*(s)G_c^*(s)G'_p(s)]^*$$
$$= R^*(s)G_c^*(s)[G'_p(s)]^* - C^*(s)G_c^*(s)[G'_p(s)]^*. \qquad [14.38]$$

Equation [14.38] can be written as

$$C^*(s)[1 + G_c^*(s)[G'_p(s)]^*] = R^*(s)G_c^*(s)[G'_p(s)]^*, \qquad [14.39]$$

**Figure 14.15 |** Block diagram of closed loop sampled data system in the $z$ plane.

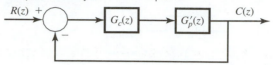

which in turn can be rewritten as

$$\frac{C^*(s)}{R^*(s)} = \frac{G_c^*(s)[G_p'(s)]^*}{1 + G_c^*(s)[G_p'(s)]^*}.$$

[14.40]

Finally, letting $s = \ln z / T$ in Eq. [14.40] yields

$$\frac{C(z)}{R(z)} = \frac{G_c(z)G_p'(z)}{1 + G_c(z)G_p'(z)}.$$

[14.41]

Equation [14.41] should look familiar. It has exactly the same form as the expression we obtained for the closed-loop transfer function in the study of *continuous* systems. As a consequence, Eq. [14.41] can be represented by the block diagram of Fig. 14.15. We are now almost ready to begin the design of the compensator $G_c(z)$. However, there is one remaining detail that we must consider and that is the determination of $G_p'(z)$.

## 14.17 | FINDING $G_p'(z)$

We begin by considering

$$G_p'(s) = \frac{1 - e^{-sT}}{s} G_p(s) = Y_{\text{step}}(s) - e^{-sT} Y_{\text{step}}(s),$$

where

$$Y_{\text{step}}(s) = \frac{G_p(s)}{s}.$$

We use this notation for the somewhat obvious reason that $Y_{\text{step}}(s)$ is the $s$ plane expression for the response of the continuous plant to a unit step input. Applying the inverse Laplace transform then yields

$$\begin{aligned}
g_p'(t) &= \mathcal{L}^{-1}\{G_p'(s)\} \\
&= \mathcal{L}^{-1}\{Y_{\text{step}}(s) - e^{-sT} Y_{\text{step}}(s)\} \\
&= \mathcal{L}^{-1}\{Y_{\text{step}}(s)\} - \mathcal{L}^{-1}\{e^{-sT} Y_{\text{step}}(s)\} \\
&= y_{\text{step}}(t)\mathbf{1}(t) - y_{\text{step}}(t - T)\mathbf{1}(t - T).
\end{aligned}$$

We now discretize $g_p'(t)$ by merely substituting $kT$ for $t$ to obtain

$$g_p'(kT) = y_{\text{step}}(kT)\mathbf{1}(kT) - y_{\text{step}}(kT - T)\mathbf{1}(kT - T).$$

**Figure 14.16** | Comparison of $G_p(s)$ and $G'_p(z)$.

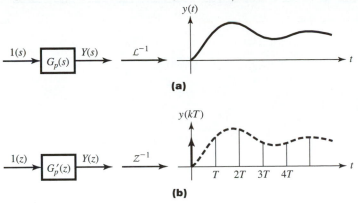

**(a)**

**(b)**

Then,

$$G'_p(z) \triangleq \mathcal{Z}\{y_{\text{step}}(kT)\mathbf{1}(kT)\} - \mathcal{Z}\{y_{\text{step}}(kT-T)\mathbf{1}(kT-T)\}$$

$$= \sum_{k=0}^{\infty} y_{\text{step}}(kT)\mathbf{1}(kT)z^{-k} - \sum_{k=0}^{\infty} y_{\text{step}}(kT-T)\mathbf{1}(kT-T)z^{-k}$$

$$= Y_{\text{step}}(z) - \{0 + y(0)z^{-1} + y(T)z^{-2} + \cdots + y(kT)z^{-(k+1)T} + \cdots\}$$

$$= Y_{\text{step}}(z) - z^{-1}\{y(0)z^0 + y(T)z^{-1} + \cdots + y(kT)z^{-kT} + \cdots\}$$

$$= Y_{\text{step}}(z) - z^{-1}Y_{\text{step}}(z)$$

$$= (1 - z^{-1})Y_{\text{step}}(z). \qquad\qquad\qquad [\mathbf{14.42}]$$

Thus, we have

$$Y_{\text{step}}(z) = \frac{z}{z-1}G'_p(z).$$

We can now draw two analogous block diagrams, as shown in Fig. 14.16. Figure 14.16 tells the following story. Applying a unit step input to $G_p(s)$ yields $Y_{\text{step}}(s)$ whose inverse Laplace transform is $y_{\text{step}}(t)$. This is shown in part (a) of Fig. 14.16. Applying the *discrete* version of the unit step to $G'_p(z)$ yields $Y_{\text{step}}(z)$ whose inverse $\mathcal{Z}$ transform is $y_{\text{step}}(kT)$. This is shown in part (b) of Fig. 14.16. A most important point is the following: *the continuous and discrete responses are identical at times $t = 0, T, 2T, \ldots, kT, \ldots$*. For this reason, $G'_p(z)$ is called the *step-invariant* transform of $G_p(s)$, where the word invariant means unchanged.

The fact that $G'_p(z)$ is the step-invariant transform of $G_p(s)$ is a result of our model for the D/A converter. We have modeled the D/A converter as a so-called "zero-order hold." As a result, we get a very specific form for $G'_p(z)$. If we had modeled the D/A converter in some other way, say as a first-order hold, we would have obtained a different formula for $G'_p(z)$. Hence, $G'_p(z)$ is sometimes called the zero-order hold transform of $G_p(s)$. However, as we have seen, it is also the step-invariant

**Table 14.3** | Impulse-invariant $\mathcal{Z}$ transforms of selected Laplace transforms.

| $X(s)$ | $x(kT)$ | $X(z)$ |
|---|---|---|
| $\frac{1}{s}$ | $1(kT)$ | $\frac{z}{z-1}$ |
| $\frac{1}{s^2}$ | $kT$ | $\frac{Tz}{(z-1)^2}$ |
| $\frac{1}{s^3}$ | $\frac{1}{2}(kT)^2$ | $\frac{T^2}{2}\frac{z(z+1)}{(z-1)^3}$ |
| $\frac{a}{s(s+a)}$ | $1-e^{-akT}$ | $\frac{z(1-e^{-aT})}{(z-1)(z-e^{-aT})}$ |
| $\frac{a^2}{s^2(s+a)}$ | $\frac{1}{a}(akT-1+e^{-akT})$ | $\frac{z[(aT-1+e^{-aT})z+(1-e^{-aT}-aTe^{-aT})]}{a(z-1)^2(z-e^{-aT})}$ |
| $\frac{a^2}{s(s+a)^2}$ | $1-e^{-akT}(1+akT)$ | $\frac{z[(1-e^{-aT}-aTe^{-aT})z+(e^{-2aT}-e^{-aT}+aTe^{-aT})]}{(z-1)(z-e^{-aT})^2}$ |
| $\frac{a^2+b^2}{s[(s+a)^2+b^2]}$ | $1-e^{-akT}\left(\cos bkT+\frac{a}{b}\sin bkT\right)$ | $\frac{z(Az+B)}{(z-1)(z^2-2e^{-aT}(\cos bT)z+e^{-2aT}}$ |
| | | $A=1-e^{-aT}\cos bT-\frac{a}{b}e^{-aT}\sin bT$ |
| | | $B=e^{-2aT}+\frac{a}{b}e^{-aT}\sin bT-e^{-aT}\cos bT$ |

transform of $G_p(s)$. In the literature, the terms step-invariant and zero-order hold are used interchangeably.

Based on our analysis, we can write down a short algorithm for finding $G'_p(z)$:

1. Form $Y_{\text{step}}(s)=\dfrac{G_p(s)}{s}$.
2. Find $y_{\text{step}}(kT)=\mathcal{L}^{-1}\{Y_{\text{step}}(s)\}|_{t=kT}$.
3. Find $Y_{\text{step}}(z)=\mathcal{Z}\{y_{\text{step}}(kT)\}$.
4. Find $G'_p(z)=(1-z^{-1})Y_{\text{step}}(z)$.

Finding $G'_p(z)$ by this algorithm can be easy or hard. It is easy if we have a table of impulse-invariant $\mathcal{Z}$ transforms such as Table 14.3.

Note that since $\mathcal{L}\{\delta(t)\}=1$, the Laplace transforms on the left can be thought of as the impulse responses of various "systems." If we then inverse Laplace transform these functions, discretize them by substituting $kT$ for $t$ and then find the $\mathcal{Z}$ transform of the discrete time function, we have the impulse-invariant response of the continuous "systems" on the left side of the table. This follows because $\mathcal{Z}\{\delta_o(kT)\}=1$. We now use this table to demonstrate the algorithm for finding $G'_p(z)$.

**EXAMPLE 14.17.1**

Let

$$G_p(s)=\frac{a}{s+a}.$$

Then,

$$Y_{\text{step}}(s)=\frac{a}{s(s+a)}.$$

The corresponding $Y_{step}(z)$, as given by the table, is

$$Y_{step}(z) = \frac{z(1 - e^{-aT})}{(z - 1)(z - e^{-aT})}.$$

Multiplying by $(1 - z^{-1})$ yields

$$G'_p(z) = (1 - z^{-1})Y_{step}(z)$$

$$= \frac{z - 1}{z} \frac{z(1 - e^{-aT})}{(z - 1)(z - e^{-aT})}$$

$$= \frac{(1 - e^{-aT})}{(z - e^{-aT})}.$$

We see that in this case, there is no zero in $G'_p(z)$. However, the reader is invited to repeat the example using

$$G_p(s) = \frac{a}{s(s + a)}.$$

In this case, $G'_p(z)$ will have a zero even though there is no zero in $G_p(s)$.

# 14.18 | NYQUIST IN THE *z* PLANE

We close this chapter with a discussion of the Nyquist criterion in the *z* plane. We will not make much use of the Nyquist criterion when analyzing discrete systems, but we include this discussion for completeness. Indeed, given the extensive foundation for the Nyquist criterion that we laid out in Chapter 10 it will not take us long to dispose of this topic.

In the *s* plane, the region of stability is infinite in extent, namely, the entire left half of the *s* plane. In the *z* plane, this is not the case. The region of stability is the interior of the unit circle. This makes drawing the contour $\Gamma$ in the $GH$ plane easier because the contour $\Omega$ in the *z* plane is finite in extent, being simply the unit circle.

We treat poles at $z = 1$ in the same way that we treated poles at $s = 0$, by detouring around them on a contour of arbitrarily small radius. We demonstrate these ideas with Example 14.18.1.

**EXAMPLE 14.18.1**

Let

$$GH(z) = \frac{K(z + 0.8)}{(z - 0.8)(z - 1)},$$

with $f_{sample} = 10$ Hz. We do not have to know the sampling frequency to apply the Nyquist criterion, but picking a sampling frequency makes it easier to relate the analysis to that we have already done in Chapter 10.

**Figure 14.17 |** (a) Contour $\Omega$ in the $z$ plane and (b) contour $\Gamma$ in $GH$ plane.

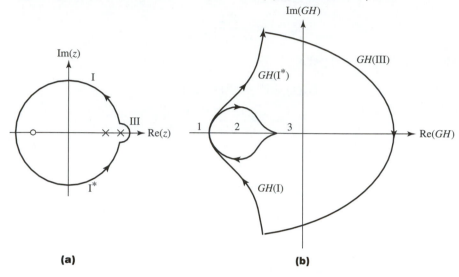

(a)                                    (b)

Figure 14.17(a) shows the contour along which we will evaluate $GH(z)$. Note that we detour around the pole at $z = 1$ on a portion of a circle of radius $\epsilon$ centered at $z = 1$. The contour $\Gamma$ in the $GH$ plane is shown in part (b) of the figure. The Bode magnitude and phase plots of $GH(e^{j\omega T})$, for $K = 1$, shown in Fig. 14.18, prove to be a great help in drawing $\Gamma$.

We see from Fig. 14.17(b) that the plot is similar to those we drew in Chapter 10 for continuous transfer functions with a single pole at $s = 0$, with the following exception. The plot does *not* touch the origin in the $z$ plane. The reason is that we evaluate $GH(e^{j\omega T})$ over a finite range of values of $\omega$, namely $0 < \omega < \pi/T$.

**Figure 14.18 |** Bode magnitude and phase plots of $GH(e^{j\omega t})$, $0 < \omega T < \pi/T$.

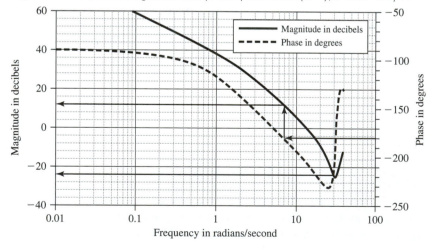

We have labeled the segments of $\Omega$ in the same fashion that we did in the *s* plane Nyquist analysis. Segment *I* is the upper half of the unit circle. Segment *I\** is the lower half the unit circle. Segment *III* is the portion of a circle of radius $\epsilon$ centered at $z = 1$. There is no segment *II* because the contour $\Omega$ in the *z* plane, unlike its counterpart in the *s* plane, is of finite extent.

We see from the Bode phase plot that for both $\omega = 7$ and $\pi / T$ rad/s,

$$\underline{/GH(e^{j\omega T})} = -180°.$$

We next find from the plot that

$$|GH(e^{j0.7})| = 10^{12/20} = 3.98 \quad \text{and} \quad |GH(e^{j\pi})| = 10^{-25/20} = 0.0562.$$

It is a simple matter to evaluate the Nyquist equation for the three cases shown in Fig. 14.17(b).

For

$$K < \frac{1}{3.98} = 0.251,$$

the point $-1$ in the *GH* plane is in region 1. The Nyquist equation is

$$Z = N + P = 0 + 2 = 2.$$

Both closed-loop poles are inside $\Omega$ in the *z* plane, that is, inside the unit circle.

For

$$0.251 < K < \frac{1}{0.0562} = 17.8,$$

the point $-1$ is in region 2, and the Nyquist equation is

$$Z = N + P = -2 + 2 = 0.$$

The two encirclements of the point $-1$ are in the clockwise direction. Since we traversed $\Omega$ in the *z* plane in the counterclockwise direction, we attach a minus sign to the two encirclements. Thus, when the point $-1$ is in region 2, we have no closed-loop poles inside the unit circle and two outside the unit circle.

Finally, for

$$K > 17.8,$$

the point $-1$ in the *GH* plane is in region 3, and the Nyquist equation is

$$Z = N + P = -1 + 2 = 1.$$

In this case, there is one pole of the closed-loop system inside the unit circle and one outside.

The root locus, shown in Fig. 14.19, should help our understanding of this analysis. For low gain, both poles are in the unit circle. After the poles break out of the real axis, they migrate toward the unit circle. For $K = 0.251$, they reach the unit circle. The two poles then travel along a circle centered at $z = -0.8$ until they break back into the real axis to the left of $z = -1$. One pole then migrates toward $z = -\infty$, the other toward the zero at $z = -0.8$. For $K \approx 17.8$ (the actual value is 18), the pole migrating toward the zero reaches the unit circle at $z = -1$. Thus, for $K > 18$, one of the closed-loop poles is inside the unit circle while the other continues its journey to $z = -\infty$.

**Figure 14.19 |** Root locus for Example 14.18.1.

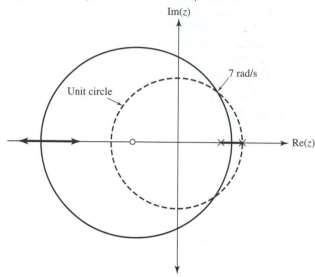

Example 14.18.1 is the extent of our investigation of Nyquist analysis in the $z$ plane. It should be clear that the procedures are similar to those we used in Chapter 10. The analysis is actually somewhat simpler because the contour $\Omega$ is of finite extent.

## 14.19 | REPRISE

In this chapter we have introduced the $\mathcal{Z}$ transform via the sampling of a continuous signal. This is the most natural development for control systems since we are primarily interested in sampled data systems, that is, the control of a continuous plant with a digital computer.

We also reviewed the properties of the $\mathcal{Z}$ transform relevant to control applications. In doing so, we saw that the $\mathcal{Z}$ transform is very closely connected to the Laplace transform. Indeed, one could argue that the $\mathcal{Z}$ transform is just a special case of the Laplace transform.

We next took a detailed look at the mappings from the $s$ plane to the $z$ plane. We saw that the left half of the $s$ plane maps to the interior of the unit circle in the $z$ plane, the imaginary axis of the $s$ plane maps to the unit circle in the $z$ plane, and the right half of the $s$ plane maps to the region exterior to the unit circle in the $z$ plane. Further, we found that the mapping is one-to-one only for the primary strip in the $s$ plane.

We also developed a mathematical model for studying sampled data systems with feedback that was analogous to the model we used in the study of continuous systems with feedback. In Chapter 15 we will put this mathematical model to work.

We concluded the chapter with a brief discussion of how to use the Nyquist criterion for stability analysis in the $z$ plane. We saw that the analysis is very similar to that for the $s$ domain, perhaps even a little easier since the contour $\Omega$ in the $z$ plane is of finite extent.

# 14.20 | PROBLEMS

## 14.20.1 Difference Equations

For each of these difference equations, find the solution using $\mathcal{Z}$ transforms. Use MATLAB to check your answers.

1. $y(k+2) - 1.5y(k+1) + 0.5y(k) = u(k)$, $u(k) = \mathbf{1}(k)$, $y(0) = 1$, and $y(1) = 1$

2. $y(k+2) - 1.6y(k+1) + 0.68y(k) = u(k)$, $u(k) = \mathbf{1}(k)$, $y(0) = 0$, and $y(1) = 0$

3. $y(k+2) - y(k+1) + 0.25y(k) = u(k)$, $u(k) = \mathbf{1}(k)$, $y(0) = 1$, and $y(1) = 0$

4. $y(k+3) - 2y(k+2) + 1.25y(k+1) - 0.25y(k) = u(k)$, $u(k) = \mathbf{1}(k)$, $y(0) = 0$, $y(1) = 0$, and $y(2) = 0$

5. $y(k+3) - 2y(k+2) + 1.25y(k+1) = u(k)$, $u(k) = \mathbf{1}(k)$, $y(0) = 1$, $y(1) = 0$, and $y(2) = 0$

6. $y(k+3) - 0.6y(k+2) + 0.09y(k+1) - 0.004y(k) = \delta_0(k)$, $y(0) = 0$, $y(1) = 0$, and $y(2) = 0$

7. $y(k+2) - 0.6y(k+1) + 0.12y(k) = 0$, $y(0) = 1$, and $y(1) = 0$

8. $y(k+3) - 1.6y(k+2) + 0.68y(k+1) - 0.08y(k) = \delta_0(k)$, $y(0) = 1$, $y(1) = 1$, and $y(2) = 1$

9. $y(k+3) - 1.1y(k+2) + 0.34y(k+1) - 0.024y(k) = \mathbf{1}(k)$, $y(0) = 1$, $y(1) = 0$, and $y(2) = 0$

10. $y(k+3) - 1.2y(k+2) + 0.36y(k+1) - 0.032y(k) = \delta_0(k)$, $y(0) = 1$, $y(1) = 1$, and $y(2) = 0$

11. $y(k+2) - y(k+1) + 0.16y(k) = k\mathbf{1}(k)$, $y(0) = 0$, and $y(1) = 0$

12. $y(k+2) - 1.2y(k+1) + 0.2y(k) = \mathbf{1}(k)$, $y(0) = 0$, and $y(1) = 1$

## 14.20.2 Partial Fraction Expansion

Expand each function $G(z)$ into a sum of partical fractions and then find the related time function $g(k)$, as well as $g(kT)$ for the given sampling frequency. Then check your answer using MATLAB.

1. $\dfrac{5z^2 - 0.6z - 0.4}{z^3 - 0.8z + 0.2z - 0.16}$, 10 Hz

2. $\dfrac{6z^2 - 7.3z + 1.75}{z^3 - 1.6z^2 + 0.65z - 0.05}$, 20 Hz

3. $\dfrac{7z^2 - 16.8z + 9}{z^3 - 2.4z^2 + z - 0.4}$, 20 Hz

4. $\dfrac{2z - 2}{z^2 - z + 0.5}$, 50 Hz

5. $\dfrac{6z^2 - 6.2z + 1.48}{z^3 - 1.6z^2 + 0.76z - 0.96}$, 20 Hz

6. $\dfrac{6z^2 - 7.5z + 3.75}{z^3 - 2.25z^2 + 1.5z - 0.25}$, 50 Hz

7. $\dfrac{2z - 0.5}{z^2 - 0.5z + 0.125}$, 20 Hz

8. $\dfrac{9z^2 - 16z + 7.5}{z^3 - 2z^2 + 1.5z - 0.5}$, 50 Hz

9. $\dfrac{4z^2 - 5.5z + 1.62}{z^3 - 2.5z^2 + 2.0625z - 0.5625}$, 10 Hz

10. $\dfrac{8z^2 - 4.2z + 0.16}{z^3 - z^2 + 0.16z}$, 50 Hz

### 14.20.3  Digital Filtering

In these problems, the poles and zeros can be either real or complex. With the exception of the first problem, the goal is to use MATLAB to design the specified filter.

1.   Classify each of the filters in Fig. 14.20 as low-pass, bandpass, or high-pass.

**Figure 14.20** | Filters: low-, band-, or high-pass.

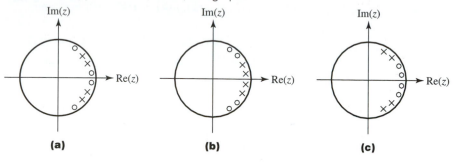

(a)                         (b)                         (c)

2.   Let $f_s = 10$ Hz. Design a bandpass filter

$$G(z) = \frac{K(z - z_1)(z - z_2)(z - z_3)}{(z - p_1)(z - p_2)(z - p_3)(z - p_4)}$$

where the pass band is from 3 rad/s to 5 rad/s.

3.   Let $f_s = 20$ Hz. Design a low-pass filter

$$G(z) = \frac{K(z - z_1)(z - z_2)}{(z - p_1)(z - p_2)(z - p_3)},$$

where
a.   $G(z = 1) = 1$.
b.   The half power point is at *approximately* 4 rad/s.

4.   Let $f_s = 10$ Hz. Design a low-pass filter

$$G(z) = \frac{K(z - z_1)}{(z - 0.9)},$$

where the half power point is approx 2 rad/s.

5.   Let $f_s = 10$ Hz. Design a high-pass filter

$$G(z) = \frac{K(z - 0.8)}{(z - p_1)},$$

where the half power point is approx 3 rad/s.

### 14.20.4  Finding $G'_p(z)$

For each of these plant transfer functions $G_p(s)$ find $G'_p(z)$. The sampling frequency is given in each case.

1. $\dfrac{10}{s+5}$, 10 Hz          2. $\dfrac{16}{s(s+4)}$, 20 Hz

3. $\dfrac{5}{s^2}$, 20 Hz          4. $\dfrac{12}{(s+2)^2}$, 50 Hz

## 14.20.5   Digital Simulation

Figure 14.21 shows the implementation using a delay for the difference equation

$$y(k+1) + 0.5y(k) = u(k).$$

**Figure 14.21 |** Implementation using a delay.

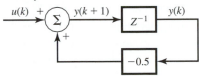

For each of these difference equations draw the implementation using delays.

1.  $y(k+3) - 1.6y(k+2) + 0.68y(k+1) - 0.08y(k) = u(k)$
2.  $y(k+3) - 1.1y(k+2) + 0.34y(k+1) - 0.024y(k) = u(k)$
3.  $y(k+3) - 1.2y(k+2) + 0.36y(k+1) - 0.032y(k) = u(k)$
4.  $y(k+2) - y(k+1) + 0.16y(k) = u(k)$
5.  $y(k+2) - 1.2y(k+1) + 0.2y(k) = u(k) + 2u(k+1)$
6.  $y(k+4) - 2.4y(k+3) + 1.96y(k+2) - 0.624y(k+1) + 0.64y(k) = u(k) + 2u(k+1) + 3u(k+2)$
7.  $y(k+4) - 4y(k+3) + 5.16y(k+2) - 2.48y(k+1) + 0.32y(k) = 3u(k) + 4u(k+1) + u(k+2)$
8.  $y(k+4) - 3y(k+3) + 3.16y(k+2) - 1.32y(k+1) + 0.16y(k) = u(k) + 2.5u(k+1) + 3u(k+2)$
9.  $y(k+3) - 1.5y(k+2) + 0.66y(k+1) - 0.8y(k) = 3u(k+1) + 2u(k)$
10. $y(k+3) - 0.33(k+2) + 0.029y(k+1) - 0.0006y(k) = 3u(k+1) + 2u(k)$

## 14.20.6   Nyquist Analysis

For each loop transfer function $GH(z)$ draw the Nyquist plot (contour $\Gamma$) in the $GH$ plane, and determine the range of gain $K$ for which the system is stable. The sampling rate is given with the loop transfer function.

1.  $\dfrac{K(z+1)(z-0.8)}{(z-1)^2(z-0.4)}$, 10 Hz          2.  $\dfrac{K(z+0.9)(z-0.6)}{(z-1)(z-0.2)}$, 20 Hz

3.  $\dfrac{Kz(z+1)}{(z-1)^2}$, 20 Hz          4.  $\dfrac{K(z+0.9)(z+0.2)}{(z-1)(z-0.8)}$, 50 Hz

5. $\dfrac{K(z-0.6)}{(z-0.2)(z-2)}$, 1 Hz

6. $\dfrac{K(z-0.2)}{(z-0.5)(z-1.5)}$, 1 Hz

7. $\dfrac{K(z+0.8)(z-0.2)}{(z+0.2)(z-0.8)^2}$, 25 Hz

8. $\dfrac{K(z-0.2)^2}{z^2(z-1)(z-0.9)}$, 10 Hz

9. $\dfrac{Kz^2}{(z-1)(z-0.9)(z+0.2)^2}$, 20 Hz

10. $\dfrac{K(z-0.2)^2}{z(z+0.4)(z-1)(z-0.9)}$, 20 Hz

## 14.20.7  Additional Problems

1. An automobile wheel is 24 in. in diameter and the rim has four equally spaced spokes. The car is in motion and is being filmed with a camera that takes 24 frames per second. At what speed do the spokes first appear to rotate backward?

2. For each transfer function, determine whether the final value theorem can be used to find the steady state value in response to a bounded input.

   a. $\dfrac{Kz}{(z-1)(z-0.9)}$

   b. $\dfrac{K(z-0.2)}{z(z-2)}$

   c. $\dfrac{Kz}{z^2-2z/\sqrt{2}+1}$

   d. $\dfrac{z^2-2z/\sqrt{2}+1}{z(z-1)}$

3. Amoritization is the name given to retiring a debt with $n$ payments of equal size. The unpaid amount is called the outstanding principal. Let
   a. $y(k) =$ the outstanding principal after the $k$th payment.
   b. $u(k) = p$ the amount of the $k$th payment.
   Write a difference equation that describes this amortization process. Then use $\mathcal{Z}$ transforms to find a formula for $p$, the payment, where N is the number of payments.

4. The Fibonacci numbers can be generated by this model of a rabbit population:
   a. Each pair of rabbits mates for life.
   b. Each pair of rabbits gives birth to one male and one female rabbit at the end of each month.
   c. Each newborn pair produces its first offspring when they are two months old.
   Write a difference equation to describe the number of rabbits at month $k$. Use $\mathcal{Z}$ transforms to find a formula for $y(k)$, thereby generating a formula for the Fibonacci numbers, or sequence.

5. The $\alpha - \beta$ tracker is an old tried but true radar tracking algorithm described as:
   a. $u(k)$ is a noise corrupted measurement of the object's range obtained from the $k$th radar pulse.
   b. $y(k)$ is the estimate of the range to the target after the $k$th radar pulse is processed.
   c. $\dot{y}(k)$ is the target's range *velocity* after the $k$th radar pulse is processed.
   d. $y_p(k)$ is the predicted target range at the $k$th radar pulse, based on the processing of all measurments up through $u(k-1)$. If $T$ is the period at which the radar pulses are sent, then the $\alpha - \beta$ tracker can be represented

by this set of difference equations.

$$y_p(k) = y(k-1) + T\dot{y}(k-1),$$

$$y(k) = y_p(k) + \alpha[u(k) - y_p(k)],$$

$$\dot{y}(k) = \dot{y}(k-1) + \frac{\beta}{T}[u(k) - y_p(k)].$$

Solve this set of difference equations.

e. A model for national income is

$$y(k) = u(k) + \alpha(1 + \beta)y(k-1) - \alpha\beta y(k-2),$$

where $y(k)$ is national income and $u(k)$ is government spending. Let $\alpha = 0.125$ and $\beta = 1$. Find the national income if

$$u(k) = \begin{cases} 0 & \text{for } k < 0 \\ 1 & \text{for } k \geq 0. \end{cases}$$

f. Consider the difference equation

$$c(k+1) - c(k) = Ac(k) - \text{cells killed by cancer therapy},$$

where $c(k)$ is the number of cancer cells at time $k$, and $A$ is a positive constant. Suppose the cancer therapy is $kB$, where $B$ is another positive constant and $k$ is the discrete time variable. In other words, the therapy is a ramp function. Let $c(0)$ be the initial number of cancer cells. Supposing that the patient doesn't die from the treatment, can the cancer be eradicated?

# FURTHER READINGS

Bracewell, Ron. 1965. *The Fourier Transform and Its Applications*. New York: McGraw-Hill.

Cadzow, James A. 1973. *Discrete Time Systems*. Englewood Cliffs, N.J.: Prentice-Hall.

Franklin, Gene F., J. David Powell, and Michael L. Workman. 1990. Reading, Mass.: Addison-Wesley.

Houpis Constantine J., and Gary B. Lamont. 1992. *Digital Control Systems, Theory, Hardware, Software,* 2nd ed. New York: McGraw-Hill.

Luenberger, David G. 1979. *Introduction to Dynamic Systems: Theory, Models, and Applications,* New York: John Wiley & Sons.

Saucedo, R. and E. E. Schiring. 1968. *Introduction to Continuous and Digital Control Systems*. New York: MacMillan.

# 15 Chapter

# Digital Control

## 15.1 | OVERVIEW

Chapter 14 was devoted to developing the mathematical machinery necessary to analyze a sampled data system. In this chapter, that machinery is used to investigate various techniques for compensating such a system. There are several approaches to designing digital compensation, and within each approach a variety of design techniques.

One approach is to design the compensation in the $s$ plane and then map the compensator to the $z$ plane. The two design techniques commonly used in this approach are root locus design and Bode design. We will look at both these techniques. One advantage of this approach is that we do not have to find $G_p'(z)$.

A second approach is to do the design in the $z$ plane. In this case, it is necessary to know $G_p'(z)$. The two techniques discussed under this approach are root locus design and direct design.

A third approach, which we will not consider is to map from the $z$ plane to the $w$ plane and do the design in the $w$ plane.

Before proceeding to the design techniques, it is worth spending some time analyzing some mappings from the $s$ domain to the $z$ domain that are related to compensator design. These mappings come into play whether the design is carried out in the $s$ plane or the $z$ plane.

We will see that all the techniques we developed for compensating continuous systems can be applied to sampled data systems. Slight modifications will have to be made in certain cases, but by and large the techniques are the same.

## 15.2 | IMPORTANT MAPPINGS

The $s$ plane root locus design techniques of Chapter 7 concentrated on two figures of merit, time to peak and percent overshoot. From these two figures of merit we determined values for the damping ratio $\zeta$ and the natural frequency $\omega_n$, the two parameters of

$$T_{N2}(s) = \frac{\omega_n^2}{s^2 + 2\zeta\omega_n s + \omega_n^2}.$$

**Figure 15.1 |** Lines of constant $\zeta$ and curves of constant $\omega_n$.

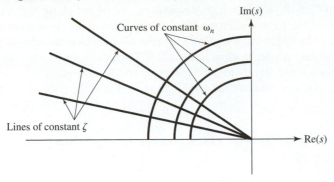

By carefully choosing values of $\zeta$ and $\omega_n$ we usually met our specifications on time to peak and percent overshoot.

In the $s$ domain, the lines of constant damping ratio are rays originating at the origin, while the curves representing constant $\omega_n$ are quarter circles, as shown in Fig. 15.1. A necessary first step for digital design is to find the equivalent curves in the $z$ plane.

## 15.2.1 Lines of Constant Damping Ratio

Figure 15.2 shows the real and imaginary parts of the complex variable $s$ expressed in terms of $\zeta$ and $\omega_n$. That is,

$$s = -\zeta\omega_n + j\omega_n\sqrt{1-\zeta^2}.$$

The equivalent point in the $z$ plane is found by applying the transformation $z = e^{sT}$ to obtain

$$z = e^{-\zeta\omega_n T}e^{j\omega_n T\sqrt{1-\zeta^2}}. \qquad\qquad \textbf{[15.1]}$$

**Figure 15.2 |** Components of line of constant damping ratio.

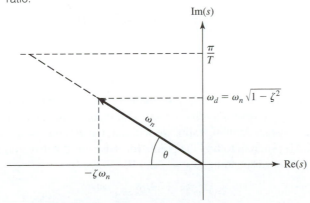

If in Eq. [15.1] we fix $\zeta$ and vary $\omega_n$ we will plot a log spiral curve, since the magnitude of $z$ will vary exponentially with $\omega_n$, while the phase varies linearly. As shown in Fig. 15.2, we only need to consider the portion of the ray of constant damping ratio between the origin and the point where the ray intersects the edge of the primary strip. It is an easy matter to write a short MATLAB program to draw the curves. In what follows we will merely find the end points of the curves.

For $\omega_n = 0$ a ray of constant damping ratio starts at the point

$$z = e^0 = 1.$$

The other end of the ray in the $s$ plane touches the edge of the primary strip. At the point of intersection

$$\omega_n \sqrt{1 - \zeta^2} = \frac{\pi}{T},$$

or, equivalently,

$$\omega_n = \frac{\pi}{T\sqrt{1 - \zeta^2}}.$$

Hence

$$z = e^{-\zeta \pi T / T \sqrt{1-\zeta^2}} e^{j\pi T \sqrt{1-\zeta^2}/T\sqrt{1-\zeta^2}} = e^{-\zeta\pi/\sqrt{1-\zeta^2}} e^{j\pi}.$$

Thus $z$ is a vector of length

$$e^{-\zeta\pi/\sqrt{1-\zeta^2}}$$

and angle $180°$. Note that the larger $\zeta$ the *shorter* the length of the vector.

The log sprial curves connecting the end points of the curves for $\zeta = 0.1, 0.2, \ldots, 0.9$ in increments of $0.1$ are shown in Fig. 15.3(a).

## 15.2.2  Curves of Constant $\omega_n$

To find the curves of constant $\omega_n$ we again use the transformation $e^{sT}$, but this time we fix $\omega_n$ and vary $\zeta$. It is customary to let

$$\omega_n = \frac{k\pi}{10T}, \qquad k = 1, 2, \ldots, 10.$$

Then

$$z = e^{-\zeta k\pi T/10T} e^{jk\pi T\sqrt{1-\zeta^2}/10T} = e^{-\zeta k\pi/10} e^{jk\pi\sqrt{1-\zeta^2}/10}. \qquad \textbf{[15.2]}$$

Equation [15.2] can be used to plot the curves of constant $\omega_n$ by holding $\omega_n$ constant and varying $\zeta$ between zero and one. Our tactic is the same one that we used for the lines of constant damping ratio: we will find the end points of the curves, and write a MATLAB program to find the points for values of $\zeta$ between zero and one.

When $\zeta = 0$, corresponding to $s = jk\pi/10$,

$$z = e^0 e^{jk\pi\sqrt{1-0^2}/10} = e^{jk\pi/10}.$$

**Figure 15.3** | Curves of (a) constant $\zeta$ and (b) constant $\omega_n$.

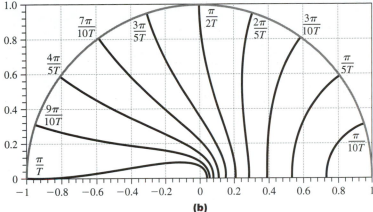

(a)

(b)

In this case $z$, is a vector of length one and angle $k\pi/10$ rad. Thus, all the curves of constant $\omega_n$ originate on the unit circle at the angles

$$k \times \frac{180°}{10} = k \times 18°, \qquad k = 1, 2, \ldots, 10.$$

At the other end of each of these curves, $\zeta = 1$, and

$$z = e^{-k\pi T/10T} e^{jk\pi T\sqrt{1-1}/10T} = e^{-k\pi/10} \qquad k = 1, 2, \ldots, 10.$$

These points lie on the positive real axis in the $z$ plane. The smaller $k$, the larger $e^{-k\pi/10}$.

The curves that connect these end points are shown in Fig. 15.3(b). We see that the curves show increasing distortion as $k$ increases. For $k = 1$, the curve is very close to a quarter circle centered at $z = 1$. The curves for $k = 2$ and $k = 3$ still have the general shape of a quarter circle, but for $k > 3$ they do not.

In the figure the lines of constant $\omega_n$ are labeled

$$\frac{\pi}{T}, \frac{\pi}{5T}, \frac{3\pi}{10T}, \ldots, \frac{\pi}{T},$$

indicating the value of $\omega_n$ that corresponds to each curve. As noted, the curves end at the angles

$$\frac{\pi}{10} = 18°, \frac{\pi}{5} = 36°, \frac{3\pi}{10} = 54°, \ldots, \pi = 180°.$$

In some texts, the curves of constant $\omega_n$ are labeled with these angles. We will use $K\pi/10T$ to denote these curves to remind ourselves that the frequency $K\pi/10T$ associated with the curve changes with the sampling rate.

By combining the curves of constant $\zeta$ and constant $\omega_n$ we can locate points in the $z$ plane with any desired combination of damping ratio and natural frequency. For instance, consider Fig. 15.4(a). In this figure, pole locations in the $s$ plane with

**Figure 15.4 |** Desired pole locations in (a) the $s$ plane and (b) the $z$ plane.

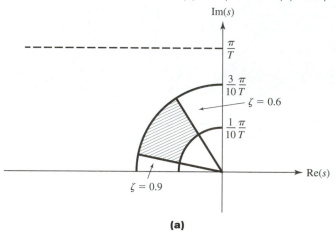

**(a)**

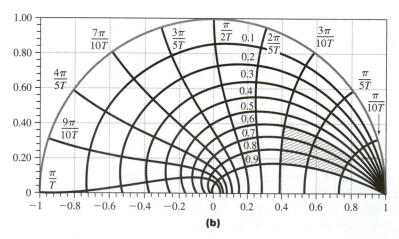

**(b)**

damping ratios between 0.6 and 0.9 and natural frequencies between $\pi/10T$ and $3\pi/10T$ are in the shaded area. The corresponding poles in the $z$ plane are shown in Fig. 15.4(b). The mapping causes some distortion but the general shape of the two shaded areas is still similar.

We note that the curves of constant $\zeta$ do not depend on $T$, but the curves of constant $\omega_n$ do. Thus, the natural frequency of a pole in the shaded region will depend on the sampling rate. For instance, for a sampling rate of 10 Hz, the poles in the shaded region will have natural frequencies between 0.5 and 1.5 Hz, or between one tenth and three tenths of the maximum frequency that can be sampled without aliasing, namely, 5 Hz. The equivalent radian frequencies are $\pi$ rad/s and $3\pi$ rad/s. On the other hand, if the sampling rate is 100 Hz poles in this same region will have natural frequencies between 5 and 15 Hz.

## 15.2.3 The Bilinear Mapping

In Section 15.2.3 we mapped the lines of constant $\zeta$ and $\omega_n$ from the $s$ plane to the $z$ plane using the mapping $z = e^{sT}$. This is the mapping we used in Chapter 14 to map the poles of the plant from the $s$ plane to the $z$ plane. We will also use this mapping to determine the desired location of the dominant poles of the closed-loop transfer function. We now investigate the first of two alternative mappings that can be used to map *compensators* from the $s$ plane to the $z$ plane.

Compensators can be mapped from the $s$ plane to the $z$ plane in a variety of ways. This is quite different from the mapping of $G_p$, the plant transfer function, from the $s$ plane to the $z$ plane. In the case of $G_p$ we had to use the step invariant transform to accurately model the effect of the zero-order hold, and the poles of $G_p(s)$ mapped from the $s$ plane to the $z$ plane under $z = e^{sT}$.

For compensators there is no such restriction on the choice of mapping. The compensator is the designer's creation, whose purpose is to place the closed-loop poles in appropriate locations. Thus, the only real constraint on our choice of a mapping is that stable poles in the $s$ plane should map to stable poles in the $z$ plane. The mapping

$$s = \frac{a}{T}\frac{z-1}{z+1}$$

is called the bilinear mapping and is a frequent choice for mapping compensators from the $s$ plane to the $z$ plane. The usual choice for $a$ is 2. For this choice of $a$, the bilinear mapping is the inverse of the trapezoidal rule for numerical integration, often referred to as Tustin's method.

To see how points map from the $s$ plane to the $z$ plane under the bilinear mapping, we use the inverse mapping

$$z = -\frac{s + 2/T}{s - 2/T}.$$

Now, consider a point $s = \sigma + j\omega$ where $-\infty < \omega < \infty$. Then

$$z = -\frac{\sigma + j\omega + 2/T}{\sigma + j\omega - 2/T} = -\frac{(\sigma + 2/T) + j\omega}{(\sigma - 2/T) + j\omega}.$$

Note that if $\sigma < 0$,

$$\left| \sigma + \frac{2}{T} \right| < \left| \sigma - \frac{2}{T} \right|,$$

and

$$|z| = \left| \frac{(\sigma + 2/T) + j\omega}{(\sigma - 2/T) + j\omega} \right| < 1.$$

On the other hand, if $\sigma > 0$,

$$|z| = \left| \frac{(\sigma + 2/T) + j\omega}{(\sigma - 2/T) + j\omega} \right| > 1.$$

Thus, the portion of the primary strip to the left of the origin of the $s$ plane maps to the interior of the unit circle, the portion of the primary strip to the right of the origin maps to the region outside the unit circle, and the imaginary axis in the $s$ plane maps to the unit circle in the $z$ plane. This means that the bilinear mapping is useful in the sense that it maps stable poles in the $s$ plane to stable poles in the $z$ plane.

Some additional information about the nature of the bilinear mapping can be obtained by considering

$$\underline{/z} = 180° + \underline{/\left(\sigma + \frac{2}{T}\right) + j\omega} - \underline{/\left(\sigma - \frac{2}{T}\right) + j\omega}.$$

Figure 15.5(a) shows the case where $\sigma < 0$ and $|\sigma| < 2/T$, and Fig. 15.5(b) the case where $\sigma < 0$ and $|\sigma| > 2/T$.

**Figure 15.5 |** Angle contributions to $z$ under bilinear mapping.

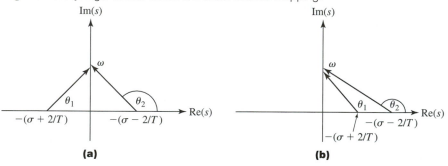

**(a)**          **(b)**

It is perhaps worth noting that to get the tips of both vectors on the imaginary axis, we have drawn each vector with its tail at the negative of the real part of the vector. This is exactly the tactic we used in root locus analysis when we represented a component $s + a$ of the loop transfer function by a vector drawn from $-a$ to $s$.

Consider first $|\sigma| < 2/T$. For $\omega = 0$,

$$\underline{/z} = 180° + \theta_1 - \theta_2$$

$$= 180° + 0° - 180°$$

$$= 0°.$$

Thus, for $\sigma < 0$ and $\omega = 0$, $z$ is a point in the interval $(0, 1)$ in the $z$ plane. If both $\sigma$ and $\omega$ are zero, then $z = 1$.

If we now increase $\omega$ while holding $\sigma$ constant,

$$\lim_{\omega \to \infty} \underline{/z} = 180° + \lim_{\omega \to \infty} \theta_1 - \lim_{\omega \to \infty} \theta_2 .$$
$$= 180° + 90° - 90°$$
$$= 180°.$$

This means a vertical line through $\sigma$ in the *left* half of the $s$ plane maps to a closed curve *inside* the unit circle in the $z$ plane, as shown in Fig. 15.6.

We see from the figure that as we begin increasing $\omega$ from very small values to larger values that $|(\sigma + 2/T) + j\omega|$ increases faster than $|(\sigma - 2/T) + j\omega|$ . Hence the curve has the cardioid shape shown.

The situation is similar for the case $\sigma < 0$ and $|\sigma| > 2/T$ except that the mapping of a vertical line through $\sigma$ is entirely to the left of the imaginary axis in the $z$ plane. To see this note that for $\omega = 0$,

$$\underline{/z} = 180° + \theta_1 - \theta_2 = 180° + 180° - 180° = 180°.$$

Further

$$\lim_{\omega \to \infty} \underline{/z} = 180° + \lim_{\omega \to \infty} \theta_1 - \lim_{\omega \to \infty} \theta_2$$
$$= 180° + 90° - 90°$$
$$= 180°.$$

As a consequence, the mapping of a vertical line starting at $s = \sigma + j0$ and ending at $s = \sigma + j\infty$ never crosses the imaginary axis, as shown in Fig. 15.6.

One major difference between the bilinear mapping and the mapping $z = e^{sT}$ is that the bilinear mapping takes the *entire* left half of the $s$ plane onto the unit circle one-to-one. This is quite different from the mapping $z = e^{sT}$ which is one-to-one only on strips of width $2\pi/T$ in the $s$ plane. The bilinear mapping is frequently used to map an $s$ plane compensator to the $z$ plane, as shown by the following example.

**Figure 15.6 |** Mapping of vertical line in the $s$ plane to the $z$ plane.

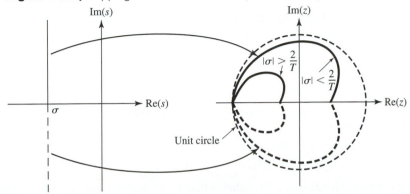

**EXAMPLE 15.2.1**

Consider the $s$ plane transfer function

$$G(s) = \frac{10(s+a)}{(s+b)(s+c)}.$$

Then,

$$
\begin{aligned}
G(z) &= G(s)\Big|_{s=\frac{2}{T}\frac{z-1}{z+1}} \\[4pt]
&= \frac{10(s+a)}{(s+b)(s+c)}\Big|_{s=\frac{2}{T}\frac{z-1}{z+1}} \\[4pt]
&= \frac{10\{(2/T)[(z-1)/(z+1)]+a\}}{\{(2/T)[(z-1)/(z+1)]+b\}\{(2/T)[(z-1)/(z+1)]+c\}} \frac{(z+1)^2}{(z+1)^2} \\[4pt]
&= \frac{10[(2/T)z-2/T+a(z+1)](z+1)}{[(2/T)z-2/T+b(z+1)][(2/T)z-2/T+c(z+1)]} \\[4pt]
&= \frac{10[(2/T+a)z-(2/T-a)](z+1)}{[(2/T+b)z-(2/T-b)][(2/T+c)z-(2/T-c)]}.
\end{aligned}
$$

We have included some detail here to emphasize several points. First, looking at the last expression, we see that we could write it down by inspection. Second, $G(z)$ has two poles and two zeros, whereas $G(s)$ has two poles and one zero. A close look at the development above shows that when the bilinear mapping is used $G(z)$ will *always* have as many zeros as poles. Third, $G(s)$ and $G(z)$ have the same dc gain.

We consider next the ad hoc mapping from the $s$ plane to the $z$ plane. So that we can compare the bilnear and ad hoc mappings, we let $T = 0.1$, $a = 2$, $b = 1$, $c = 4$, and find

$$
\begin{aligned}
G(z) &= \frac{10[(2/0.1+2)z-(2/0.1-2)](z+1)}{[(2/0.1+1)z-(2/0.1-1)][(2/0.1+4)z-(2/0.1-4)]} \\[4pt]
&= \frac{0.4365(z-0.8182)(z+1)}{(z-0.9048)(z-0.6667)}.
\end{aligned}
$$

## 15.2.4   The Ad Hoc (Pole/Zero) Mapping

Another transformation often used to map a compensator from the $s$ plane to the $z$ plane is the so called ad hoc, or pole/zero, transformation, described by the following algorithm.

1. Translate all poles from the $s$ plane to the $z$ plane using $z = e^{sT}$.
2. Translate all finite zeros using $z = e^{sT}$.
3. If the the $s$ plane transfer function has any zeros at infinity, place a zero at $z = 0$ for each zero at infinity.
4. Select a gain $G(z)$ so that

$$|G(s)|\big|_{s=j\omega} = |G(z)|\big|_{z=e^{j\omega T}}.$$

A common choice is $\omega = 0$, a choice that works unless $G(s)$ has one or more poles at $s = 0$. In the latter case, some frequency other than zero must be used.

**EXAMPLE 15.2.2**

Consider again the *s* plane transfer function

$$G(s) = \frac{10(s+2)}{(s+1)(s+4)},$$

and let $T = 0.1$ s. As discussed earlier, the number of zeros at infinity is equal to the excess of poles over finite zeros, so in the present case $G(s)$ has one zero at infinity. Then

$$G(z) = \left. \frac{Kz(z - e^{-2T})}{(z - e^{-T})(z - e^{-4T})} \right|_{T=0.1} = \frac{Kz(z - 0.8187)}{(z - 0.9048)(z - 0.6703)}.$$

We will use $K$ to match the dc gain of $G(z)$ to that of $G(s)$. For $G(z)$, the dc gain is

$$|G(z)||_{z=1} = \left| \left. \frac{Kz(z - e^{-2T})}{(z - e^{-T})(z - e^{-4T})} \right|_{z=1} \right| = \frac{K(0.1813)}{(0.0952)(0.3297)} = 5.78K.$$

The dc gain of $G(s)$ is 5. Thus, to achieve a dc gain of 5.0, means that

$$K = \frac{5}{5.778} = 0.8654.$$

For this choice of $K$

$$G(z) = \frac{0.8654z(z - 0.8187)}{(z - 0.9048)(z - 0.6703)}.$$

The ad hoc compensator is similar to the transfer function derived earlier using the bilinear mapping. The main difference is that the transfer function obtained with the bilinear mapping has a zero at $z = -1$, while the transfer function obtained from the ad hoc method has a zero at $z = 0$. If we were to put the zeros at infinity at $z = -1$ in the ad hoc method then there would be very little difference between the two transfer functions. Indeed, many designers do just that, in which case the transfer functions derived by the two methods are virtually indistinguishable for $T < 0.1$.

# 15.3 | DESIGN IN THE *s* PLANE

One approach to compensating a sampled data system is to design the compensator in the *s* plane and then map the compensator to the *z* plane using the bilinear mapping or the ad hoc procedure discussed in Example 15.2.2. A natural question that arises in this regard is how to account for the effect of the digital-to-analog converter (DAC), which we have modeled as a zero-order hold. The zero-order hold is present in the sampled data system but not in the analog system.

It is easy enough to include the effect of the zero-order hold in both Bode and root locus design. We will discuss both techniques and find, as we did for continuous systems, that the Bode design method is superior.

### 15.3.1 Root Locus Design

The easiest way to understand how the zero-order hold impacts the design of the compensator in the *s* plane is by example. In Example 15.3.1, we will first do the design ignoring the effect of the zero-order hold, and then redo the design to include these effects. As we will see, we may be able to ignore the effect of the zero-order hold, *if* the sampling rate is high enough.

**EXAMPLE 15.3.1**

Consider the sampled data system shown in Fig. 15.7. Let

$$G_p(s) = \frac{1}{s(s+1)}.$$

**Figure 15.7 |** Sampled data system.

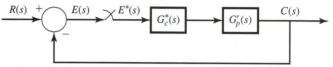

We wish to design a compensator that satisfies these simple specifications.

1. $t_p \approx 1.5$ s.
2. Percent overshoot less than 20%.

We hope that keeping the overshoot below 20% will yield an acceptable settling time.
    The first step is to do a standard *s* plane design, based on the unity feedback configuration of Fig. 15.8. The desired time to peak can be achieved by choosing a large enough damped frequency. That is,

$$\omega_d = \frac{\pi}{t_p} = \frac{\pi}{1.5} = 2.09 \rightarrow 2.$$

Making the conservative choice $\zeta = 1/\sqrt{2}$ should keep the overshoot under 20%.

**Figure 15.8 |** *s* plane block diagram.

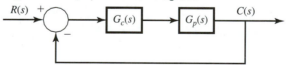

    If the zero of the lead compensator is placed at $s = -2$, then the design proceeds along the lines discussed many times in previous chapters. As shown in Fig. 15.9, the pole of the lead compensator is determined by satisfying the angle condition at $s = -2 + j2$. That is, at $s = -2 + j2$, we must have

$$\alpha - \theta_1 - \theta_2 - \theta_3 = -180°.$$

**Figure 15.9** | Vector representation of $G_c G_p$.

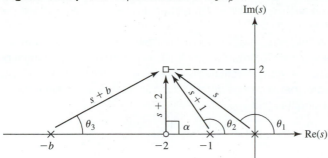

Since $\alpha$, $\theta_1$, and $\theta_2$ are known,

$$\theta_3 = \alpha + 180° - \theta_1 - \theta_2 = 18.43°.$$

Then from Fig. 15.9,

$$b = 2 + \frac{2}{\tan 18.43°} = 8.$$

The gain necessary to place closed-loop poles at $s = -2 \pm j2$ is

$$K_c = \left[ \frac{|s||s+1||s+b|}{|s+2|} \right] \Bigg|_{s=-2+j2} = 20,$$

and the lead compensator is

$$G_c = \frac{20(s+2)}{s+8}.$$

The next issue is the choice of a sampling rate. There are a number of rules of thumb for choosing a sampling rate. In the course of this chapter, we use several different rules of thumb for determining the sampling frequency. We will also try to investigate in an informal way the effect of different sampling rates on the closed-loop performance. We will find that we can sample at quite a low rate and still get good performance.

In this example we start with a common rule of thumb, namely, we require 10 samples per cycle of the output. Since the damped frequency at which the closed-loop system will oscillate is 2 rad/s, this yields a sample rate of 20 rad/s, or 3.18 Hz. Then the intersample period $T$ is

$$T = \frac{1}{3.18} = 0.314 \, s.$$

This is a very slow sampling rate and though such a slow sampling rate would work, we opt to increase the sampling rate even further to 10 Hz.

Having chosen a sampling rate, we can now map the compensator $G_c(s)$ to the $z$ plane using the bilinear mapping. Thus,

$$G_c(z) = \left[ \frac{20(s+2)}{s+8} \right] \Bigg|_{s=20\frac{z-1}{z+1}} = \frac{15.71(z-0.8182)}{z-0.4286}.$$

The gain of $G_c(z)$ is about 78% of the gain of $G_c(s)$ and the $z$ plane pole and zero have the same relative locations with respect to $z = 1$ that the $s$ plane pole and zero have relative to $s = 0$.

It is a useful exercise at this point to draw the root locus of the compensated system in the $z$ plane. To draw the root locus in the $z$ plane, $G'_p(z)$ must be known. In many cases, $G'_p(z)$ can be obtained from a table of $z$ transforms. If $G'_p(z)$ cannot be found in a table, then it can be determined from $G_p(s)$ as shown here.

The first step it to find

$$Y_{\text{step}}(s) = \frac{G_p(s)}{s} = \frac{1}{s}\frac{1}{s(s+1)} = \frac{1}{s^2(s+1)}.$$

The partial fraction expansion of $Y_{\text{step}}(s)$ is

$$\frac{1}{s^2(s+1)} = \frac{1}{s^2} - \frac{1}{s} + \frac{1}{s+1}.$$

Applying the inverse Laplace transform yields

$$y_{\text{step}}(t) = [t - 1 + e^{-t}]\mathbf{1}(t),$$

and

$$y_{\text{step}}(kT) = [kT - 1 + e^{-kT}]\mathbf{1}(kT).$$

Applying the $\mathcal{Z}$ transform then gives

$$Y_{\text{step}}(z) = \frac{Tz}{(z-1)^2} - \frac{z}{z-1} + \frac{z}{z - e^{-T}}$$

$$= z\left[\frac{T}{(z-1)^2} + \frac{z - 1 - (z - e^{-T})}{(z-1)(z - e^{-T})}\right]$$

$$= \frac{z[(T + e^{-T} - 1)z + (1 - e^{-T} - Te^{-T})]}{(z-1)^2(z - e^{-T})}.$$

Finally, we divide out the step input to obtain

$$G'_p(z) = \frac{z-1}{z}Y_{\text{step}}(z) = \frac{(T + e^{-T} - 1)z + (1 - e^{-T} - Te^{-T})}{(z-1)(z - e^{-T})}.$$

 Although the exercise just completed is worth doing once, MATLAB has a toolbox that makes it unnecessary to find $G'_p(z)$ by hand. We have engaged in this exercise primarily to illustrate how to find the step-invariant transformation.

For the chosen sample rate of 10 Hz.

$$G'_p(z) = \frac{0.004837(z + 0.9672)}{(z - 1)(z - 0.9048)},$$

and the closed-loop transfer function is

$$T_c(z) = \frac{0.0760(z - 0.8182)(z + 0.9672)}{(z - 0.6652)(z - 0.7961 - j0.1991)(z - 0.7961 + j0.1991)}.$$

The time response to a unit step input is

$$c(kT) = [1 + 0.9988e^{-4.08t} + 1.9988e^{-1.977t}\cos(2.451t - 3.134)]\mathbf{1}(kT).$$

It is worth pointing out that the actual closed-loop pole locations are not those that result from mapping $s = -2 \pm j2$ to the the *z* plane using $z = e^{sT}$. Under the mapping $z = e^{sT}$ the dominant closed-loop poles would be at

$$z = e^{(-2 \pm j2)T} = 0.8024 \pm j0.1627.$$

The reason for this discrepancy is that the compensator was initially designed in the *s* plane, ignoring the effects of the zero-order hold, and then mapped to the *z* plane using a different mapping, namely, the bilinear mapping.

The root locus is shown in Fig. 15.10. The actual dominant poles lie near the line of constant damping ratio $\zeta = 0.6$, while the dominant poles in the *s* plane were on the line of constant damping ratio $\zeta = 0.7$. Note that in the figure, the vertical axis passes through $z = 1$, rather than $z = 0$.

The unit step response of the overall sampled data system, that is, the continuous plant controlled by a digital compensator, as shown in Fig. 15.11, almost meets the stated specifications. Thus, ignoring the effects of the zero-order hold has not proven to be very detrimental, at least in this example.

We now repeat the design, this time accounting for the angle contribution of the zero-order hold. The alert reader will ask why we are accounting for the angle contribution of the zero-order hold but not the magnitude contribution. We will address that issue shortly.

**Figure 15.10 |** Root locus for $0 < K < 0.08$, Example 15.3.1.

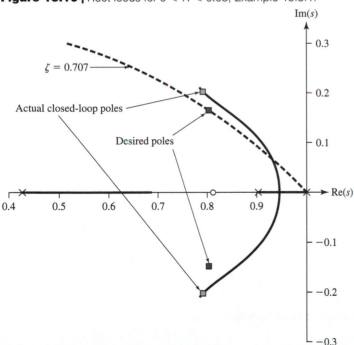

**Figure 15.11 |** Unit step responses, Example 15.3.1.

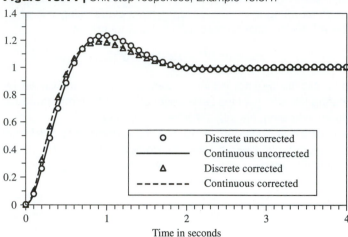

If we include the angle of the zero-order hold in our computation of the net angle of $G_c G_p(s)$ at $s = -2 + j2$, then

$$\theta_3 = \alpha + 180° - \theta_1 - \theta_2 + \left/ \frac{1 - e^{0.2} e^{-j0.2}}{-2 + j2} \right.$$

$$= 90° + 180° - (180 - \tan^{-1} 1) - (180 - \tan^{-1} 2) - 5.91°$$

$$= 12.5°.$$

Using Fig. 15.9, we compute

$$b = 2 + \frac{2}{\tan 12.5°} = 11.$$

The gain necessary to place closed-loop poles at $s = -2 \pm j2$ is

$$K_c = \left[ \frac{|s||s + 1||s + 11|}{|s + 2|} \right] \Bigg|_{s=-2+j2}$$

$$= 29.2 \rightarrow 29,$$

and the lead compensator is

$$G_c(z) = \frac{29(s + 2)}{s + 11}.$$

This compensator is slightly different than the one found earlier.
We next use the bilinear mapping to find

$$G_c(z) = \left[ \frac{29(s + 2)}{s + 11} \right] \Bigg|_{s=20\frac{z-1}{z+1}} = \frac{20.6(z - 0.8182)}{z - 0.2903}.$$

The closed-loop transfer function is then

$$T_c(z) = \frac{0.0996(z - 0.8182)(z + 0.9672)}{(z - 0.5831)(z - 0.7787 - j0.1678)(z - 0.7787 + j0.1678)}.$$

The time response to a unit step input is

$$c(kT) = [1 + 1.0562e^{-6.197t} + 2.2025e^{-2.274t}\cos(2.122t - 2.775)]\mathbf{1}(kT).$$

The damping ratio of the dominant poles has improved, as has the performance, as shown in Fig. 15.11. We will see shortly that the impact of the zero-order hold on the design is sampling frequency dependent. The higher the sampling frequency the less the impact.

---

In Example 15.3.1 we did not adjust the gain of the compensator for the magnitude of the zero-order hold. This would have made a significant difference in the gain since

$$\left| \frac{1 - e^{-0.1s}}{s} \right|_{s=-2+j2} = 0.11.$$

Adjusting the compensator gain for the magnitude of the zero-order hold would have increased the gain by nearly a factor of 10, and the response would have been very oscillatory. The reason that this gain adjustment is not made has to do with the overall process of sampling and reconstructing a signal. An analysis of this process is included in the discussion for Bode design, considered next. In that discussion, we show why we do not include the magnitude of the zero-order hold in the gain calculation. We will also see why, for a sampling rate of 10 Hz, the effects of the ZOH in Example 15.3.1 were minimal.

## 15.3.2 Bode Design

Another method for designing a digital compensator in the *s* domain is Bode's method. In designing compensators that will ultimately be mapped to the *z* plane, the Bode method has advantages in that it provides a means for choosing an adequate sampling rate and for easily accounting for the effect of the zero-order hold.

To see why it is easy to include the zero-order hold in the Bode method consider

$$
\begin{aligned}
G_{\text{ZOH}}(j\omega) &= \frac{1 - e^{-j\omega T}}{j\omega} \\
&= \frac{2e^{-j\omega T/2}}{\omega} \left[ \frac{e^{j\omega T/2} - e^{-j\omega T/2}}{2j} \right] \\
&= Te^{-j\omega T/2} \left[ \frac{\sin(\omega T/2)}{\omega T/2} \right] \\
&= Te^{-j\omega T/2}\text{sinc}\frac{\omega T}{2}.
\end{aligned}
$$

In sampled data systems, the maximum frequency that can be sampled without aliasing is $\omega_s = \pi/T$. Note that

$$\text{sinc}\left( \frac{2\pi}{T}\frac{T}{2} \right) = \frac{\sin\pi}{\pi} = 0.$$

Then $\mathrm{sinc}(\omega T/2)$ is a positive real number for $-2\pi/T < \omega < 2\pi/T$. Since the highest frequency that we can possibly sample is $\pi/T$, for any frequency of interest to us $\mathrm{sinc}(\omega T/2)$ will certainly be a positive number. As a consequence, the phase of $G_{\mathrm{ZOH}}(j\omega)$ is $-\omega T/2$. Since

$$G_{\mathrm{ZOH}}(j\omega)G_cG_p(j\omega) = |G_{\mathrm{ZOH}}(j\omega)||G_cG_p(j\omega)| \; \underline{/G_cG_p(j\omega) - \dfrac{\omega T}{2}},$$

the phase adjustment is straightforward. We simply add $-\omega T/2$ to the phase of $G_cG_p(j\omega)$.

We next determine what should be done about the magnitude

$$T \, \mathrm{sinc}\dfrac{\omega T}{2}$$

of the zero-order hold. Part of the answer to that question can be found in Fig. 14.10, which catalogs all the mappings we have discussed.

Of particular importance is the mapping from $X(s)$ to $X^*(s)$ via the convolution in the $s$ plane of $X(s)$ with $\mathcal{L}\{\delta_T(t)\}$. Although we will not do the contour integration, the result of that integration is

$$X^*(s) = \mathcal{L}\{x(t)\delta_T(t)\} = \dfrac{1}{T}\sum_{k=-\infty}^{\infty} X\left(s + \dfrac{k2\pi}{T}\right). \qquad \textbf{[15.3]}$$

From Eq. [15.3] we see that $X^*(s)$ is composed of $X(s)$ and the sum of a countably infinite number of shifted repetitions of $X(s)$ with the repetitions centered at intervals of $2\pi/T$, as shown in Fig. 15.12.

In Fig. 15.12, the transform of $X^*(j\omega)$ is bandlimited to the interval $-\pi/T \le \omega \le \pi/T$. If this is not the case, then the transform will look like that in Fig. 15.13. This is the phenomenon of aliasing, the confusion of higher frequencies with lower

**Figure 15.12 |** $X^*(j\omega)$ when $x(t)$ is bandlimited.

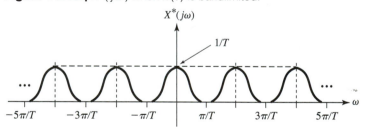

**Figure 15.13 |** $X^*(j\omega)$ when $x(t)$ is not bandlimited.

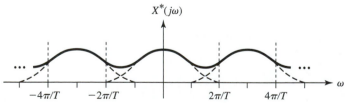

**Figure 15.14 |** Comparison of ideal and sinc reconstruction filters.

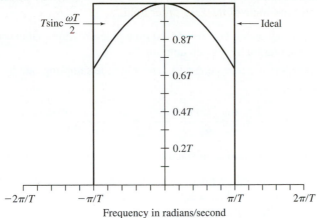

Frequency in radians/second

frequencies. It is obviously undesirable. One way to prevent aliasing is to pass $x(t)$ through an analog low-pass filter so that it will be bandlimited to the frequency range $-\pi/T \leq \omega \leq \pi/T$.

A key feature of Eq. [15.3] is the scaling factor $1/T$. If we look at the ideal reconstruction filter shown in Fig. 15.14, we see that it has a gain of $T$. Thus, the gain of the reconstruction filter is the inverse of the gain of the sampler, yielding a net gain due to sampling and reconstruction of one.

We know, of course, that the ideal reconstruction filter is not realizable. In the present case, we have replaced the ideal reconstruction filter by

$$T \operatorname{sinc} \frac{\omega T}{2}.$$

The net gain from sampling back through reconstruction using the zero-order hold is *not* one but

$$\operatorname{sinc} \frac{\omega T}{2}.$$

In Fig. 15.14 we compare the ideal reconstruction filter to $T \operatorname{sinc}(\omega T/2)$. While the magnitude of the sinc function is not flat for $-\pi/T < \omega < \pi/T$, the roll off is not that bad, especially if we are sampling at a high enough rate. For instance, suppose that the sampling rate is five times the highest frequency we expect in the output of the compensated closed-loop system. Then

$$\operatorname{sinc} \left[ \left( \frac{\pi}{5T} \right) \left( \frac{T}{2} \right) \right] = \operatorname{sinc} \frac{\pi}{10} = 0.98.$$

Since we usually sample at a rate at least five times the highest expected frequency, $T \operatorname{sinc}(\omega T/2)$ is a close approximation to the ideal reconstruction filter. This explains why we made no correction for the magnitude of the zero-order hold in the root locus design of Example 15.3.1.

Having completed our analysis of the impact of the zero-order hold on the performance of the closed-loop system, we now outline a modified Bode design strategy that accounts for the angle of the zero-order hold.

1. Do a Bode design using $G_p(j\omega)$ based on a phase margin that exceeds the desired phase margin by a given amount.

2. Use the excess phase margin $\Delta\phi$ to determine the sampling rate by using the equation

$$T = \frac{2 \times \Delta\phi \ \text{(in radians)}}{\omega_c} = \frac{\pi \times \Delta\phi \ \text{(in degrees)}}{90\omega_c}.$$

3. Iterate as necessary, until a satisfactory $T$, $\omega_c$, and phase margin are achieved.

As we will see, this procedure gives us a good deal of latitude in achieving both a satisfactory phase margin and an adequate sampling frequency. As usual, these ideas are best illustrated with an example.

**EXAMPLE 15.3.2**

Consider again the system shown in Fig. 15.8, and let

$$G_p(s) = \frac{4}{s(s+4)}.$$

We will design $G_c(z)$ by using Bode's method in the $s$ plane, accounting for the negative phase contribution of the zero-order hold, and then mapping the $s$ plane compensator to the $z$ plane using one of the mappings discussed earlier. The performance specifications are

1. Sampling rate of 20 Hz.

2. $K_v > 100$.

3. $\frac{|E(j\omega)|}{|R(j\omega)|} \leq 0.02$ for $\omega < 1$ rad/s.

4. $\frac{|C(j\omega)|}{|R(j\omega)|} \leq 0.1$ for $\omega > 100$ rad/s.

5. Crossover frequency $\omega_c$ of at least 10 rad/s.

6. Phase margin of at least 50°.

We desire the compensator to have two poles and two zeros.

In this example, the desired sampling rate is 20 Hz. Thus the goal is to meet the specifications using that sampling rate. As we will see from the analysis, it will be necessary to raise the sampling rate slightly to meet the specifications, or else settle for a design that does not quite meet the specifications.

The system is type 1 with unity feedback, and the steady state accuracy specification calls for zero steady state error to a step and finite error to a ramp. This means that the system type will not change and the compensator will be lead/lag. Figure 15.15 shows four designs. It is assumed, at this juncture, that the reader is familiar with the Bode design technique introduced in Chapter 11.

**Figure 15.15 |** Trial Bode designs.

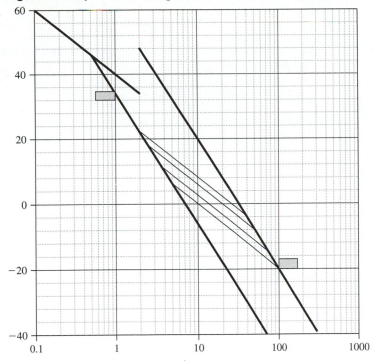

The minimum acceptable phase margin is 50°. The negative phase contribution due to the zero-order hold at the crossover frequency where phase margin is measured is

$$\phi = -\frac{\omega_c T}{2} \text{ rad.}$$

Since the sampling frequency has been initially fixed at 20 Hz, the negative phase contribution in *degrees* is

$$\phi = -\frac{\omega_c \times 0.05}{2} \times \frac{180°}{\pi} = -1.432\omega_c.$$

The four designs presented in Fig. 15.15 are now compared.

The first design,

$$G_c G_p = \frac{100(1 + s/5)}{s(1 + s/0.5)(1 + s/100)},$$

just meets the minimum crossover frequency of 10 rad/s. The phase at crossover is then

$$\underline{/G_c G_p(j10)} = \tan^{-1}\frac{10}{5} - 90° - \tan^{-1}\frac{10}{0.5} - \tan^{-1}\frac{10}{100}$$

$$= 63.4° - 90° - 87.1° - 5.7°$$

$$= -119°$$

and the resulting unadjusted phase margin is 61°.

The negative phase contribution due to the zero-order hold is

$$\phi_{ZOH} = -10 \times 0.05 \times 28.65 = -14°.$$

Then, taking into account the negative phase of the zero-order hold, the effective phase margin at crossover is

$$\phi_m = 61° - 14° = 47°,$$

or 3° short of the specified minimum phase margin.

If we repeat this analysis for the remaining three designs we generate Table 15.1. Of the designs considered, none meets the specification, but the first system we investigated comes close, and for that system

$$G_c(s) = \frac{250(s+4)(s+5)}{(s+0.5)(s+100)}.$$

It is worth noting that while none of the compensators had an effective phase margin that met the specifications for a sampling rate of 20 Hz, *all four* of the compensators could meet the specification *if* the sampling rate is increased.

For instance, in the case of system 2 there is 16° of excess phase margin to play with. An effective phase margin of 50° can be achieved by requiring that

$$T \leq \frac{\pi \times 16°}{90 \times 15} = 0.0372 \text{ s},$$

or

$$f_{sample} \geq \frac{1}{T} = 26.9 \text{ Hz}.$$

Reasonably convenient sampling rates near this frequency are 25 and 32 Hz (for both these frequencies $T$ is easy to work with being either 0.04 or 0.03125). For $f_s = 25$ Hz, the phase margin will be just slightly less than 50°, and for $f_s = 32$ Hz, just slightly more than 50°.

At this juncture, we can either accept a design whose phase margin falls a few degrees short of that specified or increase the sampling rate to diminish the impact of the zero-order hold and achieve the specified phase margin. If the choice is to stay with the sampling rate of 20 Hz, then design 1 is clearly the best choice. In this case,

**Table 15.1 |** Effective phase margin for four systems of Example 15.3.2.

| $G_c G_p$ | Unadjusted $\phi_m$ | $\phi_{ZOH}$ | Effective $\phi_m$ |
|---|---|---|---|
| $\dfrac{100(1 + s/5)}{s(1 + s/0.5)(1 + s/100)}$ | 61° | −14° | 47° |
| $\dfrac{100(1 + s/3.5)}{s(1 + s/0.5)(1 + s/66)}$ | 65° | −20° | 45° |
| $\dfrac{100(1 + s/2.5)}{s(1 + s/0.5)(1 + s/50)}$ | 62° | −29° | 33° |
| $\dfrac{100(1 + s/2)}{s(1 + s/0.5)(1 + s/40)}$ | 55° | −36° | 19° |

applying the bilinear mapping to $G_c(s)$ yields

$$G_c(z) = \frac{87.3(z - 0.8182)(z - 0.7778)}{(z - 0.9753)(z + 0.4286)}.$$

Note that under the bilinear mapping one of the poles is to the left of the origin at $z = -0.4286$.

Alternatively, using the ad hoc approach,

$$G_c(z) = \frac{K(z - 0.8187)(z - 0.7778)}{(z - 0.9753)(z - 0.00674)}.$$

For the ad hoc compensator, the gain $K$ is determined by matching up the magnitudes of the digital and analog compensators at a particular frequency. A common choice is to match up the dc gains. For that choice

$$G_c(z = 1) = \frac{K(1 - 0.8187)(1 - 0.7788)}{(1 - 0.9753)(1 - 0.00674)} = 1.6350\,K.$$

Since

$$\lim_{s \to 0} G_c(s) = \lim_{s \to 0} \frac{250(s + 4)(s + 5)}{(s + 0.5)(s + 100)} = 100,$$

we must have

$$K = \frac{100}{1.6350} = 61.2,$$

yielding

$$G_c = \frac{61.2(z - 0.8187)(z - 0.7778)}{(z - 0.9753)(z - 0.00674)}.$$

This is similar to the compensator obtained using the bilinear mapping. The main difference is the mapping of the pole at $s = -100$. The step response of the sampled data system using the ad hoc compensator is shown in Fig. 15.16. As we can see, the overshoot is substantial, due in part to the relatively small phase margin.

**Figure 15.16 |** Step response of sampled data system for Example 15.3.2.

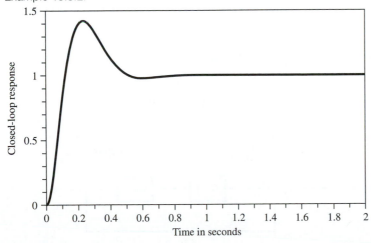

## 15.4 | DESIGN IN THE z PLANE

In this section we design in the $z$ plane. To do so, we must find $G'_p(z)$. Given the software packages available today this is much less of a problem than it was even twenty years ago. Thus, the techniques presented here are a viable alternative to those of the last section.

We will consider two design methods. In the first method we simply use the root locus techniques developed in Chapter 7. The second method is called direct design. For direct design we *specify* the closed-loop transfer function in the $z$ plane. The compensator can then be found by simple algebra.

Direct design is distinctly different than the design techniques we have considered so far. All previous methods are based on modifying the loop transfer function to obtain a satisfactory closed-loop response. The closed-loop transfer function is not specified, and in fact, we do not know exactly what it will be until we have finished designing the compensator.

The idea of specifying the closed-loop transfer function is very appealing. Despite this appeal, all the direct design methods based on this idea have a major shortcoming in that they tend to exhibit intersample oscillations, sometimes referred to as ringing. We will consider direct design first and then follow with a discussion of the root locus method.

### 15.4.1  Direct Design

We will investigate two approaches to direct design, Ragazzini's method and deadbeat design. As we will see, both exhibit ringing.

**Ragazzini's Method**    Consider the system shown in Fig. 15.17. In the root locus and Bode design procedures considered earlier, the compensator is designed to meet a set of specifications, and then the closed-loop transfer function $T_c(z)$ determined. As noted, direct design *specifies* $T_c(z)$. We then find $G_c(z)$ by a straightforward computation.

To see how this works, suppose that we have determined $T_c(z)$. How we choose $T_c(z)$ is a question still to be answered, but for the moment we will assume that $T_c(z)$ is known.

Cross multiplying in the expression

$$T_c(z) = \frac{G_c(z)G'_p(z)}{1 + G_c(z)G'_p(z)}$$

**Figure 15.17 |** Closed-loop control with unity feedback in the $z$ domain.

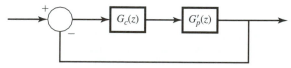

gives

$$T_c(z) + T_c(z)G_c(z)G_p'(z) = G_c(z)G_p'(z).$$

Collecting terms in $G_c(z)G_p'(z)$ results in

$$G_c(z)G_p'(z) - T_c(z)G_c(z)G_p'(z) = T_c(z),$$

or

$$[1 - T_c(z)]G_p'(z)G_c(z) = T_c(z).$$

Dividing both sides by $[1 - T_c(z)]G_p'(z)$ then yields

$$G_c(z) = \frac{1}{G_p'(z)}\frac{T_c(z)}{1 - T_c(z)}.$$

Some remarks are in order. First, the compensator cancels all the poles and all the zeros of the plant. Since, perfect cancellation is impractical, one has to hope that the residual poles left from the near cancellation do not adversely affect the performance of the system. Second, because perfect cancellation is not possible we cannot cancel plant poles outside the unit circle. Third, $T_c(z)$ must have a pole-zero excess (number of poles minus number of zeros) at least as great as that of $G_p'(z)$. If not, the compensator will be unrealizable. This is fairly easy to see because, once fractions are cleared, the numerator of

$$\frac{T_c(z)}{1 - T_c(z)}$$

will be exactly the same as the numerator of $T_c(z)$ while the denominator will be a polynomial of the same degree as $T_c(z)$. Hence, if the pole-zero excess of $T_c(z)$ is less than that of $G_p'(z)$, the compensator will have more zeros than poles and be unrealizable.

The direct design procedure already outlined provides a formula for computing $G_c(z)$. The big question is how to determine a satisfactory $T_c(z)$. The answer to that question involves some work, because $T_c(z)$ must meet specifications that are normally given in terms of figures of merit such as time to peak, percent overshoot, and steady state error to step and ramp inputs. Procedures for determining $T_c$ are now developed. The discussion is similar to that in Chapter 6 for continuous systems.

Consider first, the error signal

$$e(kT) = r(kT) - c(kT).$$

In the z domain, this becomes

$$E(z) = R(z) - C(z) = R(z) - R(z)T_c(z) = R(z)[1 - T_c(z)].$$

Then, employing the final value theorem,

$$e_{ss} \triangleq \lim_{k \to \infty} e(kT) = \lim_{z \to 1} \frac{z - 1}{z} R(z)[1 - T_c(z)].$$

If the reference input is the unit step, then

$$e_{ss} = \lim_{z \to 1} \frac{z-1}{z} \frac{z}{z-1}[1 - T_c(z)] = 1 - \lim_{z \to 1} T_c(z).$$

Zero error to a step input then requires that $\lim_{z \to 1} T_c(z) = 1$. Since the transfer functions considered in this book are simple ratios of polynomials in $z$, this reduces to $T_c(1) = 1$.

If the input is a ramp function,

$$e_{ss} = \lim_{z \to 1} \frac{z-1}{z} \frac{Tz}{(z-1)^2}[1 - T_c(z)] = \lim_{z \to 1} \frac{T[1 - T_c(z)]}{z-1}.$$

First note that if the system has finite error to a step input, then

$$1 - T_c(z) = a, \qquad a \neq 0,$$

and

$$e_{ss} = \lim_{z \to 1} \frac{T[1 - T_c(z)]}{z-1} = \lim_{z \to 1} \frac{Ta}{z-1} = \infty.$$

Thus, finite steady state error to step, implies infinite steady state error to a ramp. A necessary requirement, then, for a system to exhibit *finite* steady state error to a ramp input is that the system have zero steady state error to a step input.

Assuming that $T_c(z) = 1$, and applying L'Hospital's rule,

$$e_{ss} = \frac{\lim_{z \to 1} T\,d/dz[1 - T_c(z)]}{\lim_{z \to 1} d/dz(z-1)} = -T \lim_{z \to 1} \frac{dT_c(z)}{dz}.$$

The next task is to put this expression in a more useful form. To that end, note that

$$\frac{d}{dz} \ln T_c(z) = \frac{1}{T_c(z)} \frac{d}{dz} T_c(z),$$

Now, if $\lim_{z \to 1} T_c(z) = 1$, then

$$\lim_{z \to 1} \frac{d}{dz} \ln T_c(z) = \lim_{z \to 1} \frac{1}{T_c(z)} \frac{d}{dz} T_c(z) = \lim_{z \to 1} \frac{d}{dz} T_c(z).$$

To see how this result can be used let,

$$T_c(z) = \frac{K \prod_{i=1}^{m}(z - z_i)}{\prod_{i=1}^{n}(z - p_i)},$$

so that

$$\ln T_c(z) = \ln K + \sum_{i=1}^{m} \ln(z - z_i) - \sum_{i=1}^{n} \ln(z - p_i),$$

and

$$\frac{d}{dz} \ln T_c(z) = 0 + \sum_{i=1}^{m} \frac{d}{dz} \ln(z - z_i) - \sum_{i=1}^{n} \frac{d}{dz} \ln(z - p_i)$$

$$= \sum_{i=1}^{m} \frac{1}{z - z_i} \frac{d}{dz}(z - z_i) - \sum_{i=1}^{n} \frac{1}{z - z_i} \frac{d}{dz}(z - p_i)$$

$$= \sum_{i=1}^{m} \frac{1}{z - z_i} - \sum_{i=1}^{n} \frac{1}{z - p_i}.$$

Then,

$$e_{ss}(\text{ramp}) = T \left[ \sum_{i=1}^{n} \frac{1}{1 - p_i} - \sum_{i=1}^{m} \frac{1}{1 - z_i} \right]. \tag{15.4}$$

This result is analogous to that derived in Chapter 6 for continuous systems. Once again we see that the steady state error to a ramp input depends only on the values of the poles and zeros of the closed-loop transfer function. In particular, the steady state error does *not* depend on the gain of $T_c(z)$.

To understand why the result is so important, suppose

$$T_c(z) = \frac{K(z - \delta)}{(z - \sigma + j\omega)(z - \sigma - j\omega)}, \tag{15.5}$$

This is a very simple $T_c$, the simplest, in fact, that will give the designer control over all three key properties of a good control design, namely, satisfactory transient response, adequate stability, and the necessary steady state accuracy.

In Eq. [15.5], the denominator represents the desired dominant poles. In other words, $\sigma$ and $\omega$ can be chosen to provide the desired time to peak (transient response) and percent overshoot (stability). The zero can then be used with the two poles to obtain the desired steady state accuracy. These ideas are best illustrated with an example.

**EXAMPLE 15.4.1**

For the system of Fig. 15.17, let

$$G_p(s) = \frac{1}{s(s+1)}.$$

We wish to design a compensator that meets these specifications.

1. Time to peak $t_p = 0.2$ s.
2. Damping ratio of $\zeta = 0.8$
3. Zero steady state error to a ramp input.

The plant is of the *form*

$$G_p(s) = \frac{a}{s(s+a)},$$

with $a = 1$. Then

$$Y_{\text{step}}(s) = \frac{a}{s^2(s+a)}.$$

Using a table of $z$ transforms, such as Table 14.3, and the procedure outlined in previous examples it is easy enough to find

$$G_p'(z) = \frac{[(aT - 1 + e^{-aT})z + (1 - e^{-aT} - aTe^{-aT})]}{a(z-1)(z-e^{-aT})}$$

The specifications on $t_p$ and $\zeta$ are now used to determine the location of the dominant closed-loop poles, first in the $s$ plane and then in the $z$ plane. The first step is to determine

$$\omega_d = \frac{\pi}{t_p} = \frac{\pi}{0.2} = 15.7 \text{ rad/s},$$

and

$$\omega_n = \frac{\pi}{t_p\sqrt{1-\zeta^2}} = \frac{3.142}{0.2\sqrt{1-0.8^2}} = 26.2 \text{ rad/s}.$$

There are a couple of ways we can achieve an adequate sampling rate. One way is to make sure $f_{\text{sample}} = 10\omega_d$, where $\omega_d$ is the frequency of oscillation of the closed-loop system. In this case,

$$\omega_d = 15.7 \text{ rad/s} = 2.5 \text{ Hz}.$$

Thus a minimum sampling rate is around 25 Hz, making

$$T = \frac{1}{25} = 0.04 \text{ s}.$$

Another way to determine an adequate sampling rate is to keep the natural frequency $\omega_n$ to the *right* of the line of constant

$$\omega_n = \frac{3}{10}\frac{\pi}{T},$$

or, equivalently, keep

$$T < \frac{3}{10}\frac{\pi}{\omega_n} = 0.0359 \text{ s},$$

yielding a value of $T$ consistent with that found by the first method.

Based on the two methods just discussed, a very conservative sampling rate of 50 Hz is chosen. For this sampling rate

$$G_p'(z) = \frac{0.0001987(z + 0.9934)}{(z-1)(z-0.9802)}.$$

Note the very small value of the gain, namely, 0.0001987. As the sampling rate increases the gain of $G_p'(z)$ decreases. The stage is now set to proceed with the direct design method, often called Ragazzini's method.

As a first step, let

$$T_c(z) = \frac{K(z-\delta)}{(z-\sigma + j\omega)(z-\sigma - j\omega)}. \qquad \textbf{[15.6]}$$

This is the simplest $T_c(z)$ that will meet all the specifications. For an underdamped response $T_c(z)$ must have at least two poles. To meet the requirements on steady state accuracy a zero is required. It is also necessary that $T_c(z)$ have a pole-zero excess at least as great as $G'_p(z)$. Thus, if $T_c(z)$ has only two poles, it can have at most one zero.

The complex pole locations are already determined by the choice of damping ratio, natural frequency and sampling rate. The zero at $z = \delta$ is introduced to control the steady state error to a ramp input.

For $\zeta = 0.8$ and $\omega_n = 26.2$ rad/s, the complex poles in the z domain are at

$$z = e^{-\zeta \omega_n T} e^{\pm j(\omega_n T \sqrt{1-\zeta^2})}$$

$$= 0.6576 / \pm 18.01°$$

$$= 0.6253 \pm j0.2034.$$

All that remains is to determine $K$ and $\delta$.

Recall that for finite steady state error to a ramp input the closed-loop system must exhibit zero steady state error to a step input. That is,

$$\lim_{z \to 1} T_c(z) = 1.$$

With zero steady state error to a step input, the error to a ramp input is then

$$e_{ss}(\text{ramp}) \triangleq \frac{1}{K_v} = T \left[ \sum_{i=1}^{n} \frac{1}{1 - p_i} - \sum_{i=1}^{m} \frac{1}{1 - z_i} \right],$$

where the $p_i$ are the poles of $T_c(z)$ and the $z_i$ are the zeros of $T_c(z)$. Thus *zero* steady state error to a ramp input requires that

$$\sum_{i=1}^{n} \frac{1}{1 - p_i} - \sum_{i=1}^{m} \frac{1}{1 - z_i} = 0.$$

The same strategy used in Chapter 6 for the continuous version of $T_c(z)$ is now employed.

1. Use $\delta$ to guarantee zero steady state error to a ramp input.
2. Having found $\delta$, adjust $K$ to ensure zero steady state error to a step input.

For the $T_c(z)$ of Eq. [15.6], the formula for zero steady state error to a ramp becomes

$$\frac{1}{1 - (\sigma + j\omega)} + \frac{1}{1 - (\sigma - j\omega)} - \frac{1}{1 - \delta} = 0.$$

This expression can be rewritten as

$$\frac{[1 - (\sigma - j\omega)] + [1 - (\sigma + j\omega)]}{(1 - \sigma)^2 + \omega^2} - \frac{1}{1 - \delta} = 0,$$

or

$$\frac{2(1 - \sigma)}{(1 - \sigma)^2 + \omega^2} = \frac{1}{1 - \delta}.$$

Inverting both sides of this last equation yields

$$1 - \delta = \frac{(1-\sigma)^2 + \omega^2}{2(1-\sigma)},$$

or finally,

$$\delta = 1 - \frac{(1-\sigma)^2 + \omega^2}{2(1-\sigma)}.$$

For the complex poles determined earlier,

$$\delta = 1 - \frac{(1 - 0.6253)^2 + 0.2034^2}{2(1 - 0.6253)} = 0.7575$$

All that remains is to find $K$. To that end,

$$\lim_{z \to 1} T_c(z) = \lim_{z \to 1} \frac{K(z - 0.7575)}{(z - 0.6253 + j0.2034)(z - 0.6253 - j0.2034)}$$

$$= \frac{K(0.2425)}{0.1817}$$

Setting this last expression equal to 1, yields

$$K = 0.749.$$

The compensator can now be found from the formula

$$G_c(z) = \frac{1}{G'_p(z)} \frac{T_c(z)}{1 - T_c(z)}.$$

A necessary intermediate step is to find

$$\frac{T_c(z)}{1 - T_c(z)} = \frac{0.749(z - 0.7575)}{z^2 - 1.2508z + 0.4325 - 0.7493(z - 0.7575)}$$

$$= \frac{0.749(z - 0.7575)}{z^2 - 2z + 1}$$

$$= \frac{0.749(z - 0.7575)}{(z - 1)(z - 1)}.$$

Since

$$\frac{T_c(z)}{1 - T_c(z)} = G_c(z)G'_p(z)$$

is the overall forward loop transfer function, this last result makes sense, because with unity feedback, zero steady state error to both a step and ramp input requires that $G_c(z)G'_p(z)$ have two integrators, that is, two poles at $z = 1$. This is exactly the factorization we obtained.

The compensator in factored form is

$$G_c(z) = \frac{(z - 1)(z - 0.9802)}{0.0001987(z + 0.9934)} \frac{0.7493(z - 0.7575)}{(z - 1)^2}$$

$$= \frac{3771(z - 0.9802)(z - 0.7575)}{(z + 0.9934)(z - 1)}.$$

The discrete step response is

$$c(kT) = 1.0 + 2.0965 e^{-20.96kT} \cos(15.72kT - 2.068).$$

**Figure 15.18 |** Step response of discrete and sampled data system for Example. 15.4.1.

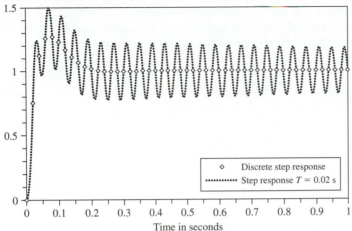

This response is shown in Fig. 15.18, along with the sampled data response. Note that the sampled data response rings. This is typical of this kind of design. The control is shown in Fig. 15.19. The control is applying a square wave of large magnitude to the system, causing the system to respond to a sequence of closely spaced positive and negative steps. A possible solution is to make the compensator third order and place the added zero on top of the pole at $z = -0.9934$. It is this pole that is the source of the oscillations in the control. This is not a very appealing idea, given the other more effective design procedures we have already discussed.

**Figure 15.19 |** Control applied to sampled data system for Example 15.4.1.

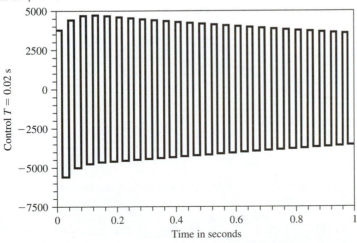

**Deadbeat Design**  A second direct design method, called "deadbeat" design, is similar to the method of Ragazzini, but specifies $c(kT)$, the response of the closed-loop system to a *specific* input in the time domain. The closed-loop transfer function $T_c(z)$ is found by applying the $\mathcal{Z}$ transform to $c(kT)$, and dividing out the $\mathcal{Z}$ transform of the input. This method is best illustrated by an example.

---

**EXAMPLE 15.4.2**

For the system

$$G_p(s) = \frac{2}{s(s+2)},$$

let $f_s = 10$ Hz. Suppose we let the time domain response to a unit step input be

$$c(kT) = \begin{cases} 0 & \text{for } k = 0 \\ 1.2 & \text{for } k = 1 \\ 1.0 & \text{for } k \geq 2. \end{cases}$$

We could specify any input we desire, but the step is by far the most useful test input. The response we have specified is designed to approximate a slightly underdamped response with zero steady state error to a unit step input.

To do a direct design we need $G_p'(z)$ and $T_c(z)$. For $T = 0.1$ s,

$$G_p'(z) = \frac{0.00937(z+0.9355)}{(z-1)(z-0.8187)}.$$

The next step is to find

$$
\begin{aligned}
C(z) &= 1.2z^{-1} + 1.0z^{-2} + z^{-3} + z^{-4} + \cdots \\
&= 1.2z^{-1} + z^{-2}\{1 + z^{-1} + z^{-2} + \cdots\} \\
&= \frac{1.2}{z} + \frac{z}{z^2(z-1)} \\
&= \frac{1.2(z-1) + 1}{z(z-1)} \\
&= \frac{1.2(z-1/6)}{z(z-1)}.
\end{aligned}
$$

To find the closed-loop transfer function $T_c(z)$ we need to divide out the input, which in this case is the unit step. Thus,

$$T_c(z) = \frac{1.2(z-1/6)}{z^2}.$$

As with the any direct design technique, the compensator is

$$G_c(z) = \frac{1}{G_p'(z)} \frac{T_c(z)}{1 - T_c(z)}.$$

**Figure 15.20** | Step response of compensated system for Example 15.4.2.

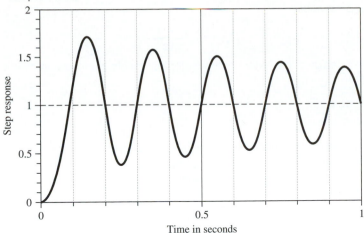

Thus, we need to compute

$$\frac{T_c(z)}{1 - T_c(z)} = \frac{1.2\,(z - 1/6)}{z^2 - 1.2z + 0.2} = \frac{1.2(z - 1/6)}{(z - 1)(z - 0.2)}$$

We can now write the compensator in factored form as

$$G_c(z) = \frac{(z - 1)(z - 0.8187)}{0.00937(z + 0.9355)} \frac{1.2(z - 0.1667)}{(z - 1)(z - 0.2)}$$

$$= \frac{128(z - 0.1667)(z - 0.8187)}{(z - 0.2)(z + 0.9355)}.$$

The step response of the sampled data system is shown in Fig. 15.20. The integration step is $h = 0.005$. Note that $c(T)$ is very close to 1.2 and $c(kT)$ very close to 1.0 for $k > 1$. If the time step were smaller, the approximation would be better. Basically, the system is right where we asked it to be every $T$ s, but oscillates in between those points in time. Like the method of Ragazzini, ringing is a problem.

Our short foray into direct design can be summarized as follows. Direct design leads to high-order compensators and ringing is a problem. Given the many other successful design techniques we have already discussed, direct design is not that appealing.

### 15.4.2 Root Locus Design in the *z* Plane

In this section, we investigate using root locus design in the *z* plane. As with direct design, this approach requires that we find $G'_p(z)$. Example 15.4.3 illustrates the technique.

**EXAMPLE 15.4.3**

Consider once again

$$G_p(s) = \frac{1}{s(s+1)}.$$

We wish to design a low-order compensator that meets the following simple specifications.

1. PO $\leq$ 10%.
2. $t_p \leq 0.5$ s.

We will use pole cancellation to make the closed-loop transfer function look as much like $T_{N2}(s)$ as possible. $G'_p(z)$ can be determined only after a sampling rate has been selected. The damped frequency is

$$\omega_d = \frac{\pi}{t_p} = \frac{\pi}{0.5} = 6.28 \text{ rad/s.}$$

Choosing $\omega_d = 7$ rad/s and $\zeta = 1/\sqrt{2}$ should prove sufficient. The sampling rate can be determined by requiring 10 samples of the damped frequency. Since 7 rad/s corresponds to 1.11 Hz, a sampling rate of 10 Hz would be adequate. A sampling rate of 20 Hz is selected, providing nearly 20 samples of one period of $\omega_d$.

For the selected sampling rate,

$$G'_p(z) = \frac{0.001229(z+0.9835)}{(z-1)(z-0.9512)}.$$

Now consider the $z$ domain equivalent of $T_{N2}(s)$. From Table 14.3 we find that the step response of $T_{N2}(s)$,

$$Y_{\text{step}}(s) = \frac{\sigma^2 + \omega_d^2}{s\left[(s+\sigma)^2 + \omega_d^2\right]},$$

has the $z$ domain equivalent

$$Y_{\text{step}}(z) = \frac{z(Az+B)}{(z-1)(z^2 - 2e^{-\sigma T}(\cos \omega_d T)z + e^{-2\sigma T})},$$

where

$$A = 1 - e^{-\sigma T}\cos \omega_d T - \frac{\sigma}{\omega_d}e^{-\sigma T}\sin \omega_d T,$$

$$B = e^{-2\sigma T} + \frac{\sigma}{\omega_d}e^{-\sigma T}\sin \omega_d T - e^{-\sigma T}\cos \omega_d T.$$

Dividing out the step yields

$$T_{N2}(z) = \frac{Az+B}{z^2 - 2e^{-\sigma T}(\cos \omega_d T)z + e^{-2\sigma T}},$$

For a sample rate of 20 Hz and the chosen complex poles $s = -7 \pm j7$,

$$A = 1 - e^{-7(0.05)}\cos[7(0.05)] - e^{-7(0.05)}\sin[7(0.05)] = 0.0964,$$

$$B = e^{-14(0.05)} + e^{-7(0.05)}\sin[7(0.05)] - e^{-7(0.05)}\cos[7(0.05)] = 0.07626.$$

Then

$$T_{N2}(z) = \frac{0.0964(z+0.7910)}{(z-0.6620 - j0.2416)(z-0.6620 + j0.2416)}.$$

We have gone to the trouble to find $T_{N2}(z)$ for the following reason. When we finish this root locus design, we will find that the closed-loop transfer function we obtain is very close to $T_{N2}(z)$.

Because we want to use pole/zero cancellation, we choose

$$G_c(z) = \frac{K_c(z-0.9512)}{z-p_1},$$

making the overall forward loop transfer function

$$G_c G_p(z) = \frac{0.001229 K_c(z+0.9835)}{(z-1)(z-p_1)}.$$

Our goal is to make the root locus pass through $s = -0.6620 \pm j0.2416$. This is simply a matter of satisfying the angle condition at the desired points, a calculation done many times before, and shown in Fig. 15.21. Thus,

$$\theta_2 = \alpha + 180° - \theta_1$$

$$= \tan^{-1}\frac{0.2416}{1.6455} + 180° - \left(180° - \tan^{-1}\frac{0.2416}{0.338}\right)$$

$$= 8.35° + 180° - 144.44°$$

$$= 43.9°.$$

Then,

$$p_1 = 0.6620 - \frac{0.2416}{\tan 43.9°} = 0.4110.$$

The gain to place the closed-loop poles at the desired locations is

$$K_c = \frac{\sqrt{0.1726} \times \sqrt{0.1214}}{\sqrt{2.767} \times 0.001229} = 70.8,$$

**Figure 15.21** | Satisfying angle condition at $z = 0.6620 + j0.2416$.

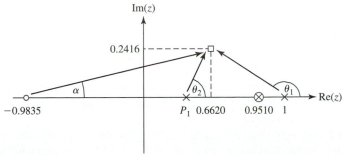

**Figure 15.22** | Discrete and sampled data unit step responses for Example 15.4.3.

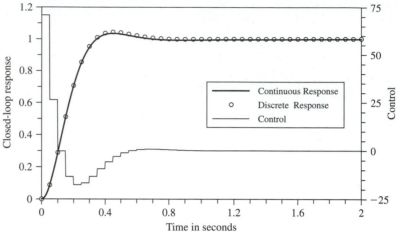

so that the compensator is

$$G_c(z) = \frac{70.8(z - 0.9512)}{z - 0.4110}.$$

Note that the only difference between $T_{N2}(z)$ and the actual closed-loop transfer function is that the zero of the actual closed-loop transfer function is slightly farther to the left than the zero of $T_{N2}(z)$. Thus our expectation is that the actual response should be very close to the ideal response.

The discrete response to the unit step is

$$c(kT) = [1 + 1.4419e^{-7kT}\cos(7kT + 2.337)]\mathbf{1}(kT).$$

The discrete response, the sampled data response and the control are shown in Fig. 15.22.

The general procedure of making $T_c(z)$ resemble $T_{N2}(z)$ proves as effective in the $z$ plane as it was in the $s$ plane. We use it again in Example 15.4.4.

**EXAMPLE 15.4.4**

Let

$$G_p(s) = \frac{4}{(s + 4)^2}.$$

We choose to let the dominant poles of the closed-loop system have a damping ratio of 0.8 and a natural frequency of 4 rad/s. As usual, the system should exhibit zero steady state error to a step input.

The first step is to choose a sampling rate. For the complex poles specified in the problem, the damped frequency at which the closed-loop system will oscillate in response to a step input is

$$\omega_d = \omega_n\sqrt{1-\zeta^2} = 4\sqrt{1-0.8^2} = 4 \times 0.6 = 2.4 \text{ rad/s}$$

$$= 0.382 \text{ Hz}.$$

To see if slower sampling will degrade the performance, we choose

$$f_s = 5 \times 0.382 \text{ Hz} \approx 2 \text{ Hz}.$$

Having chosen $f = 2$ Hz, the next step is to determine $G'_p(z)$. For this problem, $G_p(s)$ is of the form

$$G_p(s) = \frac{1}{a}\frac{a^2}{(s+a)^2},$$

with $a = 4$. Thus

$$Y_{\text{step}}(s) = \frac{1}{a}\frac{a^2}{s(s+a)^2}$$

From Table 14.3 we find that

$$\frac{a^2}{s(s+a)^2}$$

is paired with

$$\frac{z[(1-e^{-aT}-aTe^{-aT})z+(e^{-2aT}-e^{-aT}+aTe^{-aT})]}{(z-1)(z-e^{-aT})^2}.$$

Thus the transform in the table will have to be multiplied by $1/a$. For $a = 4$, we get

$$G'_p(z) = \frac{(1-e^{-4T}-4Te^{-4T})z+(e^{-8T}-e^{-4T}+aTe^{-4T})}{4(z-e^{-4T})^2}.$$

Setting $T = 0.5$ s then yields

$$G'_p(z) = \frac{(1-e^{-2}-2e^{-2})z+(e^{-4}-e^{-2}+2e^{-2})}{4(z-e^{-2})^2}$$

$$= \frac{0.594z+0.1536}{4(z-0.1353)^2}$$

$$= \frac{0.1485(z+0.2587)}{(z-0.1353)^2}.$$

Using the sampling rate of 2 Hz, the desired closed-loop poles from the $s$ plane become

$$z = e^{(-3.2\pm j2.4)T} = e^{-1.6}e^{\pm j1.2} = 0.07316 \pm j0.1882.$$

We now use a lead/PI compensator with pole cancellation to obtain

$$G_c(z) = \frac{(z-0.1353)^2}{(z-1)(z-p_1)}.$$

The calculation is based on satisfying the angle condition using the angles shown in Fig. 15.23. The angle equation is then

$$\alpha - \theta_1 - \theta_2 = -180°,$$

**Figure 15.23** | Decomposition of $G_cG_p$ into vector components.

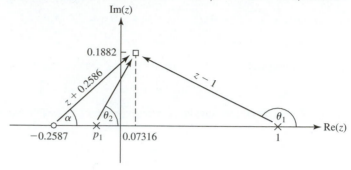

or

$$\theta_2 = \alpha + 180° - \theta_1$$

$$= \tan^{-1} \frac{0.1882}{0.3318} + 180° - \left(180° - \tan^{-1}\frac{0.1882}{0.9268}\right)$$

$$= 41.03°.$$

Then

$$p_1 = 0.07316 - \frac{0.1882}{\tan 41.03°} = -0.143.$$

All that remains is to find

$$K_c = \frac{\sqrt{0.1882^2 + 0.9268^2} \times \sqrt{0.1882^2 + 0.2162^2}}{0.1485 \times \sqrt{0.1882^2 + 0.3318^2}}$$

$$= 4.79 \rightarrow 4.8.$$

**Figure 15.24** | Step response of sampled data system.

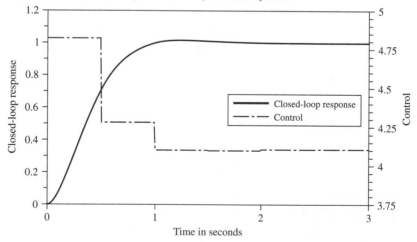

Thus

$$G_c = \frac{4.8(z - 0.1353)^2}{(z - 1)(z + 0.143)}.$$

The response of the sampled data system is shown in Fig. 15.24. At least in simulation, the slower sampling rate appears to be adequate. Whether it would prove adequate in actual implementation is another question.

## 15.5 | REPRISE

In this chapter, we introduced the design of compensators for sampled data systems. Two methods were used. In the first method, we designed the compensator in the $s$ plane and then transfered the design to the $z$ plane using either the bilinear mapping or the ad hoc transformation. In the second method, we did the design in the $z$ plane, using two different techniqes. The first was direct design, for which we specified the closed-loop transfer function $T_c(z)$. In the second technique, we used root locus analysis. The drawback to these latter two techniques is that $G_p'(z)$ must be known. If $G_p(s)$ is of high order, finding $G_p'(z)$ requires using a computer and a software package such as MATLAB.

We also found that the various methods of designing compensators for continuous systems could be applied to sampled data systems. We had to exercise a little care to make sure that we took into account the effects of the zero-order hold, but aside from that the root locus and Bode methods that worked so successfully for continuous systems worked just as well for sampled data systems.

## 15.6 | PROBLEMS

### 15.6.1  Root Locus in *z* Plane

For the feedback configuration shown in Fig. 15.25, sketch the root locus and find the gain for which the closed-loop system becomes unstable.

**Figure 15.25 |** Nonunity feedback configuration.

$$R(z) \longrightarrow \Sigma \longrightarrow \boxed{G(z)} \longrightarrow C(z)$$
$$\boxed{H(z)}$$

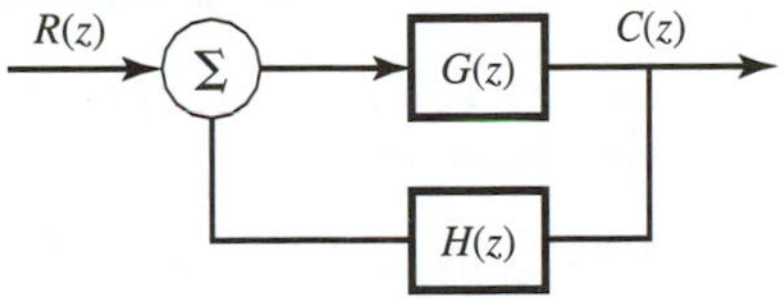

1. $GH(z) = \dfrac{K(z + 0.9)}{z(z - 0.8)(z - 1)}$

2. $GH(z) = \dfrac{K}{z(z - 1)}$

### 15.6.2 *s* Plane Root Locus Design

For these problems use the feedback configuration of Fig. 15.26. Design the compensator in the *s* plane to the stated specifications, using the root locus technique. Transfer the design to the *z* plane using the bilinear mapping or the ad hoc mapping, as directed.

**Figure 15.26 |** Unity feedback configuration.

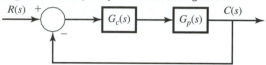

1.  Let

$$G_p(s) = \frac{1}{s^2} \quad \text{and} \quad G_c(s) = \frac{K_c(s + z_1)}{s + p_1}.$$

   a.  Time to peak $t_p$ less than 1 s.
   b.  PO less than 15%

   Transfer the compensator design to the *z* plane use the ad hoc mapping and $f_{sample} = 10$ Hz.

2.  Let

$$G_p(s) = \frac{1}{s^2} \quad \text{and} \quad G_c(s) = K_c \frac{s + z_1}{s + p_1}.$$

   a.  Time to peak $t_p$ less than 0.5 s.
   b.  PO less than 10%.

   Transfer the compensator design to the *z* plane using the ad hoc mapping and $f_{sample} = 10$ Hz.

3.  Let

$$G_p(s) = \frac{1}{s(s + 4)} \quad \text{and} \quad G_c(s) = K_c \frac{s + z_1}{s + p_1}.$$

   a.  Time to peak $t_p$ less than 1 s.
   b.  PO less than 15%.

   Transfer the compensator design to the *z* plane using the ad hoc method and $f_{sample} = 20$ Hz.

### 15.6.3 Root Locus Design in the *z* Plane

For the feedback configuration shown in Fig. 15.27, First find $G_p'(z)$ and then design the compensator to the stated specifications.

**Figure 15.27 |** Feedback configuration.

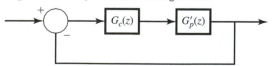

1. Let $G_p(s) = \frac{1}{s^2}$.

   a. Lead compensator.
   b. $f_{sample} = 10$ Hz.
   c. $t_p \leq 0.5$ s.
   d. PO $\leq 10\%$.

2. Let $G_p(s) = \frac{1}{s^2}$.

   a. Lead compensator.
   b. $f_{sample} = 40$ Hz.
   c. $t_p \leq 0.3$ s.
   d. PO $\leq 10\%$.

3. Let $G_p(s) = \frac{1}{s^2}$.

   a. Lead compensator.
   b. $f_{sample} = 50$ Hz.
   c. $\omega_d = 6$ rad/s.
   d. $\zeta = 0.8$.

4. Let $G_p(s) = \frac{1}{s(s+1)}$.

   a. Lead compensator.
   b. $f_{sample} = 50$ Hz.
   c. $t_p \leq 1$ s.
   d. PO $\leq 20\%$.

5. Let $G_p(s) = \frac{2}{s(s+2)}$ and $G_c(z) = \frac{K(z-0.8)}{z-b}$.

   a. $f_{sample} = 10$ Hz.
   b. $\zeta = 1/\sqrt{2}$ and $\omega_n = 3\sqrt{2}$.
   c. Find the third closed-loop pole.
   d. Find the explicit time response by partial fraction expansion.

6. Let $G_p(s) = \frac{2}{s(s+2)}$ and $G_c(z) = \frac{K(z-0.8)}{z-b}$.

   a. $f_{sample} = 100$ Hz.
   b. $\zeta = 1/\sqrt{2}$ and $\omega_n = 30\sqrt{2}$.
   c. Find the third closed-loop pole.
   d. Find the explicit time response by partial fraction expansion.

7. Let $G_p(s) = \frac{2}{s(s+2)}$ and $G(z) = \frac{K(z-z_1)}{(z-p_1)}$.

   a. $f_{sample} = 10$ Hz.
   b. Complex closed-loop poles with $\zeta = 0.8$ and $\omega_n = 4.0$ rad/s.
   c. The pole $p_1$ of the compensator is equivalent to a pole at $s = 20$.

8. Let $G_p(s) = \frac{2}{s(s+2)}$ and $G(z) = \frac{K(z-z_1)}{z-p_1}$, so that

   a. PD compensator.
   b. $f_{sample} = 10$ Hz.

   c.   Complex closed-loop poles $\zeta = 0.8$ and $\omega_n = 4.0$ rad/s.
   d.   The pole $p_1$ of the compensator is equivalent to a pole at $s = -\infty$.

9.   Let $G_p(s) = \dfrac{2}{s(s+2)}$ and $G(z) = \dfrac{K(z-z_1)}{z-p_1}$.

   a.   $f_{sample} = 10$ Hz.
   b.   Complex closed-loop poles with $\zeta = 0.8$ and $\omega_n = 4.0$ rad/s.
   c.   One pole of $G_c(z)$ at the equivalent of a pole at $s = -\infty$.
   d.   The closed-loop system is second order.
   e.   Find the step response of the closed-loop system.

10.   Let $G_p(s) = \dfrac{2}{s(s+2)}$ and $G(z) = \dfrac{K(z-z_1)(z-z_2)}{(z-p_1)(z-p_2)}$, so that

   a.   $f_{sample} = 10$ Hz.
   b.   Complex closed-loop poles with $\zeta = 0.8$ and $\omega_n = 4.0$ rad/s.
   c.   The pole $p_1$ of the compensator is equivalent to a pole at $s = -\infty$.
   d.   The closed-loop system is third order.
   e.   The system has zero steady state error to a ramp input.
   f.   Find the step response of the closed-loop system.

11.   Let $G_p(s) = \dfrac{4}{(s+4)^2}$ and $G(z) = \dfrac{K(z-z_1)(z-z_2)}{(z-p_1)(z-1)}$.

   a.   Complex closed-loop poles $\zeta = 0.8$ and $\omega_n = 4.0$ rad/s.
   b.   $f_{sample}$ chosen so that response of the closed-loop system to a step is
         sampled at least 10 times per cycle (based on the damped frequency).

12.   Let $G_p(s) = \dfrac{4}{s(s+4)}$ and $G(z) = \dfrac{K(z-a)}{z-0.1}$.

   a.   Complex closed-loop poles $\zeta = 0.8$ and $\omega_n = 4.0$ rad/s.
   b.   $T$ chosen so that response of the closed-loop system to a step response is
         sampled at least five times per cycle (based on specified damped
         frequency).

13.   Let $G_p(s) = \dfrac{1}{s(s+1)}$.

   a.   Complex closed-loop poles $\zeta = 0.8$ and $\omega_n = 5.0$ rad/s.
   b.   The closed-loop transfer function $T_c(z)$ has only one zero, that of $G_p'(z)$.
   c.   Zero steady state error to a step input.
   d.   $f_{sample} = 40$ Hz.

### 15.6.4  Direct Design

For each problem use either Ragazzini's method or deadbeat design techniques, as
directed, to find the compensation that meets the stated specifications.

1.   $G_p(s) = \dfrac{1}{s(s+1)}$.

   a.   Deabeat design.
   b.   $G_c(z)$ third order.
   c.   $f_{sample} = 10$ Hz.
   d.   $t_p = 0.2$ s.

   e.   $\zeta = 0.6$.

   f.   Zero steady state error to a sep input.

**2.**  $G_p(s) = \dfrac{4}{s(s+2)}$.

   a.   Ragazzini's method.

   b.   $f_{sample} = 10$ Hz.

   c.   Zero steady state error to a step input.

   d.   Ten percent error to a unit ramp input.

   e.   Complex closed-loop poles with $\omega_n = 4$ rad/s and $\zeta = 0.6$.

**3.**  $G_p(s) = \dfrac{4}{(s+2)^2}$.

   a.   Ragazzini's method.

   b.   Zero steady state error to a step input.

   c.   Ten percent error to a unit ramp input.

   d.   $f_{sample} = 10$ Hz.

   e.   Complex closed-closed loop poles with $\omega_n = 4$ rad/s and $\zeta = 0.6$.

**4.**  $G_p(s) = \dfrac{1}{s(s+1)}$.

   a.   Ragazzini's method.

   b.   $f_{sample} = 50$ Hz.

   c.   Time to peak $t_p = 0.2$ s.

   d.   Damping ratio of $\zeta = 0.8$.

   e.   Zero steady state error to a ramp input.

**5.**  $G_p(s) = \dfrac{1}{s(s+1)}$.

   a.   Ragazzini's method.

   b   $f_{sample} = 50$ Hz.

   c.   Time to peak $t_p = 0.2$ s.

   d.   $\zeta = 0.8$.

   e.   Zero steady state error to a step input.

   f.   $K_v = 100$.

## 15.6.5 Bode Design

For these problems use Bode's method to design the compensator to the stated specifications. Assume the feedback configuration of Fig. 15.26.

**1.**  $G_p(s) = \dfrac{40}{s(s+4)(s+10)}$.

   a.   Sample rate: $f_{sample} \leq 50$ Hz.

   b.   $K_v > 100$.

   c.   $\dfrac{|E(j\omega)|}{|R(j\omega)|} \leq 0.02$ for $\omega < 1$ rad/s.

   d.   $\dfrac{|C(j\omega)|}{|R(j\omega)|} \leq 0.05$ for $\omega > 200$ rad/s.

   e.   Crossover frequency $\omega_c$ of at least 10 rad/s.

   f.   Phase margin of at least $50°$.

g.  $G_c(s) = \dfrac{K_c \prod_{i=1}^{n}(s + z_i)}{\prod_{i=1}^{n}(s + p_i)}$, with the order of the compensator as low as possible.

Transfer the design the the $z$ plane using the bilinear mapping.

2.  $G_p(s) = \dfrac{40}{s(s + 4)(s + 10)}$.

   a.  Sample rate: $f_{sample} \le 50$ Hz.

   b.  $K_v > 100$.

   c.  $\dfrac{|E(j\omega)|}{|R(j\omega)|} \le 0.01$ for $\omega < 1$ rad/s.

   d.  $\dfrac{|C(j\omega)|}{|R(j\omega)|} \le 0.1$ for $\omega > 500$ rad/s.

   e.  Crossover frequency $\omega_c$ of at least 10 rad/s.

   f.  Phase margin of at least 50°.

   g.  $G_c(s) = \dfrac{K_c \prod_{i=1}^{n}(s + z_i)}{\prod_{i=1}^{n}(s + p_i)}$, with the order of the compensator as low as possible.

Transfer the design to the $z$ plane using the ad hoc method, placing zeros at infinity at $z = -1$.

3.  $G_p(s) = \dfrac{40}{s(s + 4)(s + 10)}$.

   a.  Sample rate: $f_{sample} \le 50$ Hz.

   b.  $K_v > 100$.

   c.  $\dfrac{|E(j\omega)|}{|R(j\omega)|} \le 0.02$ for $\omega < 1$ rad/s.

   d.  $\dfrac{|C(j\omega)|}{|R(j\omega)|} \le 0.1$ for $\omega > 400$ rad/s.

   e.  Crossover frequency $\omega_c$ of at least 20 rad/s.

   f.  Phase margin of at least 50°.

   g.  $G_c(s) = \dfrac{K_c \prod_{i=1}^{n}(s + z_i)}{\prod_{i=1}^{n}(s + p_i)}$, with the order of the compensator as low as possible.

Transfer the compensator to the $z$ plane using the bilinear mapping.

4.  $G_p(s) = \dfrac{50(s + 2)}{s(s + 10)(s + 50)}$.

   a.  Sample rate of 50 Hz or less.

   b.  $K_v > 100$.

   c.  $\dfrac{|E(j\omega)|}{|R(j\omega)|} \le 0.02$ for $\omega < 1$ rad/s.

   d.  $\dfrac{|C(j\omega)|}{|R(j\omega)|} \le 0.1$ for $\omega > 120$ rad/s.

   e.  Crossover frequency $\omega_c$ of at least 15 rad/s.

   f.  Phase margin of at least 50°.

   g.  $G_c(s) = \dfrac{K_c \prod_{i=1}^{n}(s + z_i)}{\prod_{i=1}^{n}(s + p_i)}$, with the order of the compensator as low as possible.

Transfer the compensator to the $z$ plane using the bilinear mapping.

5. $G_p(s) = \dfrac{50(s+2)}{s(s+10)(s+50)}$.

   a. Sample rate of 100 Hz or less.
   b. $K_v > 100$.
   c. $\dfrac{|E(j\omega)|}{|R(j\omega)|} \leq 0.02$ for $\omega < 1$ rad/s.
   d. $\dfrac{|C(j\omega)|}{|R(j\omega)|} \leq 0.05$ for $\omega > 200$ rad/s.
   e. Crossover frequency $\omega_c$ of at least 15 rad/s.
   f. Phase margin of at least $50°$.
   g. $G_c(s) = \dfrac{K_c \prod_{i=1}^{n}(s+z_i)}{\prod_{i=1}^{n}(s+p_i)}$, with the order of the compensator as low as possible.

   Transfer the compensator to the $z$ plane using the ad hoc mapping.

6. $G_p(s) = \dfrac{100}{(s+4)(s+50)}$.

   a. Sample rate of 50 Hz or less.
   b. $K_v > 100$.
   c. $\dfrac{|E(j\omega)|}{|R(j\omega)|} \leq 0.02$ for $\omega < 1$ rad/s.
   d. $\dfrac{|C(j\omega)|}{|R(j\omega)|} \leq 0.1$ for $\omega > 100$ rad/s.
   e. Crossover frequency $\omega_c$ of at least 15 rad/s.
   f. Phase margin of at least $50°$.
   g. $G_c(s) = \dfrac{K_c \prod_{i=1}^{n}(s+z_i)}{\prod_{i=1}^{n}(s+p_i)}$, with the order of the compensator as low as possible.

   Determine $G_c(z)$ using the bilinear mapping.

7. $G_p(s) = \dfrac{10}{s(s+5)}$ and $G_c(s) = K_c\dfrac{(1+s/z_1)(1+s/z_2)}{(1+s/p_1)(1+s/p_2)}$.

   a. $K_v \geq 100$.
   b. $\left|\dfrac{E(j\omega)}{R(j\omega)}\right| \leq 0.1$ for $\omega \leq 0.1$ rad/s.
   c. $\left|\dfrac{C(j\omega)}{R(j\omega)}\right| \leq 0.1$ for $\omega \geq 30$ rad/s.
   d. Phase margin: $\phi_m \geq 60$.
   e. $f_{sample} = 10$ Hz.
   f. Crossover frequency, $\omega_c \geq 3$ rad/s and *maximized* consistent with specifications a–e.

8. $G_p(s) = \dfrac{9}{(s+3)(s+30)}$. Design a compensator

   $$G_c(s) = K_c\dfrac{(1+s/z_1)(1+s/z_2)}{(1+s/p_1)(1+s/p_2)}$$

   that will meet these specifications:
   a. $K_v \geq 100$.

    b.   $\left|\dfrac{E(j\omega)}{R(j\omega)}\right| \leq 0.02$ for $\omega \leq 1$ rad/s.

    c.   $\left|\dfrac{C(j\omega)}{R(j\omega)}\right| \leq 0.05$ for $\omega \geq 200$ rad/s.

    d.   Phase margin: $\phi_m \geq 55$.

    e.   $f_{sample} \leq 100$ Hz.

    f.   Crossover frequency, $\omega_c \geq 10$ rad/s and *maximized* consistent with specifications a–e.

**9.**  $G_p(s) = \dfrac{9}{(s+3)(s+30)}$ and $G_c(s) = K_c \dfrac{(1+s/z_1)(1+s/z_2)}{(1+s/p_1)(1+s/p_2)}$.

    a.   $K_v \geq 100$.

    b.   $\left|\dfrac{E(j\omega)}{R(j\omega)}\right| \leq 0.02$ for $\omega \leq 1$ rad/s.

    c.   $\left|\dfrac{C(j\omega)}{R(j\omega)}\right| \leq 0.1$ for $\omega \geq 400$ rad/s.

    d.   Phase margin: $\phi_m \geq 50$.

    e.   $f_{sample} \leq 40$ Hz.

    f.   Crossover frequency, $\omega_c \geq 20$ rad/s and *maximized* consistent with specifications a–e.

### 15.6.6   Additional Problems

**1.**  Draw a picture showing the locations of poles with $0.5 < \zeta < 0.8$ and $7\pi/10T < \omega_n < 9\pi/10T$ in both the $s$ plane and the $z$ plane.

**2.**  Show analytically that if $G(s)$ has no poles at $s = 0$ and we map it to the $z$ plane using the bilinear mapping

$$s = \frac{2}{T}\frac{z-1}{z+1},$$

then $G(s)$ and $G(z)$ have the same dc gain.

**3.**  Reconsider the "smart" missile control problem first introduced in Chapter 7, as shown in Fig. 15.28. The missile has a TV camera in its nose that relays a picture to the pilot. The pilot then directs the missile by centering the target on a display in the cockpit with a joystick. The signal from the pilot then causes the

**Figure 15.28 |** Smartbomb system.

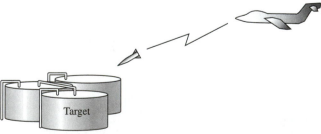

Target

guidance system of the missile to move towards the target. Let the dynamics of the missile and its control system be

$$G_p(s) = \frac{200}{s(s+5)(s+15)}.$$

For the unity feedback, cascade compensation configuration used in this chapter, design the compensator $G_c$ to these specifications:

a.  $f_{\text{sample}} \leq 25$ Hz.
b.  $K_v \geq 100$.
c.  $\left| \dfrac{E(j\omega)}{R(j\omega)} \right| \leq 0.01$ for $\omega \leq 0.2$ rad/s.
d.  $\left| \dfrac{C(j\omega)}{R(j\omega)} \right| \leq 0.1$ for $\omega \geq \omega_\ell$, $\omega_\ell$ as small as possible.
e.  $\phi_m \geq 50°$.
f.  PO $\leq 10\%$.
g.  Rise time to 90% of final value $\leq 0.2$ s.

4.  Redo Problem 3, using these specifications:

a.  $f_{\text{sample}} \leq 100$ Hz.
b.  $K_v \geq 100$.
c.  $\left| \dfrac{E(j\omega)}{R(j\omega)} \right| \leq 0.01$ for $\omega \leq 0.2$ rad/s.
d.  $\left| \dfrac{C(j\omega)}{R(j\omega)} \right| \leq 0.1$ for $\omega \geq 100$ rad/s.
e.  $\phi_m \geq 50°$.
f.  PO $\leq 10\%$.
g.  Compensator gain as low as possible.

Use Bode design in the $s$ plane and transfer the compensator to the $z$ plane using the bilinear mapping.

5.  Figure 15.29 shows a block diagram of a speed controller for an automobile that we considered in Chapter 7, where

$$G_{\text{spdc}}(s) = \frac{10}{(s+3)(s+3.2)} \qquad G_{\text{car}}(s) = \frac{1}{s+2.5}.$$

**Figure 15.29 |** Block diagram of automobile speed control.

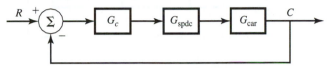

Design a controller $G_c$ that meets these specifications:

a.  $f_{\text{sample}} \leq 20$ Hz.
b.  $K_p \geq 10$.
c.  Rise time to 63% of final value less than 0.3 s.
d.  The response to a step input is critically damped.

Find $G_p'(z)$ using MATLAB. Then design the compensator in the $z$ plane using root locus design.

6. Consider again the system shown in Fig. 15.30, first considered in Chapter 7, where the plant has a feedback loop. Let

$$G_1(s) = \frac{1}{s^2} \qquad G_2(s) = \frac{120s + 100}{s^2 + 12s + 72}.$$

**Figure 15.30 |** Multiloop control.

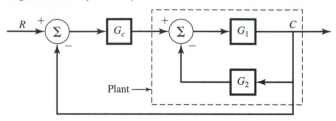

Design a controller $G_c$ to meet these specifications:
a.  $f_{\text{sample}} \le 50$ Hz.
b.  $t_p \le 1$ s.
c.  PO $\le 30\%$.

Find $G_p'(z)$ using MATLAB. Then design the compensator in the $z$ plane using root locus design.

7. Figure 15.31 shows a unity feedback loop for the pitch control of an aircraft, first considered in Chapter 7, where

$$G_{\text{flap}}(s) = \frac{4000}{(s + 8)} \qquad G_p(s) = \frac{(s + 6)(s + 15)}{s(s + 3 - j12)(s + 3 + j12)}.$$

**Figure 15.31 |** Pitch control of aircraft.

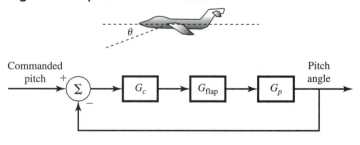

Design a compensator to meet these specifications:
a.  $K_v \ge 130$.
b.  PO $\le 15\%$.
c.  $t_p \le 0.7$ s.
d.  $f_{sample} \le 100$ Hz.
Find $G_p'(z)$ and design the compensator in the $z$ plane using the root locus method.

8. In Chapter 7 we considered the the roll characteristics of a missile about its longitudinal axis, as shown in Fig. 15.32. The dynamics about the longitudinal axis are given by

$$G_m(s) = \frac{1}{s(s+15)}.$$

**Figure 15.32** | Roll control of a missile.

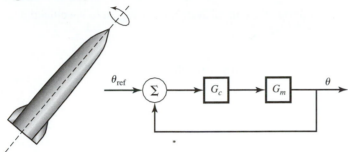

Redesign the the compensator $G_c$ using the methods of this chapter to meet these specifications:
a. $f_{\text{sample}} \le 50$ Hz.
b. $K_v \ge 150$.
c. $\left|\dfrac{E(j\omega)}{R(j\omega)}\right| \le 0.01$ for $\omega \le 0.2$ rad/s.
d. $\left|\dfrac{C(j\omega)}{R(j\omega)}\right| \le 0.1$ for $\omega \ge 100$ rad/s.
e. $\phi_m \ge 55°$.
f. Compensator gain as low as possible.
Use Bode design in the $s$ plane and adjust for the negative phase of the zero-order hold. Map the compensator to the $z$ plane using the bilinear mapping.

9. Consider again the high-speed magnetic levitation train of Fig. 15.33, first considered in Chapter 7. On curves it is desired to bank the train into the turn. The block diagram shows how this might be accompished with a rate gyro.

**Figure 15.33** | Roll control of maglev train.

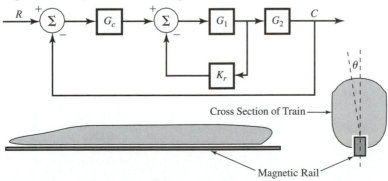

Since the train is floating, its dynamics have been modeled as

$$G_{\text{maglev}}(s) = \frac{1}{Js^2},$$

where $J$ is the moment of inertia of the train. Assume the ratio

$$\frac{K_r}{J}$$

is known. Redesign the control system $G_c$ using these specifications:

a.  $f_{\text{sample}} \leq 25$ Hz.

b.  $K_v \geq 100$.

c.  $\left|\dfrac{E(j\omega)}{R(j\omega)}\right| \leq 0.01$ for $\omega \leq 1.0$ rad/s.

d.  $\left|\dfrac{C(j\omega)}{R(j\omega)}\right| \leq 0.1$ for $\omega \geq 600$ rad/s.

e.  $\phi_m \geq 70°$.

f.  $K_r/J \leq 50$.

Map the compensator to the $z$ plane using the bilinear mapping.

## FURTHER READINGS

Astrom, Karl J. and Bjorn Wittenmark. 1997. *Computer Controlled Systems—Theory and Design,* 3rd ed., Saddle River, NJ: Prentice Hall.

Cadzow, James A. 1973. *Discrete Time Systems—An Introduction with Interdisciplinary Applications.* Englewood Cliffs, NJ: Prentice Hall.

Franklin, Gene F., J. David Powell, and Michael L. Workman. 1998. *Digital Control of Dynamic Systems,* 3rd ed., Menlo Park, CA.: Addison-Wesley.

Houpis, Constantine H. and Gary B. Lamont. 1992. *Digital Control Systems—Theory, Hardware, Software,* 2nd ed., New York: McGraw-Hill.

Saucedo, Roberto and Earl E. Schiring. 1968. *Introduction To Continuous And Digital Control Systems.* New York: MacMillan.

# Chapter 16

# Aircraft Pitch Control
*A Case Study*

## 16.1 | OVERVIEW

This chapter offers us another chance to step through the entire design cycle. As usual we will begin by finding an appropriate model for the plant to be controlled, and then follow that with an identification of the parameters of the model. We will then design and implement a compensator. This time, we will do the design and implementation using digital control.

The system to be controlled, or "plant" as we sometimes call it, is shown in Fig. 16.1. The device consists of a carriage that can rotate. Affixed to the carriage is a weight used to adjust the dynamcis of the carriage. Inside the box are two springs that restore the carriage to a horizontal position if the carriage is deflected and then released. The carriage is attached to the shaft of a dc motor at one end, and to a heliopot at the other end. The motor provides the torque to pitch the carriage at a requested angle.

**Figure 16.1 |** Stable platform.

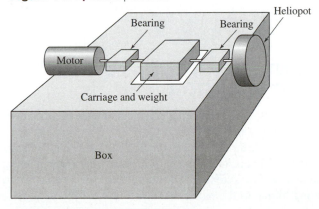

531

**Figure 16.2 |** Inner workings of a heliopot.

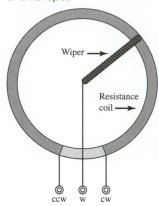

Wiper →

Resistance coil →

ccw   w   cw

**Figure 16.3 |** Attitude of a plane.

$\theta$

The heliopot senses the angle the carriage makes to the horizontal. The heliopot used here is identical to that used for the positioning table studied in Chapter 13. It is simply a very high quality rheostat, with no stops. An idea of what the heliopot looks like is shown in Fig. 16.2. As discussed in Chapter 13, by applying a voltage across CW and CCW, we can use the wiper voltage to measure the pitch angle of the carriage relative to the horizontal.

The device shown in Fig. 16.1 is a reasonable approximation to the pitch, or attitude, dynamics of an airplane, as defined in Fig. 16.3. As we will see, the transfer function is quite interesting, type 0, with dominant complex poles.

Our plan of action is familiar by now: first find an appropriate model for the plant and then identify the parameters of the plant.

# 16.2 | PLANT MODELING AND IDENTIFICATION

It may come as a surprise to the reader that the model for the plant, shown in Fig. 16.2, is our old friend the dc motor.

However, with a little thought we see that the carriage simply changes the overall moment of inertia $J$. That is, the moment of inertia of the carriage is combined with the moment of inertia of the rotor of the dc motor. The springs attached to the carriage apply a restoring torque to the motor shaft. In Fig. 16.4 the cylinder of revolution

**Figure 16.4 |** A dc motor with load.

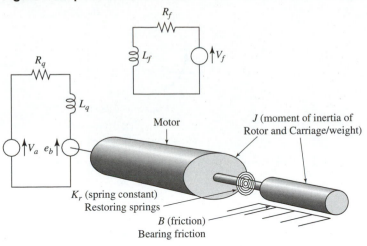

represents the carriage and $K_r$ accounts for the restoring torque of the springs. Thus, the transfer function of our system, as derived in Chapter 3, is

$$G_p(s) = \frac{K_m}{[s^2 + (B/J)s + (K_r/J)][s + (R_q/L_q)] + K_v K_m s}, \qquad \textbf{[16.1]}$$

where $K_v$ and $K_m$ are constants defined in the orginal derivation of the model in Chapter 3.

Our next goal is to find the roots of the characteristic equation

$$\left(s^2 + \frac{B}{J}s + \frac{K_r}{J}\right)\left(s + \frac{R_q}{L_q}\right) + K_v K_m s = 0. \qquad \textbf{[16.2]}$$

As noted, we cannot ignore $K_r$ since it accounts for the restoring torque of the springs.

If we divide both sides of the Eq. [16.2] by

$$\left(s^2 + \frac{B}{J}s + \frac{K_r}{J}\right)\left(s + \frac{R_q}{L_q}\right),$$

we obtain

$$1 + \frac{K_v K_m s}{[s^2 + (B/J)s + (K_r/J)][s + (R_q/L_q)]} = 0.$$

Treating $K_v K_m$ as the variable gain, we obtain the root locus shown in Fig. 16.5.

The root locus is based on the assumption that $B$ is very small compared to $J$ and $K_r$, so that the roots of the quadratic term will be a complex conjugate pair. The third pole, which depends largely on the electrical time constant of the dc motor, will be far to the left in the $s$ plane. This is reminiscent of our indentification results in Chapter 13. In this case we will finally decide to ignore the third pole.

**Figure 16.5 |** Root locus to determine closed-loop pole locations.

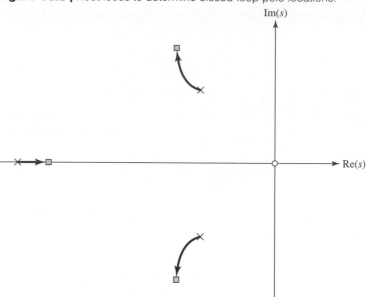

Thus, although the transfer function is third order, the complex poles will turn out to be very dominant. This information will be essential for obtaining the transfer function experimentally.

### 16.2.1  Plant Parameter Identification

A block diagram of the laboratory setup to measure the frequency response of the plant is shown in Fig. 16.6. This diagram is identical to Fig. 13.3. In the present case, the heliopot voltage measures the pitch angle of the carriage.

**Figure 16.6 |** Block diagram of laboratory setup for taking frequency response data.

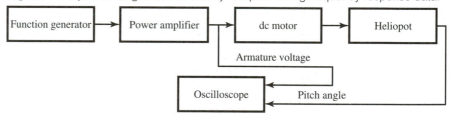

The actual laboratory setup to collect the frequency response data necessary to identify the parameters of the transfer function is shown in Fig. 16.7.

We enumerate some of the details of the setup:

1. A dual power supply is used to apply ±10 V across the CW and CCW inputs of the heliopot.

**Figure 16.7** | Laboratory setup for taking frequency response data.

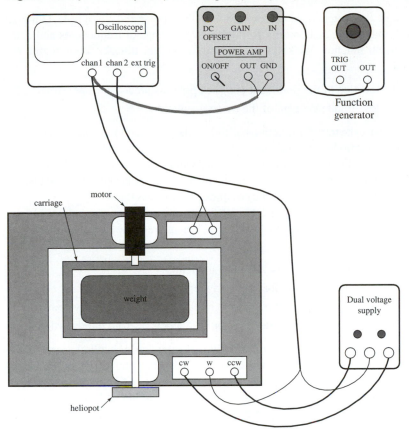

2. The w output of the heliopot goes to channel 2 of the oscilloscope. The ground of the connection to the oscilloscope has to be connected to the ground of the dual power supply. The lead connected to the oscilloscope is a shielded conductor so that the ground of the oscilloscope is not visible. It is, however, connected to the ground of the dual power supply.

3. Before connecting the output of the heliopot to the oscilloscope, we first connect it to a digital voltmeter (not shown) and adjust the rest position of the carriage to zero. The heliopot has a clamp that that can be loosened allowing the heliopot to be turned, so that the the horizontal rest position corresponds to 0 V. Once the zero setting is made the clamp is retightened.

4. The function generator shown in the figure will be used to apply sinusoidal voltages to a power amplifier, which in turn, is connected to the armature winding of the dc motor.

5. The "thicker" leads in the figure are multiconductor leads. The thin leads at the ends represent individual conductors.

## 16.2.2  Data Collection

As noted, the system has two complex conjugate poles and a real pole. Our goal is to collect magnitude and phase information over a range of frequencies and determine the transfer function. We know the general form of the transfer function, but we need to find

1.  The location of the dominant complex poles as precisely as possible.
2.  The low-frequency gain of the transfer function.

Because the transfer function has lightly damped complex poles, we expect to see a peak or "hump" in the Bode magnitude plot at $\omega_r$, the so-called resonant frequency of the system. For small damping ratios, $\omega_r$ will be close to $\omega_n$, the natural frequency of the complex conjugate poles. For this plant, the peak is very high because we will find that the damping ratio of the complex poles is less than 0.1.

We could just start taking data, and find the resonant frequency by trial and error. Instead, we get a good estimate of the resonant frequency by using this four-step procedure.

1.  Depress the carriage about an inch and a half.
2.  Set up the oscilloscope for single trigger operation.
3.  Release the carriage and record the impulse response of the system.
4.  Determine the approximate resonant frequency $\omega_r$ from the recorded response.

Finding an approximate value for $\omega_r$ will make the data collection more efficient.

In making these measuements, we will keep the oscillation of the carriage to moderate size. A vertical displacement from the rest position of no more than 1.5 in. will keep the restoring force of the spring reasonably linear. We will take measurements down to the lowest frequency possible so that we can locate the low-frequency asymptote. We need to find the low-frequency asymptote, as well as the size and location of the peak magnitude, in order to find the damping ratio $\zeta$.

Before collecting and analyzing the frequency response data, we develop some formulas that will make that analysis easier.

The open-loop transfer function will be of the form

$$\bar{G}_p(s) = \frac{\bar{K}}{\left(s^2 + 2\zeta\omega_n s + \omega_n^2\right)(s + \gamma)},$$

where $\gamma$ is very large. Since $\gamma$ is very large, we will ultimately decide to not include it in our model, and hence we ignore it in the analysis. Thus, we let

$$G_p(s) = \frac{K\omega_n^2}{s^2 + 2\zeta\omega_n s + \omega_n^2}. \qquad \textbf{[16.3]}$$

We now see that the plant is simply $T_{N2}(s)$ scaled by $K$, enabling us to use all the results that we have developed for $T_{N2}(s)$, particularly those in Chapter 9. As we showed in Chapter 9, the maximum value of the magnitude of $G_p(j\omega)$ will occur for

$$\omega_r = \omega_n \sqrt{1 - 2\zeta^2}.$$

Since the plant has lightly damped complex poles, the magnitude plot will have a distinct maximum at $\omega = \omega_r$. If the maximum is known, then $\zeta$ can be determined as shown next.

We first find by direct substitution that

$$|G_p(j\omega_r)| = \left| \frac{K\omega_n^2}{(j\omega_n\sqrt{1-2\zeta^2})^2 + j2\zeta\omega_n^2\sqrt{1-2\zeta^2} + \omega_n^2} \right|$$

$$= \frac{K\omega_n^2}{\left\{ \left[\omega_n^2 - \omega_n^2(1-2\zeta^2)\right]^2 + 4\omega_n^4\zeta^2(1-2\zeta^2) \right\}^{1/2}}$$

$$= \frac{K}{[4\zeta^4 + 4\zeta^2(1-2\zeta^2)]^{1/2}}$$

$$= \frac{K}{[4\zeta^2 - 4\zeta^4]^{1/2}}$$

$$= \frac{K}{2\zeta\sqrt{1-\zeta^2}}.$$

Then, since

$$|G_p(j0)| = K,$$

we have

$$M_r \triangleq \frac{|G_p(j\omega_r)|}{|G_p(j0)|} = \frac{1}{2\zeta\sqrt{1-\zeta^2}}. \qquad \textbf{[16.4]}$$

Since $M_r$ can be determined from the experimental data, we can first find $\zeta$, and finally $\omega_n$. Because $\zeta$ and $\omega_n$ determine the location of the dominant plant poles we can then identify the plant transfer function, with the exception of the real pole. As it turns out, the data that we collect will convince us that we can ignore the real pole.

We are now ready to collect and analyze the data. Figures 16.8(a) and 16.8(b) show the shape of the magnitude and phase plots for

$$\frac{1}{(j\hat{\omega})^2 + 2\zeta j\hat{\omega} + 1)}, \qquad \hat{\omega} = \frac{\omega}{\omega_n}.$$

These plots provide a sanity check when we determine the transfer function.

Our first step is to approximate the resonant frequency as just suggested. Figure 16.9 shows the waveform captured when the carriage was depressed and then released. We see that $\omega_r$ is between 1.5 and 1.6 Hz. This gives us a good starting point for determining the frequency response. It is now just a matter of finding the magnitude and phase data at selected frequencies above and below 1.5 Hz. The data are shown in Fig. 16.10. We are now ready to identify the parameters of our model.

**Figure 16.8 |** (a) Magnitude and (b) phase of normalized second-order transfer function.

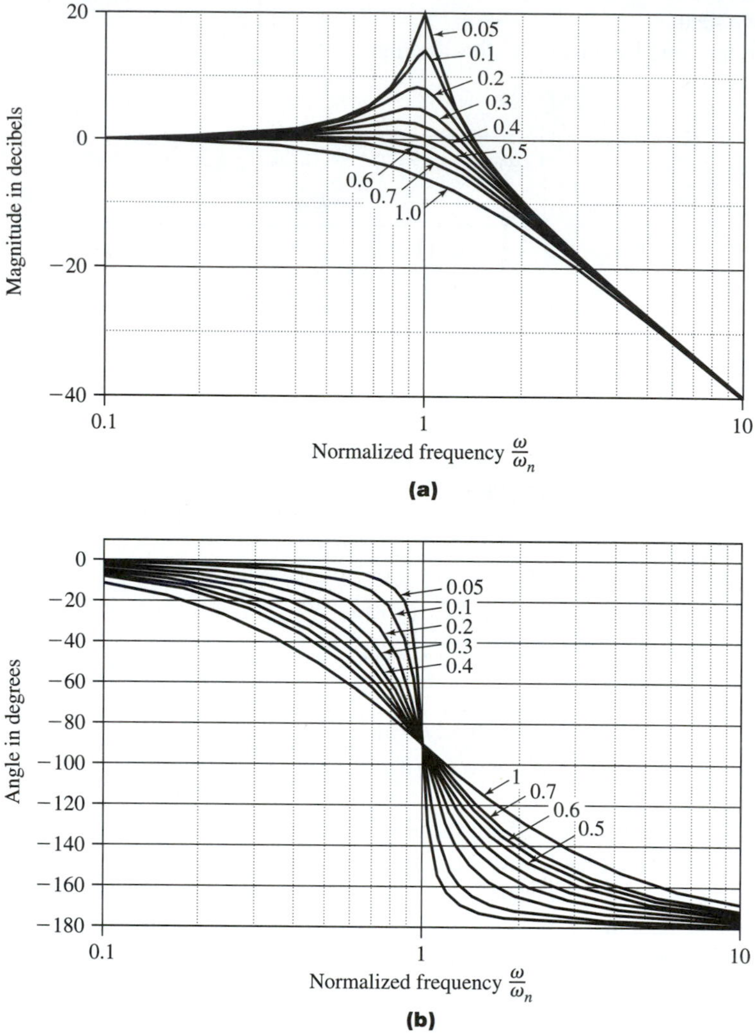

**(a)**

**(b)**

## 16.2.3  Analyzing the Data

We see from Fig. 16.10 that the peak magnitude is almost exactly $-10$ dB, and the steady state value is about $-31$ dB. Thus,

$$M_r = \frac{|G_p(j\omega_r)|}{|G_p(j0)|} = 11.22.$$

We next recast Eq. [16.4] as

$$4(\zeta^2)^2 - 4\zeta^2 + \frac{1}{M_r^2} = 0. \qquad \qquad \textbf{[16.5]}$$

**Figure 16.9 |** Impulse response of platform.

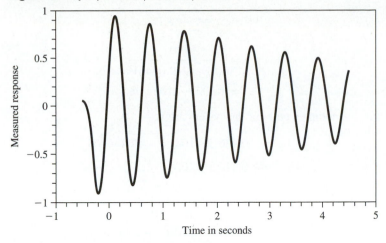

**Figure 16.10 |** Bode phase and magnitude plots for platform.

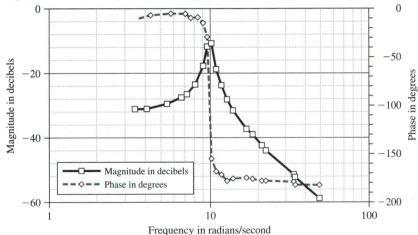

Solving Eq. [16.5] yields

$$\zeta^2 = 0.00199, 0.998.$$

Taking the smaller of the two roots we get

$$\zeta = 0.0446.$$

Then, examining Fig. 16.8 we see that this value makes sense. We also see from the Bode magnitude data that

$$\omega_r = 10 \text{ rad/s}.$$

Since

$$\omega_r = \omega_n \sqrt{1 - 2\zeta^2},$$

we can now find

$$\omega_n = \frac{\omega_r}{\sqrt{1 - 2\zeta^2}}$$

$$= \frac{10}{\sqrt{1 - 2(0.0446)^2}}$$

$$= 10.02 \rightarrow 10 \text{ rad/s}.$$

Thus, the complex poles of the system are at

$$s = -0.446 \pm j10\sqrt{1 - 0.0446^2}$$

$$= -0.446 \pm j10.$$

We can now write

$$G_p(s) = \frac{K \times 10^2}{(s + 0.446 - j10)(s + 0.446 + j10)}.$$

Since

$$K = |G_p(j0)| = -10 \text{ dB} = 0.3162,$$

we finally have

$$G_p(s) = \frac{31.6}{(s + 0.446 - j10)(s + 0.446 + j10)}.$$

## 16.3 | CONTROL DESIGN

We now wish to design a digital controller for the stable platform whose transfer function we identified in Section 16.2. We will transform the plant to the $z$ domain and design the compensator there. The compensator will be based on pole/zero cancellation.

### 16.3.1  Transferring Plant to the $z$ Plane

We find $G_p'(s)$ by taking the step invariant transform of $G_p(s)$. The first step is to find

$$Y_{\text{step}}(s) = \frac{a^2 + b^2}{s[(s + a)^2 + b^2]}.$$

From Table 14.3 we find that

$$Y_{\text{step}}(z) = \frac{z(Az + B)}{(z - 1)[z^2 - (2e^{-aT} \cos bT)z + e^{-2aT}]},$$

where

$$A = 1 - e^{-aT} \cos bT - \frac{a}{b} e^{-aT} \sin bT,$$

$$B = e^{-2aT} + \frac{a}{b} e^{-aT} \sin bT - e^{-aT} \cos bT.$$

Dividing out the step input, we have

$$G_p'(z) = (1 - z^{-1})Y_{\text{step}}(z)$$

$$= \frac{Az + B}{z^2 - (2e^{-aT}\cos bT)z + e^{-2aT}}.$$

In the present case,

$$G_p(s) = \frac{0316}{(s + 0.446 - j10)(s + 0.446 + j10)}$$

$$= 0.3162\left[\frac{100}{(s + 0.446 - j10)(s + 0.446 + j10)}\right].$$

Letting $a = 0.446$, $b = 10$, and $f_s = 40$ Hz, we find that

$$A = 0.030919 \quad \text{and} \quad B = 0.0306896.$$

Thus

$$G_p'(z) = \frac{0.3162A(z + B/A)}{z^2 - \left(2e^{-0.446(0.025)}\cos\{(10)(0.025)\}\right)z + e^{-2(0.446)(0.025)}}$$

$$= \frac{0.009757(z + 0.9926)}{(z - 0.9582 - j0.2444)(z - 0.9582 + j0.2444)}.$$

With $G_p'(z)$ in hand, we can now proceed to the design of the compensator. We elect to cancel the plant poles with zeros and then add two additional poles. To ensure zero steady state error to a step input, one of the poles will have to be at $z = 1$. The compensator will then be

$$G_c(z) = \frac{K_c(z - 0.9582 - j0.2444)(z - 0.9582 + j0.2444)}{(z - 1)(z - p)}.$$

The general shape of the root locus is shown in Fig. 16.11.

Suppose our specifications are

1. $t_p \leq 0.5$ s.
2. PO $\leq 10\%$.

Then

$$b = \frac{\pi}{t_p} = 6.28 \text{ rad/s}.$$

For numerical convenience we round $b$ to 6 rad/s. Then, if we choose $\zeta = 0.8$, the system will be nearly critically damped.

We will proceed with the design and implementation of this compensator shortly, but we pause here to discuss the implications of the design. This is the first real system we have studied that is susceptible to noise. We know that this system has a very strong resonance at 10 rad/s, or 1.6 Hz. We have chosen a damped frequency of 6 Hz. A check of Fig. 16.8(a) shows that we are about a third of the way up the hump. We need to be careful here. We need to check the bandwidth of the system carefully, especially if we expect sensor noise. In this particular system, there may be sensor

**Figure 16.11 |** Root locus of proposed control.

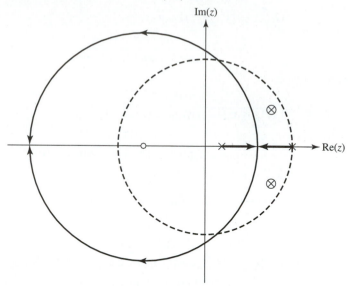

noise because inside the heliopot we have a metal wiper rubbing on a coil of wire. This may be one of those cases where the performance specifications come into conflict with the realities of the plant we are trying to control. We will leave these issues as problems at the end of the chapter. We now complete the design.

For $f_{sample} = 40$ Hz, the dominant poles will be at

$$z = e^{-(8)(0.025)}e^{\pm j(6)(0.025)} = 0.8095 \pm j0.1223.$$

We leave the calculation of $p$ and the gain of the compensator as an exercise.

## 16.4 | LABORATORY SETUP

A block diagram of the laboratory setup to implement the compensator is shown in Fig. 16.12. Note that the feedback now goes through an A/D converter to the computer. The compensator is simply a software routine that implements the difference equation that corresponds to $G_c(z)$.

**Figure 16.12 |** Block diagram of setup for digital control of pitch angle.

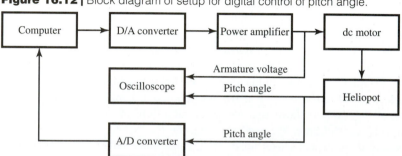

**Figure 16.13 |** Actual laboratory setup for digital control of pitch angle.

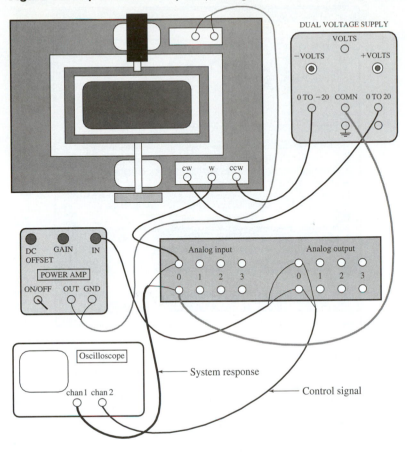

The actual laboratory setup to apply digital control to the stable platform is shown in Fig. 16.13. Both the A/D and the D/A converters are on the same input/output (I/O) board in the computer. As discussed in Chapters 8 and 13, the panel shown in the figure simply brings the inputs for the A/D and D/A channels out to a point where they can be conveniently connected to the other components of the setup.

Once the heliopot has been zeroed, a software program called DCSP (for Digital Compensation Software Package) is opened on the computer. DCSP is a menu driven program that takes care of the details of applying the digital compensation.

The Main Menu for DCSP, shown in Fig. 16.14, will appear first. The next step is to select the Single Input/Single Output option. This brings up the pole/zero editor shown in Fig. 16.15

By clicking on the COMPENSATOR bar, we can enter the poles and zeros of the compensator. The procedure is quite straightforward. To create a real pole or zero, we click on one of the R buttons next to either POLES or ZEROS. For a complex pole or zero we click on one of the C buttons.

**Figure 16.14 |** Main menu for DCSP.

**Figure 16.15 |** Pole/zero editor.

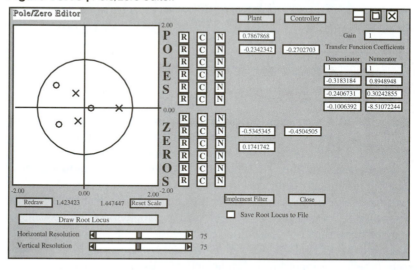

Clicking on an R or C button opens a data entry window to the right of the button panel. We then type in the desired pole or zero location. A pole or zero can be removed by clicking the N button next to the pole or zero to be removed. In addition, once a pole or zero is created, its location can be changed by dragging it with the mouse. We enter the gain of the comensator in the data entry window at the top right. It goes

**Figure 16.16 |** Filter implementation screen.

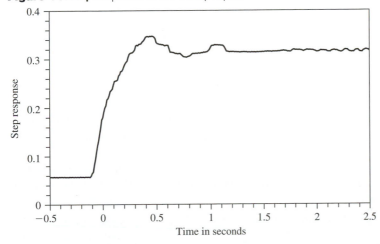

without saying that we have to have selected a sampling rate before we can do the data entry in this menu.

Having set up the compensator, we can click on the IMPLEMENT FILTER option and bring up the screen shown in Fig. 16.16. Now we can select the sample rate, in this case 40 Hz, and the type of input, a step of 0.3 V. If we now turn on the power amplifier, we are ready to click on the IMPLEMENT FILTER button to start the control of the system.

Figure 16.17 shows the closed-loop system response to a 0.3-V step input. The percent overshoot is about 17%. It is clear that the system is mildly nonlinear, mostly

**Figure 16.17 |** Response to 0.3-V step input.

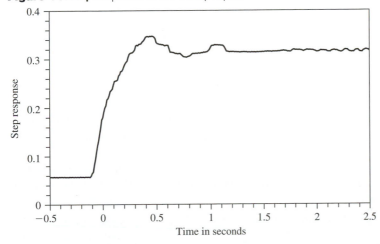

due to bearing friction and the springs. We have met our requirement on rise time, but we have more overshoot than expected. The next step is a redesign. We leave the redesign as an exercise.

## 16.5 | REPRISE

In this chapter we have once again done a complete design, starting with the modeling of the plant, followed by the identification of the parameters of the model, continuing with the design of a compensator and finishing with the implementation of the compensator.

This particular plant exhibits more nonlinearity than any system we have investigated to this point, and the control is more difficult. Nonetheless, the implementation shows that with some work we can achieve our design objectives. In this chapter, we have left the reader with some problems to solve with regard to the final design and implementation. This is as it should be. At this point we have been traveling along together for some time, crossing a variety of intellecutal terrains. It is time for the reader to do a little bit more of the work, and let the author rest a bit.

## 16.6 | PROBLEMS

The CD-ROM that comes with the text contains the frequency response data for five devices like the one described in the text. The data files are labeled spfid1, spfid2, spfid3, spfid4, and spfid5. The data for the plant used in the text is spfid5.

1. Find the bandwidth of the the loop transfer function for the design in the text.
2. Find the gain of the compensator designed in the text.
3. Using any of the listed data files, identify the paramters of one of the five plants.
4. For any of the five plants redesign the compensator so that the dominant closed-loop poles have a natural frequency of 20 rad/s. Use $f_{sample} = 50$ Hz. This problem requires working Problem 3 first. Note: this design will help us test questions raised in the text about the practical maximum bandwidth of this system. The implementation of a design that meets the specifications on the actual system will be available in the solutions manual.
5. Repeat Problem 4 for $f_{sample} = 10$ Hz.
6. Instead of canceling the plant poles, design a compensator using root locus in the $z$ plane that pulls the plant poles down and to the left so that they have a natural frequency of of 20 rad/s and a damping ratio of 0.8. Use $f_{sample} = 40$ Hz. This problem requires working Problem 3 first. Note: this design will help us test questions raised in the text about the practical maximum bandwidth of this system. The implementation of a design that meets the specifications on the actual system will be available in the solutions manual.
7. Repeat Problem 6 for $f_{sample} = 10$ Hz.

8. Find the difference equation that corresponds to the compensator designed in the text. Note: you need to do Problem 1 first.

9. Using the Tow-Thomas biquadractic opamp design in Chapter 3, implement the analog version of the compensator in the text. Note: you need to do Problem 1 first.

10. Redesign the compensator in the text for any of the five plants on the CD-ROM using the Bode design methods of Chapter 15. The specifications are

    a. $K_v \geq 50$.

    b. $\dfrac{|E(j\omega)|}{|R(j\omega)|} \leq 0.02 \; \omega \leq 0.1$ rad/s.

    c. $\dfrac{|C(j\omega)|}{|R(j\omega)|} \leq 0.05 \; \omega \leq \omega_h$, where $\omega_h \leq 0.5\omega_r$, and $\omega_r$ is the resonant frequency.

       Use a sampling frequency of 25 Hz. The implementation of a design that meets the specifications on the actual system will be available in the solutions manual.

11. Redo Problem 10 but without canceling the poles of the plant for these specifications:

    a. $K_v \geq 50$.

    b. $\dfrac{|E(j\omega)|}{|R(j\omega)|} \leq 0.02 \; \omega \leq 0.1$ rad/s.

    c. $\dfrac{|C(j\omega)|}{|R(j\omega)|} \leq 0.05 \; \omega \leq \omega_h$, where $\omega_h \leq 0.5\omega_r$, and $\omega_r$ is the resonant frequency.

       Use a sampling rate of 50 Hz. The implementation of a design that meets the specifications on the actual system will be available in the solutions manual.

# FURTHER READINGS

Eykhoff, P. 1974. *System Identification*. London: John Wiley.

Graupe, D. 1972. *Identification of Systems*. New York: Van Nostrand-Reinholt.

Rake, H. 1981. *Step Response and Frequency Response Methods*. IFAC System Identification Tutorial. Oxford: Pergamon Press.

# 17 Chapter

# The Transportation Lag

## 17.1 | OVERVIEW

A transportation lag is the delay between the time an input signal is applied to a system and the time the system reacts to that input signal. A time domain block diagram of the transportation lag itself is shown in Fig. 17.1. We see that the output signal is the input signal delayed by $\tau$ units of time. If we look back at all the systems we have studied previously, we find that in every case there is no delay between the application of the input and the system response to that input. In reality, most systems have a transportation lag. If the delay is small enough we can ignore it; if not then we have to account for its effects.

**Figure 17.1 |** Time domain representation of transportation lag.

$x(t) \longrightarrow$ | Transportation lag | $\xrightarrow{x(t - \tau)}$

In this chapter we will first find a mathematical model of the transportation lag, and then turn our attention to designing compensators for systems that have a substantial delay. We will find that we can design effective compensators, but the presence of the transportation lag causes the transient response to be much slower.

In Chapter 15 we got our first look at something line a transportation lag when we developed the $s$-domain model of the digital to analog converter (DAC). In that development we saw that the main effect of the DAC was to add negative phase to the total angle of $G_c G_p(j\omega)$. A transportation lag has a similar effect and forces us to modify our design techniques. In this chapter we will see that the presence of a transportation lag makes us lower our expectation of system performance.

Our plan of attack is to first analyze the effect of a transportation lag on a continuous system, and then repeat the analysis for sampled data systems. We will find that the transportation lag is easiest to manage if we use Bode design. At the same time, we will show that it is also possible to incorporate the transportation lag into root locus design with only slightly more effort than in the case of Bode design.

# 17.2 | TRANSPORTATION LAG IN A CONTINUOUS SYSTEM

Transportation lags are quite common in industrial applications where they are sometimes called "dead time." In a continuous system, this simple delay is represented by the term $e^{-\tau s}$. That is,

$$\mathcal{L}\{x(t-\tau)\mathbf{1}(t-\tau)\} = e^{-\tau s}X(s), \qquad \overset{\circ}{.}$$

where

$$X(s) = \mathcal{L}\{x(t)\}.$$

The block diagram in the $s$ plane that corresponds to Fig. 17.1 is shown in Fig. 17.2.

**Figure 17.2** | Frequency domain representation of transportation lag.

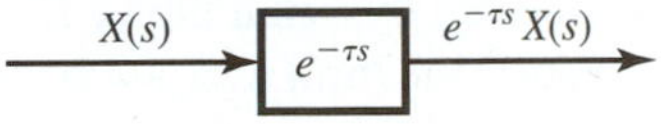

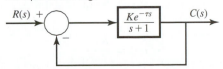

Now consider the system shown in Fig. 17.3. The addition of the transportation lag changes things dramatically. For one thing, we now have a closed-loop system that is *infinite* dimensional. This is easy enough to see from the equation

$$\frac{Ke^{-\tau s}}{s+1} = 1\underline{/-180^{\circ}}.$$

For $K$ fixed and finite, if we let $s = -\sigma \pm j\omega,\ \sigma > 0$, then

$$\lim_{\sigma\to\infty}\frac{Ke^{-\tau s}}{s+1} = \lim_{\sigma\to\infty}\frac{Ke^{-\tau(-\sigma\pm j\omega)}}{(-\sigma\pm j\omega)+1}$$

$$= \lim_{\sigma\to\infty}\frac{Ke^{\tau\sigma}e^{\pm j\omega\tau}}{(-\sigma\pm j\omega)+1}$$

$$= -\infty\underline{/-\pi\pm\omega\tau}.$$

The last step follows from the fact that $e^x$ always dominates $x^n$ for any integer $n$, and hence the term $e^{\tau\sigma}$ in the numerator will dominate the term $(-\sigma + 1) \pm j\omega$ in the denominator. Note that to satisfy the characteristic equation for the closed-loop system, we must make $K$ arbitrarily small to keep $|G_cG_p| = 1$. Further, to satisfy the

**Figure 17.3** | Closed-loop system with transportation lag.

angle condition the poles must be infinite in number and regularly spaced, because to satisfy the angle condition we must have

$$-\pi \pm \omega\tau = -\pi,$$

or

$$\pm \omega\tau = 0,$$

implying that

$$\omega = \frac{\pm 2n\pi}{\tau} \quad n = 0, 1, 2, \ldots.$$

We can, of course, move these poles by increasing the gain, which we will do shortly, but for $K$ arbitrarily small the closed-loop system will have poles at

$$s = -1 \quad \text{and} \quad s = -\infty \pm j\frac{2n\pi}{\tau}, \qquad n = 0, 1, 2, \ldots.$$

As $K$ then increases, the closed-loop poles will migrate to an infinite set of zeros at infinity. These zeros can be located by again fixing $K$ at some finite value, letting $s = \sigma \pm j\omega, \sigma > 0$, and then taking the limit as $\sigma \to \infty$ of the loop transfer function to obtain

$$\lim_{\sigma \to \infty} \frac{Ke^{-\tau s}}{s+1} = \lim_{\sigma \to \infty} \frac{Ke^{-\tau(\sigma \pm j\omega)}}{(\sigma \pm j\omega) + 1}$$

$$= \lim_{\sigma \to \infty} \frac{Ke^{-\tau\sigma}e^{\pm j\omega\tau}}{(\sigma \pm j\omega) + 1}$$

$$= 0\underline{/\pm j\omega\tau}.$$

Then the only way to satisfy the characteristic equation is to let $K \to \infty$ so that

$$\left| \frac{Ke^{-\sigma\tau}}{\sigma + 1 \pm j\omega} \right| = 1.$$

Note that the pole at $s = -1$ makes no angle contribution as $\sigma \to \infty$. To satisfy the angle condition we must have

$$\pm \omega\tau = -\pi$$

or

$$\omega = \pm \frac{m\pi}{\tau} \qquad m = 1, 3, 5, \ldots.$$

Thus, as $K$ increases, the closed-loop poles migrate from left to right, as shown in Fig. 17.4. The closed-loop poles pass into the right half plane in pairs. The first two poles to cross are the pair closest to the origin, followed by the next closest pair, and so on. This can be shown by using the Nyquist stability criterion.

Consider

$$G(j\omega) = \frac{Ke^{-j\omega\tau}}{j\omega + 1}.$$

**Figure 17.4 |** Root locus for $G(s) = \dfrac{Ke^{-\tau s}}{s+1}$.

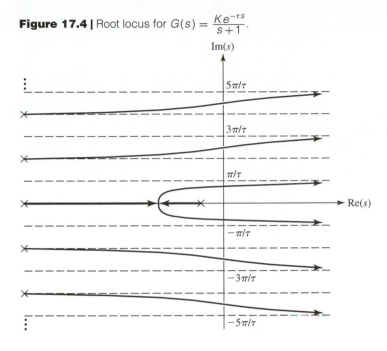

Then, it is easy to show that the transportation lag has *no* effect on the *magnitude* plot. That is,

$$|G(j\omega)| = \left| \frac{Ke^{-j\omega\tau}}{j\omega + 1} \right| = \frac{K|e^{-j\omega\tau}|}{|j\omega + 1|} = \frac{K}{|j\omega + 1|}.$$

Thus, the magnitude plot of the system with the transportation lag is identical to that of the system *without* the transportation lag.

The transportation lag does, however, have a significant effect on the Bode phase plot since the term $e^{-j\omega\tau}$ adds $-\omega\tau$ to the phase of $G(j\omega)$. That is,

$$\underline{/G(j\omega)} = -\tan^{-1}\omega - \omega\tau.$$

Thus the transportation lag makes a negative angle contribution that is linear in frequency. The polar plot of $G(j\omega)$ for $0 < \omega < \infty$ is shown in Fig. 17.5(a). The complete Nyquist plot is shown in Fig. 17.5(b).

Actually, as shown in Fig. 17.5(b), we can't draw the whole Nyquist plot since it has an infinite number of encirclements. We can envision it, however, and what it tells us is that as the gain increases, there are first zero, then two, then four, then six, and so on encirclements of $G = -1$. This shows that there are an infinite number of closed-loop poles and that they pass into the right half plane in pairs. The first pair to cross is the pair closest to the origin of the $s$ plane, followed by the next closest pair, and so on. Indeed, if we begin increasing the gain from zero through larger and larger values, we would see a wedge of poles traveling from left to right across the $s$ plane, much like a flight of Canadian geese winging southward in the late fall.

**Figure 17.5** | Polar (a) and Nyquist (b) plots of $G(j\omega) = \dfrac{Ke^{-j\omega\tau}}{j\omega + 1}$.

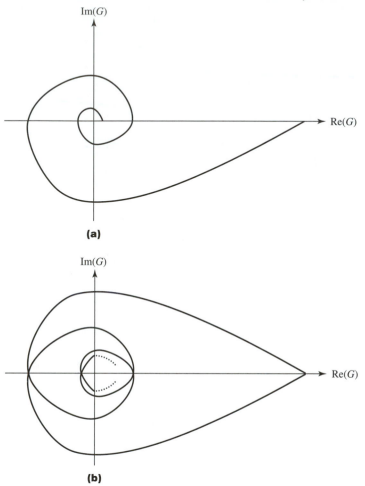

(a)

(b)

A little thought should convince the reader that this is always the case for any transfer function that consists of a ratio of polynomials in $s$ to which a transportation lag is added. Even for more complex transfer functions, the constraint of satisfying the angle condition causes the poles to migrate from left to right, and to cross the imaginary axis in pairs. All that changes is the location of these poles along a vertical line through $s = -\infty$.

For instance, for unity feedback consider

$$G(s) = \frac{Ke^{-\tau s}}{s(s+4)}.$$

The Nyquist plot is shown in Fig. 17.6 and the root locus in Fig. 17.7.

**Figure 17.6 |** Nyquist plot for $G(s) = \dfrac{Ke^{-\tau s}}{s(s+4)}$.

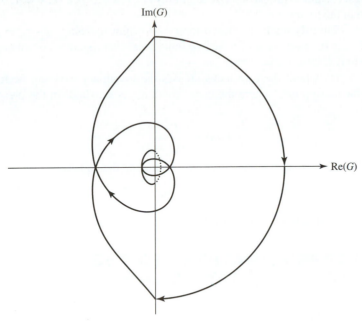

**Figure 17.7 |** Root locus for $G(s) = \dfrac{Ke^{-\tau s}}{s(s+4)}$.

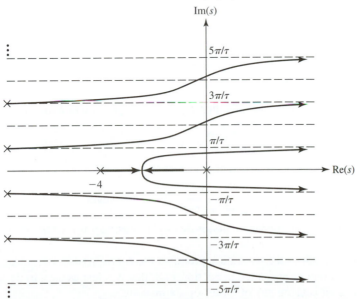

Note that in this case the closed-loop poles originate at $s = -\infty \pm jk\pi/\tau$, $k = 1, 3, 5, \ldots$ and terminate at zeros at infinity at $s = \infty \pm jk\pi/\tau, k = 1, 3, 5, \ldots$, as shown in the figure.

For $K$ arbitrarily small, the closed-loop poles originate from $s = -\infty \pm jn\pi/T$, $n = 1, 3, \ldots$, because we now have *two* finite poles that together contribute $-360°$ of phase to $GH(s)$ for $s = -\infty \pm j\omega, -\infty < \omega < \infty$.

The points where the root locus crosses the imaginary axis can be found by looking for those points where the angle condition is satisfied. In the present case with

$$G(s) = \frac{Ke^{-\tau s}}{s(s+4)},$$

we simply search along the imaginary axis evaluating the equation

$$\underline{/G(j\omega)} = -\frac{\pi}{2} - \tan^{-1}\frac{\omega}{4} - \omega\tau.$$

To do so, we would have to have a value for $\tau$.

# 17.3 | APPROXIMATIONS TO THE TRANSPORTATION LAG

There are several approximations to the transportation lag. The simplest is just the Taylor series approximation. That is

$$e^{-\tau s} = \left[e^{-\tau s}\right]_{|s=0} + \left[\frac{d}{ds}e^{-\tau s}\right]_{|s=0} s + \text{HOT}$$

$$= 1 - \tau s + \text{HOT}$$

$$\approx 1 - \tau s.$$

Another is

$$e^{-\tau s} \approx \frac{1}{1+\tau s} = 1 - \tau s + \text{HOT},$$

which amounts to the same thing.

A better approximation is the first order Pade approximation given by

$$e^{-\tau s} \approx \frac{1 - \tau s/2}{1 + \tau s/2}.$$

Another, and perhaps better, approximation is

$$e^{-\tau s} \approx \frac{1}{[1 + \tau s/n]^n}, \quad n \text{ an integer.}$$

The advantage of this approximation is that by increasing $n$ we make the approximation better.

Having cataloged the possible approximations for the transportation lag, we will find, in the examples presented in Section 17.4, that it is just as easy to design using $e^{-\tau s}$ itself, as it is using any of these approximations.

# 17.4 | COMPENSATOR DESIGN FOR CONTINUOUS SYSTEMS

In this section we will consider the design of compensation for continuous systems with a transportation lag using both root locus and Bode techniques. As a rule, most practitioners prefer Bode design, but root locus design has its place. For both techniques we can account for the effects of the transportation lag with very little extra computational effort.

## 17.4.1 Root Locus Design

Design using root locus techniques proceeds almost as it would if the transportation lag were not present. The only difference is that at a point $s = \sigma + j\omega$ we have to determine the magnitude and angle angle contributions due to

$$e^{-(\sigma+j\omega)\tau} = e^{-\sigma\tau}e^{-j\omega\tau} = e^{-\sigma\tau}\underline{/-\omega\tau}.$$

Clearly, the angle contribution in radians is $-\omega\tau$. Example 17.4.1 illustrates how the transportation lag is incorporated into the design.

**EXAMPLE 17.4.1**

Let

$$G_p(s) = \frac{10e^{-\tau s}}{s(s+4)},$$

where $\tau = 0.5$ s. For unity feedback we wish to design a cascade compensator that will meet these specifications:

**1.** $t_p \leq 0.5$ s.

**2.** PO $\leq 10\%$.

We begin by determining what we can get from simple gain compensation. The root locus for the dominant poles is shown in Fig. 17.8. If we choose $\zeta = 1/\sqrt{2}$, then it is a reasonably simple matter to find where the root locus crosses the chosen line of constant damping ratio. As always, what we have to do is satisfy the angle condition. That equation is

$$\underline{/e^{-\tau s}} - \underline{/s} - \underline{/s+4} = -180°.$$

The only new term is

$$\underline{/e^{-\tau s}}.$$

For a point along the chosen line of constant damping ratio, $s = -a + ja$, and

$$e^{-\tau s} = e^{-(-a+ja)\tau} = e^{a\tau}e^{-ja\tau} = e^{a\tau}\underline{/-a\tau},$$

where the angle is given in radians. Expressed in degrees we have

$$\underline{/e^{-(-a+ja)\tau}} = -a\tau \times \frac{180°}{\pi} = -a\tau \times 57.3°.$$

**Figure 17.8 |** Root locus for dominant poles $G_p = \dfrac{10e^{-\tau s}}{s(s+4)}$ for Example 17.4.1.

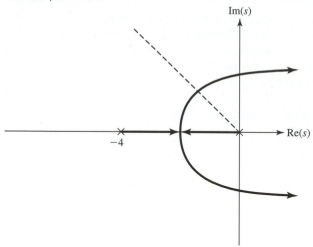

Thus our angle equation becomes

$$-a\tau \times 57.3° - \underline{/s} - \underline{/s+4} = -180°.$$

All that is required now is to find where the root locus crosses the chosen line of constant damping ratio. As usual, we do this with a convergent trial and error search. That is, we simply evaluate the equation at a particular point and then use the result to move outward or inward along the line of constant damping ratio. Table 17.1 summarizes the search. From the table, we see that a damping ratio $\zeta = 1/\sqrt{2}$ is achieved at $s = -0.96 + j0.96$. All that is left to do is compute

$$
\begin{aligned}
K &= \left[ \frac{|s| \times |s+4|}{10 \times |e^{-\tau s}|} \right]_{s=-0.96+j0.96} \\
&= \frac{|-0.96 + j0.96| \times |3.04 + j0.96|}{10 \times e^{(0.96)(0.5)}} \\
&= \frac{1.358 \times 3.188}{10 \times 1.616} \\
&= 0.268.
\end{aligned}
$$

Note the factor

$$e^{(0.96)(0.5)} = 1.616.$$

**Table 17.1 |** Summary of search with line of constant damping ratio.

| $a$ | 1 | 0.9 | 0.95 | 0.96 |
|---|---|---|---|---|
| $\underline{/G_p}$ | $-182.1°$ | $-177°$ | $-179.5°$ | $180°$ |

**Figure 17.9** | Step response of system $G_p = \dfrac{10e^{-\tau s}}{s(s+4)}$ for Example 17.4.1.

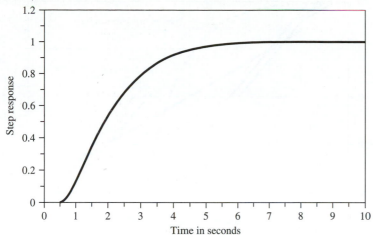

This is the contribution to the gain from the transportation lag. The step response is shown in Fig. 17.9.

In this case, we have used simple gain compensation, but it should be clear that the design procedure is no more difficult if we add lead, lag, or PID compensation. The design will be more tedious because we have to compute more angles in the process of locating the desired closed-loop poles, but there is no increase in conceptual complexity.

In Example 17.4.2, we use the Bode design technique of Chapter 15 that includes the ZOH. Again, the only modification is the need to compute the phase contribution of the transportation lag at the crossover frequency.

**EXAMPLE 17.4.2**

Let

$$G_p(s) = \frac{10e^{-\tau s}}{s(s+1)}$$

with $\tau = 0.5$ s. We wish to design a lead/lag compensator. The specifications are

1. Crossover frequency $\omega_c \approx 1$ rad/s.
2. Phase margin $\phi_m \geq 55°$.
3. Velocity error constant $K_v$ as large as possible.

The specifications are not as complete as they have been in the past. One reason is that the negative phase contribution of the transportation lag will force the crossover frequency down so low that noise suppression will not even be an issue. We could

**Figure 17.10 |** Two designs for $G_p(s) = \dfrac{10e^{-0.5s}}{s(s+1)}$ for Example 17.4.2.

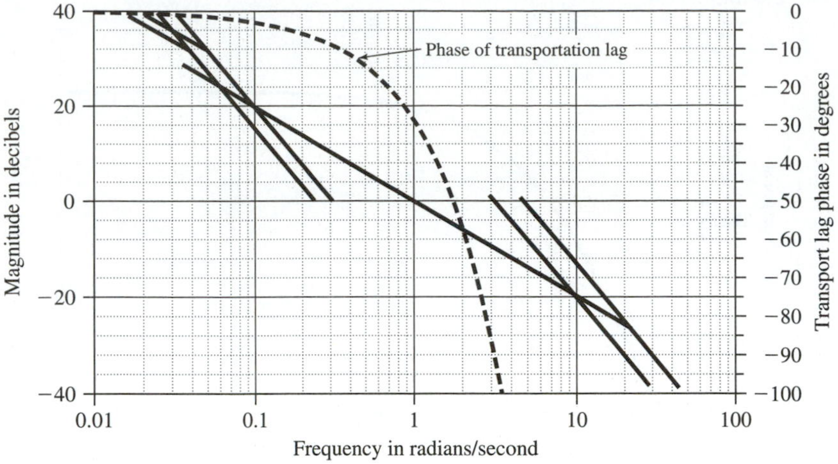

have added a specification on midfrequency gain but we will get a reasonable idea of the speed of response from $\omega_c$ anyway, so we omit this specification as well.

Two designs are shown in Fig. 17.10. We have added to the plot the negative phase contribution of the transportation lag as a design aid. By examining this phase plot, it becomes clear that getting the crossover frequency above 2 rad/s would be extraordinarily difficult. As can be seen, at $\omega_c = 1$ rad/s the transportation lag adds $-28.6°$ of phase. This is quite a lot of negative phase. Further, if we move $\omega_c$ up to 2 rad/s, the negative phase *doubles* to 60°. Thus, it is clear that getting the crossover frequency much above 1 rad/s is going to be difficult, at least if we use a low-order compensator.

The first design that we try is

$$G_c G_p(s) = \frac{2(1 + s/0.1)e^{-0.5s}}{s(1 + s/0.05)(1 + s/10)},$$

with $\omega_c = 1$ rad/s. Then,

$$\underline{/G_c G_p(j1)} = \tan^{-1} \frac{1}{0.1} - 90° - \tan^{-1} \frac{1}{0.05} - \tan^{-1} \frac{1}{10} - 28.6°$$

$$= 84.3° - 90° - 87.1° - 5.7° - 28.6°$$

$$= -127°.$$

Thus the phase margin is

$$180° - 129° = 53°.$$

For the second design, we leave the crossover frequency at $\omega_c = 1$ rad/s, but move the zero of the compensator to the left and pole to the right. In moving the zero to the left, we reduce $K_v$ thereby lowering the steady accuracy to a ramp input. However, raising the crossover frequency is not possible because we will not be able to meet the phase margin specification if we do.

Thus, for the second system

$$G_c G_p(s) = \frac{1.6(1 + s/0.06)e^{-0.5s}}{s(1 + s/0.04)(1 + s/20)}$$

and

$$\underline{/G_c G_p(j1)} = \tan^{-1} \frac{1}{0.06} - 90° - \tan^{-1} \frac{1}{0.04} - \tan^{-1} \frac{1}{20} - 28.6°$$

$$= 86.6° - 90° - 87.7° - 2.9° - 28.6°$$

$$= -123°,$$

and the phase margin is

$$180° - 123° = 57°.$$

For the second design

$$G_c(s) = \frac{\dfrac{1.6(1 + s/0.06)e^{-0.5s}}{s(1 + s/0.04)(1 + s/20)}}{\dfrac{10e^{-0.5s}}{s(1 + s)}}$$

$$= \frac{2.13(s + 0.06)(s + 1)}{(s + 0.04)(s + 20)}.$$

The step response for the second design is shown in Fig. 17.11. As we can see from the figure, the response is about what we could expect for the phase margin achieved.

**Figure 17.11 |** Step response for Example 17.4.2.

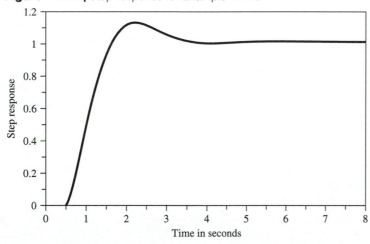

Using Example 17.4.2 we can now outline a general design procedure when a transportation lag is present.

1. Pick a crossover frequency where the negative phase contribution of the transportation lag is the maximum that can be overcome. This will probably be in the range of 30° to 50°.
2. Lay an asymptote of −20 dB/decade through the chosen crossover frequency.
3. Go down 1 decade below crossover and lay in an asymptote of slope −40 dB/decade. Connect this asymptote to the desired low-frequency asymptote.
4. Go up 1 decade above crossover and lay in an asymptote of slope −40 dB/decade. Add poles at higher frequencies if the pole-zero excess of $G_p$ (finite poles minus finite zeros) is greater than two.
5. Check the phase margin. If it is too low, widen the design corridor and try again.

A final observation is the following. The design in Example 17.4.2 has poor steady state error characteristics for a ramp input. This can be rectified by replacing the pole at $s = -0.04$ by a pole at $s = 0$. The net change in phase margin is only −2.3°. The resulting system has zero steady state error to both a step and ramp input. The only difficulty with this may be the implementation of the compensator using analog electronics, since we would have to build a double integrator.

Example 17.4.3 is designed to show the limitations that a transportation lag puts on our ability to control a system remotely.

**EXAMPLE 17.4.3**

Suppose we wish to put a lunar rover on the moon that has a simple robot arm. We want to control the rover and its robot arm from earth. Our design calls for a TV camera on the rover that transmits a picture of what the rover sees, as well as the position of the robot arm, back to earth. An operator sitting at a console manuevers the rover and the robot arm using a joystick. That is, the output of the joystick is transmitted to the rover via the communication link that transmits the TV picture to earth.

It takes 1.27 s for a signal sent from earth to reach the rover on the moon. It takes another 1.27 s for the TV image to be transmitted back to earth. Our goal is to compensate this system so that it behaves in a stable fashion and allows the operator to position the robot arm with sufficient accuracy. The specifications are simple:

1. Steady state accuracy to a step of 5%.
2. As quick a response as possible.

A block diagram of this system is shown in Fig. 17.12, with the robot arm dynamics represented as

$$G_{rover}(s) = \frac{1}{s+1}.$$

As we know from our analysis of the positioning table, which is really an elementary

**Figure 17.12 |** Block diagram of lunar robot control.

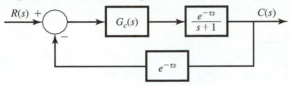

robot arm, this model is a bit of a simplification. A more realistic model would be

$$G_{rover}(s) = \frac{K}{s(s+a)}.$$

As we will see, it would be easy enough to incorporate the more complicated model in a redesign.

As we see from Fig. 17.12, we do *not* have unity feedback, so we need to determine the steady state error using the closed loop formulation, namely,

$$e_{ss} = \lim_{s \to 0} sR(s)[1 - T_c(s)].$$

For a unit step input

$$e_{ss} = \lim_{s \to 0}[1 - T_c(s)].$$

However,

$$\lim_{s \to 0}[1 - T_c(s)] = \lim_{s \to 0}\left[1 - \frac{e^{-\tau s}G_c(s)G_p(s)}{1 + e^{-2\tau s}G_c(s)G_p(s)}\right]$$

$$= \lim_{s \to 0} \frac{1 + e^{-2\tau s}G_c(s)G_p(s) - e^{-\tau s}G_c(s)G_p(s)}{1 + e^{-2\tau s}G_c(s)G_p(s)}$$

$$= \frac{1}{1 + \lim_{s \to 0} G_c(s)G_p(s)}$$

$$= \frac{1}{1 + K_p},$$

with

$$K_p \triangleq \lim_{s \to 0} G_c(s)G_p(s).$$

Thus, even though we do not have unity feedback, we can use the standard Bode design techniques as if we did. In particular we can use the formula for the position error constant, to write

$$e_{ss} = \frac{1}{1 + K_p} \le 0.05,$$

or $K_p \ge 19$.

Suppose we decide to build a simple lag compensator as shown in Fig. 17.13. For this choice

$$G_cG_pH(s) = \frac{19(1 + s/0.1)e^{-2.54s}}{(1 + s/0.002)(1 + s)} = \frac{0.38(s + 0.1)e^{-2.54s}}{(s + 0.002)(s + 1)},$$

and $\omega_c = 0.04$ rad/s, clearly indicating that the transient response will be very slow.

**Figure 17.13 |** Simple lag compensation.

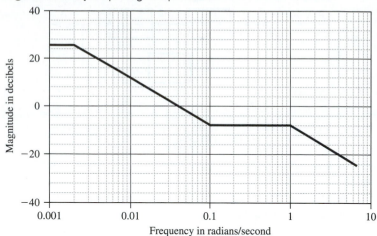

To compute the phase margin we first find

$$\underline{/G_cG_pH(j0.04)} = \tan^{-1}\frac{0.04}{0.1} - \tan^{-1}\frac{0.04}{0.002} - \tan^{-1}\frac{0.04}{1}$$
$$- (0.04)(2.54)(180/\pi)$$
$$= 21.8° - 87.14° - 2.3° - 5.82°$$
$$= -73.5°.$$

Then

$$\phi_m = 180° - 73.5° = 107°.$$

This is a large phase margin, but in systems with a transportation lag it is often necessary to have a very large phase margin to obtain a reasonable gain margin. To illustrate this, consider that a decade or so higher in frequency at $\omega = 0.9$ rad/s we have

$$\underline{/G_cG_pH(j0.9)} = \tan^{-1}\frac{0.9}{0.1} - \tan^{-1}\frac{0.9}{0.002} - \tan^{-1}\frac{0.9}{1}$$
$$- (0.9)(2.54)\frac{180}{\pi}$$
$$= 83.7° - 89.9° - 42° - 131°$$
$$= -179°.$$

Accurate Bode phase and magnitude plots of the compensated system are shown in Fig. 17.14. Note how rapidly the phase changes after crossover due to the contribution of the transportation lag. As a result the system has less than 8 dB of gain margin even though it has 107° of phase margin. The step response is shown in Fig. 17.15, and is clearly unsatisfactory.

**Figure 17.14 |** Bode magnitude plots of lag design of lunar rover $G_pH(s) = \dfrac{e^{-2\tau s}}{s+1}$.

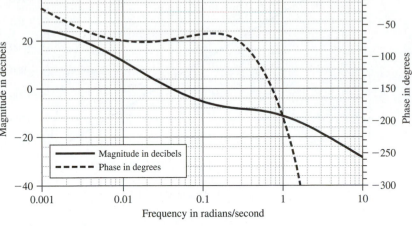

**Figure 17.15 |** Step response of lag design of lunar rover $G_pH(s) = \dfrac{e^{-2\tau s}}{s+1}$, Example 17.4.3.

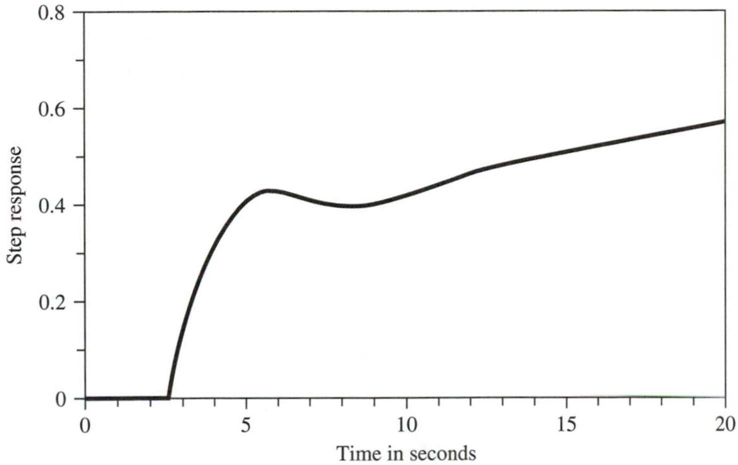

An improved design is shown in Fig. 17.16. The compensator is

$$G_c(s) = \frac{0.2(s+1)}{s}.$$

This is simply proportional plus integral control with the the zero of the PI compensator canceling the pole of the plant at $s = -1$, yielding

$$G_cG_pH(s) = \frac{0.2e^{-2.54s}}{s}.$$

Included along with the asymptotic Bode magnitude plot is the phase contribution of the transportation lag. As can be seen the transportation lag by itself contributes

**Figure 17.16 |** Bode plot for PI design of lunar rover for Example 17.4.3.

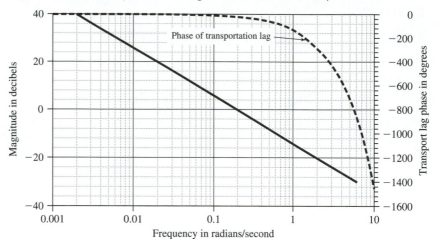

over −200° of negative phase at $\omega = 1.1$ rad/s. Because of the very large negative phase contribution from the transportation lag, we simply cannot raise the crossover frequency much above 0.5 rad/s.

This improved design increases the crossover frequency to 0.2 rad/s. The resulting rise time will be about 5 s. Not great, but this is better than the first design. In addition, the steady state error is zero and the gain margin has increased to 18 dB.

The unit step response is shown in Fig. 17.17. As we see the response is very smooth, and about as fast as could be expected given the crossover frequency. As

**Figure 17.17 |** Step response of PI design of lunar rover for Example 17.4.3.

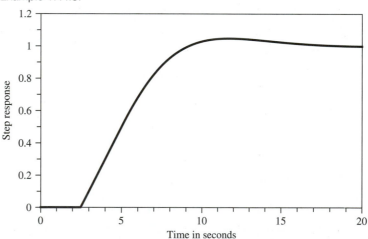

it turns out this is about as good a response as we are likely to obtain with a simple compensator. We might be able to improve the crossover frequency somewhat by introducing multiple zeros in the region of 0.5 rad/s to try to overcome the negative phase of the transportation lag, but we will not attempt that here.

## 17.5 | SAMPLED DATA SYSTEMS

We now turn our attention to the design of sampled data systems when the continuous plant has a transportation lag. We will use both root locus and Bode design techniques. As has been the case in the past, Bode design will prove to be superior to root locus design, primarily because we can can specify the system performance more completely using Bode design.

### 17.5.1 Bode s Plane Design

The Bode design procedure for a sampled data system with a transportation lag is very similar to that developed in Chapter 15 where we had to account for the negative phase of the zero-order hold. If a transportation lag is added, then we also have to account for the negative phase contribution of the lag. The two phase contributions are very similar. The negative phase contribution of the zero-order hold at frequency $\omega$ is

$$\phi_{\text{ZOH}} = -\frac{\omega T}{2} \text{ rad} = -28.7\omega T \text{ deg}, \qquad \text{[17.1]}$$

while that of the transportation lag is

$$\phi_{\text{lag}} = -\omega\tau \text{ rad} = -57.3\omega\tau \text{ deg}. \qquad \text{[17.2]}$$

Thus, as we did in Chapter 15, we will use excess phase margin to offset these negative phase contributions at the crossover frequency $\omega_c$.

**EXAMPLE 17.5.1**

Consider again the system shown in Fig. 17.18, and let

$$G_p(s) = \frac{4e^{-\tau s}}{s(s+4)},$$

with $\tau = 0.5$ s. We will design $G_c(z)$ using Bode's method in the $s$ plane, accounting for the negative phase contribution of the zero-order hold and that of the transportation

**Figure 17.18 |** Sampled data system with unity feedback.

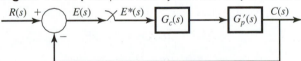

**Figure 17.19** | Two designs for $G_p(s) = \dfrac{4e^{-\tau s}}{s(s+4)}$.

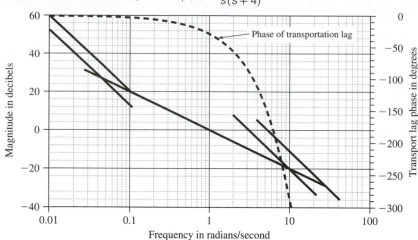

lag. $G_c(s)$ can then transferred to the $z$ domain using either the bilinear or ad hoc mapping. The performance specifications are:

1.  Sampling rate as low as possible, preferably below 50 Hz.
2.  $K_v > 100$.
3.  Crossover frequency $\omega_c \geq 1$ rad/s.
4.  Phase margin of at least $50°$.

Figure 17.19 shows two designs. At this juncture, we assume that the reader is familiar with the Bode design procedures introduced in Chapters 11 and 15. As before, we will design a sequence of systems in an effort to maximize performance.

Design 1, shown in Fig. 17.19, is

$$G_c G_p(s) = \frac{0.1(1 + s/0.1)e^{-0.5s}}{s^2(1 + s/10)}.$$

Note that we have elected to build a PI/Lead compensator. Since the plant is itself type 1, the overall forward loop transfer function will be type 2. This means that we exceed the specification on steady state accuracy. The rationale is that if we leave the system type at 1, we will end up with a second pole very near the origin anyway, so we might just as well put the pole at the origin. As we know from Chapter 15, it is easy to implement a double integrator *digitally*.

With $\omega_c = 1$ rad/s, accounting for the negative phase of the transportation lag but not the negative phase of the zero-order hold, we have

$$\underline{/G_c G_p} = \tan^{-1} \frac{1}{0.1} - 180° - \tan^{-1} \frac{1}{10} + \phi_\tau$$

$$= 84.3° - 180° - 5.7° - 28.6°$$

$$= -130°,$$

where $\phi_\tau$ is the negative phase contribution of the transportation lag. This puts us right at the minimum required phase margin *without* accounting for the negative phase of the zero-order hold. Thus, we have to choose the maximum allowable sampling rate $f_s = 50$ Hz. At this sampling frequency

$$\phi_{ZOH} = -\frac{1.0 \times 0.02 \times 90}{\pi}$$

$$= -0.57°.$$

We see that at the desired crossover frequency the negative phase contribution of the transportation lag dominates. If we now push the zero of the compensator at $s = -0.1$ to the left and the pole at $s = -10$ to the right we should be able to obtain the desired phase margin. Therefore we consider

$$G_c G_p(s) = \frac{0.0398(1 + s/0.04)e^{-0.5s}}{s^2(1 + s/30)}.$$

Then

$$\underline{/G_c G_p} = \tan^{-1} \frac{1}{0.04} - 180° - \tan^{-1} \frac{1}{30} + \phi_\tau$$

$$= 87.7° - 180° - 1.9° - 28.6°$$

$$= -123°.$$

If we now account for the negative phase contribution of the zero-order hold at $f_s = 50$ Hz, we have

$$\phi_m = 57° - 0.57° = 56°.$$

This means that we can more than meet the specifications for phase margin and crossover frequency. A satisfactory compensator is

$$G_c(s) = \frac{G_c(s)G_p(s)}{G_p(s)} = \frac{7.5(s + 0.04)(s + 4)}{s(s + 30)}.$$

Using the ad hoc method to transfer the compensator to the $z$ domain, we obtain

$$G_c(z) = \frac{7.5(z - 0.9992)(z - 0.9231)}{(z - 1)(z - 0.5488)}.$$

The alert reader will question using the same gain in $G_z(z)$ as in $G_c(s)$. For $f_{sample} = 50$ Hz, we will not be far off in doing so. To verify this, we could find $G_z(z)$ using the bilinear mapping and conclude that the gain is little high, but not much (see Problem 11 of Section 17.7.5). For the ad hoc compensator, matching the magnitudes of $G_c(s)$ and $G_c(z)$ at $\omega = 1$ rad/s, yields $K_c = 5.9$.

The step responses for $K_c = 5.9$ and 7.5 are shown in Fig. 17.20. The two responses provide us with a trade off between speed of response and per cent overshoot.

**Figure 17.20** | Step responses $K_c = 7.5$ and 5.9 for Example 17.5.1.

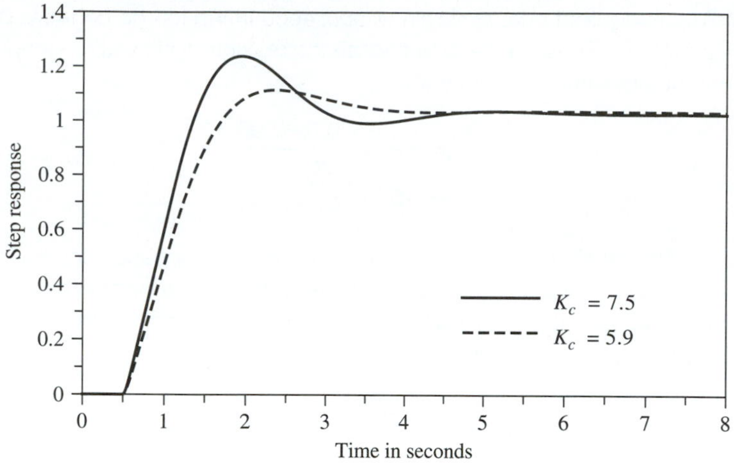

## 17.5.2 Design in the z Plane

We can also design the compensation for a sampled data system with a transportation lag directly in the $z$ plane. At first glance it would seem a fairly daunting task to do the design in this way, but as we will see it is not that much more difficult than a $z$-plane design without the transportation lag. We will have to find $G_p'(z)$. Example 17.5.2 is devoted to showing how to find $G_p'(z)$ when a transportation lag is present.

**EXAMPLE 17.5.2**

Let

$$G_p(s) = \frac{ae^{-\tau s}}{s+a}.$$

If we let $T = 1/f_{\text{sample}}$, then we can write

$$\tau = \ell T - \gamma T,$$

where

$$0 < \gamma < 1,$$

and $\ell$ is an integer. We will find $G_p'(z)$ using this formulation. Given the capabilities of the modern microprocessor we can always adjust the sampling frequency slightly so that

$$\tau = \ell T.$$

This assumption would simplify the following derivation of $G_p'(z)$, and in most cases we make this adjustment in the sampling frequency. However, leaving $\gamma$ in the formulation doesn't really complicate the following derivation very much, and it leads to a very interesting question (see Problem 1 in Section 17.7.5).

To find $G'_p(z)$ we first find

$$Y_{step}(s) = \frac{ae^{-(\ell-\gamma)Ts}}{s(s+a)}$$

$$= e^{-(\ell-\gamma)Ts}\left[\frac{a}{s(s+a)}\right]$$

$$= e^{-(\ell-\gamma)Ts}\left[\frac{1}{s} - \frac{1}{s+a}\right].$$

Applying the inverse Laplace-transform yields

$$y_{step}(t) = \mathbf{1}[t - (\ell-\gamma)T] - e^{-a[t-(\ell-\gamma)T]}\mathbf{1}[t - (\ell-\gamma)T]$$

$$y_{step}(kT) = \mathbf{1}[kT - (\ell-\gamma)T] - e^{-a[kT-(\ell-\gamma)T]}\mathbf{1}[kT - (\ell-\gamma)T].$$

We now find the $\mathcal{Z}$ transforms of the *delayed* discrete unit step and discrete exponential functions and finally assemble $Y_{step}(s)$.

We have

$$\mathcal{Z}\{\mathbf{1}[kT - (\ell-\gamma)T]\} = \sum_{k=0}^{\infty} \mathbf{1}[(k-\ell)T + \gamma T]z^{-k}$$

$$= 0 \times z^0 + 0 \times z^{-1} + \cdots + 0 \times z^{-(\ell-1)}$$

$$+ 1 \times z^{-\ell} + 1 \times z^{-(\ell+1)} + \cdots$$

$$= z^{-\ell}\sum_{k=0}^{\infty} z^{-k}$$

$$= \frac{1}{z^\ell}\frac{z}{z-1}$$

$$= \frac{z}{z^\ell(z-1)},$$

$$\mathcal{Z}\{e^{-a[kT-(\ell-\gamma)T]}\mathbf{1}[kT - (\ell-\gamma)T]\} = \sum_{k=0}^{\infty} e^{-a[kT-(\ell-\gamma)T]}\mathbf{1}[(k-\ell)T + \gamma T]z^{-k}$$

$$= 0 \times z^0 + 0 \times z^{-1} + \cdots + 0 \times z^{-(\ell-1)}$$

$$+ 1 \times e^{-a\gamma T}z^{-\ell} + 1 \times e^{-aT}e^{-a\gamma T}z^{-(\ell+1)} + \cdots$$

$$= z^{-\ell}e^{-a\gamma T}\sum_{k=0}^{\infty} e^{-akT}z^{-k}$$

$$= \frac{e^{-a\gamma T}}{z^\ell}\frac{z}{z-e^{-aT}}$$

$$= \frac{ze^{-a\gamma T}}{z^\ell(z-e^{-aT})}.$$

We are now ready for the final assembly of

$$Y_{step}(z) = \frac{1}{z^\ell}\frac{z}{z-1} - \frac{e^{-a\gamma T}}{z^\ell}\frac{z}{z-e^{-aT}}$$

$$= \frac{1}{z^\ell}\left\{\frac{z[z-e^{-aT}-(z-1)e^{-a\gamma T}]}{(z-1)(z-e^{-aT})}\right\}$$

$$= \frac{1}{z^\ell}\left\{\frac{z[(1-e^{-a\gamma T})z+(e^{-a\gamma T}-e^{-aT})]}{(z-1)(z-e^{-aT})}\right\}.$$

Finally, dividing out the discrete step, we have

$$G'_p(z) = (1-z^{-1})Y_{step}(z) = \frac{(1-e^{-a\gamma T})z+(e^{-a\gamma T}-e^{-aT})}{z^\ell(z-e^{-aT})}.$$

Note that if $\gamma = 0$, then

$$G'_p(z) = z^{-\ell}\bar{G}'_p(z),$$

where

$$\bar{G}_p(s) = \frac{a}{s+a}.$$

Thus, for $\gamma = 0$, we merely find $\bar{G}'_p(z)$ and multiply by $z^{-\ell}$. Note that if $\gamma \neq 0$ then $G'_p(z)$ has a zero that it would not have were $\gamma = 0$. The process is essentially the same, albeit more tedious, if $G_p(s)$ has more poles.

---

We now design a compensator in the $z$ plane using the root locus method we first used for continuous systems. In Example 17.5.3, we explore the impact of the sampling rate on the ease of design. Our natural inclination will be to slow the sampling rate to minimize the degree of the characteristic equation. The example shows that our natural inclination is wrong.

**EXAMPLE 17.5.3**

---

Consider once again

$$G_p(s) = \frac{e^{-\tau s}}{s(s+1)},$$

with $\tau = 0.5$ s. The specifications on the closed-loop system are

1.  PO $\leq$ 10%.
2.  $t_p \leq 2.5$ s.

The specification on time to peak takes into account the half second delay due to the transportation lag. We will use a sampling rate of 50 Hz, which seems counterintuitive since it will lead to a very high order compensator. However, as we will see that is not the problem that it might seem.

For $f_s = 50$ Hz,

$$G_p'(z) = \frac{(0.02 + e^{-0.02} - 1)z + (1 - e^{-0.02} - 0.02e^{-0.02})}{z^{(0.5)(50)}(z - 1)(z - e^{-0.02})}$$

$$= \frac{0.00019867(z + 0.000197353)}{z^{25}(z - 1)(z - 0.9802)}$$

$$= \frac{0.0002(z + 0.9934)}{z^{25}(z - 1)(z - 0.9802)}.$$

We now have a 27th order system. This may seem intractable, but it does not prove to be. What we are concerned with is the *total* negative phase contribution of the transportation lag. As long as this total negative phase contribution is manageable, we don't really care whether it is generated by 1 pole or 25 poles. One thing is certain, however. If we wish to draw the root locus, we will need the assistance of a computer.

For a time to peak of 2.5 s, we use 2 s in our computation because of the delay of 0.5 s. To satisfy the specifications we then choose dominant poles at $s = -1.5 \pm j1.5$. This yields $\zeta = 1/\sqrt{2}$. In the $z$ plane, the dominant poles are at

$$z = e^{-(1.5)(0.02)}e^{\pm j(1.5)(0.02)}$$

$$= 0.9704 \underline{/\pm 1.719°}$$

$$= 0.97 \pm j0.0291.$$

At the location of the desired closed-loop poles, as shown in Fig. 17.21,

$$\underline{/G_p'(z)} = \alpha - \theta_1 - \theta_2 - 25\theta_3$$

$$= \tan^{-1}\frac{0.02911}{1.96341} - \left[180° - \tan^{-1}\frac{0.02911}{0.02999}\right] - \left[180° - \tan^{-1}\frac{0.02911}{0.0102}\right]$$

$$\quad - 25 \times 1.7189°$$

$$= 0.8494° - 135.86° - 109.3° - 42.972°$$

$$= -287.27°.$$

Then, we need

$$287.27° - 180° = 107.27°$$

from our compensator.

Suppose we use pole/zero cancellation and a simple lead compensator. The zero of the lead will cancel the plant pole at $z = 0.9802$, as shown in Fig. 17.22, and the location of the pole of the compensator can be found by noting that with the plant pole canceled by the zero of the lead compensator the angle equation becomes

$$\underline{/G_p'(z)} + \theta_2 - \theta_4 = -180°.$$

Thus,

$$\theta_4 = 2.022°.$$

**Figure 17.21 |** Angle contributions at desired closed-loop pole locations.

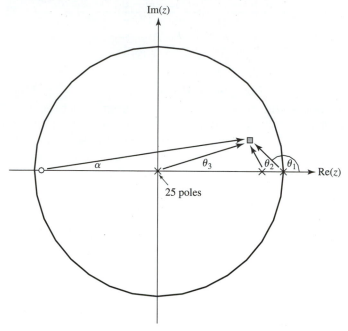

**Figure 17.22 |** Pole and zero locations of $G_c(z)$.

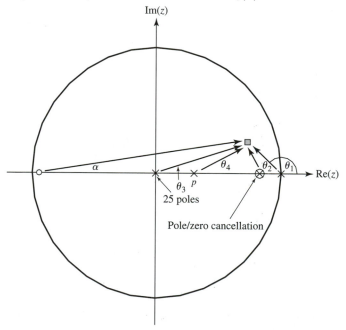

**Figure 17.23 |** Step response of compensated system, Example 17.5.3.

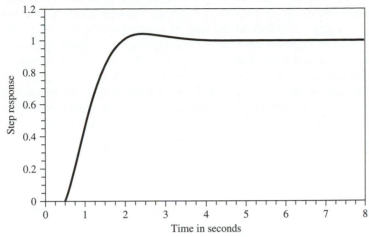

Then

$$p = 0.9700 - \frac{0.02911}{\tan 2.022°} = 0.1457.$$

Our compensator is then

$$G_c(z) = \frac{K_c(z - 0.9802)}{z - 0.2022},$$

where

$$K_c = \left[ \frac{|z|^{25}|z - 1||z - 0.255|}{(0.0002)|z + 0.9934|} \right] \Big|_{z = 0.97 + j0.0291}$$

$$= 41.47$$

The step response, shown in Fig. 17.23, meets the specifications.

In the continuous domain, we included the negative phase contribution due to the transportation lag from $e^{-\tau s}$. In the $z$ domain, that negative phase contribution is represented by the 25 poles at the origin. As we see, it is possible to overcome a large amount of negative phase, in this case about 43°. However, as we see from the step response, we cannot expect an extremely fast response. That is, with a transportation lag of 0.5 s, we have to settle for a slower response.

## 17.6 | REPRISE

In this chapter, we have analyzed systems that have a transportation lag and shown that all the design techniques we had previously developed could be applied to such systems with only minor modification. The main lesson learned is that the presence of a transportation lag forces us to lower our expectation of system performance, as regards the *speed* of the transient response.

For Bode design, the transportation lag significantly reduces the phase margin at higher frequencies, forcing the crossover frequency to the left. In the case of root locus design, effectively the same thing happens, although it appears in the form of a large negative angle contribution from the poles generated by the transportation lag. To overcome this large negative angle contribution, the dominant poles have to be moved downward and to the right in the $z$ plane, reducing the damped frequency and hence the bandwidth and the speed of response.

The design techniques presented in this chapter all meet the transportation lag head on. There are a number of approximations to the zero-order hold, but the design examples presented show that it is possible, with only a small amount of additional effort, to account exactly for the effects of the lag.

## 17.7 | PROBLEMS

### 17.7.1 Continuous Systems—Root Locus Design

1.  For the unity feedback case, let

$$G_p(s) = \frac{e^{-0.3s}}{(s+2)(s+6)} \quad \text{and} \quad G_c(s) = \frac{K_c(s+2)}{s}.$$

Find $K_c$ so that the so that the damping ratio of the dominant closed-loop poles is 0.8.

2.  For the unity feedback case let

$$G_p(s) = \frac{e^{-0.2s}}{s(s+0.5)} \quad \text{and} \quad G_c(s) = \frac{K_c(s+0.5)}{s+b}.$$

Design the compensator so that
a. $\zeta = 0.8$.
b. $\omega_d = 4$ rad/s.

3.  For the unity feedback case let

$$G_p(s) = \frac{e^{-0.2s}}{s(s+4)} \quad \text{and} \quad G_c(s) = \frac{K_c(s+4)}{s+b}.$$

Design the compensator so that
a. $\zeta = 0.8$.
b. $\omega_d > 4$ rad/s.
c. $K_c$ minimized consistent with a and b.

4.  For the unity feedback case let

$$G_p(s) = \frac{e^{-0.1s}}{(s+2)(s+4)} \quad \text{and} \quad G_c(s) = \frac{K_c(s+2)(s+4)}{s(s+b)}.$$

Design a compensator so that

a. $\zeta = 0.8$.

b. $\omega_d > 5$ rad/s.

c. $K_c$ minimized consistent with a and b.

## 17.7.2 Continuous Systems—Bode Design

For each system use Bode design to find a compensator that meets the stated specifications.

1. $G_p(s) = \dfrac{10e^{-\tau s}}{(s+1)(s+3)}$, $\tau = 0.3$ s. Design the lowest order compensator that satisfies

   a. $K_p \geq 20$.

   b. $\omega_c$ as large as possible.

   c. Phase margin $\phi_m$ of at least $50°$.

2. $G_p(s) = \dfrac{10e^{-0.4s}}{(s+1)(s+3)}$ and $G_c(s) = \dfrac{K_c \prod_{i=1}^n (s+zi)}{\prod_{i=1}^n (s+p_i)}$. Design a compensator that meets these specifications:

   a. $K_p \geq 100$.

   b. $\omega_c$ as large as possible.

   c. Phase margin $\phi_m$ of at least $50°$.

   d. Compensator no more than second order.

   e. $K_c < 20$.

3. $G_p(s) = \dfrac{10e^{-\tau s}}{s(s+5)}$ with $\tau = 0.1$ s. Design

   $$G_c(s) = \frac{K_c(1 + s/z_1)(1 + s/z_2)}{(1 + s/p_1)(1 + s/p_2)}$$

   that meets these specifications:

   a. $K_v \geq 50$.

   b. $\left| \dfrac{E(j\omega)}{R(j\omega)} \right| \leq 0.1$ for $\omega \leq 0.5$ rad/s.

   c. $\left| \dfrac{C(j\omega)}{R(j\omega)} \right| \leq 0.1$ for $\omega \geq 150$ rad/s.

   d. Phase margin $\phi_m \geq 50°$.

   e. Crossover frequency $\omega_c$ maximized consistent with specifications a–d.

4. $G_p(s) = \dfrac{10e^{-0.1s}}{s(s+5)}$ and $G_c(s) = \dfrac{K_c(1 + s/z_1)(1 + s/z_2)}{(1 + s/p_1)(1 + s/p_2)}$. Design $G_c$ to meet these specifications:

   a. $K_v \geq 50$.

   b. $\left| \dfrac{E(j\omega)}{R(j\omega)} \right| \leq 0.1$ for $\omega \leq 0.5$ rad/s.

   c. $\left| \dfrac{C(j\omega)}{R(j\omega)} \right| \leq 0.1$ for $\omega \geq 150$ rad/s.

   d. Crossover frequency $\omega_c > 2$ rad/s.

   e. Phase margin maximized.

5. $G_p(s) = \dfrac{100e^{-\tau s}}{s(s+1)(s+10)}$, with $\tau = 0.2$ s. Design

$$G_c(s) = \frac{K_c(1 + s/z_1)(1 + s/z_2)}{(1 + s/p_1)(1 + s/100)}$$

that meets these specifications:
   a.  $K_v \geq 50$.
   b.  $\left|\dfrac{E(j\omega)}{R(j\omega)}\right| \leq 0.05$ for $\omega \leq 0.1$ rad/s.
   c.  $\left|\dfrac{C(j\omega)}{R(j\omega)}\right| \leq 0.1$ for $\omega \geq 200$ rad/s.
   d.  Phase margin: 50°.
   e.  Crossover frequency $\omega_c$ maximized consistent with specifications a–d.

6. $G_p(s) = \dfrac{100e^{-0.2s}}{s(s+1)(s+10)}$ and $G_c(s) = \dfrac{K_c(s+z_1)(s+z_2)}{(s+p_1)(s+100)}$. Design $G_c(s)$ to meet these specifications:
   a.  $K_a \geq 0.5$.
   b.  $\left|\dfrac{E(j\omega)}{R(j\omega)}\right| \leq 0.02$ for $\omega \leq 0.1$ rad/s.
   c.  $\left|\dfrac{C(j\omega)}{R(j\omega)}\right| \leq 0.1$ for $\omega \geq 100$ rad/s.
   d.  $\omega_c \geq 1$ rad/s.
   e.  Phase margin maximized consistent with specifications a–d.

7. $G_p(s) = \dfrac{100e^{-\tau s}}{s(s+1)(s+10)}$, with $\tau = 0.2$ s. Design

$$G_c(s) = \frac{K_c(1 + s/z_1)(1 + s/z_2)}{(1 + s/p_1)(1 + s/100)}$$

that meets these specifications:
   a.  $K_a \geq 0.1$.
   b.  $\left|\dfrac{E(j\omega)}{R(j\omega)}\right| \leq 0.1$ for $\omega \leq 0.1$ rad/s.
   c.  $\left|\dfrac{C(j\omega)}{R(j\omega)}\right| \leq 0.1$ for $\omega \geq 100$ rad/s.
   d.  Phase margin: 50°.
   e.  Crossover frequency $\omega_c$ maximized consistent with specifications a–d.

8. $G_p(s) = \dfrac{e^{-0.2s}}{s(s+1)}$ and $G_c(z) = \dfrac{K_c(z-z_1)}{(z-p_1)}$.
   a.  Find $G_p'(z)$ for $f_s = 50$ Hz.
   b.  $t_p \approx 2$ s.
   c.  PO is less than 20%.

9. $G_p(s) = \dfrac{e^{-0.2s}}{s(s+1)}$ and $G_c(z) = \dfrac{K_c(z-z_1)}{(z-p_1)}$.
   a.  Find $G_p'(z)$ for $f_s = 100$ Hz.

b. $t_p \approx 2$ s.

c. PO is less than 20%.

**10.** $G_p(s) = \dfrac{10e^{-\tau s}}{s(s+5)}$, $\tau = 0.2$ s. Design the lowest order compensator that meets these specifications:

a. $K_v \geq 20$.

b. $\left|\dfrac{E(j\omega)}{R(j\omega)}\right| \leq 0.02$ $\omega \leq 0.1$ rad/s.

c. $\left|\dfrac{C(j\omega)}{R(j\omega)}\right| \leq 0.05$ $\omega \geq 5$ rad/s.

d. $\omega_c$ as large as possible.

e. Phase margin $\phi_m$ of at least $50°$.

**11.** $G_p(s) = \dfrac{e^{-\tau s}}{s^2}$, with $\tau = 0.3$ s. Design a compensator

$$G_c(s) = \frac{K_c(1 + s/z_1)}{(1 + s/p_1)}$$

that will meet these specifications:

a. $K_a > 0.1$.

b. $\left|\dfrac{C(j\omega)}{R(j\omega)}\right| \leq 0.1$ for $\omega \geq 40$ rad/s.

c. Phase margin: $50°$.

d. Crossover frequency $\omega_c \geq 2$ rad/s.

**12.** $G_p(s) = \dfrac{180e^{-\tau s}}{(s+6)(s+30)}$, with $\tau = 0.3$ s. Design a compensator

$$G_c(s) = \frac{K_c(1 + s/z_1)(1 + z/z_2)}{(1 + s/p_1)(1 + s/p_2)}$$

that will meet these specifications:

a. $K_v > 100$.

b. $\left|\dfrac{E(j\omega)}{R(j\omega)}\right| \leq 0.02$ for $\omega \leq 0.1$ rad/s.

c. $\left|\dfrac{C(j\omega)}{R(j\omega)}\right| \leq 0.1$ for $\omega \geq 40$ rad/s.

d. $\omega_c \geq 10$ rad/s.

d. $\phi_m$ maximized.

## 17.7.3 Sampled Data Systems—Root Locus Design

For each problem find $G_p'(z)$ and then design the specified compensator to meet the given specifications using root locus techniques directly in the $z$ plane.

**1.** $G_p(s) = \dfrac{e^{-0.2s}}{s^2}$. Design a lead compensator that meets these specifications:

a. $f_s = 50$ Hz.

b. $\omega_n = 3\sqrt{2}$ rad/s.

c. $\zeta = 1/\sqrt{2}$.

2. $G_p(s) = \dfrac{e^{-\tau s}}{s(s+1)}$, with $\tau = 0.2$ s. Specifications:
   a. For $f_s = 50$ Hz.
   b. $t_p \approx 2$ s.
   c. PO $\leq 20\%$.

### 17.7.4 Sampled Data Systems—Bode Design

For these problems, assume unity feedback and design the specified compensators by Bode's method.

1. $G_p(s) = \dfrac{e^{-0.2s}}{s^2}$. Let the sampling frequency be 50 Hz.
   a. Find $G'_p(z)$.
   b. Design a lead compenstor directly in the $z$ plane that meets these specifications: (i) $\omega_n = 3\sqrt{2}$ rad/s and (ii) $\zeta = 1/\sqrt{2}$.

2. $G_p(s) = \dfrac{e^{-0.2s}}{s^2}$. Let the sampling frequency be 50 Hz.
   a. Find $G'_p(z)$.
   b. Design a lead compenstor directly in the $z$ plane that meets these specifications: (i) 4 rad/s and (ii) $\zeta = 0.8$.

3. $G_p(s) = \dfrac{e^{-0.2s}}{s^2}$. Let the sampling frequency be 100 Hz.
   a. Find $G'_p(z)$.
   b. Design a lead compenstor directly in the $z$ plane that meets these specifications: (i) 5 rad/s and (ii) $\zeta = 0.8$.

### 17.7.5 Additional Problems

1. For the $G'_p(z)$ derived in Example 17.5.2, let
   a. $a = 2$.
   b. $f_{sample} = 10$ Hz.
   c. $\gamma = 0.05$ s.
   Where is the zero caused by $\gamma$? Zeros can be of use in a compensator design. Can we use this zero to our advantage? What happens if we let $f_{sample} = 50$ Hz?

2. Same as Problem 1 but for $f_{sample} = 2$, 4, and 8 Hz.
3. For the unity feedback configuration of Fig. 17.24 let

$$G(s) = \frac{1}{s+1}.$$

**Figure 17.24 |** Closed-loop system with transportation lag.

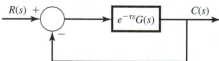

For $\tau = 0.4$ s, use MATLAB to find where the root locus crosses the imaginary axis.

4. For the unity feedback configuration of Fig. 17.24 let

$$G(s) = \frac{1}{s+1}.$$

For $\tau = 0.4$ s, approximate $e^{-\tau s}$:

$$G_\tau = 1 - \tau s.$$

Use MATLAB to draw the root locus and find the points, where the locus crosses the imaginary axis. Compare the crossing points with those of Problem 2.

5. Same as Problem 4 but $e^{-\tau s}$ approximated by

$$G_\tau = \frac{1}{1 + \tau s}.$$

6. Same as Problem 4 but $e^{-\tau s}$ approximated by

$$G_\tau = \frac{1 - \tau s/2}{1 + \tau s/2}.$$

7. Same as Problem 4 but $e^{-\tau s}$ approximated by

$$G_\tau = \frac{1}{[1 + \tau s/n]^n}, n = 3.$$

8. Same as Problem 4 but $e^{-\tau s}$ approximated by

$$G_\tau = \frac{1}{[1 + \tau s/n]^n}, n = 7.$$

9. Same as Problem 4 but $e^{-\tau s}$ approximated by

$$G_\tau = \frac{1}{[1 + \tau s/n]^n}, n = 10.$$

10. Rework Example 17.4.1, approximating $e^{-\tau s}$ by

$$G_\tau = 1 - \tau s.$$

11. For Example 17.5.1, use the bilinear mapping to find $G_c(z)$ and then find the step response.

12. Draw a picture showing the locations of poles with $0.5 < \zeta < 0.8$ and $7\pi/10T < \omega_n < 9\pi/10T$ in both the $s$ plane and the $z$ plane.

13. Show analytically that if $G(s)$ has no poles at $s = 0$ and we map it to the $z$ plane using the bilinear mapping

$$s = \frac{2}{T} \frac{z-1}{z+1},$$

$G(s)$ and $G(z)$ have the same dc gain.

14.  Reconsider the "smart" missile control problem first introduced in Chapter 7, as shown in Fig. 17.25. The missile has a TV camera in its nose that relays a picture to the pilot. The pilot then directs the missile by centering the target on a display in the cockpit with a joystick. The signal from the pilot then causes the guidance system of the missile to move toward the target. Let the dynamics of the missile and its control system be

$$G_p(s) = \frac{200e^{-\tau s}}{s(s+5)(s+15)},$$

with $\tau = 0.05$ s. For the unity feedback, cascade compensation configuration used in this chapter, design the compensator $G_c$ to these specifications:

a.  $f_{\text{sample}} \le 40$ Hz.

b.  $K_v \ge 100$.

c.  $\left|\dfrac{E(j\omega)}{R(j\omega)}\right| \le 0.01$ for $\omega \le 0.2$ rad/s.

d.  $\left|\dfrac{C(j\omega)}{R(j\omega)}\right| \le 0.1$ for $\omega \ge 200$ rad/s.

e.  $\phi_m \ge 50°$.

f.  PO $\le 10\%$.

g.  Compensator gain as low as possible.

**Figure 17.25 |** Smartbomb system.

Target

15.  Figure 17.26 shows a block diagram of a speed controller for an automobile that we considered in Chapter 7, where

$$G_{\text{spdc}}(s) = \frac{10}{(s+3)(s+3.2)} \qquad G_{\text{car}}(s) = \frac{e^{-\tau s}}{s+2.5},$$

where $\tau = 0.05$ s. Design a controller $G_c$ that meets these specifications:

a.  $f_{\text{sample}} \le 40$ Hz.

b.  $K_p \ge 10$.

**Figure 17.26 |** Block diagram of automobile speed control.

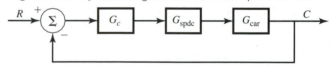

c. Rise time to 63% of final value less than 0.3 s.
d. The response to a step input is critically damped.
Use Bode design in the $s$ plane and adjust for the negative phase of the transportation lag and the zero-order hold. Map the compensator to the $z$ plane using the bilinear mapping.

16. Consider again the system shown in Fig. 17.27, first considered in Chapter 7, where the plant has a feedback loop. Let

$$G_1(s) = \frac{e^{-\tau s}}{s^2} \qquad G_2(s) = \frac{120s + 100}{s^2 + 12s + 72},$$

$\tau = 0.1$ s. Design a controller $G_c$ to meet these specifications:
a. $t_p \le 3$ s.
b. PO $\le 30\%$.
Use the root locus method in the $s$ plane to design the compensator.

**Figure 17.27** | Multiloop control.

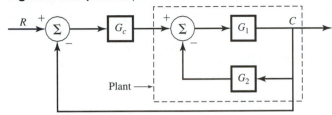

17. Figure 17.28 shows a unity feedback loop for the pitch control of an aircraft, first considered in Chapter 7, where

$$G_{\text{flap}}(s) = \frac{4000e^{-\tau s}}{s + 8} \qquad G_p(s) = \frac{(s + 6)(s + 15)}{s(s + 3 - j12)(s + 3 + j12)},$$

$\tau = 0.1$ s. Design a compensator to meet these specifications:
a. $f_{\text{sample}} \le 100$ Hz.
b. $K_v \ge 130$.
c. PO $\le 30\%$.
d. $t_p \le 5$ s.
Find $G'_p(z)$ and design the compensator in the $z$ plane using the root locus

**Figure 17.28** | Pitch control of aircraft.

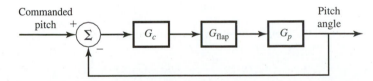

method. Let $\tau = mT$, where $m$ is an integer.

18.  In Chapter 7, we considered the the roll characteristics of a missile about its longitudinal axis, as shown in Fig. 17.29. The dynamics about the longitudinal axis are given by

$$G_m(s) = \frac{e^{-\tau s}}{s(s+15)},$$

$\tau = 0.3$ s. Redesign the the compensator $G_c$ using the methods of this chapter to meet the following specifications.

a.  $f_{sample} \le 100$ Hz.
b.  $K_v \ge 150$.
c.  $\left| \dfrac{E(j\omega)}{R(j\omega)} \right| \le 0.01$ for $\omega \le 0.2$ rad/s.
d.  $\left| \dfrac{C(j\omega)}{R(j\omega)} \right| \le 0.1$ for $\omega \ge 400$ rad/s.
e.  $\phi_m \ge 50°$.
f.  PO $\le 20\%$.

**Figure 17.29** | Roll control of a missile.

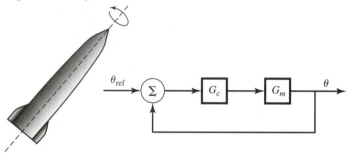

Use Bode design in the $s$ plane and adjust for the negative phase of the zero-order hold. Map the compensator to the $z$ plane using the bilinear mapping.

19.  Figure 17.30 shows a high-speed magnetic levitation train. On curves it is necessary to bank the train to match the bank of rail. The block diagram shows how this might be accomplished with a rate gyro. $R$ is a bank command in degrees and $C$ is the actual amount of bank, also in degrees. Since the train is floating, its dynamics have been modeled as

$$G_{maglev}(s) = \frac{1}{Js^2}.$$

In the figure, the transfer function has been broken down into

$$G_1(s) = \frac{e^{-\tau s}}{Js} \quad \text{and} \quad G_2(s) = \frac{1}{s},$$

**Figure 17.30 |** Roll control of maglev train.

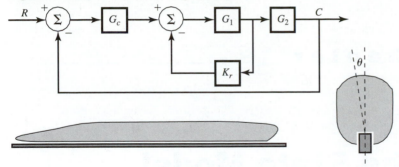

with $\tau = 0.2$ s. We do not need to know $J$. We simply assume the ratio

$$\frac{K_r}{J}$$

is known. Design an analog compensator $G_c(s)$ to meet these specifications:

a.  $K_v \geq 500$.

b.  $\left| \dfrac{E(j\omega)}{R(j\omega)} \right| \leq 0.02$ for $\omega \leq 0.3$ rad/s.

c.  $\left| \dfrac{C(j\omega)}{R(j\omega)} \right| \leq 0.1$ for $\omega \geq 300$ rad/s.

d.  $\phi_m \geq 70°$

e.  PO $\leq 10\%$.

f.  Rise time to 90% of final value $\leq 0.2$ s.

# FURTHER READINGS

Chestnut, Harold, and R. W. Mayer. 1951. *Servomechanisms and Regulating Systems Design,*
   Vol. 1. New York: John Wiley & Sons.

D'Azzo, John J., and Constantine H. Houpis. 1988. *Linear Control System Design:
   Conventional and Modern.* New York: McGraw-Hill.

James, H. M., N. B. Nichols, and R. S. Phillips. 1947. *Theory of Servomechanisms.*
   New York: McGraw Hill.

Kuo, Benjamin C. 1982. *Automatic Control,* 4th ed. Englewood Cliffs, N.J.: Prentice-Hall.

Ogata, K. 1970. *Modern Control Engineering.* Englewood Cliffs. N.J.: Prentice-Hall.

Saucedo, R., and E. E. Schiring. 1968. *Introduction to Continuous and Digital Control
   Systems.* New York: MacMillan.

# 18 Chapter

# The State Model

## 18.1 | OVERVIEW

In this chapter we introduce a new representation of the physical system, or plant, that we wish to control. In previous chapters we have represented the plant with a transfer function. The compensators that we designed to improve the performance of the closed-loop system were also represented as transfer functions. In this chapter we introduce the state model representation of a physical system.

The state model representation of a physical system has some advantages. One is that it can easily accommodate more complex plants that may have multiple inputs and multiple outputs. The transfer function representation is not well suited to these more complex plants. Another advantage of the state model is that it provides us with information about the internal behavior of the plant. The transfer function representation, by contrast, tells us nothing about the internal behavior of the plant because all we have is a single output signal from the plant.

The fact that we have access to all the states of the plant will lead us first to the ideas of controllability and observability and then to a very different kind of control, called state feedback control. We will then introduce the concept of an observer and finally formulate a control strategy called the controller/observer.

Most of these topics will unfold in Chapters 19 and 20. In this chapter we will first introduce the state model and then discuss the stability characteristics of simple second-order state models at length. Once we fully understand the stability of these second-order systems, we can very rapidly extend the analysis to state models of higher dimension, because we will be able to find matrix transformations that decouple the states of the higher dimension models into low dimension subsystems. Generally, these subsystems will be of dimension one and two. Occasionally we may encounter a subsystem of dimension three or more, but only rarely.

This chapter will be the last to contain very many pictures. That in itself speaks volumes about the state model, or state space, approach. The analysis of the state model is essentially an exercise in linear algebra, and the pictures in this chapter, representing the stability behavior of two-dimensional systems, will be our primary source of intuition for understanding higher dimension state models.

# 18.2 | RELATION TO THE TRANSFER FUNCTION

Consider the system shown in Fig. 18.1. and let

$$G(s) = \frac{K}{s^3 + a_2 s^2 + a_1 s + a_0}.$$

**Figure 18.1 | Open-loop system.**

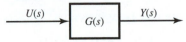

Then

$$Y(s) = G(s)U(s) = \frac{KU(s)}{s^3 + a_2 s^2 + a_1 s + a_0}.$$

Cross multiplying yields

$$s^3 Y(s) + a_2 s^2 Y(s) + a_1 s Y(s) + a_0 Y(s) = KU(s).$$

Assuming zero initial conditions and applying the inverse Laplace transform, yields the differential equation

$$\frac{d^3}{dt^3} y(t) + a_2 \frac{d^2}{dt^2} y(t) + a_1 \frac{d}{dt} y(t) + a_0 y(t) = K u(t). \qquad [18.1]$$

Now let

$$x_1(t) = y(t), \qquad x_2(t) = \frac{d}{dt} x_1(t) = \frac{d}{dt} y(t), \qquad x_3(t) = \frac{d}{dt} x_2(t) = \frac{d^2}{dt^2} y(t).$$

Using these definitions of "states," Eq. [18.1] can be written as

$$\frac{d}{dt} x_3(t) + a_2 x_3(t) + a_1 x_2(t) + a_0 x_1(t) = K u(t),$$

or

$$\frac{d}{dt} x_3(t) = -a_2 x_3(t) - a_1 x_2(t) - a_0 x_1(t) + K u(t).$$

Combining this last equation with the earlier definitions of $x_1(t)$ and $x_2(t)$ yields

$$\frac{d}{dt} x_1(t) = x_2(t),$$

$$\frac{d}{dt} x_2(t) = x_3(t),$$

$$\frac{d}{dt} x_3(t) = -a_2 x_3(t) - a_1 x_2(t) - a_0 x_1(t) + K u(t).$$

Letting $\dot{x}(t) = (d/dt)x(t)$ and putting the equations in matrix form yields

$$\begin{bmatrix} \dot{x}_1(t) \\ \dot{x}_2(t) \\ \dot{x}_3(t) \end{bmatrix} = \begin{bmatrix} 0 & 1 & 0 \\ 0 & 0 & 1 \\ -a_0 & -a_1 & -a_2 \end{bmatrix} \begin{bmatrix} x_1 \\ x_2 \\ x_3 \end{bmatrix} + \begin{bmatrix} 0 \\ 0 \\ K \end{bmatrix} u(t).$$

Defining

$$\mathbf{x}(t) \triangleq \begin{bmatrix} \dot{x}_1(t) \\ \dot{x}_2(t) \\ \dot{x}_3(t) \end{bmatrix}, \qquad \mathbf{A} \triangleq \begin{bmatrix} 0 & 1 & 0 \\ 0 & 0 & 1 \\ -a_0 & -a_1 & -a_2 \end{bmatrix}, \quad \text{and} \quad \mathbf{b} \triangleq \begin{bmatrix} 0 \\ 0 \\ K \end{bmatrix},$$

the so-called state model can now be written in the very compact matrix form

$$\dot{\mathbf{x}}(t) = \mathbf{A}\mathbf{x}(t) + \mathbf{b}u(t). \tag{18.2}$$

It is worth commenting on the structure of the matrices $\mathbf{A}$ and $\mathbf{b}$. The bottom row of the $\mathbf{A}$ matrix contains the negatives of the coefficients of the characteristic equation, starting on the left with $-a_0$ and ending on the right with $-a_2$. Above the bottom row is a column of zeros on the left and a $2 \times 2$ identity matrix on the right. All the information about the original system is contained in the bottom row. The $\mathbf{b}$ matrix is similarly very simple. All the elements are zero except for the bottom element, which is the gain $K$ from the original system.

We will see this formulation again later. There we will call it the "controllable canonical form." It is worth noting here that this formulation, also called the "phase variable model" arises naturally when we obtain the state model equivalent of a transfer function.

## 18.3 | THE TRANSITION MATRIX

Applying the Laplace transform to Eq. [18.2], we obtain

$$s\mathbf{x}(s) - \mathbf{x}(0) = \mathbf{A}\mathbf{x}(s) + \mathbf{b}U(s). \tag{18.3}$$

Before proceeding we note a slight deviation in notation. We will use lowercase bold letters for vectors in both the time domain and the Laplace domain. We do it to make it easier to distinguish vector quantities from matrix quantities like $\mathbf{A}$.

Equation [18.3] can be rewritten as

$$s\mathbf{x}(s) - \mathbf{A}\mathbf{x}(s) = \mathbf{x}(0) + \mathbf{b}U(s),$$

and then as

$$s\mathbf{I}\mathbf{x}(s) - \mathbf{A}\mathbf{x}(s) = \mathbf{x}(0) + \mathbf{b}U(s),$$

where $\mathbf{I}$ is an $n \times n$ identity matrix. Factoring out $\mathbf{x}(s)$ on the left-hand side yields

$$[s\mathbf{I} - \mathbf{A}]\mathbf{x}(s) = \mathbf{x(0)} + \mathbf{b}U(s), \tag{18.4}$$

where $s\mathbf{I} - \mathbf{A}$ is an $n \times n$ matrix whose individual elements are polynomials in the complex variable $s$. If this matrix has an inverse, then we can solve Eq. [18.4] for

$\mathbf{x}(s)$ and then apply the inverse Laplace transform to obtain $\mathbf{x}(t)$. The invertibility of $s\mathbf{I} - \mathbf{A}$ depends on its determinant. If

$$\text{Det}\,\{s\mathbf{I} - \mathbf{A}\} \neq 0,$$

then the matrix is invertible. Under the assumption that $s\mathbf{I} - \mathbf{A}$ is indeed invertible, we can write

$$\mathbf{x}(s) = [s\mathbf{I} - \mathbf{A}]^{-1}\mathbf{x}(0) + [s\mathbf{I} - \mathbf{A}]^{-1}\mathbf{b}U(s). \qquad [18.5]$$

The conditions for which $s\mathbf{I} - \mathbf{A}$ is invertible will be investigated later. The values of the Laplace variable $s$ for which this matrix is not invertible are important, and correspond to the singular points, or poles, of a transfer function.

Applying the inverse Laplace transform to both sides of Eq. [18.5], we obtain

$$\mathcal{L}^{-1}\{\mathbf{x}(s)\} = \mathbf{x}(t) = \mathcal{L}^{-1}\{[s\mathbf{I} - \mathbf{A}]^{-1}\}\mathbf{x}(0) + \mathcal{L}^{-1}\{[s\mathbf{I} - \mathbf{A}]^{-1}U(s)\}\mathbf{b}. \qquad [18.6]$$

Note that the order of multiplication of $U(s)$ and $\mathbf{b}$ has been reversed, which is permissible since $U(s)$ is a *scalar* input.

Now

$$\mathcal{L}^{-1}\{[s\mathbf{I} - \mathbf{A}]^{-1}\}$$

is a matrix, each of whose elements is a *time* function. This may not be totally clear at this juncture, but it will be shortly after we have worked an example. We need a convenient compact symbol to represent this matrix of time functions, so we write

$$\mathcal{L}^{-1}\{[s\mathbf{I} - \mathbf{A}]^{-1}\} \triangleq e^{\mathbf{A}t},$$

where $e^{\mathbf{A}t}$ is called the matrix exponential or the transition matrix. The motivation for these names will be clear shortly.

We next recall the following theorem from Laplace transform theory.

> **Theorem 18.3.1**
>
> Let $f_1(t)$ and $f_2(t)$ be time functions whose Laplace transforms, $F_1(s)$ and $F_2(s)$, exist. Then,
>
> $$\mathcal{L}^{-1}\{F_1(s)F_2(s)\} = \int_0^t f_1(\tau)\,f_2(t-\tau)\,d\tau.$$

Using theorem 18.3.1 we can rewrite Eq. [18.6] as

$$\mathbf{x}(t) = e^{\mathbf{A}t}\mathbf{x}(0) + \left[\int_0^t e^{\mathbf{A}(t-\tau)}u(\tau)\,d\tau\right]\mathbf{b}. \qquad [18.7]$$

We now see that the symbol $e^{\mathbf{A}t}$ is not chosen arbitrarily, but is based on the analogy between the *vector* Eq. [18.2],

$$\dot{\mathbf{x}}(t) = \mathbf{A}\mathbf{x}(t) + \mathbf{b}u(t),$$

repeated here for convenience, and the *scalar* differential equation

$$\dot{x}(t) = \alpha x(t) + bu(t). \qquad \textbf{[18.8]}$$

We know from elementary differential equation theory that the solution of Eq. [18.8] is

$$x(t) = e^{\alpha t}x(0) + b\int_0^t e^{\alpha(t-\tau)}u(\tau)\,d\tau.$$

Thus, the symbol $e^{\mathbf{A}t}$ for the *matrix* of time functions in the solution of the *vector* differential equation *corresponds* to $e^{\alpha t}$ in the solution of the *scalar* equation. We will subsequently show that $e^{\mathbf{A}t}$ has many of the properties of $e^{\alpha t}$.

At this stage, it is perhaps best to consider a simple example that illustrates most of the comments made to this point.

**EXAMPLE 18.3.1**

Consider the system

$$\begin{bmatrix} \dot{x}_1(t) \\ \dot{x}_2(t) \end{bmatrix} = \begin{bmatrix} -2 & 2 \\ 0 & -4 \end{bmatrix} \begin{bmatrix} x_1(t) \\ x_2(t) \end{bmatrix} + \begin{bmatrix} 1 \\ 2 \end{bmatrix} u(t). \qquad \textbf{[18.9]}$$

We first form

$$s\mathbf{I} - \mathbf{A} = \begin{bmatrix} s & 0 \\ 0 & s \end{bmatrix} - \begin{bmatrix} -2 & 2 \\ 0 & -4 \end{bmatrix} = \begin{bmatrix} s+2 & -2 \\ 0 & s+4 \end{bmatrix}.$$

Then,

$$[s\mathbf{I} - \mathbf{A}]^{-1} = \frac{\text{Adj}\{s\mathbf{I} - \mathbf{A}\}}{\text{Det}\{s\mathbf{I} - \mathbf{A}\}}$$

$$= \frac{\begin{bmatrix} s+4 & 2 \\ 0 & s+2 \end{bmatrix}}{(s+2)(s+4)}$$

$$= \begin{bmatrix} \frac{1}{s+2} & \frac{1}{s+2} - \frac{1}{s+4} \\ 0 & \frac{1}{s+4} \end{bmatrix}.$$

This development assumes a minimal background in linear algebra. From this last result we see that $[s\mathbf{I} - \mathbf{A}]$ is nonsingular as long as $s \neq -2$ and $s \neq -4$. These particular values will shortly be referred to as "eigenvalues." They play the same role in the state model that poles play in a transfer function.

For the case of a $2 \times 2$ matrix the adjoint matrix is formed by interchanging the on-diagonal elements and changing the sign of the off-diagonal elements. For square matrices of dimension three or greater the adjoint matrix is formed as follows. For a square $n \times n$ matrix $\mathbf{A}$ we define

$$\mathbf{A}_{ij}$$

to be the element in the $i$th row and $j$th column. We then define

$$\mathbf{M}_{ij}(\mathbf{A}),$$

to be the $n-1 \times n-1$ *matrix* obtained by crossing out the $i$th row and $j$th column of **A**. $\mathbf{M}_{ij}(\mathbf{A})$ is called the *minor* of $\mathbf{A}_{ij}$. Then,

$$(-1)^{i+j}\text{Det}\,[\mathbf{M}_{ij}(\mathbf{A})],$$

is called the cofactor of $\mathbf{A}_{ij}$. Finally, Adj(**A**) is defined as the transpose of the matrix formed by replacing each element $\mathbf{A}_{ij}$ by its corresponding cofactor. Symbolically, we have

$$[\text{Adj}(\mathbf{A})]_{ij} = (-1)^{j+i}\,\text{Det}\,[\mathbf{M}_{ji}(\mathbf{A})].$$

We will not often invert matrices that are of dimension three or higher, but we do need to understand how the adjoint is formed.

Returning, to the problem at hand, we can now write

$$e^{\mathbf{A}t} = \mathcal{L}^{-1}\left\{\begin{bmatrix} \frac{1}{s+2} & \frac{1}{s+2} - \frac{1}{s+4} \\ 0 & \frac{1}{s+4} \end{bmatrix}\right\}$$

$$= \begin{bmatrix} \mathcal{L}^{-1}\left\{\frac{1}{s+2}\right\} & \mathcal{L}^{-1}\left\{\frac{1}{s+2} - \frac{1}{s+4}\right\} \\ 0 & \mathcal{L}^{-1}\left\{\frac{1}{s+4}\right\} \end{bmatrix}$$

$$= \begin{bmatrix} e^{-2t} & e^{-2t} - e^{-4t} \\ 0 & e^{-4t} \end{bmatrix}.$$

Then,

$$\begin{bmatrix} x_1(t) \\ x_2(t) \end{bmatrix} = \begin{bmatrix} e^{-2t} & e^{-2t} - e^{-4t} \\ 0 & e^{-4t} \end{bmatrix}\begin{bmatrix} x_1(0) \\ x_2(0) \end{bmatrix}$$

$$+ \int_0^t \left\{\begin{bmatrix} e^{-2(t-\tau)} & e^{-2(t-\tau)} - e^{-4(t-\tau)} \\ 0 & e^{-4(t-\tau)} \end{bmatrix} u(\tau)\,d\tau\right\}\mathbf{b}$$

$$= \begin{bmatrix} e^{-2t} & e^{-2t} - e^{-4t} \\ 0 & e^{-4t} \end{bmatrix}\begin{bmatrix} x_1(0) \\ x_2(0) \end{bmatrix}$$

$$+ \begin{bmatrix} \int_0^t e^{-2(t-\tau)}u(\tau)\,d\tau & \int_0^t [e^{-2(t-\tau)} - e^{-4(t-\tau)}]u(\tau)\,d\tau \\ 0 & \int_0^t e^{-4(t-\tau)}u(\tau)\,d\tau \end{bmatrix}\mathbf{b}.$$

From this last equation, we see that the matrix $e^{\mathbf{A}t}$ is composed of time functions that are all exponentials that decay with time.

Note carefully that the eigenvalues $\lambda = -2$ and $\lambda = -4$ determine the time functions in $e^{\mathbf{A}t}$, just as the poles of a transfer function determine the time functions that appear in the response of the system represented by the transfer function.

The matrix product

$$
\begin{bmatrix} e^{-2t} & e^{-2t} - e^{-4t} \\ 0 & e^{-4t} \end{bmatrix}
\begin{bmatrix} x_1(0) \\ x_2(0) \end{bmatrix}
$$

will decay to zero as $t \to \infty$.

All the elements in

$$
\int_0^t e^{\mathbf{A}(t-\tau)} u(\tau)\, d\tau =
\begin{bmatrix}
\int_0^t e^{-2(t-\tau)} u(\tau)\, d\tau & \int_0^t \left[ e^{-2(t-\tau)} - e^{-4(t-\tau)} \right] u(\tau)\, d\tau \\
0 & \int_0^t e^{-4(t-\tau)} u(\tau)\, d\tau
\end{bmatrix}
$$

will be finite as long as $u(t)$ is a bounded function. Thus, for a bounded input $u$, $x_1(t)$ and $x_2(t)$ are both bounded and the fact that they are is a consequence of the time functions in $e^{\mathbf{A}t}$. This means that from a stability point of view we might just as well examine

$$
\dot{\mathbf{x}}(t) = \mathbf{A}\mathbf{x}(t), \qquad\qquad\qquad \textbf{[18.10]}
$$

since the homogeneous equation has all the stability information. The same, of course, is true of ordinary differential equations, where the homogeneous solution contains all the information about the behavior of the system itself. That said, we turn our attention to the study of Eq. [18.10].

## 18.4 | PHASE PORTRAITS

In this section, we examine three examples that illustrate all the essential features of the stability of state space models of arbitrary dimension. The examples are all second order, and one might well ask how the basic information about the stability of large dimension state models can be contained in second-order examples.

The answer lies in the fact that we will always be able to find a transformation matrix that puts the state model in a *preferred* coordinate system where it consists of *decoupled* subsystems of low dimension, typically dimension one and two. Thus, the study of these two-dimensional examples is central to understanding the behavior of systems of higher dimension.

We have seen that if we want the total solution to Eq. [18.2] then we need to find $e^{\mathbf{A}t}$ and then do a vector convolution integral. In most cases, we are less interested in specific solutions and more interested in the overall stability of the system. In that regard, state models are no different than the transfer functions we have studied up to now.

In previous chapters we have used root locus analysis, Bode analysis, and Nyquist analysis to study the stability of the closed-loop system. These methods were graphical in nature and were not compuationally intensive. We will follow a similar path with the state model. By looking at the structure of $e^{\mathbf{A}t}$ we will be able to determine the stability of the state model with minimal computational effort.

It is possible to obtain the required stability information without explicitly finding $e^{At}$, or solving the convolution integral. To motivate this approach we consider drawing so-called "portraits" or "flows" of the two-dimensional systems considered in the following examples. This "portrait" is just that, a picture that captures all possible solutions, or "trajectories," for all possible initial conditions.

## 18.4.1 Real Distinct Roots

Consider again

$$\begin{bmatrix} \dot{x}_1(t) \\ \dot{x}_2(t) \end{bmatrix} = \begin{bmatrix} -2 & 2 \\ 0 & -4 \end{bmatrix} \begin{bmatrix} x_1(t) \\ x_2(t) \end{bmatrix}.$$  [18.11]

As a first step, we introduce the concept of a vector field. Consider describing the evolution of a solution to Eq. [18.11] by a two-dimensional picture consisting of a set of Cartesian coordinates, where the abscissa represents $x_1(t)$ and the ordinate $x_2(t)$. Such a system is shown in Fig. 18.2. A solution, or trajectory, is shown in this figure, along with the derivative $\dot{x}$ of the trajectory at selected points.

Equation [18.11] provides a means of computing these derivatives. In fact it provides a means of plotting the derivative at *every* point in the so-called "phase space," or "state space," defined by the Cartesian coordinate system of Fig. 18.2.

If we plot the derivative of the state model of Eq. [18.11] at each point in the cartesian coordinate system of Fig. 18.2, we create what is known as a vector field. The concept is exactly the same as computing the electric field at every point in three space for a given charge configuration. Our next goal is to create such a vector field for the state model of Eq. [18.11].

At first glance it would seem that computing the derivative at every point is a hopeless task, but, in fact, it is possible to quickly determine the vector field by examining a few *selected* points in the state space.

**Figure 18.2** | Typical trajectory with derivative shown at selected points.

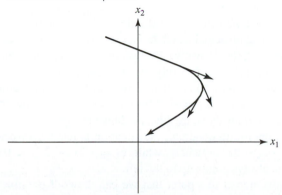

The formulas for the components of the derivative, as obtained from Eq. [18.11], are

$$\dot{x}_1(t) = -2x_1 + 2x_2,$$

$$\dot{x}_2(t) = -4x_2.$$

We now investigate the derivatives at selected points.

Along the $x_1$ axis, $x_1 > 0$ and $x_2 = 0$, and we have

$$\dot{x}_1(t) = -2x_1,$$

$$\dot{x}_2(t) = 0.$$

Thus, for any point along the $x_1$ axis, the derivative points *along* the $x_1$ axis. To the left of the origin, the derivative points to the right, while to the right of the origin, the derivative points to the left. Thus, any trajectory starting on the $x_1$ axis will stay on the $x_1$ axis and move toward the origin as time progresses. As we will see shortly this is a very special behavior.

At any point along the trajectory, the rate at which the solution is moving toward the origin is indicated by the magnitude of the derivative. If we imagine a point traveling along the trajectory from some initial condition, the point travels slower and slower as it approaches the origin. In fact, it takes an infinite amount of time to reach the origin.

In the first quadrant, $x_1 > 0$ and $x_2 > 0$ so that the components of the derivative are

$$\dot{x}_1(t) = -2x_1 + 2x_2,$$

$$\dot{x}_2(t) = -4x_2,$$

we see that since $x_2 > 0$ the component of the derivative in the $x_2$ direction always points down. The component of the derivative in the $x_1$ direction can be negative, positive, or zero. Along the line $x_1 = x_2$, it is zero, so that all along this line the derivative points straight down. Such a line along which the ratio $\dot{x}_2/\dot{x}_1$ is constant is called an isocline. Above the line, where $x_1 < x_2$, the component of the derivative in the $x_1$ direction is positive and points to the right, while below the line it points to the left, as shown in Fig. 18.3.

In the second quadrant, where $x_1 < 0$ and $x_2 > 0$, the component of the derivative in the $x_2$ direction is again negative, while $\dot{x}_1 = -2x_1 + 2x_2 > 0$ everywhere. Hence, in the second quadrant, the derivative always points down to the right.

In the third quadrant, we can rely on our analysis from the first quadrant. It requires only a little thought to see that in the third quadrant the derivative points (1) straight up along the line $x_1 = x_2$, (2) to the left and up below the line $x_1 = x_2$, and (3) to the right and up above the line, as shown in Fig. 18.3.

Similarly, in the fourth quadrant, the situation is just the reverse of that in the second: $\dot{x}_2 = -4x_2 > 0$ everywhere, while $\dot{x}_1 = -2x_1 + 2x_2 < 0$ everywhere, so that the derivative always points up to the left.

We might conclude at this point that we can draw all possible trajectories by simply sketching smooth curves through the derivatives in the vector field. However,

**Figure 18.3 |** Vector field.

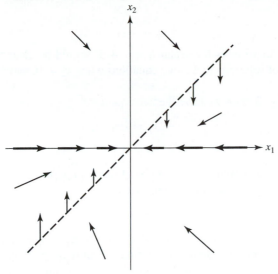

that conclusion would prove to be a bit hasty. To see why, consider again the very first point we analyzed, namely, the point on the $x_1$ axis.

In that case, we found that

$$\begin{bmatrix} -2 & 2 \\ 0 & -4 \end{bmatrix} \begin{bmatrix} x_1 \\ 0 \end{bmatrix} = \begin{bmatrix} -2x_1 \\ 0 \end{bmatrix} = -2 \begin{bmatrix} x_1 \\ 0 \end{bmatrix}. \qquad \text{[18.12]}$$

That is, the derivative of **x** is a scaled version of **x**.

The generalization of Eq. [18.12] is

$$\dot{\mathbf{x}} = \mathbf{A}\mathbf{x} = \lambda\mathbf{x}, \qquad \text{[18.13]}$$

where $\lambda$ is a scalar. What we wish to do now is locate any other straight-line trajectories in the state space.

Our two equations, for an arbitrary unknown $\lambda$ then become

$$-2x_1 + 2x_2 = \lambda x_1,$$

$$-4x_2 = \lambda x_2.$$

As it turns out there are an infinite number of solutions to this set of equations, but only two solutions that are distinctly different. If we assume $x_2 \neq 0$, then the second equation yields

$$\lambda = -4.$$

Substituting this value into the first equation then yields

$$x_1 = -x_2.$$

We now have identified a second straight-line trajectory in the phase plane, namely, the line

$$x_2 = -x_1.$$

Associated with that line is the scalar $\lambda = -4$. It should be clear that there are an infinite number of solutions to the two equations when $x_2 \neq 0$, namely, all the points on this line.

If we let $x_2 = 0$, then we have the two equations

$$-2x_1 = \lambda x_1,$$

$$0 = 0.$$

The second equation would not seem to be of much importance, but it is, as we will see later in the chapter. The first equation yields

$$\lambda = -2,$$

and we see that this equation is satisfied by any point on the $x_1$ axis. Thus, even though there are an infinite number of solutions to our two equations, all the solutions lie along two lines, with each line associated with a specific scalar. These two lines and their associated scalars are of great importance, because as we will see next they characterize the state model of Eq. [18.11].

Even though we have managed to solve Eq. [18.13], for this example, we need a better way of understanding the problem in general, especially if we want to investigate state models of higher dimension. To that end, we rewrite Eq. [18.13] as

$$[\mathbf{A} - \lambda \mathbf{I}]\,\mathbf{x} = \mathbf{0}. \qquad [18.14]$$

We are looking for nontrivial solutions to Eq. [18.14]. Note that if the *square* matrix $[\mathbf{A} - \lambda \mathbf{I}]$ is nonsingular, then it has an inverse, and

$$\mathbf{x} = [\mathbf{A} - \lambda \mathbf{I}]^{-1}\,\mathbf{0} = \mathbf{0}.$$

Thus, if $[\mathbf{A} - \lambda \mathbf{I}]$ is nonsingular, the only solution is the trivial solution $\mathbf{x} = \mathbf{0}$.

However, if $[\mathbf{A} - \lambda \mathbf{I}]$ is singular, then nontrivial solutions exist. Therefore, we write

$$
\begin{aligned}
\text{Det}\,[\mathbf{A} - \lambda \mathbf{I}] &= \text{Det}\left\{ \begin{bmatrix} -2 & 2 \\ 0 & -4 \end{bmatrix} - \begin{bmatrix} \lambda & 0 \\ 0 & \lambda \end{bmatrix} \right\} \\
&= \text{Det}\begin{bmatrix} -(2+\lambda) & 2 \\ 0 & -(4+\lambda) \end{bmatrix} \\
&= (\lambda + 2)(\lambda + 4).
\end{aligned}
$$

Equating this last expression to zero yields

$$(\lambda + 2)(\lambda + 4) = 0. \qquad [18.15]$$

Equation [18.15] is called the "characteristic" equation or "eigenequation." The name comes from the fact that the two solutions to this equation characterize the behavior of the linear homogeneous system we are studying. For this second-order system, these two values, $\lambda = -2$ and $\lambda = -4$, determine the two straight-line trajectories in the state space, *and* the time functions that are present in $e^{At}$. It is worth recalling here that for this system, which we first studied in Example 18.3.1, the time functions in $e^{At}$ were $e^{-2t}$ and $e^{-4t}$. As one might suspect, this is not a coincidence.

If we now go back and solve Eq. [18.14] for these two *specific* values of $\lambda$ we can find the straight-line paths. For $\lambda = -2$ we have

$$\begin{bmatrix} -(2+\lambda) & 2 \\ 0 & -(4+\lambda) \end{bmatrix}_{\lambda=-2} \begin{bmatrix} x_1 \\ x_2 \end{bmatrix} = \begin{bmatrix} 0 & 2 \\ 0 & -2 \end{bmatrix} \begin{bmatrix} x_1 \\ x_2 \end{bmatrix}$$

Then, if we solve

$$\begin{bmatrix} 0 & 2 \\ 0 & -2 \end{bmatrix} \begin{bmatrix} x_1 \\ x_2 \end{bmatrix} = \begin{bmatrix} 0 \\ 0 \end{bmatrix},$$

we find that we have the two equations

$$2x_2 = 0,$$

$$-2x_2 = 0.$$

The only information here is that $x_2 = 0$. Since nothing is said about $x_1$, it can have any value we choose. Thus, the direction, or eigenvector, associated with $\lambda = -2$ is

$$\mathbf{e}_1 = \begin{bmatrix} a \\ 0 \end{bmatrix},$$

with $-\infty < a < \infty$. This is old news because we have already found this vector when we drew the initial vector field for this system. We call $\mathbf{e}_1$ the eigenvector associated with the eigenvalue $\lambda = -2$.

If we now repeat this process for $\lambda = -4$, we have

$$\begin{bmatrix} -(2+\lambda) & 2 \\ 0 & -(4+\lambda) \end{bmatrix}_{\lambda=-4} \begin{bmatrix} x_1 \\ x_2 \end{bmatrix} = \begin{bmatrix} 2 & 2 \\ 0 & 0 \end{bmatrix} \begin{bmatrix} x_1 \\ x_2 \end{bmatrix}$$

Then solving

$$\begin{bmatrix} 2 & 2 \\ 0 & 0 \end{bmatrix} \begin{bmatrix} x_1 \\ x_2 \end{bmatrix} = \begin{bmatrix} 0 \\ 0 \end{bmatrix}$$

yields the two equations

$$2x_1 + 2x_2 = 0,$$

$$0 = 0.$$

The first equation tells us that

$$x_2 = -x_1.$$

The second equation doesn't seem to tell us anything. However, when we subsequently discuss generalized eigenvectors, equations of this form will have significance.

**Figure 18.4 |** (a) Vector field and (b) phase portrait.

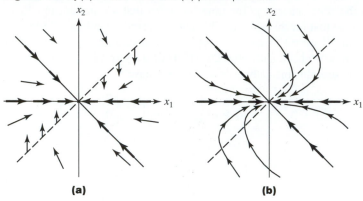

(a)          (b)

Returning to the first equation, we see that it tells us that the eigenvector associated with the eigenvalue $\lambda = -4$ is

$$\mathbf{e}_2 = \begin{bmatrix} a \\ -a \end{bmatrix},$$

with $-\infty < a < \infty$. We can choose any $a$ we desire, so we choose an easy value: $a = 1$. Then a *specific* eigenvector associated with $\lambda = -4$ is

$$\mathbf{e}_2 = \begin{bmatrix} -1 \\ 1 \end{bmatrix}.$$

We are now in a position to sketch the complete vector field as shown in Fig. 18.4(a). Having completed the vector field we can now draw the phase portrait, a sketch of all the possible trajectories in the phase space. This is shown in Fig. 18.4(b).

## 18.4.2 Isoclines and the Jordan Form

The determination of the curvature of the paths in Fig. 18.4 may not seem easy. In most cases, we can find this curvature without too much difficulty, and, in point of fact, in most cases we don't really care that much anyway. In some cases, however, the curvature may be of some interest, and so we introduce here a method of drawing the phase portrait that can resolve the issue of curvature, if it becomes an issue.

The technique we will use to determine the curvature is called the method of isoclines and is first illustrated by considering the system

$$\begin{bmatrix} \dot{x}_1(t) \\ \dot{x}_2(t) \end{bmatrix} = \begin{bmatrix} -2 & 0 \\ 0 & -4 \end{bmatrix} \begin{bmatrix} x_1(t) \\ x_2(t) \end{bmatrix}.$$

The alert reader will note that this system is very similar to the one we introduced in Example 18.3.1. There is a reason we have chosen this particular system, and that reason will be clear soon.

In the method of isoclines, we determine curves along which

$$\frac{\Delta x_2}{\Delta x_1} = \frac{\dot{x}_2}{\dot{x}_1} = a,$$

where $a$ is a constant. Having found these curves it is a simple matter to sketch in the trajectories.

For this system the curves are actually the straight lines defined by

$$\frac{\dot{x}_2}{\dot{x}_1} = \frac{-4x_2}{-2x_1} = 2\frac{x_2}{x_1} = a.$$

The equation

$$\frac{x_2}{x_1} = \frac{a}{2},$$

rewritten as

$$x_2 = \frac{a}{2}x_1,$$

is the equation of a straight line passing through the origin with slope $a/2$. The isoclines for the values $a = \pm 1, \pm 2$, and $\pm 3$ are shown in Fig. 18.5. Typical trajectories are also shown by matching the slope of the trajectory to the slopes along the isoclines. The method of isoclines can be used to deterimine the curvature of the trajectories for the state model of Example 18.3.1 (see Problem 3 in Section 18.9.8). However, we can get at that curvature in a more enlightening way, as shown next.

We now ask the following question: is there a *preferred* coordinate system in which to study the stability of a state model? We already have a partial answer to this question from the system for which we drew the flow using the method of isoclines. That system has the same eignevalues as the system of Example 18.3.1. So it would appear that the answer to our question is yes. We can find that preferred

**Figure 18.5 |** Isoclines and trajectories.

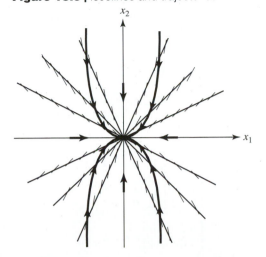

coordinate system, called the "Jordan canonical coordinate system" by making use of the eigenvectors.

Suppose for the system defined by Eq. [18.11] we use the eigenvectors as coordinate axes. That is, we determine new coordinates $z_1$ and $z_2$ such that

$$\begin{bmatrix} x_1 \\ x_2 \end{bmatrix} = x_1 \begin{bmatrix} 1 \\ 0 \end{bmatrix} + x_2 \begin{bmatrix} 0 \\ 1 \end{bmatrix} = z_1 \begin{bmatrix} 1 \\ 0 \end{bmatrix} + z_1 \begin{bmatrix} -1 \\ 1 \end{bmatrix} = \begin{bmatrix} z_1 - z_2 \\ z_2 \end{bmatrix}$$

$$= \begin{bmatrix} 1 & -1 \\ 0 & 1 \end{bmatrix} \begin{bmatrix} z_1 \\ z_2 \end{bmatrix}.$$

We now have a transformation of variables

$$\mathbf{x} = \mathbf{Tz},$$

with

$$\mathbf{T} = \begin{bmatrix} 1 & -1 \\ 0 & 1 \end{bmatrix},$$

that takes us from the $z_1$-$z_2$ coordinate system to the $x_1$-$x_2$ coordinate system. Note carefully that

$$\mathbf{T} = [\, \mathbf{e}_1 \quad \mathbf{e}_2 \,].$$

Since $\mathbf{T}$ is a matrix of constants,

$$\dot{\mathbf{x}} = \mathbf{T}\dot{\mathbf{z}}.$$

Therefore, we can write

$$\mathbf{T}\dot{\mathbf{z}} = \mathbf{ATz}.$$

Since $\mathbf{T}$ is invertible, we can then write

$$\dot{\mathbf{z}} = \mathbf{T}^{-1}\mathbf{ATz} = [\mathbf{T}^{-1}\mathbf{AT}]\mathbf{z} = \boldsymbol{\Lambda}\mathbf{z},$$

where

$$\boldsymbol{\Lambda} = \mathbf{T}^{-1}\mathbf{AT}.$$

To see if we have achieved any simplification, we compute

$$\boldsymbol{\Lambda} = \mathbf{T}^{-1}\mathbf{AT}$$
$$= \begin{bmatrix} 1 & 1 \\ 0 & 1 \end{bmatrix} \begin{bmatrix} -2 & 2 \\ 0 & -4 \end{bmatrix} \begin{bmatrix} 1 & -1 \\ 0 & 1 \end{bmatrix}$$
$$= \begin{bmatrix} 1 & 1 \\ 0 & 1 \end{bmatrix} \begin{bmatrix} -2 & 4 \\ 0 & -4 \end{bmatrix}$$
$$= \begin{bmatrix} -2 & 0 \\ 0 & -4 \end{bmatrix}.$$

In the canonical coordinates, the system looks like

$$\begin{bmatrix} \dot{z}_1 \\ \dot{z}_2 \end{bmatrix} = \begin{bmatrix} -2 & 0 \\ 0 & -4 \end{bmatrix} \begin{bmatrix} z_1 \\ z_2 \end{bmatrix}.$$

Note that $\Lambda$ is *diagonal* and hence, in the new coordinate system, the original system has been decomposed into two one dimensional *decoupled* subsystems.

Further, we see that

$$\begin{aligned} \mathrm{Det}\,\{[\Lambda - \lambda \mathbf{I}]\} &= \mathrm{Det}\left\{\begin{bmatrix} -2 & 0 \\ 0 & -4 \end{bmatrix} - \begin{bmatrix} -\lambda & 0 \\ 0 & -\lambda \end{bmatrix}\right\} \\ &= \mathrm{Det}\left\{\begin{matrix} -(\lambda + 2) & 0 \\ 0 & -(\lambda + 4) \end{matrix}\right\} \\ &= (\lambda + 2)(\lambda + 4). \end{aligned}$$

Thus, the canonical system has the same eigenvalues as the original system.

If we now solve the eigenvector equation

$$\begin{bmatrix} -(2 + \lambda) & 0 \\ 0 & -(4 + \lambda) \end{bmatrix}_{\lambda = -2} \begin{bmatrix} x_1 \\ x_2 \end{bmatrix} = \begin{bmatrix} 0 \\ 0 \end{bmatrix},$$

we obtain

$$\begin{bmatrix} 0 & 0 \\ 0 & -2 \end{bmatrix} \begin{bmatrix} x_1 \\ x_2 \end{bmatrix} = \begin{bmatrix} 0 \\ 0 \end{bmatrix},$$

or, equivalently,

$$0 = 0$$
$$-2x_2 = 0.$$

These equations indicate that $x_2 = 0$ and $x_1$ is arbitrary. Hence the eigenvector associated with $\lambda = -2$ is

$$\mathbf{e}_1 = \begin{bmatrix} a \\ 0 \end{bmatrix},$$

with $-\infty < a < \infty$. That is, the eigenvector lies along the $z_1$ axis.

In like manner, if we solve the eigenvector equation

$$\begin{bmatrix} -(2 + \lambda) & 0 \\ 0 & -(4 + \lambda) \end{bmatrix}_{\lambda = -4} \begin{bmatrix} x_1 \\ x_2 \end{bmatrix} = \begin{bmatrix} 0 \\ 0 \end{bmatrix},$$

we obtain the two equations

$$2x_1 = 0,$$
$$0 = 0,$$

indicating that $x_1 = 0$ and $x_2$ is arbitrary. Hence the eigenvector associated with $\lambda = -4$ is

$$\mathbf{e}_1 = \begin{bmatrix} 0 \\ a \end{bmatrix},$$

with $-\infty < a < \infty$. Thus we see that the new system not only has the same eigenvalues as the original system, the eigenvectors are *orthogonal* and lie along the coordinates axes. This shouldn't come as too much of a surprise since we selected the eigenvalues as the coordinate axes. The phase portrait for this system is shown in Figure 18.5.

The solution of the canonical system is trivial, since the equations are decoupled. Thus

$$\begin{bmatrix} z_1(t) \\ z_2(t) \end{bmatrix} = \begin{bmatrix} e^{-2t} & 0 \\ 0 & e^{-4t} \end{bmatrix} \begin{bmatrix} z_1(0) \\ z_2(0) \end{bmatrix},$$

where $z_1(0)$ and $z_2(0)$ are the initial conditions necessary to solve the state equation, and

$$\begin{bmatrix} e^{-2t} & 0 \\ 0 & e^{-4t} \end{bmatrix} = e^{\Lambda t},$$

is the transition matrix for the canonical system.

Finally, we can find the state transition matrix for the original coordinate system using the matrix $\mathbf{T}$. We know that $\mathbf{x} = \mathbf{Tz}$. Hence,

$$\begin{aligned} \mathbf{x}(t) &= \mathbf{Tz}(t) \\ &= \mathbf{T}e^{\Lambda t}\mathbf{z}(0) \\ &= \mathbf{T}e^{\Lambda t}\mathbf{T}^{-1}\mathbf{x}(0) \\ &= [\mathbf{T}e^{\Lambda t}\mathbf{T}^{-1}]\mathbf{x}(0), \end{aligned}$$

with

$$\begin{aligned} e^{\mathbf{A}t} &= \mathbf{T}e^{\Lambda t}\mathbf{T}^{-1} \\ &= \begin{bmatrix} 1 & -1 \\ 0 & 1 \end{bmatrix} \begin{bmatrix} e^{-2t} & 0 \\ 0 & e^{-4t} \end{bmatrix} \begin{bmatrix} 1 & 1 \\ 0 & 1 \end{bmatrix} \\ &= \begin{bmatrix} 1 & -1 \\ 0 & 1 \end{bmatrix} \begin{bmatrix} e^{-2t} & e^{-2t} \\ 0 & e^{-4t} \end{bmatrix} \\ &= \begin{bmatrix} e^{-2t} & e^{-2t} - e^{-4t} \\ 0 & e^{-4t} \end{bmatrix}. \end{aligned}$$

This gives us an alternative to the Laplace transform for determining $e^{\mathbf{A}t}$.

We can also use the transformation $\mathbf{T}^{-1}$ to go from the original phase portrait to the canonical phase portrait. Using a superscript "$\mathbf{A}$" to designate eigenvectors in the original coordinate system and superscript "$\Lambda$" to designate the eigenvectors in the canonical coordinate system, we have

$$\mathbf{e}_1^\Lambda = \mathbf{T}^{-1}\mathbf{e}_1^\mathbf{A} = \begin{bmatrix} 1 & 1 \\ 0 & 1 \end{bmatrix} \begin{bmatrix} 1 \\ 0 \end{bmatrix} = \begin{bmatrix} 1 \\ 0 \end{bmatrix},$$

**Figure 18.6** | Transformation between original and canonical coordinate systems $\phi$.

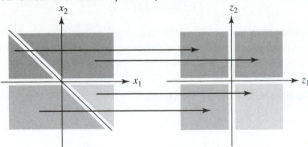

and

$$e_2^\Lambda = T^{-1}e_2^A = \begin{bmatrix} 1 & 1 \\ 0 & 1 \end{bmatrix} \begin{bmatrix} -1 \\ 1 \end{bmatrix} = \begin{bmatrix} 0 \\ 1 \end{bmatrix}.$$

Then the eigenvector associated with $\lambda = -2$ is unchanged, but the eigenvector associated with $\lambda = -4$ gets rotated clockwise. The result is that the area above the $x_1$ axis and the line $x_1 = -x_2$ in the original coordinate system is compressed and becomes the first quadrant in the canonical coordinate system. In similar fashion, the region between the negative half of the $x_1$ axis and the line $x_1 = -x_2$ gets stretched out to become the second quadrant of the canonical coordinate system. The effect is similar for the regions below and above the line $x_1 = -x_2$ in the third and fourth quadrants of the $x_1$-$x_2$ coordinate systems. This reshaping is shown in Fig. 18.6. Based on Figs. 18.5 and 18.6 the curvature in the phase portrait of the original system from Example 18.3.1 should now be clear.

At this juncture, we summarize our results for the second-order system of Eq. [18.11].

1. The system is characterized by two eigenvalues and their associated eigenvectors.
2. For the case of two distinct real eigenvalues, the eigenvectors determine straight-line trajectories in the phase space.
3. The eigenvectors determine a transformation that puts the system in Jordan canonical form, that is in the coordinate system where its behavior is the easiest to determine.
4. In the canonical coordinate system we see that the eigenvalues determine the time functions that show up in the transition matrix.
5. The transition matrix for the original coordinate system is determined to be

$$e^{At} = Te^{\Lambda t}T^{-1},$$

where $T$ is the same transformation that we used to get to the canonical coordinate system, and $e^{At}$ can be determined by inspection.

It is clear that the determination of the eigenvalues from the equation

$$\text{Det}\,[\mathbf{A} - \lambda\mathbf{I}] = 0$$

is the key step, and one of our goals will be to generalize this result to higher dimension systems. Before doing so we examine another second-order system where there are no straight-line trajectories.

### 18.4.3  Complex Eigenvalues

Consider the system

$$\begin{bmatrix} \dot{x}_1 \\ \dot{x}_2 \end{bmatrix} = \begin{bmatrix} 1 & 3 \\ -6 & -5 \end{bmatrix} \begin{bmatrix} x_1 \\ x_2 \end{bmatrix}.$$
  **[18.16]**

Based on the results of Example 18.3.1, and our subsequent discussion of the state model from that example, the first step is to determine the eigenvalues. To that end, we compute

$$\text{Det}\,[\mathbf{A} - \lambda\mathbf{I}] = \text{Det}\left\{\begin{bmatrix} 1 & 3 \\ -6 & -5 \end{bmatrix} - \begin{bmatrix} \lambda & 0 \\ 0 & \lambda \end{bmatrix}\right\}$$

$$= \text{Det}\begin{bmatrix} 1 - \lambda & 3 \\ -6 & -5 - \lambda \end{bmatrix}$$

$$= \lambda^2 + 4\lambda + 13$$

$$= (\lambda + 2 - j3)(\lambda + 2 + j3).$$

We next find the eigenvectors associated with the eigenvalues and the diagonalizing transformation composed of those eigenvectors.

We first find

$$\begin{bmatrix} 1 - \lambda & 3 \\ -6 & -5 - \lambda \end{bmatrix}_{\lambda = -2 + j3} = \begin{bmatrix} 3 - j3 & 3 \\ -6 & -3 - j3 \end{bmatrix}.$$

Then to find the related eigenvector we solve

$$\begin{bmatrix} 3 - j3 & 3 \\ -6 & -3 - j3 \end{bmatrix} \begin{bmatrix} x_1 \\ x_2 \end{bmatrix} = \begin{bmatrix} 0 \\ 0 \end{bmatrix},$$

which results in the two equations

$$3x_1(1 - j) + 3x_2 = 0,$$

$$-6x_1 - 3x_2(1 + j) = 0,$$

or

$$x_2 = -(1 - j)x_1.$$

Thus, if we choose $x_1 = 1$,

$$\mathbf{e}_1 = \begin{bmatrix} 1 \\ -1 + j \end{bmatrix}.$$

To find the other eigenvector we note that if

$$[A - \lambda I] x = 0,$$

then conjugating both sides yields

$$[A - \lambda^* I] x^* = 0,$$

so that the other eigenvector is just the conjugate of the one we have already found. Thus,

$$e_2 = \begin{bmatrix} 1 \\ -1 - j \end{bmatrix}.$$

Then our transformation matrix $\bar{T}$ such that $x = \bar{T}z$ is

$$\bar{T} = \begin{bmatrix} 1 & 1 \\ -1 + j & -1 - j \end{bmatrix},$$

and it follows that

$$\bar{T}^{-1} = \frac{1}{2} \begin{bmatrix} 1 - j & -j \\ 1 + j & j \end{bmatrix},$$

and

$$T^{-1}AT = \frac{1}{2} \begin{bmatrix} 1 - j & -j \\ 1 + j & j \end{bmatrix} \begin{bmatrix} 1 & 3 \\ -6 & -5 \end{bmatrix} \begin{bmatrix} 1 & 1 \\ -1 + j & -1 - j \end{bmatrix}$$

$$= \begin{bmatrix} -2 + j3 & 0 \\ 0 & -2 - j3 \end{bmatrix}.$$

The system in the canonical coordinate system is then

$$\begin{bmatrix} \dot{z}_1 \\ \dot{z}_2 \end{bmatrix} = \begin{bmatrix} -2 + j3 & 0 \\ 0 & -2 - j3 \end{bmatrix} \begin{bmatrix} z_1 \\ z_2 \end{bmatrix},$$

and the solution is

$$\begin{bmatrix} z_1(t) \\ z_2(t) \end{bmatrix} = \begin{bmatrix} e^{(-2+j3)t} & 0 \\ 0 & e^{(-2-j3)t} \end{bmatrix} \begin{bmatrix} z_1(0) \\ z_2(0) \end{bmatrix},$$

where

$$z(0) = \begin{bmatrix} z_1(0) \\ z_2(0) \end{bmatrix} = T^{-1}x(0).$$

The difficulty with this result is that it involves complex exponential functions. The solution to this problem is to find a useful transformation of

$$\begin{bmatrix} -2 + j3 & 0 \\ 0 & -2 - j3 \end{bmatrix},$$

that results in a real matrix.

To accomplish this consider, the system

$$\begin{bmatrix} \dot{x}_1 \\ \dot{x}_2 \end{bmatrix} = \begin{bmatrix} \sigma & \omega \\ -\omega & \sigma \end{bmatrix} \begin{bmatrix} x_1 \\ x_2 \end{bmatrix}, \qquad \qquad [18.17]$$

where $\sigma$ and $\omega$ are real with $-\infty < \sigma < \infty$ and $\omega \geq 0$. Based on the results of Example 18.3.1, we begin by finding

$$\text{Det}\,[\mathbf{A} - \lambda \mathbf{I}] = \text{Det}\left[\begin{bmatrix} \sigma & \omega \\ -\omega & \sigma \end{bmatrix} - \begin{bmatrix} \lambda & 0 \\ 0 & \lambda \end{bmatrix}\right]$$

$$= \text{Det}\begin{bmatrix} \sigma - \lambda & \omega \\ -\omega & \sigma - \lambda \end{bmatrix}$$

$$= \lambda^2 - 2\sigma\lambda + (\sigma^2 + \omega^2)$$

$$= (\lambda - \sigma - j\omega)(\lambda - \sigma + j\omega).$$

In this case, the eigenvalues are a complex conjugate pair, and more importantly, the real part of the complex eigenvalues appears in the diagonal positions of the matrix and the imaginary part in the off-diagonal positions. Thus the matrix

$$\begin{bmatrix} \sigma & \omega \\ -\omega & \sigma \end{bmatrix}$$

can be thought of as the *real* canonical form for the case of complex eigenvalues. In this form, it is reasonably easy to draw the phase portrait. We begin by letting

$$\rho = \sqrt{\sigma^2 + \omega^2} \quad \text{and} \quad \phi = \tan^{-1}\frac{\omega}{\sigma}.$$

Then

$$\begin{bmatrix} \sigma & \omega \\ -\omega & \sigma \end{bmatrix} = \begin{bmatrix} \rho\cos\phi & \rho\sin\phi \\ -\rho\sin\phi & \rho\cos\phi \end{bmatrix}$$

$$= \rho\begin{bmatrix} \cos\phi & \sin\phi \\ -\sin\phi & \cos\phi \end{bmatrix}.$$

The matrix

$$\begin{bmatrix} \cos\phi & \sin\phi \\ -\sin\phi & \cos\phi \end{bmatrix}$$

is a rotation matrix. If we multiply a vector $\mathbf{x}$ by this matrix, $\mathbf{x}$ is rotated through an angle $\phi$. To see this consider

$$\begin{bmatrix} \cos\phi & \sin\phi \\ -\sin\phi & \cos\phi \end{bmatrix}\begin{bmatrix} x_1 \\ x_2 \end{bmatrix} = \begin{bmatrix} x_1\cos\phi + x_2\sin\phi \\ -x_1\sin\phi + x_2\cos\phi \end{bmatrix}$$

$$= x_1\begin{bmatrix} \cos\phi \\ -\sin\phi \end{bmatrix} + x_2\begin{bmatrix} \sin\phi \\ \cos\phi \end{bmatrix}.$$

Figure 18.7 shows that the effect is to rotate each component of $\mathbf{x}$ through an angle $\phi$. Hence the vector itself is rotated through an angle $\phi$. This rotated version of $\mathbf{x}$ is then scaled by the factor $\rho$.

Referring to Fig. 18.8, we see that if $0 < \phi < 90°$, the derivative points out and the trajectories spiral outward. If $90° < \phi < 180°$ the trajectories spiral inward. The magnitude of $\phi$ depends on the sign of $\sigma$ the real part of the complex root. If $\sigma$ is negative the trajectories spiral inward. If $\sigma$ is positive the trajectories spiral outward.

**Figure 18.7 |** Rotation of vector **x** through an angle $\phi$.

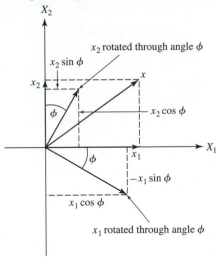

**Figure 18.8 |** Rotation of vector **x** as a function of $\phi$.

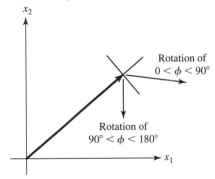

For

$$\mathbf{A} = \begin{bmatrix} \sigma & \omega \\ -\omega & \sigma \end{bmatrix},$$

the trajectories spiral clockwise, and for

$$\bar{\mathbf{A}} = \begin{bmatrix} \sigma & -\omega \\ \omega & \sigma \end{bmatrix},$$

they spiral counterclockwise.

To get a solution to Eq. [18.17], we convert to polar coordinates using the variables.

$$r(t) = \sqrt{x_1^2(t) + x_2^2(t)} \qquad \theta(t) = \tan^{-1}\frac{x_2(t)}{x_1(t)}.$$

Then, in terms of **A**,

$$\dot{x}_1 = \sigma x_1 + \omega x_2,$$

$$\dot{x}_2 = -\omega x_1 + \sigma x_2,$$

we can now write

$$\dot{r} = \frac{d}{dt}\sqrt{x_1^2 + x_2^2}$$

$$= \frac{1}{2}\left[x_1^2 + x_2^2\right]^{-1/2}\left[2x_1\dot{x}_1 + 2x_2\dot{x}_2\right]$$

$$= \frac{2x_1(\sigma x_1 + \omega x_2) + 2x_2(-\omega x_1 + \sigma x_2)}{2\sqrt{x_1^2 + x_2^2}}$$

$$= \frac{2\sigma x_1^2 + 2\sigma x_2^2 + 2\omega x_1 x_2 - 2\omega x_1 x_2}{2\sqrt{x_1^2 + x_2^2}}$$

$$= \frac{\sigma r^2}{r}$$

$$= \sigma r.$$

We note that the equation for $r(t)$ does not contain $\theta(t)$. To find the equation for $\theta(t)$, we have

$$\frac{d}{dt}\theta(t) = \frac{d}{dt}\tan^{-1}\frac{x_2(t)}{x_1(t)}$$

$$= \frac{1}{1 + [x_2/x_1]^2}\frac{d}{dt}\frac{x_2}{x_1}$$

$$= \frac{x_1^2}{x_1^2 + x_2^2}\left[\frac{-x_2\dot{x}_1}{x_1^2} + \frac{\dot{x}_2}{x_1}\right]$$

$$= \frac{x_1^2}{x_1^2 + x_2^2}\frac{x_1\dot{x}_2 - \dot{x}_1 x_2}{x_1^2}$$

$$= \frac{x_1(-\omega x_1 + \sigma x_2) - (\sigma x_1 + \omega x_2)x_2}{x_1^2 + x_2^2}$$

$$= \frac{-\omega x_1^2 - \omega x_2^2 + \sigma x_1 x_2 - \sigma x_1 x_2}{x_1^2 + x_2^2}$$

$$= \frac{-\omega\left(x_1^2 + x_2^2\right)}{x_1^2 + x_2^2}$$

$$= -\omega.$$

We now have the two *decoupled* equations

$$\dot{r} = \sigma r,$$

$$\dot{\theta} = -\omega,$$

with solution

$$r(t) = e^{\sigma t} r(0),$$

$$\theta(t) = -\omega t + \theta(0),$$

where

$$r(0) = \sqrt{x_1^2(0) + x_2^2(0)} \quad \text{and} \quad \theta(0) = \tan^{-1} \frac{x_2(0)}{x_1(0)}.$$

The trajectories, or solutions, are log-spiral curves.

Our final goal, for the example under study, is to determine how to get from the original system

$$\begin{bmatrix} \dot{x}_1 \\ \dot{x}_2 \end{bmatrix} = \begin{bmatrix} 1 & 3 \\ -6 & -5 \end{bmatrix} \begin{bmatrix} x_1 \\ x_2 \end{bmatrix},$$

repeated here for convenience, to the real canonical system

$$\begin{bmatrix} \dot{x}_1 \\ \dot{x}_2 \end{bmatrix} = \begin{bmatrix} -2 & 3 \\ -3 & -2 \end{bmatrix} \begin{bmatrix} x_1 \\ x_2 \end{bmatrix}.$$

We already have the transformation that takes us from the original system to the complex canonical system with the complex eigenvalues along the diagonal. If we can now determine a transformation from the complex canonical system to the real canonical system, we can cascade the transformations and go directly from the original system to the real canonical system.

Finding the transformation from the complex to real canonical form is straightforward, because what we are looking for is the *inverse* of the transformation that takes us from the real to the complex canonical form, and this latter transformation can be found by applying the same transformation techniques we have used previously. That is, we can write

$$\begin{bmatrix} \sigma - \lambda & \omega \\ -\omega & \sigma - \lambda \end{bmatrix}_{\Big|_{\lambda=\sigma+j\omega}} \begin{bmatrix} x_1 \\ x_2 \end{bmatrix} = \begin{bmatrix} -j\omega & \omega \\ -\omega & -j\omega \end{bmatrix} \begin{bmatrix} x_1 \\ x_2 \end{bmatrix}$$

$$= \begin{bmatrix} 0 \\ 0 \end{bmatrix}.$$

This yields the equations

$$-j\omega x_1 + \omega x_2 = 0,$$

$$-\omega x_1 - j\omega x_2 = 0,$$

both of which yield

$$x_2 = j x_1.$$

Thus the general form of the eigenvector is

$$\mathbf{e}_1 = \begin{bmatrix} \alpha \\ j\alpha \end{bmatrix}.$$

For $\lambda = \sigma - j\omega$ the result is

$$\mathbf{e}_2 = \begin{bmatrix} \alpha \\ -j\alpha \end{bmatrix},$$

and the transformation matrix is

$$\hat{\mathbf{T}} = \alpha \begin{bmatrix} 1 & 1 \\ j & -j \end{bmatrix}.$$

It follows that the transformation from the complex to the real canonical form is just

$$\tilde{\mathbf{T}} = \hat{\mathbf{T}}^{-1}$$

$$= \frac{1}{2\alpha} \begin{bmatrix} 1 & -j \\ 1 & j \end{bmatrix}$$

$$= \frac{1}{2} \begin{bmatrix} 1 & -j \\ 1 & j \end{bmatrix},$$

where we have chosen $\alpha = 1$.

Now let

$$\mathbf{A} = \begin{bmatrix} 1 & 3 \\ -6 & -5 \end{bmatrix} \qquad \mathbf{\Lambda}_{\text{cmplx}} = \begin{bmatrix} -2+j3 & 0 \\ 0 & -2-j3 \end{bmatrix} \qquad \mathbf{\Lambda}_{\text{real}} = \begin{bmatrix} -2 & 3 \\ -3 & -2 \end{bmatrix}.$$

Then

$$\mathbf{\Lambda}_{\text{cmplx}} = \bar{\mathbf{T}}^{-1} \mathbf{A} \bar{\mathbf{T}},$$

and

$$\mathbf{\Lambda}_{\text{real}} = \tilde{\mathbf{T}}^{-1} \mathbf{\Lambda}_{\text{cmplx}} \tilde{\mathbf{T}}$$

$$= \tilde{\mathbf{T}}^{-1} \bar{\mathbf{T}}^{-1} \mathbf{A} \bar{\mathbf{T}} \tilde{\mathbf{T}}$$

$$= [\bar{\mathbf{T}} \tilde{\mathbf{T}}]^{-1} \mathbf{A} [\bar{\mathbf{T}} \tilde{\mathbf{T}}]$$

Thus the overall transformation to get from the original system to the real canonical system is

$$\mathbf{T} = \bar{\mathbf{T}} \tilde{\mathbf{T}}$$

$$= \frac{1}{2} \begin{bmatrix} 1 & 1 \\ -1+j & -1-j \end{bmatrix} \begin{bmatrix} 1 & -j \\ 1 & j \end{bmatrix}$$

$$= \begin{bmatrix} 1 & 0 \\ -1 & 1 \end{bmatrix}$$

Then

$$\mathbf{T}^{-1} = \begin{bmatrix} 1 & 0 \\ -1 & 1 \end{bmatrix}^{-1} = \begin{bmatrix} 1 & 0 \\ 1 & 1 \end{bmatrix}.$$

Finally,

$$\mathbf{T}^{-1}\mathbf{A}\mathbf{T} = \begin{bmatrix} 1 & 0 \\ 1 & 1 \end{bmatrix} \begin{bmatrix} 1 & 3 \\ -6 & -5 \end{bmatrix} \begin{bmatrix} 1 & 0 \\ -1 & 1 \end{bmatrix}$$

$$= \begin{bmatrix} 1 & 0 \\ 1 & 1 \end{bmatrix} \begin{bmatrix} -2 & 3 \\ -1 & -5 \end{bmatrix}$$

$$= \begin{bmatrix} -2 & 3 \\ -3 & -2 \end{bmatrix}.$$

We note the following. The eigenvector associated with $\lambda = -2 + j3$ is

$$\mathbf{e}_1 = \begin{bmatrix} 1 \\ -1+j \end{bmatrix} = \begin{bmatrix} 1 \\ -1 \end{bmatrix} + j \begin{bmatrix} 0 \\ 1 \end{bmatrix}.$$

Then the transformation matrix can be written

$$\mathbf{T} = [\, \text{Re}\{\mathbf{e}_1\} \quad \text{Im}\{\mathbf{e}_1\}\,].$$

This result is easy enough to show. Noting that $\mathbf{e}_2 = \mathbf{e}_1^*$, we can write

$$\bar{\mathbf{T}}\tilde{\mathbf{T}} = [\mathbf{e}_1 \quad \mathbf{e}_1^*] \begin{bmatrix} 1/2 & -j/2 \\ 1/2 & j/2 \end{bmatrix}$$

$$= [(\mathbf{e}_1 + \mathbf{e}_q^*)/2 \quad -j(\mathbf{e}_1 - \mathbf{e}_1^*])/2]$$

$$= [\text{Re}\{\mathbf{e}_1\} \quad \text{Im}\{\mathbf{e}_1\}].$$

### 18.4.4 Repeated Real Roots

The two examples considered so far in this section represent almost all the possibilities for two-dimensional systems. There is one remaining special case to be considered and that is the case of repeated real roots. To that end, we now look at a specific system with repeated roots.

**EXAMPLE 18.4.1**

Consider the state model

$$\begin{bmatrix} \dot{x}_1 \\ \dot{x}_2 \end{bmatrix} = \begin{bmatrix} 2 & -8 \\ 2 & -6 \end{bmatrix} \begin{bmatrix} x_1 \\ x_2 \end{bmatrix}. \qquad \text{[18.18]}$$

Again, our first step is to find the eigenvalues by finding

$$\text{Det}\left\{ \begin{bmatrix} 2 & -8 \\ 2 & -6 \end{bmatrix} - \begin{bmatrix} \lambda & 0 \\ 0 & \lambda \end{bmatrix} \right\} = \text{Det}\begin{bmatrix} 2-\lambda & -8 \\ 2 & -6-\lambda \end{bmatrix}$$

$$= \lambda^2 + 4\lambda - 12 + 16$$

$$= \lambda^2 + 4\lambda + 4$$

$$= (\lambda + 2)(\lambda + 2).$$

Thus, the system has only the one eigenvalue $\lambda = -2$. We can find the eigenvector for $\lambda = -2$ by solving

$$\begin{bmatrix} 2 - \lambda & -8 \\ 2 & -6 - \lambda \end{bmatrix}_{\lambda = -2} \begin{bmatrix} x_1 \\ x_2 \end{bmatrix} = \begin{bmatrix} 0 \\ 0 \end{bmatrix}.$$

Making the substitution $\lambda = -2$ in the matrix yields

$$\begin{bmatrix} 4 & -8 \\ 2 & -4 \end{bmatrix} \begin{bmatrix} x_1 \\ x_2 \end{bmatrix} = \begin{bmatrix} 0 \\ 0 \end{bmatrix},$$

resulting in the equations

$$4x_1 - 8x_2 = 0,$$

$$2x_1 - 4x_2 = 0.$$

Both equations tell us the same thing, namely, that

$$x_1 = 2x_2.$$

Thus, one choice for the eigenvector is

$$\mathbf{e}_1 = \begin{bmatrix} 2 \\ 1 \end{bmatrix}.$$

Now we have something of a dilemma. We would like to find a transformation matrix **T** to take us to the canonical form, but we only have one eigenvector. Thus, becaues of the repeated root, the canonical form will not be diagonal. Then we have to settle for the simplest form possible and we choose

$$\mathbf{\Lambda} = \begin{bmatrix} -2 & 1 \\ 0 & -2 \end{bmatrix}.$$

This is a *nearly* diagonal matrix and the simplest that we can find. Having chosen this canonical matrix, we now turn our attention to finding the transformation matrix **T**.

Since we have computed the single eigenvector

$$\mathbf{e}_1 = \begin{bmatrix} 2 \\ 1 \end{bmatrix},$$

we can use that for one column of the matrix

To find the second column for the transformation matrix, we use a variation of the equation we used to find the eigenvector. That is, we write

$$\begin{bmatrix} 2 - \lambda & -8 \\ 2 & -6 - \lambda \end{bmatrix}_{\lambda = -2} \begin{bmatrix} g_1 \\ g_2 \end{bmatrix} = \begin{bmatrix} 2 \\ 1 \end{bmatrix},$$

where we have replaced the column of zeros on the right hand side by the eigenvector $\mathbf{e}_1$. Although it should be obvious that we can use any variable name in solving this equation, we have used

$$\mathbf{g} = \begin{bmatrix} g_1 \\ g_2 \end{bmatrix}$$

to make it *totally* clear that we are solving for what we call a *generalized* eigenvector.

Substituting $\lambda = -2$ we get

$$\begin{bmatrix} 4 & -8 \\ 2 & -4 \end{bmatrix} \begin{bmatrix} g_1 \\ g_2 \end{bmatrix} = \begin{bmatrix} 2 \\ 1 \end{bmatrix},$$

which yields the equations

$$4g_1 - 8g_2 = 2,$$
$$2g_1 - 4g_2 = 1.$$

Either of these equations yields

$$g_2 = \frac{2g_1 - 1}{4}.$$

Choosing $g_1 = 1/2$ yields

$$\mathbf{e}_{11} = \begin{bmatrix} \frac{1}{2} \\ 0 \end{bmatrix},$$

and the transformation matrix is

$$\mathbf{T} = [\mathbf{e}_1 \quad \mathbf{e}_{11}] = \begin{bmatrix} 2 & \frac{1}{2} \\ 1 & 0 \end{bmatrix}.$$

Note that the equation

$$[\mathbf{A} - \lambda \mathbf{I}]\big|_{\lambda = -2} \mathbf{e}_{11} = \mathbf{e}_1$$

can be rewritten as

$$\mathbf{A}\mathbf{e}_{11} - \lambda \mathbf{e}_{11} = \mathbf{e}_1, \qquad \lambda = -2,$$

or

$$\mathbf{A}\mathbf{e}_{11} = \mathbf{e}_1 + \lambda \mathbf{e}_{11}, \qquad \lambda = -2.$$

Now consider the equation

$$\Lambda = \mathbf{T}^{-1}\mathbf{A}\mathbf{T},$$

which we rewrite as

$$\mathbf{T}\Lambda = \mathbf{A}\mathbf{T}$$
$$= \mathbf{A}[\mathbf{e}_1 \quad \mathbf{e}_{11}]$$
$$= [\mathbf{A}\mathbf{e}_1 \quad \mathbf{A}\mathbf{e}_{11}]$$
$$= [\lambda\mathbf{e}_1 \quad \mathbf{e}_1 + \lambda\mathbf{e}_{11}], \qquad \lambda = -2.$$

Letting

$$\mathbf{e}_1 = \begin{bmatrix} a_1 \\ a_2 \end{bmatrix} \quad \text{and} \quad \mathbf{e}_{11} = \begin{bmatrix} b_1 \\ b_2 \end{bmatrix},$$

**Figure 18.9 |** Isoclines for the case of a repeated root.

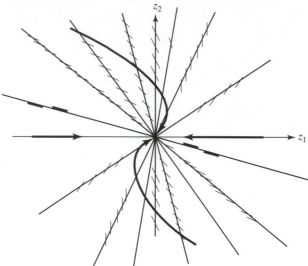

we have

$$\mathbf{T}\Lambda = [\mathbf{e}_1 \quad \mathbf{e}_{11}]\Lambda$$

$$= \begin{bmatrix} a_1 & b_1 \\ a_2 & b_2 \end{bmatrix} \begin{bmatrix} \lambda & 1 \\ 0 & \lambda \end{bmatrix}$$

$$= \begin{bmatrix} \lambda a_1 & a_1 + \lambda b_1 \\ \lambda a_2 & a_2 + \lambda b_2 \end{bmatrix}$$

$$= [\lambda \mathbf{e}_1 \quad \mathbf{e}_1 + \lambda \mathbf{e}_{11}], \quad \lambda = -2.$$

This example can be easily generalized to the *n*-dimensional case. The phase portrait is shown in Fig. 18.9. We leave the drawing of the phase portrait by the method of isoclines as an exercise.

---

We have invested significant effort in studying three state models of dimension two. That effort will pay handsome dividends because these three models embody all the fundamental behaviors that we will find in higher dimension state models. Thus, in Section 18.5, we will be able to very quickly extend our analysis to these seemingly more complicated higher dimension state models.

## 18.5 | STATE MODELS OF HIGHER DIMENSION

In this section, we will rapidly retrace the mathematical path we have already trodden for state models of dimension two, extending our results to state models of arbitrary dimension. We will be able to move quite rapidly because we have already done most of the analysis.

Suppose that $\mathbf{A}$ is $n \times n$. We compute the eigenvalues just as we did for the two dimensional case by solving

$$\text{Det}\,[\mathbf{A} - \lambda\mathbf{I}] = 0.$$

If the elements of $\mathbf{A}$ are real, then

$$\text{Det}\,[\mathbf{A} - \lambda\mathbf{I}] = \lambda^n + \alpha_{n-1}\lambda^{n-1} + \cdots + \alpha_1\lambda + \alpha_0,$$

and the so-called characteristic equation is then

$$\lambda^n + \alpha_{n-1}\lambda^{n-1} + \cdots + \alpha_1\lambda + \alpha_0 = 0,$$

where the $\alpha_i$ are sums of products of the elements of $\mathbf{A}$ and hence real.

The solutions of the characteristic equation are the eigenvalues, and if the elements in the matrix $\mathbf{A}$ are all real, then these eigenvalues will be either real or complex conjugate pairs. This follows from the fact that the coefficients in the characteristic equation are real. Thus, the situation is identical to that for the characteristic equation we studied earlier for transfer functions. The only difference is we are using $\lambda$ instead of the Laplace variable $s$.

## 18.5.1 Distinct Roots

In general, the $n$ roots of the characteristic equation are distinct. Note that a complex conjugate pair constitutes two distinct roots. If the roots are all distinct, then we can find $n$ distinct eigenvectors, one associated with each distinct eigenvalue. By distinct we mean that the eigenvectors are linearly independent. We will not show this is so, but the proof is not difficult.

Given that the $n$ eigenvectors are linearly independent, consider using the eigenvectors as the basis for a canonical coordinate system for the equation

$$\dot{\mathbf{x}} = \mathbf{A}\mathbf{x} + \mathbf{b}u, \qquad\qquad [18.19]$$

where $\mathbf{A}$ is $n \times n$ and $\mathbf{b}$ is $n \times 1$.

Then we have

$$
\begin{bmatrix} x_1 \\ \vdots \\ x_i \\ \vdots \\ x_n \end{bmatrix}
= x_1 \begin{bmatrix} 1 \\ 0 \\ 0 \\ \vdots \\ 0 \end{bmatrix}
+ x_2 \begin{bmatrix} 0 \\ 1 \\ 0 \\ \vdots \\ 0 \end{bmatrix}
+ \cdots + x_i \begin{bmatrix} 0 \\ 0 \\ 1 \\ \vdots \\ 0 \end{bmatrix}
+ \cdots + x_n \begin{bmatrix} 0 \\ 0 \\ \vdots \\ 0 \\ 1 \end{bmatrix}
$$

$$= z_1\mathbf{e}_1 + z_2\mathbf{e}_2 + \cdots + z_i\mathbf{e}_i + \cdots + z_n\mathbf{e}_n$$

$$= \begin{bmatrix} \mathbf{e}_1 & \mathbf{e}_2 & \cdots & \mathbf{e}_i & \cdots & \mathbf{e}_n \end{bmatrix}
\begin{bmatrix} z_1 \\ \vdots \\ z_i \\ \vdots \\ z_n \end{bmatrix}.$$

The matrix

$$\mathbf{T} = [\mathbf{e}_1 \quad \mathbf{e}_2 \quad \cdots \quad \mathbf{e}_i \quad \cdots \quad \mathbf{e}_n] \qquad [18.20]$$

is then a transformation from one coordinate system to another. If we use the distinct eigenvectors as the basis for our coordinate system, then, since

$$\mathbf{x} = \mathbf{T}\mathbf{z},$$

the differential equation in this new coordinate system will be

$$\dot{\mathbf{z}} = \mathbf{\Lambda}\mathbf{z},$$

where

$$\mathbf{\Lambda} = \mathbf{T}^{-1}\mathbf{A}\mathbf{T}. \qquad [18.21]$$

We are interested in the structure of the matrix $\mathbf{\Lambda}$. To investigate this structure we rewrite Eq. [18.21] as

$$\mathbf{T}\mathbf{\Lambda} = \mathbf{A}\mathbf{T}. \qquad [18.22]$$

The right-hand side of Eq. [18.22] can be expanded as

$$\mathbf{A}\mathbf{T} = \mathbf{A}[\mathbf{e}_1 \quad \mathbf{e}_2 \quad \ldots \quad \mathbf{e}_i \quad \ldots \quad \mathbf{e}_n]$$
$$= [\mathbf{A}\mathbf{e}_1 \quad \mathbf{A}\mathbf{e}_2 \quad \ldots \quad \mathbf{A}\mathbf{e}_i \quad \ldots \quad \mathbf{A}\mathbf{e}_n]$$
$$= [\lambda_1\mathbf{e}_1 \quad \lambda_2\mathbf{e}_2 \quad \ldots \quad \lambda_i\mathbf{e}_i \quad \ldots \quad \lambda_n\mathbf{e}_n].$$

We now have to determine the form of $\mathbf{\Lambda}$. One approach would be to equate the left-hand side, element by element, to the right-hand side. A better approach is to note that for a given $\mathbf{T}$ the matrix $\mathbf{\Lambda}$ is unique, and then simply choose a $\mathbf{\Lambda}$ and see if it satisfies the equation. If it does, we are done. Therefore, we choose

$$\mathbf{\Lambda} = \begin{bmatrix} \lambda_1 & 0 & \ldots & 0 & \ldots & 0 \\ 0 & \lambda_2 & \ldots & 0 & \ldots & 0 \\ \vdots & & \ddots & & & \vdots \\ 0 & \ldots & 0 & \lambda_i & \ldots & 0 \\ \vdots & & & & \ddots & \\ 0 & 0 & \ldots & 0 & \ldots & \lambda_n \end{bmatrix}.$$

Then,

$$\mathbf{T}\mathbf{\Lambda} = \begin{bmatrix} T_{11} & T_{12} & \ldots & T_{1i} & \ldots & T_{1n} \\ \vdots & & & & & \vdots \\ T_{i1} & T_{i2} & \ldots & T_{ii} & \ldots & T_{in} \\ \vdots & & & & & \vdots \\ T_{n1} & T_{n2} & \ldots & T_{ni} & \ldots & T_{nn} \end{bmatrix} \begin{bmatrix} \lambda_1 & 0 & \ldots & 0 & \ldots & 0 \\ 0 & \lambda_2 & \ldots & 0 & \ldots & 0 \\ \vdots & & \ddots & & & \vdots \\ 0 & \ldots & 0 & \lambda_i & \ldots & 0 \\ \vdots & & & & \ddots & \vdots \\ 0 & 0 & \ldots & 0 & \ldots & \lambda_n \end{bmatrix}$$

$$
= \begin{bmatrix}
\lambda_1 T_{11} & \lambda_2 T_{12} & \cdots & \lambda_i T_{1i} & \cdots & \lambda_n T_{1n} \\
\vdots & & & & & \vdots \\
\lambda_1 T_{i1} & \lambda_2 T_{i2} & \cdots & \lambda_i T_{ii} & \cdots & \lambda_n T_{in} \\
\vdots & & & & & \vdots \\
\lambda_1 T_{n1} & \lambda_2 T_{n2} & \cdots & \lambda_i T_{ni} & \cdots & \lambda_n T_{nn}
\end{bmatrix}
$$

$$
= [\lambda_1 \mathbf{e}_1 \quad \lambda_2 \mathbf{e}_2 \quad \cdots \quad \lambda_i \mathbf{e}_i \quad \cdots \quad \lambda_n \mathbf{e}_n].
$$

Thus, our choice of $\Lambda$ is the correct one.

If we have distinct complex roots, we may wish to replace the complex roots by the real canonical form that expresses the subsystem in terms of the real and imaginary parts of the complex eigenvalue $\Lambda = \sigma + j\omega$. That is, if we have

$$
\Lambda = \begin{bmatrix}
\lambda_1 & 0 & \cdots & 0 & \cdots & 0 \\
0 & \lambda_2 & \cdots & 0 & \cdots & 0 \\
\vdots & & \ddots & & & \vdots \\
0 & \cdots & \lambda_i & 0 & \cdots & 0 \\
0 & \cdots & 0 & \lambda_i^* & \cdots & 0 \\
\vdots & & & & \ddots & \vdots \\
0 & 0 & \cdots & 0 & \cdots & \lambda_n
\end{bmatrix},
$$

where $\lambda_i = \sigma + j\omega$, then we will probably prefer the form

$$
\Lambda = \begin{bmatrix}
\lambda_1 & 0 & \cdots & 0 & \cdots & 0 \\
0 & \lambda_2 & \cdots & 0 & \cdots & 0 \\
\vdots & & \ddots & & & \vdots \\
0 & \cdots & \sigma & \omega & \cdots & 0 \\
0 & \cdots & -\omega & \sigma & \cdots & 0 \\
\vdots & & & & \ddots & \vdots \\
0 & 0 & \cdots & 0 & \cdots & \lambda_n
\end{bmatrix}.
$$

In the case of the state models of dimension two studied earlier, we found that for a pair of complex eigenvalues the total transformation from the original coordinate system to the real canonical form was

$$
\mathbf{T} = \bar{\mathbf{T}}\tilde{\mathbf{T}} = [\text{Re}(\mathbf{e}_1) \quad \text{Im}(\mathbf{e}_1)],
$$

where

$$
\bar{\mathbf{T}} = [\mathbf{e}_1 \quad \mathbf{e}_1^*]
$$

and

$$
\tilde{\mathbf{T}} = \frac{1}{2}\begin{bmatrix} 1 & -j \\ 1 & j \end{bmatrix}.
$$

The two-dimensional case can be easily extended to the $n$-dimensional case. Suppose

$$
\bar{\mathbf{T}} = [\mathbf{e}_1 \quad \mathbf{e}_2 \quad \cdots \quad \mathbf{e}_i \quad \mathbf{e}_i^* \quad \cdots \quad \mathbf{e}_n],
$$

where $\mathbf{e}_i$ is the eigenvector for $\lambda = \sigma + j\omega$. Then let

$$
\tilde{\mathbf{T}} =
\begin{bmatrix}
1 & 0 & \cdots & 0 & 0 & 0 & \cdots & 0 \\
0 & 1 & 0 & \cdots & 0 & 0 & \cdots & 0 \\
\vdots & & \ddots & 1 & \vdots & \vdots & & \vdots \\
0 & \cdots & 0 & \frac{1}{2} & -\frac{j}{2} & 0 & \cdots & 0 \\
0 & \cdots & 0 & \frac{1}{2} & \frac{j}{2} & 0 & \cdots & 0 \\
\vdots & & & & \ddots & 1 & & \vdots \\
0 & 0 & 0 & 0 & \cdots & 0 & 1 & 0 \\
0 & 0 & 0 & 0 & \cdots & 0 & 0 & 1
\end{bmatrix},
$$

where $\tilde{\mathbf{T}}$ is the identity matrix except for the $2 \times 2$ block in rows $i$ and $i+1$. It is easy to verify that

$$
\mathbf{T} = \bar{\mathbf{T}}\tilde{\mathbf{T}} = [\mathbf{e}_1 \quad \mathbf{e}_2 \quad \cdots \quad \mathrm{Re}(\mathbf{e}_i) \quad \mathrm{Im}(\mathbf{e}_i) \quad \cdots \quad \mathbf{e}_n],
$$

and we have a transformation that takes us directly from the original coordinate system to the real Jordan canonical coordinate system.

## 18.5.2  Repeated Eigenvalues

It is possible to encounter systems that have repeated eigenvalues. These repeated eigenvalues can be either real or complex. If they are complex, then there are, of course, repeated *pairs* of eigenvalues. We will treat the case of repeated real eigenvalues in some detail. Repeated complex pairs of eigenvalues can be treated by the techniques introduced here for repeated real eigenvalues, but repeated complex eigenvalues are so rare that discussing them in detail is not easily justified. As it is, we will spend more time on the case of repeated real eigenvalues than is warranted, given the rarity of such eigenvalues in engineering problems.

We have already treated the case of repeated eigenvalues for a two-dimensional system. All we need to do now is extend those ideas a little. We do so by way of Example 18.5.1.

**EXAMPLE 18.5.1**

Consider the system

$$
\dot{\mathbf{x}} = \mathbf{A}\mathbf{x},
$$

with

$$
\mathbf{A} =
\begin{bmatrix}
-2 & 2 & 0 & 1 \\
0 & -2 & 4 & 0 \\
0 & 0 & -2 & 0 \\
0 & 0 & 0 & -2
\end{bmatrix}.
$$

Our goal is to transform the system to Jordan canonical form. The first step is to find the eigenvalues, which is not hard because the matrix is upper triangular. Thus,

$$\text{Det}\,[\mathbf{A} - \lambda\mathbf{I}] = \text{Det} \begin{bmatrix} -2-\lambda & 2 & 0 & 1 \\ 0 & -2-\lambda & 4 & 0 \\ 0 & 0 & -2-\lambda & 0 \\ 0 & 0 & 0 & -2-\lambda \end{bmatrix}$$

$$= (\lambda + 2)^4.$$

In obtaining this result we have used the fact that the determinant of an upper triangular matrix is simply the product of the diagonal elements of the matrix (see Problem 5 in Section 18.9.8.) Thus, the only eigenvalue the system has is $\lambda = -2$. The next question is: how many true eigenvectors does the system have?

To answer that question we have to solve the eigenequation

$$[\mathbf{A} - \lambda\mathbf{I}]\big|_{\lambda=-2} = \mathbf{0}.$$

For the system at hand

$$[\mathbf{A} - \lambda\mathbf{I}]\big|_{\lambda=-2} = \begin{bmatrix} 0 & 2 & 0 & 1 \\ 0 & 0 & 4 & 0 \\ 0 & 0 & 0 & 0 \\ 0 & 0 & 0 & 0 \end{bmatrix}.$$

Then the equation to determine the eigenvectors is

$$\begin{bmatrix} 0 & 2 & 0 & 1 \\ 0 & 0 & 4 & 0 \\ 0 & 0 & 0 & 0 \\ 0 & 0 & 0 & 0 \end{bmatrix} \begin{bmatrix} x_1 \\ x_2 \\ x_3 \\ x_4 \end{bmatrix} = \begin{bmatrix} 0 \\ 0 \\ 0 \\ 0 \end{bmatrix}. \qquad \textbf{[18.23]}$$

Note that the matrix

$$\begin{bmatrix} 0 & 2 & 0 & 1 \\ 0 & 0 & 4 & 0 \\ 0 & 0 & 0 & 0 \\ 0 & 0 & 0 & 0 \end{bmatrix}$$

is not full rank. If it were of full rank four, the matrix would have an inverse and the only solution would be $\mathbf{x} = \mathbf{0}$. However, the matrix is rank two, as can be seen by the fact that it has only two linearly independent rows (columns).

Technically, there are an infinite number of solutions to Eq. [18.23]. The situation is no different than it was for the state model of Eq. [18.11]. In that case our analysis of a second-order state model also showed that that there were an infinite number of solutions, but all the solutions lay along two lines: the $x_1$ axis and the line

$$x_2 = -x_1.$$

In the present case we have a system of dimension four, but if we think of each solution as a vector, then among all the solutions (vectors) there will be a finite set of linearly independent solutions (vectors) that we can use to generate all the remaining solutions (vectors).

The number of finite, linearly independent solutions (vectors) is equal to the dimension of the matrix minus its rank. In this case, the dimension is four and the rank two so there are $4 - 2 = 2$ nonzero linearly independent solutions. If the rank had been three there would have been one nonzero solution, whereas if the rank had been one there would have been three nonzero linearly independent solutions. That is, the higher the rank, the fewer the number of nonzero linearly independent solutions.

*Each nonzero linearly independent solution corresponds to a true eigenvector.* In this case, there will be two linearly independent eigenvectors. These two eigenvectors provide two of the four columns of the transformation matrix **T** that will transform the system to the Jordan canonical form. We need to determine two more columns that are linearly independent of the two true eigenvectors. We do that by the process set forward in Example 18.4.1.

To find the two true eigenvectors we use Eq. [18.23], which yields the equations

$$2x_2 + x_4 = 0,$$

$$4x_3 = 0,$$

$$0 = 0,$$

$$0 = 0.$$

The last two equations don't seem particularly important, or relevant, but they are, as we will see shortly. From the first two equations we determine that

$$x_4 = -2x_2,$$

$$x_3 = 0,$$

$$x_1 = \text{anything}.$$

Thus the eigenvectors are of the form:

$$\mathbf{e}_i = \begin{bmatrix} \text{anything} \\ a \\ 0 \\ -2a \end{bmatrix}.$$

In Example 18.4.1, we generated the necessary column of **T** by replacing the vector of zeros on the right-hand side of the eigenequation by the eigenvector $\mathbf{e}_1$. In this case, one might suppose that we could generate a so-called generalized eigenvector from each of the true eigenvectors by this same method. That, however, does not happen to be the case. What we will find is that we can generate two generalized eigenvectors from one of the true eigenvectors and none from the other. To see how this happens we first pick, for simplicity,

$$\mathbf{e}_1 = \begin{bmatrix} 1 \\ 0 \\ 0 \\ 0 \end{bmatrix} \quad and \quad \mathbf{e}_2 = \begin{bmatrix} 0 \\ 1 \\ 0 \\ -2 \end{bmatrix}.$$

There are an infinite number of choices, but for hand calculations this is one of the simplest. The equation to find the generalized eigenvectors is

$$[\mathbf{A} - \lambda \mathbf{I}]\big|_{\lambda=-2} \mathbf{g} = \mathbf{e}_i \quad i = 1, 2.$$

For $\mathbf{e}_1$, we have

$$\begin{bmatrix} 0 & 2 & 0 & 1 \\ 0 & 0 & 4 & 0 \\ 0 & 0 & 0 & 0 \\ 0 & 0 & 0 & 0 \end{bmatrix} \begin{bmatrix} g_1 \\ g_2 \\ g_3 \\ g_4 \end{bmatrix} = \begin{bmatrix} 1 \\ 0 \\ 0 \\ 0 \end{bmatrix},$$

which results in the equations

$$2g_2 + g_4 = 1,$$

$$4g_3 = 0,$$

$$0 = 0,$$

$$0 = 0.$$

The last two equations are trivial, but important nonetheless, because we must have agreement on both sides of the equation for all four entries. The importance of this will be apparent shortly when we look for a generalized eigenvector for $\mathbf{e}_2$.

The result of solving these equations is

$$g_1 = \text{anything},$$

$$g_4 = 1 - 2g_2$$

$$g_3 = 0. \qquad\qquad\qquad\qquad \textbf{[18.24]}$$

We can make $g_1$ anything we want to because it never shows up in the equations. Thus, we can find at least one generalized eigenvector associated with $\mathbf{e}_1$, and we pick $g_1 = 0$, $g_2 = 1$, so that

$$\mathbf{e}_{11} = \begin{bmatrix} 0 \\ 1 \\ 0 \\ -1 \end{bmatrix}.$$

We will see shortly that this was not the best, or final, choice for $\mathbf{e}_{11}$. The reason for this statement becomes clear as we now try to find another generalized eigenvector associated with $\mathbf{e}_1$.

To do so we now replace $\mathbf{e}_1$ on the right-hand side of the eigenequation by $\mathbf{e}_{11}$. This yields

$$2g_2 + g_4 = 0,$$

$$4g_3 = 1,$$

$$0 = 0,$$

$$0 = -1.$$

The last equation $0 = -1$ seems to indicate that we cannot find a second generalized eigenvector for $\mathbf{e}_1$, at least based on our particular *choice* of $\mathbf{e}_{11}$. However, if we go back to Eqs. [18.24] and let $g_1 = 0$, $g_2 = 0.5$, then

$$\mathbf{e}_{11} = \begin{bmatrix} 0 \\ 0.5 \\ 0 \\ 0 \end{bmatrix}.$$

Now re-solving for $\mathbf{e}_{12}$, we have

$$2g_2 + g_4 = 0,$$

$$4g_3 = 0.5,$$

$$0 = 0,$$

$$0 = 0.$$

These equations are consistent and can be reduced to

$$g_1 = \text{anything},$$

$$g_4 = -2g_2,$$

$$g_3 = \frac{1}{8}.$$

Choosing $g_2 = 0$, we get

$$\mathbf{e}_{12} = \begin{bmatrix} 0 \\ 0 \\ \frac{1}{8} \\ 0 \end{bmatrix}.$$

This last result should convince us that we *cannot* find a generalized eigenvector associated with $\mathbf{e}_2$. We check this by writing

$$\begin{bmatrix} 0 & 2 & 0 & 1 \\ 0 & 0 & 4 & 0 \\ 0 & 0 & 0 & 0 \\ 0 & 0 & 0 & 0 \end{bmatrix} \begin{bmatrix} g_1 \\ g_2 \\ g_3 \\ g_4 \end{bmatrix} = \begin{bmatrix} 0 \\ 1 \\ 0 \\ -2 \end{bmatrix},$$

yielding

$$2g_2 + 4g_4 = 0,$$

$$g_3 = 1,$$

$$0 = 0,$$

$$0 = -2.$$

It is the last of these equations that does us in. There is no way to construct a generalized eigenvector that will satisfy this last equation. Further, recalling the form of the true eigenvectors:

$$\mathbf{e} = \begin{bmatrix} \text{anything} \\ a \\ 0 \\ -2a \end{bmatrix},$$

it becomes apparent that we must choose at least one true eigenvector with $a \neq 0$, and for that eigenvector, we will not be able to find a generalized eigenvector. Thus,

$$\mathbf{T} = [\mathbf{e}_1 \quad \mathbf{e}_{11} \quad \mathbf{e}_{12} \quad \mathbf{e}_2]$$

$$= \begin{bmatrix} 1 & 0 & 0 & 0 \\ 0 & \frac{1}{2} & 0 & 1 \\ 0 & 0 & \frac{1}{8} & 0 \\ 0 & 0 & 0 & -2 \end{bmatrix}.$$

It is easy enough to check that

$$\mathbf{T}^{-1}\mathbf{AT} = \begin{bmatrix} 1 & 0 & 0 & 0 \\ 0 & 2 & 0 & 1 \\ 0 & 0 & 8 & 0 \\ 0 & 0 & 0 & -\frac{1}{2} \end{bmatrix} \begin{bmatrix} -2 & 2 & 0 & 1 \\ 0 & -2 & 4 & 0 \\ 0 & 0 & -2 & 0 \\ 0 & 0 & 0 & -2 \end{bmatrix} \begin{bmatrix} 1 & 0 & 0 & 0 \\ 0 & \frac{1}{2} & 0 & 1 \\ 0 & 0 & \frac{1}{8} & 0 \\ 0 & 0 & 0 & -2 \end{bmatrix}$$

$$= \begin{bmatrix} 1 & 0 & 0 & 0 \\ 0 & 2 & 0 & 1 \\ 0 & 0 & 8 & 0 \\ 0 & 0 & 0 & -\frac{1}{2} \end{bmatrix} \begin{bmatrix} -2 & 1 & 0 & 0 \\ 0 & -1 & \frac{1}{2} & -2 \\ 0 & 0 & -\frac{1}{4} & 0 \\ 0 & 0 & 0 & 4 \end{bmatrix}$$

$$= \begin{bmatrix} -2 & 1 & 0 & 0 \\ 0 & -2 & 1 & 0 \\ 0 & 0 & -2 & 0 \\ 0 & 0 & 0 & -2 \end{bmatrix}.$$

We now show that the final form of $\mathbf{\Lambda}$ can be ascertained without actually finding, $\mathbf{T}$ numerically. In this example,

$$\mathbf{T} = [\mathbf{e}_1 \quad \mathbf{e}_{11} \quad \mathbf{e}_{12} \quad \mathbf{e}_2].$$

Then

$$\mathbf{AT} = \mathbf{A}[\mathbf{e}_1 \quad \mathbf{e}_{11} \quad \mathbf{e}_{12} \quad \mathbf{e}_2]$$

$$= [\mathbf{Ae}_1 \quad \mathbf{Ae}_{11} \quad \mathbf{Ae}_{12} \quad \mathbf{Ae}_2].$$

Next, using the fact that

$$\mathbf{Ae}_{11} = \mathbf{e}_1 + \lambda\mathbf{e}_{11} \quad \text{and} \quad \mathbf{Ae}_{12} = \mathbf{e}_{11} + \lambda\mathbf{e}_{12}, \qquad \lambda = -2,$$

we can write

$$\mathbf{AT} = [\lambda\mathbf{e}_1 \quad \mathbf{e}_1 + \lambda\mathbf{e}_{11} \quad \mathbf{e}_{11} + \lambda\mathbf{e}_{12} \quad \lambda\mathbf{e}_2], \qquad \lambda = -2.$$

Now suppose that

$$\Lambda = \begin{bmatrix} \lambda & 1 & 0 & 0 \\ 0 & \lambda & 1 & 0 \\ 0 & 0 & \lambda & 0 \\ 0 & 0 & 0 & \lambda \end{bmatrix}, \qquad \lambda = -2.$$

Then

$$\mathbf{TA} = [\mathbf{e}_1 \quad \mathbf{e}_{11} \quad \mathbf{e}_{12} \quad \mathbf{e}_2] \begin{bmatrix} \lambda & 1 & 0 & 0 \\ 0 & \lambda & 1 & 0 \\ 0 & 0 & \lambda & 0 \\ 0 & 0 & 0 & \lambda \end{bmatrix}$$

$$= [\lambda\mathbf{e}_1 \quad \mathbf{e}_1 + \lambda\mathbf{e}_{11} \quad \mathbf{e}_{11} + \lambda\mathbf{e}_{12} \quad \lambda\mathbf{e}_2], \qquad \lambda = -2.$$

Since for this particular choice of $\mathbf{T}$, $\Lambda$ is unique, we have found $\Lambda$. The system is now in an optimum coordinate system. The matrix $\Lambda$ is diagonal except for the two ones above the diagonal. We can't make things any simpler than this.

---

From this last example, we obtain a good deal of valuable information about generating the transformation matrix for the case of repeated roots, which we now summarize.

1.  The number of true eigenvectors associated with a repeated root $\lambda_\eta$ is the dimension of $\mathbf{A}$ *minus* the rank of the matrix

$$\mathbf{A} - \lambda_\eta\mathbf{I}.$$

2.  The generalized eigenvectors form so-called "chains" with the true eigenvectors. That is, there may be several generalized eigenvectors associated with one true eigenvector and one or none associated with another true eigenvector. In Example 18.5.1, the chains were

$$\mathbf{e}_1 \to \mathbf{e}_{11} \to \mathbf{e}_{12}$$

$$\mathbf{e}_2.$$

For a different $\mathbf{A}$ matrix of dimension four, the chains may be

$$\mathbf{e}_1 \to \mathbf{e}_{11}$$

$$\mathbf{e}_2 \to \mathbf{e}_{21}.$$

It is possible to treat the case of repeated roots in a more rigorous way than is done here. The reason for not doing so is that repeated roots occur in engineering problems, but not that often. Hence, for the problems normally encountered, the techniques presented in Examples 18.4.1 and 18.5.1 are sufficient to find the necessary generalized eigenvectors to fill out the transformation matrix. Further, as we will see in Section 18.6, we rarely compute eigenvectors or generalized eignevectors anyway. What we really want to know is the *form* of the Jordan canonical matrix $\Lambda$. This Jordan canonical form plays the same role for a state model that factoring the denominator of the closed-loop transfer function played when we analyzed single-input, single-output systems.

# 18.6 | THE JORDAN CANONICAL FORM

We have now developed transformation matrices for all the cases we are likely to encounter: distinct roots, complex roots, and repeated roots. By combining these transformations we can transform a vector differential equation of the form

$$\dot{\mathbf{x}} = \mathbf{A}\mathbf{x}$$

into the coordinate system that lays bare its fundamental behavior. This form as we have already noted several times is called the Jordan canonical form. In many recent textbooks, the Jordan form has been relegated to an appendix as the current vogue has been to concentrate on the case of distinct eigenvalues. We will not do so. We will not linger here very long, but we wish to give the Jordan form a place in our discussion. We do so with Example 18.6.1, which has both real distinct, repeated real, and complex roots.

---

**EXAMPLE 18.6.1**

Consider the system

$$\dot{\mathbf{x}} = \mathbf{A}\mathbf{x},$$

where

$$\mathbf{A} = \begin{bmatrix} -1 & 0 & 1 & 0 & 1 \\ 0 & -2 & 3 & 1 & 0 \\ 0 & 0 & -2 & 0 & 0 \\ 0 & 0 & 0 & 3 & 5 \\ 0 & 0 & 0 & -4 & -5 \end{bmatrix}.$$

Then

$$\text{Det} \begin{bmatrix} -1-\lambda & 0 & 1 & 0 & 1 \\ 0 & -2-\lambda & 3 & 1 & 0 \\ 0 & 0 & -2-\lambda & 0 & 0 \\ 0 & 0 & 0 & 3-\lambda & 5 \\ 0 & 0 & 0 & -4 & -5-\lambda \end{bmatrix}$$

$$= (-\lambda - 1)(-\lambda - 2)(-\lambda - 2)[(3 - \lambda)(-5 - \lambda) - (4)(5)]$$

$$= (-1)^3(\lambda + 1)(\lambda + 2)^2(\lambda^2 + 2\lambda + 5).$$

Since the matrix is block diagnonal, with all entries zero below the diagonal blocks, the characteristic equation can be found by simply multiplying together the determinants of the diagonal blocks. Then the characteristic equation is

$$(\lambda + 1)(\lambda + 2)^2(\lambda + 1 - j2)(\lambda + 1 + j2) = 0.$$

As advertised, the system has both repeated real roots and complex roots. We next find the transformation matrix that will put the system in canonical form.

### ■ Eigenvector for $\lambda = -1$

We first form

$$[\mathbf{A} - \lambda\mathbf{I}]\Big|_{\lambda=-1} = \begin{bmatrix} -1-\lambda & 0 & 1 & 0 & 1 \\ 0 & -2-\lambda & 3 & 1 & 0 \\ 0 & 0 & -2-\lambda & 0 & 0 \\ 0 & 0 & 0 & 3-\lambda & 5 \\ 0 & 0 & 0 & -4 & -5-\lambda \end{bmatrix}\Bigg|_{\lambda=-1}$$

$$= \begin{bmatrix} 0 & 0 & 1 & 0 & 1 \\ 0 & -1 & 3 & 1 & 0 \\ 0 & 0 & -1 & 0 & 0 \\ 0 & 0 & 0 & 4 & 5 \\ 0 & 0 & 0 & -4 & -4 \end{bmatrix}.$$

Then the equation to find $\mathbf{e}_1$ is

$$\begin{bmatrix} 0 & 0 & 1 & 0 & 1 \\ 0 & -1 & 3 & 1 & 0 \\ 0 & 0 & -1 & 0 & 0 \\ 0 & 0 & 0 & 4 & 5 \\ 0 & 0 & 0 & -4 & -4 \end{bmatrix} \begin{bmatrix} x_1 \\ x_2 \\ x_3 \\ x_4 \\ x_5 \end{bmatrix} = \begin{bmatrix} 0 \\ 0 \\ 0 \\ 0 \\ 0 \end{bmatrix},$$

which yields the equations

$$x_3 + x_5 = 0,$$

$$-x_2 + 3x_3 + x_4 = 0,$$

$$-x_3 = 0,$$

$$4x_4 + 5x_5 = 0,$$

$$-4x_4 - 4x_5 = 0.$$

From the third equation, we see that $x_3 = 0$. Using this information and the first equation then gives $x_5 = 0$. We can then use the fourth or fifth equations to show show that $x_4 = 0$. Finally, knowing that $x_3 = x_4 = 0$, we can use the second equation to show that $x_2 = 0$. The general form of the of the eigenvector for $\mathbf{e}_1$ is thus

$$\mathbf{e}_1 = \begin{bmatrix} \text{anything} \\ 0 \\ 0 \\ 0 \\ 0 \end{bmatrix}.$$

We choose the specific eigenvector

$$
\mathbf{e}_1 = \begin{bmatrix} 1 \\ 0 \\ 0 \\ 0 \\ 0 \end{bmatrix}.
$$

## ■ Eigenvector(s) for $\lambda = -2$

For the repeated root $\lambda = -2$ we may find either one or two true eigenvectors. If we find only one true eigenvector, then we will have to generate a generalized eigenvector from the true eigenvector.

Again, the first step is to form

$$
[\mathbf{A} - \lambda \mathbf{I}]\Big|_{\lambda=-2} = \begin{bmatrix} -1-\lambda & 0 & 1 & 0 & 1 \\ 0 & -2-\lambda & 3 & 1 & 0 \\ 0 & 0 & -2-\lambda & 0 & 0 \\ 0 & 0 & 0 & 3-\lambda & 5 \\ 0 & 0 & 0 & -4 & -5-\lambda \end{bmatrix}\Bigg|_{\lambda=-2}
$$

$$
= \begin{bmatrix} 1 & 0 & 1 & 0 & 1 \\ 0 & 0 & 3 & 1 & 0 \\ 0 & 0 & 0 & 0 & 0 \\ 0 & 0 & 0 & 5 & 5 \\ 0 & 0 & 0 & -4 & -3 \end{bmatrix}.
$$

Then the equation to find $\mathbf{e}_2$ is

$$
\begin{bmatrix} 1 & 0 & 1 & 0 & 1 \\ 0 & 0 & 3 & 1 & 0 \\ 0 & 0 & 0 & 0 & 0 \\ 0 & 0 & 0 & 5 & 5 \\ 0 & 0 & 0 & -4 & -3 \end{bmatrix} \begin{bmatrix} x_1 \\ x_2 \\ x_3 \\ x_4 \\ x_5 \end{bmatrix} = \begin{bmatrix} 0 \\ 0 \\ 0 \\ 0 \\ 0 \end{bmatrix},
$$

which yields the equations

$$
x_1 + x_3 + x_5 = 0,
$$
$$
3x_3 + x_4 = 0,
$$
$$
0 = 0,
$$
$$
5x_4 + 5x_5 = 0,
$$
$$
-4x_4 - 3x_5 = 0.
$$

The only solution to the last two equations is $x_4 = x_5 = 0$. Knowing that $x_4 = 0$, we can use the second equation to show that $x_3 = 0$. Substituting $x_3 = x_5 = 0$ in the first equation yields $x_1 = 0$. The only variable that has not been set to zero is $x_2$, about which we have no information.

Thus, the general form of the eigenvector is

$$
\mathbf{e}_2 = \begin{bmatrix} 0 \\ \text{anything} \\ 0 \\ 0 \\ 0 \end{bmatrix}.
$$

We choose

$$
\mathbf{e}_2 = \begin{bmatrix} 0 \\ 1 \\ 0 \\ 0 \\ 0 \end{bmatrix}.
$$

Since there is only one true eigenvector, we must find a generalized eigenvector, so we solve

$$
\begin{bmatrix} 1 & 0 & 1 & 0 & 1 \\ 0 & 0 & 3 & 1 & 0 \\ 0 & 0 & 0 & 0 & 0 \\ 0 & 0 & 0 & 5 & 5 \\ 0 & 0 & 0 & -4 & -3 \end{bmatrix} \begin{bmatrix} g_1 \\ g_2 \\ g_3 \\ g_4 \\ g_5 \end{bmatrix} = \begin{bmatrix} 0 \\ 1 \\ 0 \\ 0 \\ 0 \end{bmatrix}.
$$

The resulting equations are

$$
g_1 + g_3 + g_5 = 0,
$$

$$
3g_3 + g_4 = 1,
$$

$$
0 = 0,
$$

$$
5g_4 + 5g_5 = 0,
$$

$$
-4g_4 - 3g_5 = 0.
$$

Once again, $g_4 = g_5 = 0$. However, we now have

$$
g_3 = \frac{1}{3} \quad \text{and} \quad g_1 = -g_3 = -\frac{1}{3}.
$$

Again, nothing is said about $g_2$, so the general form of the eigenvector is

$$
\mathbf{e}_{21} = \begin{bmatrix} -\frac{1}{3} \\ \text{anything} \\ \frac{1}{3} \\ 0 \\ 0 \end{bmatrix}.
$$

For simplicity we choose $g_2 = 0$. Then

$$\mathbf{e}_{21} = \begin{bmatrix} -\frac{1}{3} \\ 0 \\ \frac{1}{3} \\ 0 \\ 0 \end{bmatrix}.$$

## ■ Eigenvector for $\lambda = -1 + j2$

For the complex roots $\lambda = -1 \pm j2$ the procedure is to find the eigenvector for $\lambda = -1 + j2$ and break it into a real and imaginary part to form the two columns of the transformation matrix. Again the first step is to form

$$[\mathbf{A} - \lambda \mathbf{I}]\Big|_{\lambda=-1+j2} = \begin{bmatrix} -1-\lambda & 0 & 1 & 0 & 1 \\ 0 & -2-\lambda & 3 & 1 & 0 \\ 0 & 0 & -2-\lambda & 0 & 0 \\ 0 & 0 & 0 & 3-\lambda & 5 \\ 0 & 0 & 0 & -4 & -5-\lambda \end{bmatrix}\Bigg|_{\lambda=-1+j2}$$

$$= \begin{bmatrix} -j2 & 0 & 1 & 0 & 1 \\ 0 & -1-j2 & 3 & 1 & 0 \\ 0 & 0 & -1-j2 & 0 & 0 \\ 0 & 0 & 0 & 4-j2 & 5 \\ 0 & 0 & 0 & -4 & -4-j2 \end{bmatrix}.$$

Then the equation to find $\mathbf{e}_3$ is

$$\begin{bmatrix} -j2 & 0 & 1 & 0 & 1 \\ 0 & -1-j2 & 3 & 1 & 0 \\ 0 & 0 & -1-j2 & 0 & 0 \\ 0 & 0 & 0 & 4-j2 & 5 \\ 0 & 0 & 0 & -4 & -4-j2 \end{bmatrix} \begin{bmatrix} x_1 \\ x_2 \\ x_3 \\ x_4 \\ x_5 \end{bmatrix} = \begin{bmatrix} 0 \\ 0 \\ 0 \\ 0 \\ 0 \end{bmatrix},$$

yielding the equations

$$-j2x_1 + x_3 + x_5 = 0,$$

$$(-1 - j2)x_2 + 3x_3 + x_4 = 0,$$

$$(-1 - j2)x_3 = 0,$$

$$(4 - j2)x_4 + 5x_5 = 0,$$

$$-4x_4 - (4 + j2)x_5 = 0.$$

From the third equation we see that $x_3 = 0$, which, in turn, reduces the first equation to $x_1 = -j(0.5)x_5$. From either the fourth or fifth equation we find that

$$x_5 = \frac{4x_4}{-4 - j2}$$

$$= (-0.8 + j0.4)x_4.$$

From the second equation, knowing that $x_3 = 0$, we obtain

$$x_2 = \frac{x_4}{1 + j2} = (0.2 - j0.4)x_4.$$

Then, letting $x_4 = 1$, and remembering that $x_3 = 0$, we can determine the other three elements of the eigenvector to be.

$$x_1 = -j(0.5)x_5$$

$$= -j(0.5)(-0.8 + j0.4)$$

$$= 0.2 + j0.4,$$

$$x_2 = 0.2 - j0.4,$$

$$x_5 = -0.8 + j0.4.$$

Then

$$\mathbf{e}_3 = \begin{bmatrix} 0.2 + j0.4 \\ 0.2 - j0.4 \\ 0 \\ 1 \\ -0.8 + j0.4 \end{bmatrix}.$$

We next break $\mathbf{e}_3$ into a real and an imaginary part:

$$\mathbf{e}_3 = \begin{bmatrix} 0.2 \\ 0.2 \\ 0 \\ 1 \\ -0.8 \end{bmatrix} + j \begin{bmatrix} 0.4 \\ -0.4 \\ 0 \\ 0 \\ 0.4 \end{bmatrix}.$$

Finally, the overall transformation matrix is

$$\mathbf{T} = [\mathbf{e}_1 \quad \mathbf{e}_2 \quad \mathbf{e}_{21} \quad \text{Re}\{\mathbf{e}_3\} \quad \text{Im}\{\mathbf{e}_3\}]$$

$$= \begin{bmatrix} 1 & 0 & -\frac{1}{3} & 0.2 & 0.4 \\ 0 & 1 & 0 & 0.2 & -0.4 \\ 0 & 0 & \frac{1}{3} & 0 & 0 \\ 0 & 0 & 0 & 1 & 0 \\ 0 & 0 & 0 & -0.8 & 0.4 \end{bmatrix},$$

and

$$\mathbf{T}^{-1} = \begin{bmatrix} 1 & 0 & 1 & -1 & -1 \\ 0 & 1 & 0 & 0.6 & 1 \\ 0 & 0 & 3 & 0 & 0 \\ 0 & 0 & 0 & 1 & 0 \\ 0 & 0 & 0 & 2 & 2.5 \end{bmatrix}.$$

To complete the problem we do the arithmetic to find that, just as we knew it would,

$$\Lambda = T^{-1}AT$$

$$= \begin{bmatrix} 1 & 0 & 1 & -1 & -1 \\ 0 & 1 & 0 & 0.6 & 1 \\ 0 & 0 & 3 & 0 & 0 \\ 0 & 0 & 0 & 1 & 0 \\ 0 & 0 & 0 & 2 & 2.5 \end{bmatrix} \begin{bmatrix} -1 & 0 & 1 & 0 & 1 \\ 0 & -2 & 3 & 1 & 0 \\ 0 & 0 & -2 & 0 & 0 \\ 0 & 0 & 0 & 3 & 5 \\ 0 & 0 & 0 & -4 & -5 \end{bmatrix}$$

$$\times \begin{bmatrix} 1 & 0 & -\frac{1}{3} & 0.2 & 0.4 \\ 0 & 1 & 0 & 0.2 & -0.4 \\ 0 & 0 & \frac{1}{3} & 0 & 0 \\ 0 & 0 & 0 & 1 & 0 \\ 0 & 0 & 0 & -0.8 & 0.4 \end{bmatrix}$$

$$= \begin{bmatrix} 1 & 0 & 1 & -1 & -1 \\ 0 & 1 & 0 & 0.6 & 1 \\ 0 & 0 & 3 & 0 & 0 \\ 0 & 0 & 0 & 1 & 0 \\ 0 & 0 & 0 & 2 & 2.5 \end{bmatrix} \begin{bmatrix} -1 & 0 & \frac{2}{3} & -1 & 0 \\ 0 & -2 & 1 & 0.6 & 0.8 \\ 0 & 0 & -\frac{2}{3} & 0 & 0 \\ 0 & 0 & 0 & -1 & 2 \\ 0 & 0 & 0 & 0 & -2 \end{bmatrix}$$

$$= \begin{bmatrix} -1 & 0 & 0 & 0 & 0 \\ 0 & -2 & 1 & 0 & 0 \\ 0 & 0 & -2 & 0 & 0 \\ 0 & 0 & 0 & -1 & 2 \\ 0 & 0 & 0 & -2 & -1 \end{bmatrix}.$$

Example 18.6.1 reveals just about everything we need to know to determine the Jordan canonical form for any state model we will encounter. The "about" comes from the fact that we have not treated the case of repeated complex roots, and we will not do so. Based on our development of generalized eigenvectors we can pretty much guess how the Jordan form would look in that case.

We can now state a general procedure for finding the Jordan canonical form.

1. Find the eigenvalues for the **A** matrix.
2. Find the eigenvectors for each of the real distinct eigenvalues.
3. For the repeated eigenvalues, find the generalized eigenvector(s) associated with each true eigenvector.
4. For the complex eigenvalues find the eigenvector for $\lambda = a + jb$.
5. In the matrix **T**
   a. Stack in the eigenvectors of the distinct roots.
   b. For each repeated root, stack the generalized eigenvectors to the right of its true eigenvector.
   c. For each pair of complex roots break the eigenvector into a real and an imaginary part and stack the real and imaginary parts side by side.

Having transformed to canonical coordinates our system will be segregated into decoupled subsystems of low dimension, typically dimension one or two. The stability analysis is then easy. If all the subsystems are stable, then the overall system is stable. Since the stability of the subsystems can be determined by inspection, we can see at a glance whether or not the overall system is stable.

And now comes a very surprising statement. Having gone to the trouble to show how the Jordan canonical form can be generated, we will seldom, if ever, go to the trouble to find $\mathbf{T}$ explicitly. The reason is that all the Jordan canonical form does is rearrange things to maximize the decoupling between the states so that we can visualize the behavior of the system more easily.

In the end, if all the eigenvalues have negative real parts, we know the system is stable. The Jordan form just helps us visualize the behavior of the system more easily. Furthermore, if someone gave us the eigenvalues and corresponding eigenvectors and generalized eigenvectors we could write the Jordan form down immediately. After doing such an exercise a few times, we probably would not even bother to write down the Jordan form. We would just visualize it mentally, just as we learned to do for the partial fraction expansion of the factored closed-loop transfer function earlier in the book.

## 18.7 | INVARIANCE OF EIGENVALUES

We have one last detail to consider, namely, we need to show that the eigenvalues are invariant under the transformation to canonical form. That fact is evident in every example we have considered, but we need to show it formally. To do so we compute

$$\text{Det}[\lambda \mathbf{I} - \mathbf{\Lambda}] = \text{Det}[\lambda \mathbf{T}^{-1}\mathbf{T} - \mathbf{T}^{-1}\mathbf{A}\mathbf{T}]$$
$$= \text{Det}\{\mathbf{T}^{-1}[\lambda \mathbf{I} - \mathbf{A}]\mathbf{T}\}$$
$$= \text{Det}\{\mathbf{T}^{-1}\} \times \text{Det}[\lambda \mathbf{I} - \mathbf{A}] \times \text{Det}\{\mathbf{T}\}.$$

Now, if

$$\text{Det } \mathbf{T} = \alpha,$$

where $\alpha$ is a scalar, it follows that since

$$\mathbf{T}^{-1}\mathbf{T} = \mathbf{I},$$

$$\text{Det}\{\mathbf{T}^{-1}\mathbf{T}\} = \text{Det}\{\mathbf{T}^{-1}\} \times \text{Det}\{\mathbf{T}\}$$
$$= \alpha \times \text{Det}\{\mathbf{T}^{-1}\}$$
$$= \text{Det}\{\mathbf{I}\}$$
$$= 1.$$

Since

$$\alpha \times \text{Det}\{\mathbf{T}^{-1}\} = 1,$$

we must have

$$\text{Det}\{\mathbf{T}^{-1}\} = \frac{1}{\alpha}.$$

Finally, we have

$$\text{Det}[\lambda\mathbf{I} - \boldsymbol{\Lambda}] = \text{Det}\{\mathbf{T}^{-1}\} \times \text{Det}[\lambda\mathbf{I} - \mathbf{A}] \times \text{Det}\{\mathbf{T}\}$$

$$= \alpha \times \frac{1}{\alpha} \times \text{Det}[\lambda\mathbf{I} - \mathbf{A}]$$

$$= \text{Det}[\lambda\mathbf{I} - \mathbf{A}].$$

Thus, we see that the eigenvalues are invariant (unchanged) under the transformation to the Jordan canonical form. This was obvious all along, but we have now formally established this fact.

## 18.8 | REPRISE

In this chapter, we introduced the continuous state model representation of a physical system or plant. We arrived at the state model via the transfer function of a single-input, single-output system. For such systems, the state model formulation offers only marginal advantage over the transfer function formulation. However, the state model can very easily accommodate multi-input, multi-output systems.

Having shown how to derive a state model from a transfer function, we then found the general solution using Laplace transforms. We next noted that the stability analysis could be done using the homogeneous state equation. We then spent considerable time studying the behavior of state models of dimension two. In particular, we looked at state models with two distinct real roots, a repeated real root, and a pair of complex roots. We put all three of these systems into what we would subsequently call the Jordan canonical form.

We then generalized our results for state models of dimesion two to state models of arbitrary dimension. We found that we could transform the state model to a preferred or canonical coordinate system where the model was segregated into decoupled systems of low order, enabling us to determine the stability characteristics of both the unforced and forced state model by inspection. This led to a result of the utmost importance. For a state model to be stable, for bounded inputs, all the eigenvalues must have negative real part. On reflection this is not so surprising given that for a transfer function that represents a physical system to be stable for bounded inputs, all the poles of the tranfer function must have negative real parts.

We then discussed the Jordan canonical form by way of some examples. We showed in detail how to construct the various transformations necessary to put a system in Jordan canonical form. Having gone to all this trouble, we then noted that we are free to *not* have to actually construct those transformations. We simply compute the eigenvalues of the original system and realize that the transformations exists that will put the system in Jordan canonical form.

Finally, we showed formally that since the eigenvalues do not change under transformation, the system's stability properties will not change either. Hence, we can just write down the Jordan canonical form and examine the stability of each decoupled subsystem. If every subsystem is stable, the system is stable. If *any one* of the decoupled subsystems is unstable, the system as a whole is unstable. Thus, by simply computing eigenvalues, we can determine everything about the stability of a linear time-invariant state model.

In Chapter 19, we will first discretize the continuous model, and then discuss two properties of the state model, controllability and observability, that must be understood before we can move on to begin building control systems based on the state model.

## 18.9 | PROBLEMS

### 18.9.1   Phase Portraits

For the state equation

$$\dot{\mathbf{x}}(t) + \mathbf{A}\mathbf{x}(t),$$

draw the phase portrait for each matrix $\mathbf{A}$.

**1.** $\begin{bmatrix} -1 & 0 \\ 0 & 2 \end{bmatrix}$ 　　　　　　 **2.** $\begin{bmatrix} -1 & 1 \\ 0 & -1 \end{bmatrix}$

**3.** $\begin{bmatrix} 0 & 1 \\ 0 & 0 \end{bmatrix}$ 　　　　　　 **4.** $\begin{bmatrix} 1 & 0 \\ 0 & 0 \end{bmatrix}$

**5.** $\begin{bmatrix} -2 & -3 \\ 3 & -2 \end{bmatrix}$ 　　　　　 **6.** $\begin{bmatrix} 2 & 1 \\ 0 & 2 \end{bmatrix}$

**7.** $\begin{bmatrix} 0 & 1 \\ -1 & 0 \end{bmatrix}$ 　　　　　 **8.** $\begin{bmatrix} 2 & 4 \\ -4 & -6 \end{bmatrix}$

**9.** $\begin{bmatrix} 2 & 0 & 0 \\ 0 & -2 & -4 \\ 0 & 4 & -2 \end{bmatrix}$ 　　　 **10.** $\begin{bmatrix} -4 & -3 \\ 2 & 1 \end{bmatrix}$

**11.** $\begin{bmatrix} 0 & 1 \\ 1 & 0 \end{bmatrix}$ 　　　　　 **12.** $\begin{bmatrix} -1 & 0 \\ 0 & 2 \end{bmatrix}$

**13.** $\begin{bmatrix} -1 & 1 \\ 0 & -1 \end{bmatrix}$ 　　　　 **14.** $\begin{bmatrix} -1 & 0 \\ -3 & -4 \end{bmatrix}$

**15.** $\begin{bmatrix} -4 & -5 \\ 2 & 3 \end{bmatrix}$ 　　　　 **16.** $\begin{bmatrix} -6 & -2 \\ 5 & 1 \end{bmatrix}$

### 18.9.2   Canonical Phase Portraits

For these problems, assume the state model is in the canonical form

$$\dot{\mathbf{z}}(t) = \mathbf{\Lambda}\mathbf{z}(t).$$

Draw the phase portrait for each matrix $\mathbf{\Lambda}$. Let $\lambda_1$ be the eigenvalue associated with $z_1$ and $\lambda_2$ the eigenvector associated with $z_2$.

1. Both $\lambda_1$ and $\lambda_2$ real, $\lambda_2 < \lambda_1 < 0$
2. Both $\lambda_1$ and $\lambda_2$ real, $\lambda_1 < \lambda_2 < 0$
3. Both $\lambda_1$ and $\lambda_2$ real, $\lambda_2 > \lambda_1 > 0$
4. Both $\lambda_1$ and $\lambda_2$ real, $\lambda_1 > \lambda_2 > 0$
5. Both $\lambda_1$ and $\lambda_2$ real, $\lambda_1 > 0, \lambda_2 < 0$
6. Both $\lambda_1$ and $\lambda_2$ real, $\lambda_2 > 0, \lambda_1 < 0$
7. $\lambda_1, \lambda_2 = \sigma \pm j\omega, \sigma > 0, \omega > 0$
8. $\lambda_1, \lambda_2 = \sigma \pm j\omega, \sigma < 0, \omega > 0$
9. $\lambda_1, \lambda_2 = \sigma \pm j\omega, \sigma = 0, \omega > 0$
10. $\lambda_1 = \lambda_2 = 0$
11. $\lambda_1 < 0, \lambda_2 = 0$
12. $\lambda_1 = 0, \lambda_2 < 0$
13. $\lambda_1 > 0, \lambda_2 = 0$
14. $\lambda_1 = 0, \lambda_2 > 0$
15. $\lambda_1 = \lambda_2 = \lambda > 0$
16. $\lambda_1 = \lambda_2 = \lambda < 0$

### 18.9.3  State Transition Matrix

For each matrix $\mathbf{A}$, find the state transition matrix $e^{\mathbf{A}t}$ using Laplace transforms. Check with MATLAB.

1. $\begin{bmatrix} -2 & 2 & 0 \\ 0 & -3 & 1 \\ 0 & 0 & -4 \end{bmatrix}$
2. $\begin{bmatrix} -3 & 1 \\ 0 & -3 \end{bmatrix}$

3. $\begin{bmatrix} \lambda & 1 & 1 \\ 0 & \lambda & 1 \\ 0 & 0 & \lambda \end{bmatrix}$
4. $\begin{bmatrix} a & b \\ -b & a \end{bmatrix}$

5. $\begin{bmatrix} 0 & 1 \\ -4 & -3 \end{bmatrix}$
6. $\begin{bmatrix} 0 & 1 \\ 1 & 0 \end{bmatrix}$

7. $\begin{bmatrix} -1 & 1 \\ 0 & -2 \end{bmatrix}$
8. $\begin{bmatrix} 0 & 1 \\ -4 & -2 \end{bmatrix}$

### 18.9.4  Canonical Form

Each of these matrices is the matrix $\mathbf{A}$ for the state model

$$\dot{\mathbf{x}}(t) = \mathbf{A}\mathbf{x}(t).$$

Find the transformation matrix $\mathbf{T}$ that puts the system in canonical form $\dot{\mathbf{z}}(t) = \mathbf{A}\mathbf{z}(t)$. Check with MATLAB.

1. $\begin{bmatrix} -6 & 4 \\ -4 & 2 \end{bmatrix}$
2. $\begin{bmatrix} -2 & 2 \\ 0 & -2 \end{bmatrix}$

**3.** $\begin{bmatrix} -1 & -1 \\ 1 & -1 \end{bmatrix}$

**4.** $\begin{bmatrix} 2 & 1 \\ -13 & -4 \end{bmatrix}$

**5.** $\begin{bmatrix} -4 & 9 \\ -2 & 5 \end{bmatrix}$

**6.** $\begin{bmatrix} -1 & 1 \\ 0 & -3 \end{bmatrix}$

**7.** $\begin{bmatrix} -1 & -1 \\ 1 & -1 \end{bmatrix}$

**8.** $\begin{bmatrix} 0 & 1 \\ -4 & -4 \end{bmatrix}$

## 18.9.5 Phase Variable State Model

For each transfer function $G$ or differential equation, find the phase variable state model

**1.** $G(s) = \dfrac{\alpha_1 s + \alpha_0}{s^3 + \beta_2 s^2 + \beta_1 s + \beta_0}$

**2.** $G(s) = \dfrac{16(s+4)}{s^3 + 12s^2 + 40s + 64}$

**3.** $\dfrac{d^3}{dt^3} y(t) + 7 \dfrac{d^2}{dt^2} y(t) + 14 \dfrac{d}{dt} y(t) + 8y(t) = u(t)$

## 18.9.6 Jordan Form—Quantitative Problems

For each matrix $\mathbf{A}$, find the transformation matrix that puts the matrix in Jordan canonical form. These problems should be done by hand and checked with MATLAB.

**1.** $\begin{bmatrix} -1 & 2 & 1 \\ 0 & -2 & 3 \\ 0 & -3 & -2 \end{bmatrix}$

**2.** $\begin{bmatrix} -1 & 0 & 0 & 0 & 5 \\ 0 & -3 & 10 & 1 & 0 \\ 0 & 0 & -2 & 0 & 0 \\ 0 & 0 & 0 & -2 & 0 \\ 0 & 0 & 0 & 0 & -2 \end{bmatrix}$

**3.** $\begin{bmatrix} -1 & 0 & 0 & 0 & 5 \\ 0 & -3 & 10 & 1 & 0 \\ 0 & 0 & -2 & 0 & 0 \\ 0 & 0 & 0 & 1 & -3 \\ 0 & 0 & 0 & 3 & -5 \end{bmatrix}$

**4.** $\begin{bmatrix} -1 & 0 & 0 & 0 & 5 \\ 0 & -3 & 10 & 1 & 0 \\ 0 & 0 & -2 & 0 & 0 \\ 0 & 0 & 0 & 1 & 5 \\ 0 & 0 & 0 & -2 & -5 \end{bmatrix}$

**5.** $\begin{bmatrix} -1 & 1 \\ -2 & -4 \end{bmatrix}$

**6.** $\begin{bmatrix} -4 & 9 \\ -1 & -2 \end{bmatrix}$

**7.** $\begin{bmatrix} -2 & 1 \\ 1 & -2 \end{bmatrix}$

**8.** $\begin{bmatrix} 2 & 2 \\ 2 & -1 \end{bmatrix}$

**9.** $\begin{bmatrix} -3 & 4 \\ -2 & 1 \end{bmatrix}$

**10.** $\begin{bmatrix} -1 & 2 & 1 \\ 0 & -2 & 1 \\ 0 & 0 & -3 \end{bmatrix}$

**11.** $\begin{bmatrix} -1 & 2 & 3 \\ 0 & -2 & 4 \\ 0 & -4 & -2 \end{bmatrix}$

**12.** $\begin{bmatrix} -1 & 2 & 4 & 1 \\ 0 & -1 & 0 & 3 \\ 0 & 0 & -1 & 0 \\ 0 & 0 & 0 & -1 \end{bmatrix}$

13.
$$\begin{bmatrix} -1 & 0 & 1 \\ 0 & -4 & -2 \\ 0 & 5 & 2 \end{bmatrix}$$

14.
$$\begin{bmatrix} -4 & -3 & 0 & 0 \\ 3 & 2 & 0 & 0 \\ 0 & 0 & -5 & -3 \\ 0 & 0 & 4 & 2 \end{bmatrix}$$

15.
$$\begin{bmatrix} -1 & 0 & 0 & 0 & 5 \\ 0 & -3 & 10 & 1 & 0 \\ 0 & 0 & -2 & 0 & 0 \\ 0 & 0 & 0 & -2 & 0 \\ 0 & 0 & 0 & 0 & -2 \end{bmatrix}$$

16.
$$\begin{bmatrix} -1 & 0 & 0 & 2 & 0 \\ 0 & -3 & 10 & 1 & 5 \\ 0 & 0 & -2 & 0 & 0 \\ 0 & 0 & 0 & -2 & 0 \\ 0 & 0 & 0 & 0 & -2 \end{bmatrix}$$

## 18.9.7 Jordan Form—Qualitative Problems

Each of these problems is based on the system

$$\dot{\mathbf{x}}(t) = \mathbf{A}\mathbf{x}(t).$$

1.  Suppose the eigenvalues of **A** are

$$\lambda = -1, -3, -3, -1 + j2, -1 - j2.$$

If the rank of

$$\text{Det}[\mathbf{A} - \lambda\mathbf{I}]|_{\lambda=-3}$$

is four, determine **T** *symbolically* and then write down

$$\mathbf{\Lambda} = \mathbf{T}^{-1}\mathbf{A}\mathbf{T}$$

for the **T** you have chosen.

2.  Suppose the eigenvalues of **A** are

$$\lambda = -1, -2, -2, -2.$$

If the rank of

$$\text{Det}[\mathbf{A} - \lambda\mathbf{I}]|_{\lambda=-2}$$

is three, find

$$\mathbf{\Lambda} = \mathbf{T}^{-1}\mathbf{A}\mathbf{T}.$$

3.  Suppose the eigenvalues of **A** are

$$\lambda = -1, -2, -2, -2, -3.$$

If the rank of

$$[\mathbf{A} - \lambda\mathbf{I}]|_{\lambda=-2}$$

is three, determine **T** *symbolically* and then write down

$$\mathbf{\Lambda} = \mathbf{T}^{-1}\mathbf{A}\mathbf{T}$$

for the **T** you have chosen.

4. Suppose

$$A = \begin{bmatrix} -2 & 2 & 0 \\ 0 & -3 & 2 \\ 0 & 0 & -5 \end{bmatrix}$$

   a.  For an arbitrary initial condition $x_0$ is the system stable? Why or why not?
   b.  What is the form of the canonical matrix $\Lambda$?

5. Suppose

$$A = \begin{bmatrix} -1 & 1 & 0 & 1 \\ 0 & -3 & 0 & 2 \\ 0 & 0 & -3 & 0 \\ 0 & 0 & 0 & -2 \end{bmatrix}.$$

   a.  What is the characteristic equation?
   b.  Write down in symbolic form a transformation matrix $\mathbf{T}$ that will put the system in canonical form.
   c.  What is

$$\Lambda = \mathbf{T}^{-1}\mathbf{A}\mathbf{T},$$

   for the $\mathbf{T}$ of part (b)?

6. $\text{Det}\{\lambda \mathbf{I} - \mathbf{A}\} = (\lambda + 2)^3(\lambda + 1)(\lambda + 3)$.

   The matrix

$$[\mathbf{A} - \lambda \mathbf{I}]\,|_{\lambda=-2}$$

   has rank three. Write down a Jordan canonical form for this system.

7. Discuss the truth of the following statement: "*The Jordan canonical form of a matrix is unique.*"

## 18.9.8   Additional Problems

1. Suppose we define

$$e^{\mathbf{A}t} = \mathbf{I} + \mathbf{A}t + \mathbf{A}^2\frac{t^2}{2!} + \cdots.$$

   Suppose further that

$$\mathbf{A} = \Sigma + \mathbf{N},$$

   where

$$\Sigma \mathbf{N} = \mathbf{N}\Sigma.$$

   Using the basic definition of $e^{\mathbf{A}t}$ show that

$$e^{\mathbf{A}t} = e^{(\Sigma+\mathbf{N})t} = e^{\Sigma t}e^{\mathbf{N}t}.$$

2.  Let $\mathbf{A}$ be an $n \times n$ matrix and suppose we define

$$\text{Trace } \mathbf{A} = \sum_{i=1}^{n} a_{ii}.$$

Show that

$$\text{Trace } \mathbf{A} = \sum_{i=1}^{n} \lambda_i.$$

3.  Use the method of isoclines to determine the curvature of the trajectories in the phase portrait of Example 18.3.1 for the region above the negative real axis and below the eigenvector associated with the eigenvalue -4.

4.  For the state model of Eq. [18.18], draw the phase portrait or the *canonical* representation using the method of isoclines.

5.  Show that if a matrix is upper triangular, then the determinant of the matrix is just the product of the diagonal elements of the matrix.

# FURTHER READINGS

Arnold, V. I. 1973. *Ordinary Differential Equations*. Cambridge, MA: MIT Press.

Brogan, William L. 1985. *Modern Control Theory*, 2nd ed. Englewood Cliffs, N.J.: Prentice-Hall.

D'Azzo, John J., and Constantine H. Houpis. 1988. *Linear Control System Design: Conventional and Modern*. New York: McGraw-Hill.

Dorny, C. Nelson. 1980. *A Vector Space Approach to Models and Optimization*. Huntington, N.Y.: Robert Krieger Publishing.

Luenberger, David G. 1979. *Introduction to Dynamics Systems: Theory, Models, Applications*, Vol. 1. New York: John Wiley & Sons.

Ogata, Katsuhiko. 1967. *State Space Analysis of Control Systems*. Englewood Cliffs, N.J.: Prentice-Hall.

Ogata, K. 1970. *Modern Control Engineering*. Englewood Cliffs, N.J.: Prentice-Hall.

Porter, William A. 1966. *Modern Foundations of Systems Engineering*. New York: Macmillan.

Saucedo, R., and E. E. Schiring. 1968. *Introduction to Continuous and Digital Control Systems*. New York: MacMillan.

Schultz, Donald G., and James L. Melsa. 1967. *State Functions and Linear Control Systems*. New York: McGraw-Hill.

# 19 Chapter

# Observability and Controllability

## 19.1 | OVERVIEW

In this chapter, we first find the discrete equivalent for the continuous state model we introduced in Chapter 18. The reason for discretizing the state model is that all the control applications developed in Chapter 20 use the discrete state model. The reason is simple. These control algorithms are very hard to implement with analog circuitry and very easy to implement using a digital computer.

In discretizing the state model, we will have to be careful to obtain a discrete state model that is equivalent to $G'_p(z)$, the step-invariant transformation of $G_p(s)$. We will demonstrate the equivalence of the two discretizations with an example.

Having obtained the discrete state model, we then turn our attention to some fundamental properties of both the continuous and discrete state models. These properties are controllablity and observability. An understanding of these two properties is essential when we begin designing compensators in Chapter 20.

More specifically, if a system is controllable, then we will find that we can place the eigenvalues (poles) of the closed-loop system anywhere we wish, provided we can feed back all the states of the system. If the system is observable, then we find that we don't have to measure all the states. Instead we can measure only the output of the system and use this one measurement to generate accurate estimates of all the states of the system.

We will discuss controllability and observability for both the continuous and discrete state models. The concepts are essentially the same for both types of models. However, the concepts are much easier to understand for the discrete state model. Furthermore, it is the discrete state model that is of importance for control design.

# 19.2 | DISCRETIZING THE STATE MODEL

Consider the continuous state model

$$\dot{\mathbf{x}}(t) = \mathbf{A}\mathbf{x}(t) + \mathbf{b}u(t),$$

$$y(t) = \mathbf{c}^T \mathbf{x}(t). \qquad [19.1]$$

Note that we have added the expression

$$y(t) = \mathbf{c}^T \mathbf{x}(t)$$

so that the system has a *scalar* output.

The solution of Eq. [19.1], as derived earlier using Laplace transforms, is

$$\mathbf{x}(t) = e^{\mathbf{A}t}\mathbf{x}(0) + \left( \int_0^t e^{\mathbf{A}(t-\tau)} u(\tau)\, d\tau \right) \mathbf{b}.$$

We can generalize this result slightly. If the initial conditions are $\mathbf{x}(t_0)$ for time $t_0$, then the solution is

$$\mathbf{x}(t) = e^{\mathbf{A}(t-t_0)}\mathbf{x}(t_0) + \left( \int_{t_0}^t e^{\mathbf{A}(t-\tau)} u(\tau)\, d\tau \right) \mathbf{b}.$$

Using this latter form, we now let $t = (k+1)T$ and $t_0 = kT$, where $T$ is the intersample time, to obtain

$$\mathbf{x}((k+1)T) = e^{\mathbf{A}(kT+T-kT)}\mathbf{x}(kT) + \left( \int_{kT}^{(k+1)T} e^{\mathbf{A}(kT+T-\tau)} u(\tau)\, d\tau \right) \mathbf{b}$$

$$= e^{\mathbf{A}T}\mathbf{x}(kT) + \left( \int_{kT}^{(k+1)T} e^{\mathbf{A}(kT+T-\tau)} u(\tau)\, d\tau \right) \mathbf{b}. \qquad [19.2]$$

We next let $u(\tau) = u(kT)$. This approximation is consistent with the model of the D/A converter that we made for single-input, single-output systems, namely, that the input to the system is constant over a sample interval. This is an important point, because we would like our discrete state model of the plant $G_p(s)$ to be consistent with $G_p'(z)$ the step-invariant transform of $G_p(s)$ that we have used throughout most of the book. The state models that we use in this text are state models of single-input, single-output systems that could be represented by a transfer function. Therefore, we need the discrete state model to be equivalent to our discrete transfer function model of a continuous system, and that discrete equivalent is $G_p'(z)$.

That said, our equation now becomes

$$\mathbf{x}((k+1)T) = e^{\mathbf{A}T}\mathbf{x}(kT) + \left( \int_{kT}^{(k+1)T} e^{\mathbf{A}(kT+T-\tau)}\, d\tau \right) \mathbf{b}u(kT). \qquad [19.3]$$

We next make the substitution of variables

$$\eta = kT + T - \tau,$$

for which we note that

$$d\eta = -d\tau, \qquad \tau = kT \Rightarrow \eta = T, \qquad \tau = kT + T \Rightarrow \eta = 0.$$

Then Eq. [19.3] can be rewritten as

$$\mathbf{x}((k+1)T) = e^{\mathbf{A}T}\mathbf{x}(kT) + \left(\int_T^0 e^{\mathbf{A}\eta}(-d\eta)\right)\mathbf{b}u(kT)$$

$$= e^{\mathbf{A}T}\mathbf{x}(kT) + \left(\int_0^T e^{\mathbf{A}\eta}\,d\eta\right)\mathbf{b}u(kT).$$

Letting

$$\mathbf{F} \triangleq e^{\mathbf{A}T}, \qquad \mathbf{g} \triangleq \left(\int_0^T e^{\mathbf{A}\eta}\,d\eta\right)\mathbf{b}, \qquad \mathbf{h}^T \triangleq \mathbf{c}^T,$$

we have the discrete system

$$\mathbf{x}((k+1)T) = \mathbf{F}\mathbf{x}(kT) + \mathbf{g}u(kT),$$

$$y(kT) = \mathbf{h}^T\mathbf{x}(kT). \tag{19.4}$$

It is common practice to suppress the $T$ and write

$$\mathbf{x}(k+1) = \mathbf{F}\mathbf{x}(k) + \mathbf{g}u(k),$$

$$y(k) = \mathbf{h}^T\mathbf{x}(k). \tag{19.5}$$

Equation [19.4] can be analyzed just as we analyzed the continuous state model, but using the $\mathcal{Z}$ transform instead of the Laplace transform. That is, if we $\mathcal{Z}$ transform both sides of Eq. [19.4], we obtain

$$z\mathbf{x}(z) - z\mathbf{x}(0) = \mathbf{F}\mathbf{x}(z) + \mathbf{g}u(z),$$

which can be rewritten as

$$[z\mathbf{I} - \mathbf{F}]\mathbf{x}(z) = z\mathbf{x}(0) + \mathbf{g}u(z),$$

which leads to

$$\mathbf{x}(z) = z[z\mathbf{I} - \mathbf{F}]^{-1}\mathbf{x}(0) + ([z\mathbf{I} - \mathbf{F}]^{-1}u(z))\mathbf{g}.$$

Applying the inverse $\mathcal{Z}$ transform to both sides then yields

$$\mathbf{x}(kT) = \mathcal{Z}^{-1}\{z[z\mathbf{I} - \mathbf{F}]^{-1}\}\mathbf{x}(0) + \mathcal{Z}^{-1}\{[z\mathbf{I} - \mathbf{F}]^{-1}u(z)\}\mathbf{g}.$$

The term

$$\mathcal{Z}^{-1}\{z[z\mathbf{I} - \mathbf{F}]^{-1}\}$$

is the analog of the term

$$\mathcal{L}^{-1}\{[s\mathbf{I} - \mathbf{A}]^{-1}\}$$

from our analysis of continuous systems.

Now recall that

$$\mathcal{L}^{-1}\{[s\mathbf{I} - \mathbf{A}]^{-1}\} \overset{\Delta}{=} e^{\mathbf{A}t},$$

the state transition matrix of a continuous system. Similarly,

$$\mathcal{Z}^{-1}\{z[z\mathbf{I} - \mathbf{F}]^{-1}\} = e^{\mathbf{A}kT} \overset{\Delta}{=} \mathbf{\Phi}(k, 0).$$

Note that with

$$\mathbf{F} \overset{\Delta}{=} e^{\mathbf{A}T},$$

we can write

$$\mathbf{\Phi}(k, 0) = F^k.$$

As with the continuous case, this result can be generalized slightly. If we let

$$\mathbf{x}(mT)$$

be the *known* initial condition, then the homogenous state equation becomes

$$\mathbf{x}(k) = \mathbf{F}^{k-m}\mathbf{x}(m), \ \ k > m,$$

where

$$\mathbf{F}^{k-m} = (e^{\mathbf{A}T})^{k-m} = e^{\mathbf{A}(kT-mT)} \overset{\Delta}{=} \mathbf{\Phi}(k, m)$$

is the state transition matrix for the *discrete* model with initial condition $\mathbf{x}(mT)$ at time $mT$.

The interpretation of

$$\mathcal{Z}^{-1}\{[z\mathbf{I} - \mathbf{F}]^{-1}\}$$

requires a little more thought. First, note that

$$[z\mathbf{I} - \mathbf{F}]^{-1} = z^{-1}\{z[z\mathbf{I} - \mathbf{F}]^{-1}\}.$$

Then,

$$\mathcal{Z}^{-1}\{[z\mathbf{I} - \mathbf{F}]^{-1}\} = \mathbf{\Phi}(k - 1, 0),$$

the state transition matrix delayed by one time step. Recalling that

$$\mathcal{L}^{-1}\{[s\mathbf{I} - \mathbf{A}]^{-1}U(s)\} = \int_0^t e^{\mathbf{A}(t-\tau)}u(\tau)\,d\tau,$$

the convolution of $e^{\mathbf{A}t}$ with $u(t)$, we must then have

$$\mathcal{Z}^{-1}\{[z\mathbf{I} - \mathbf{F}]^{-1}u(z)\} = \sum_{i=0}^{k-1} \Phi(k - i - 1, 0)u(i).$$

The total solution is not difficult to "derive" recursively from the original vector difference equation. That is,

$$\mathbf{x}(1) = \mathbf{F}\mathbf{x}(0) + \mathbf{g}u(0),$$

$$\mathbf{x}(2) = \mathbf{F}\mathbf{x}(1) + \mathbf{g}u(1)$$

$$= \mathbf{F}[\mathbf{F}\mathbf{x}(0) + \mathbf{g}u(0)] + \mathbf{g}u(1)$$

$$= \mathbf{F}^2\mathbf{x}(0) + \{u(1) + \mathbf{F}u(0)\}\mathbf{g},$$

$$\mathbf{x}(3) = \mathbf{F}\mathbf{x}(2) + \mathbf{g}u(2)$$

$$= \mathbf{F}[\mathbf{F}^2\mathbf{x}(0) + \{u(1) + \mathbf{F}u(0)\}\mathbf{g}] + \mathbf{g}u(2)$$

$$= \mathbf{F}^3\mathbf{x}(0) + \{u(2) + \mathbf{F}u(1) + \mathbf{F}^2u(0)\}\mathbf{g},$$

$$\vdots$$

$$\mathbf{x}(k) = \mathbf{F}^k\mathbf{x}(0) + \left(\sum_{i=0}^{k-1} \Phi(k - 1 - i, \ 0)u(i)\right)\mathbf{g}.$$

At this juncture an example is long overdue. The example should make these concepts more concrete.

**EXAMPLE 19.2.1**

Consider the transfer function

$$G(s) = \frac{a}{s(s + a)}.$$

For the proper choice of $a$, this is a reasonably good model for a small dc motor connected by a rigid shaft to an inertia, with the input being armature voltage $e_q$ and the output being shaft position $\theta$. Thus, we have

$$\Theta(s) = G(s) = \frac{a}{s(s + a)} E_q(s).$$

Cross multiplying yields

$$s^2\Theta(s) + as\Theta(s) = aE_q(s),$$

which under the inverse Laplace transform yields the differential equation

$$\ddot{\theta}(t) + a\dot{\theta}(t) = ae_q(t).$$

Letting

$$x_1(t) = \theta(t) \quad \text{and} \quad x_2(t) = \dot{x}_1(t),$$

we can write

$$\dot{x}_1(t) = x_2(t),$$
$$\dot{x}_2(t) = -ax_2(t) + ae_q(t),$$

which, in matrix form, is

$$\begin{bmatrix} \dot{x}_1 \\ \dot{x}_2 \end{bmatrix} = \begin{bmatrix} 0 & 1 \\ 0 & -a \end{bmatrix} \begin{bmatrix} x_1 \\ x_2 \end{bmatrix} + \begin{bmatrix} 0 \\ a \end{bmatrix} e_q(t),$$

$$y(t) = \theta(t) = \begin{bmatrix} 1 & 0 \end{bmatrix} \begin{bmatrix} x_1 \\ x_2 \end{bmatrix}.$$

We first find the transition matrix for the continuous system. The first step is to form

$$[s\mathbf{I} - \mathbf{A}] = \begin{bmatrix} s & 0 \\ 0 & s \end{bmatrix} - \begin{bmatrix} 0 & 1 \\ 0 & -a \end{bmatrix}$$

$$= \begin{bmatrix} s & -1 \\ 0 & s+a \end{bmatrix}.$$

Then,

$$[s\mathbf{I} - \mathbf{A}]^{-1} = \begin{bmatrix} s & -1 \\ 0 & s+a \end{bmatrix}^{-1}$$

$$= \begin{bmatrix} \frac{s+a}{s(s+a)} & \frac{1}{s(s+a)} \\ 0 & \frac{s}{s(s+a)} \end{bmatrix}$$

$$= \begin{bmatrix} \frac{1}{s} & \frac{1}{a}\left(\frac{1}{s} - \frac{1}{s+a}\right) \\ 0 & \frac{1}{s+a} \end{bmatrix},$$

and

$$e^{\mathbf{A}t} = \mathcal{L}^{-1}\left\{ \begin{bmatrix} \frac{1}{s} & \frac{1}{a}\left(\frac{1}{s} - \frac{1}{s+a}\right) \\ 0 & \frac{1}{s+a} \end{bmatrix} \right\}$$

$$= \begin{bmatrix} 1 & \frac{1}{a}(1 - e^{-at}) \\ 0 & e^{-at} \end{bmatrix}.$$

By substituting $T$ for $t$, we then have

$$\mathbf{F} = e^{\mathbf{A}T} = \begin{bmatrix} 1 & \frac{1}{a}(1 - e^{-aT}) \\ 0 & e^{-aT} \end{bmatrix}.$$

With a little more work we can find

$$\mathbf{g} = \left( \int_0^T e^{\mathbf{A}\eta} \, d\eta \right) \mathbf{b}$$

$$= \begin{bmatrix} \int_0^T d\eta & \frac{1}{a} \int_0^T (1 - e^{-a\eta}) \, d\eta \\ 0 & \int_0^T e^{-a\eta} \, d\eta \end{bmatrix} \begin{bmatrix} 0 \\ a \end{bmatrix}$$

$$= \begin{bmatrix} T & \frac{1}{a}\left(T + \frac{1}{a}(e^{-aT} - 1)\right) \\ 0 & \frac{1}{a}(1 - e^{-aT}) \end{bmatrix} \begin{bmatrix} 0 \\ a \end{bmatrix}$$

$$= \begin{bmatrix} \frac{aT + e^{-aT} - 1}{a} \\ 1 - e^{-aT} \end{bmatrix}.$$

We can now determine

$$\Phi(k, 0) = \mathcal{Z}^{-1}\{z[z\mathbf{I} - \mathbf{F}]^{-1}\}$$

$$= \mathcal{Z}^{-1}\left\{ z \left[ \begin{bmatrix} z & 0 \\ 0 & z \end{bmatrix} - \begin{bmatrix} 1 & \frac{1}{a}(1 - e^{-aT}) \\ 0 & e^{-aT} \end{bmatrix} \right]^{-1} \right\}$$

$$= \mathcal{Z}^{-1}\left\{ z \begin{bmatrix} z - 1 & -\frac{1}{a}(1 - e^{-aT}) \\ 0 & z - e^{-aT} \end{bmatrix}^{-1} \right\}$$

$$= \mathcal{Z}^{-1}\left\{ z \begin{bmatrix} \frac{z - e^{-aT}}{(z-1)(z-e^{-aT})} & \frac{1}{a}\frac{(1 - e^{-aT})}{(z-1)(z-e^{-aT})} \\ 0 & \frac{z-1}{(z-1)(z-e^{-aT})} \end{bmatrix} \right\}$$

$$= \mathcal{Z}^{-1}\left\{ \begin{bmatrix} \frac{z}{z-1} & \frac{1}{a}\left[\frac{z}{z-1} - \frac{z(e^{-aT})}{z-e^{-aT}}\right] \\ 0 & \frac{z}{z-e^{-aT}} \end{bmatrix} \right\}$$

$$= \begin{bmatrix} 1 & \frac{1}{a}[1 - e^{-akT}] \\ 0 & e^{-akT} \end{bmatrix}$$

After a little thought, this result should not be too surprising, because $\Phi(k, 0)$ is the *impulse*-invariant transformation of $e^{\mathbf{A}t}$.

## 19.3 | EQUIVALENT TRANSFER FUNCTION

The discrete state model we found in Example 19.2.1 came from a continuous transfer function. We now want to show that the discrete state model is equivalent to the transfer function $G'_p(z)$ that we would obtain by finding the step-invariant transformation of this same continuous transfer function. We do so by taking the $\mathcal{Z}$ transform of the discrete state model and then manipulating the resulting equations until they become a transfer function. The transfer function we obain by this process is, in fact, $G'_p(z)$.

The first step is to take the $\mathcal{Z}$ transform of the equations

$$\mathbf{x}(k+1) = \mathbf{F}\mathbf{x}(k) + \mathbf{g}u(k),$$

$$y(k) = \mathbf{h}^T\mathbf{x}(k),$$

with zero initial conditions, to obtain

$$z\mathbf{x}(z) = \mathbf{F}\mathbf{x}(z) + \mathbf{g}u(z),$$

$$y(z) = \mathbf{h}^T\mathbf{x}(z).$$

The first of these equations yields

$$\mathbf{x}(z) = [z\mathbf{I} - \mathbf{F}]^{-1}\mathbf{g}u(z).$$

Substituting into the second equation yields

$$y(z) = \mathbf{h}^T[z\mathbf{I} - \mathbf{F}]^{-1}\mathbf{g}u(z),$$

and since $y(z)$ and $u(z)$ are *scalars*, we have

$$\frac{y(z)}{u(z)} = \mathbf{h}^T[z\mathbf{I} - \mathbf{F}]^{-1}\mathbf{g}. \qquad [19.6]$$

The right-hand side of Eq. [19.6] is the *step*-invariant transform of the plant. This results from the approximation $u(\tau) = u(kT)$ we made to the continuous convolution integral in deriving the discrete model. We verify this result in Example 19.3.1.

**EXAMPLE 19.3.1**

For the transfer function

$$G_p(s) = \frac{a}{s(s+a)},$$

we have found the discrete state model to be

$$\begin{bmatrix} x_1(k+1) \\ x_2(k+1) \end{bmatrix} = \begin{bmatrix} 1 & \frac{1}{a}(1-e^{-aT}) \\ 0 & e^{-aT} \end{bmatrix} \begin{bmatrix} x_1(k) \\ x_2(k) \end{bmatrix} + \begin{bmatrix} \frac{aT+e^{-aT}-1}{a} \\ 1-e^{-aT} \end{bmatrix} u(k),$$

$$y(k) = \begin{bmatrix} 1 & 0 \end{bmatrix} \begin{bmatrix} x_1(k) \\ x_2(k) \end{bmatrix}.$$

Then,

$$\mathbf{h}^T\text{Adj}[z\mathbf{I} - \mathbf{F}]\mathbf{g} = \begin{bmatrix} 1 & 0 \end{bmatrix} \left\{ \text{Adj} \begin{bmatrix} z-1 & -\frac{1}{a}(1-e^{-aT}) \\ 0 & z-e^{-aT} \end{bmatrix} \right\} \begin{bmatrix} \frac{aT+e^{-aT}-1}{a} \\ 1-e^{-aT} \end{bmatrix}$$

$$= \begin{bmatrix} 1 & 0 \end{bmatrix} \begin{bmatrix} z-e^{-aT} & \frac{(1-e^{-aT})}{a} \\ 0 & z-1 \end{bmatrix} \begin{bmatrix} \frac{aT+e^{-aT}-1}{a} \\ 1-e^{-aT} \end{bmatrix}$$

$$= \begin{bmatrix} 1 & 0 \end{bmatrix} \begin{bmatrix} \frac{(z-e^{-aT})(aT+e^{-aT}-1)}{a} + \frac{(1-e^{-aT})^2}{a} \\ (z-1)(1-e^{-aT}) \end{bmatrix}$$

$$= \frac{z(aT + e^{-aT} - 1) - e^{-aT}(aT + e^{-aT} - 1) + (1 - 2e^{-aT} + e^{-2aT})}{a}$$

$$= \frac{z(aT + e^{-aT} - 1) + e^{-aT} - e^{-2aT} - aTe^{-aT} + 1 - 2e^{-aT} + e^{-2aT}}{a}$$

$$= \frac{z(aT + e^{-aT} - 1) + (1 - e^{-aT} - aTe^{-aT})}{a}.$$

Also

$$\text{Det}[z\mathbf{I} - \mathbf{F}] = \text{Det} \begin{bmatrix} z - e^{-aT} & -\frac{1}{a}(1 - e^{-aT}) \\ 0 & z - 1 \end{bmatrix}$$

$$= (z - 1)(z - e^{-aT}).$$

Finally,

$$\frac{y(z)}{u(z)} = \mathbf{h}^T[z\mathbf{I} - \mathbf{F}]^{-1}\mathbf{g}$$

$$= \frac{\mathbf{h}^T \text{Adj}[z\mathbf{I} - \mathbf{F}]\mathbf{g}}{\text{Det}[z\mathbf{I} - \mathbf{F}]}$$

$$= \frac{[z(aT + e^{-aT} - 1) + (1 - e^{-aT} - aTe^{-aT})]/a}{(z - 1)(z - e^{-aT})}$$

$$= \frac{z(aT + e^{-aT} - 1) + (1 - e^{-aT} - aTe^{-aT})}{a(z - 1)(z - e^{-aT})}.$$

We have previously derived the $G'_p(z)$ that corresponds to

$$G_p(s) = \frac{a}{s(s + a)},$$

by first defining

$$Y_{\text{step}}(s) = \frac{a}{s^2(s + a)}$$

and then using any standard table relating Laplace and $\mathcal{Z}$ transforms, such as Table 14.3, to obtain the $\mathcal{Z}$ transform corresponding to $Y_{\text{step}}(s)$. In this case, the companion transfer function is

$$Y_{\text{step}}(z) = \frac{z[z(aT + e^{-aT} - 1) + (1 - e^{-aT} - aTe^{-aT})]}{a(z - 1)^2(z - e^{-aT})}.$$

Dividing out the unit step gives the same answer we have already obtained.

---

With the discrete state model in hand, we are now positioned to discuss some fundamental properties that apply to both the continuous and discrete state models, concepts that are needed to properly formulate feedback compensation using the state model formulation.

# 19.4 | THE REGULATOR PROBLEM

In this section we develop through Examples 19.4.1 and 19.4.2 a feedback strategy based on the assumption that we can measure all the states of the system. We will find that this feedback strategy enables us to place *all* the eigenvalues of the closed-loop state model *anywhere* we desire. This feedback strategy, known as a regulator, is very different from the one we used with SISO systems where we only fed back the output of the system.

For examples 19.4.1 and 19.4.2, we will be able to place the eigenvalues of the closed-loop system arbitrarily. This, of course, begs the question: what is the property of the *plant* state model that will allow us to gain complete control of the eigenvalues of the *closed-loop* system? That property is called controllability, which we will define and discuss in Section 19.5.

The value of the dual of controllability, called observability, is not so obvious at this juncture. Its value stems from the fact that complete state feedback, while appealing from a theoretical standpoint, is of very little practical use. Observability is a property of the plant state model that will, in Chapter 20, enable us to modify complete state feedback so that it becomes a very powerful and practical design strategy.

We now develop the concepts of pole placement and regulation, first for a continuous state model and then for a discrete state model. Example 19.4.1 and 19.4.2 show that the concepts are identical for continuous and discrete systems.

**EXAMPLE 19.4.1**

Consider the system

$$\dot{\mathbf{x}}(t) = \mathbf{A}\mathbf{x}(t) + \mathbf{b}u(t), \qquad [19.7]$$

where

$$\mathbf{A} = \begin{bmatrix} -4 & 5 \\ -2 & 3 \end{bmatrix} \quad \text{and} \quad \mathbf{b} = \begin{bmatrix} 1 \\ 2 \end{bmatrix}.$$

Our first step is to build some block diagrams of the system. Figure 19.1 shows our system in a very general way. This diagram suggests that there is feedback present, but there is *not*. Figure 19.1 simply is a model of the plant.

**Figure 19.1 |** Block diagram representation of a forced state equation.

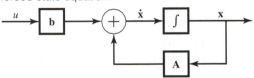

We now add feedback by letting

$$u = -\mathbf{k}^T\mathbf{x},$$

where for the problem at hand

$$\mathbf{k}^T = [k_1 \quad k_2].$$

If we make this substitution, then our state equation becomes:

$$\dot{\mathbf{x}} = \mathbf{A}\mathbf{x} - \mathbf{b}\mathbf{k}^T\mathbf{x}$$

$$= [\mathbf{A} - \mathbf{b}\mathbf{k}^T]\mathbf{x}$$

$$= \tilde{\mathbf{A}}\mathbf{x},$$

where we have the obvious definition

$$\tilde{\mathbf{A}} \triangleq [\mathbf{A} - \mathbf{b}\mathbf{k}^T].$$

We now have the homogeneous system of Fig. 19.2.

**Figure 19.2 |** Block diagram representation with $\mathbf{u} = -\mathbf{k}^T\mathbf{x}$.

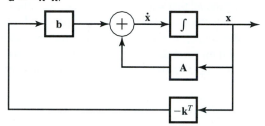

For the system under study in this example,

$$\tilde{\mathbf{A}} = \begin{bmatrix} -4 & 5 \\ -2 & 3 \end{bmatrix} - \begin{bmatrix} 1 \\ 2 \end{bmatrix} [k_1 \quad k_2]$$

$$= \begin{bmatrix} -4 & 5 \\ -2 & 3 \end{bmatrix} - \begin{bmatrix} k_1 & k_2 \\ 2k_1 & 2k_2 \end{bmatrix}$$

$$= \begin{bmatrix} -4 - k_1 & 5 - k_2 \\ -2 - 2k_1 & 3 - 2k_2 \end{bmatrix}$$

We next find the eigenvalues of the homogeneous system

$$\dot{\mathbf{x}} = \tilde{\mathbf{A}}\mathbf{x}.$$

We have

$$\text{Det}[\lambda\mathbf{I} - \tilde{\mathbf{A}}] = \text{Det}\left\{ \begin{bmatrix} \lambda + (4 + k_1) & -5 + k_2 \\ 2 + 2k_1 & \lambda + (-3 + 2k_2) \end{bmatrix} \right\}$$

$$= \lambda^2 + (4 - 3 + k_1 + 2k_2)\lambda + (-12 - 3k_1 + 8k_2 + 2k_1 k_2)$$

$$- (-10 - 10k_1 + 2k_2 + 2k_1 k_2)$$

$$= \lambda^2 + (1 + k_1 + 2k_2)\lambda + (-2 + 7k_1 + 6k_2).$$

An important point to note is that the cross term $k_1 k_2$ is not present. This is not a fluke of this particular problem, it is *always* the case. Why this is so will become clear in Section 19.6.

The characteristic equation for the system with feedback is then

$$\lambda^2 + (1 + k_1 + 2k_2)\lambda + (-2 + 7k_1 + 6k_2) = 0. \qquad \textbf{[19.8]}$$

This is a most remarkable equation, because, supposing that we can make $k_1$ and $k_2$ assume any values we desire, we can make the *eigenvalues* of the system with feedback assume *any* values we desire. Suppose for instance we wish the eigenvalues to be

$$\lambda = -3 \quad \text{and} \quad \lambda = -4.$$

Then the *desired* characteristic equation is

$$\lambda^2 + 7\lambda + 12 = 0. \qquad \textbf{[19.9]}$$

To achieve this we have only to equate coefficients of like powers of $\lambda$ in Eqs. [19.8] and [19.9]. Doing so yields

$$1 + k_1 + 2k_2 = 7,$$

$$-2 + 7k_1 + 6k_2 = 12,$$

which can be rearranged as

$$k_1 + 2k_2 = 6,$$

$$7k_1 + 6k_2 = 14.$$

These are *linear* equations in the two unknowns $k_1$ and $k_2$. They are easily solved yielding

$$k_1 = -1 \quad \text{and} \quad k_2 = 3.5.$$

Thus, by applying so-called state feedback, we have achieved a stable system. More remarkably, it appears that we can choose any eigenvalues we desire for the system with feedback.

---

So far, we have only shown that we can achieve this result for a specific system of dimension two. What we would like to be able to show is that this same result holds for a system of arbitrary dimension $n$. To get at this more general result we need to introduce the concept of controllability and then look for an appropriate transformation. We address these two tasks after we show, in Example 19.4.2, that the same results hold for discrete systems. Our development in Example 19.4.2 is brief because it should be obvious that everything we have developed for the continuous state model will hold for the discrete state model. Figure 19.3 shows the discrete state model with

$$u(k) = -\mathbf{k}^T \mathbf{x}(k).$$

The basic homogeneous discrete state equation is shown inside the dotted rectangle. The determination of the control is exactly the same as for the continuous case as example 19.4.2 shows

**Figure 19.3 |** Block diagram representation with $\mathbf{u} = -\mathbf{k}^T\mathbf{x}$.

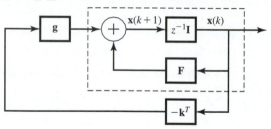

## EXAMPLE 19.4.2

Consider again the transfer function of Example 19.2.1

$$G(s) = \frac{a}{s(s+a)}.$$

In that example, we first found the continuous state model, and then the discrete state model

$$\begin{bmatrix} x_1(k+1) \\ x_2(k+1) \end{bmatrix} = \begin{bmatrix} 1 & \frac{1}{a}(1-e^{-aT}) \\ 0 & e^{-aT} \end{bmatrix} \begin{bmatrix} x_1(k) \\ x_2(k) \end{bmatrix} + \begin{bmatrix} \frac{aT+e^{-aT}-1}{a} \\ 1-e^{-aT} \end{bmatrix} u(k),$$

$$y(k) = [1 \quad 0] \begin{bmatrix} x_1(k) \\ x_2(k) \end{bmatrix}.$$

For $a = 4$, $T = 0.1$ s, we obtain

$$\mathbf{F} = \begin{bmatrix} 1 & 0.08242 \\ 0 & 0.67032 \end{bmatrix}, \qquad \mathbf{g} = \begin{bmatrix} 0.01758 \\ 0.03297 \end{bmatrix}.$$

One of the things we see right away is that the numbers are not as easy to work with. The ultimate solution for systems of large dimension is to write some simple computer programs to do the arithmetic drudgery. For the simple two-dimensional case under study, we can do the manipulations symbolically without too much difficulty. There is a second, more important benefit. A good deal of understanding of the state model approach can be derived from pushing first some symbols and then some numbers around. Once we have done so, and understand what the computer will be doing for us, we can engage it.

We begin by finding

$$\mathbf{F} - \mathbf{g}\mathbf{k}^T = \begin{bmatrix} f_{11} & f_{12} \\ f_{21} & f_{22} \end{bmatrix} - \begin{bmatrix} g_1 \\ g_2 \end{bmatrix} [k_1 \quad k_2]$$

$$= \begin{bmatrix} f_{11} & f_{12} \\ f_{21} & f_{22} \end{bmatrix} - \begin{bmatrix} g_1 k_1 & g_1 k_2 \\ g_2 k_1 & g_2 k_2 \end{bmatrix}$$

$$= \begin{bmatrix} f_{11} - g_1 k_1 & f_{12} - g_1 k_2 \\ f_{21} - g_2 k_1 & f_{22} - g_2 k_2 \end{bmatrix}.$$

Then

$$\text{Det}\{z\mathbf{I} - [\mathbf{F} - \mathbf{g}\mathbf{k}^T]\} = \text{Det}\begin{bmatrix} z - (f_{11} - g_1 k_1) & -(f_{12} - g_1 k_2) \\ -(f_{21} - g_2 k_1) & z - (f_{22} - g_2 k_2) \end{bmatrix}$$

$$= z^2 - (f_{11} - g_1 k_1 + f_{22} - g_2 k_2)z$$

$$+ (f_{11} - g_1 k_1)(f_{22} - g_2 k_2) - (f_{12} - g_1 k_2)(f_{21} - g_2 k_1)$$

$$= z^2 - [f_{11} + f_{22} - g_1 k_1 - g_2 k_2]z$$

$$+ f_{11} f_{22} - f_{11} g_2 k_2 - f_{22} g_1 k_1 + g_1 g_2 k_1 k_2$$

$$- (f_{12} f_{21} - f_{12} g_2 k_1 - f_{21} g_1 k_2 + g_1 g_2 k_1 k_2)$$

$$= z^2 - [f_{11} + f_{22} - g_1 k_1 - g_2 k_2]z + (f_{11} f_{22} - f_{12} f_{21})$$

$$+ (f_{12} g_2 - f_{22} g_1)k_1 + (f_{21} g_1 - f_{11} g_2)k_2$$

$$= z^2 - [\text{Trace}(\mathbf{F}) - g_1 k_1 - g_2 k_2]z$$

$$+ [\text{Det}(\mathbf{F}) + (f_{12} g_2 - f_{22} g_1)k_1 + (f_{21} g_1 - f_{11} g_2)k_2].$$

Note that the cross term $g_1 g_2 k_1 k_2$ disappears, just as it did for the continuous case. The reader may not be familiar with Trace $\mathbf{F}$; it merely stands for the sum of the diagonal elements of $\mathbf{F}$.

At this juncture we have the characteristic equation expressed in terms of $k_1$ and $k_2$ and the *known constants* from the matrices $\mathbf{F}$ and $\mathbf{g}$. Suppose we want the characteristic equation to be

$$p(z) = (z - \sigma + j\omega)(z - \sigma - j\omega) = z^2 - 2\sigma z + (\sigma^2 + \omega^2). \qquad \text{[19.10]}$$

Then equating coefficients of like powers of $z$ in our two expressions for the characteristic equation, we obtain

$$\text{Trace}(\mathbf{F}) - g_1 k_1 - g_2 k_2 = 2\sigma,$$

$$\text{Det}(\mathbf{F}) + (f_{12} g_2 - f_{22} g_1)k_1 + (f_{21} g_1 - f_{11} g_2)k_2 = \sigma^2 + \omega^2.$$

These equations can be rearranged as

$$\begin{bmatrix} g_1 & g_2 \\ f_{22} g_1 - f_{12} g_2 & f_{11} g_2 - f_{21} g_1 \end{bmatrix} \begin{bmatrix} k_1 \\ k_2 \end{bmatrix} = \begin{bmatrix} \text{Trace}(\mathbf{F}) - 2\sigma \\ \text{Det}(\mathbf{F}) - (\sigma^2 + \omega^2) \end{bmatrix}. \qquad \text{[19.11]}$$

We now have the general solution to the controller problem for two-dimensional state models. All that is left is to choose some values for $\sigma$ and $\omega$.

Suppose we choose closed-loop poles with a natural frequency $\omega_n = 5$ rad/s and a damping ratio of $\zeta = 0.8$. For a sampling rate of 10 Hz, the corresponding poles in the $z$ plane are

$$z = e^{sT} = e^{(-4 \pm j3)(0.1)} = 0.64038 \pm j0.19809.$$

Substituting these values into Eq. [19.11] yields

$$\begin{bmatrix} 0.01758 & 0.32968 \\ -0.01539 & 0.32968 \end{bmatrix} \begin{bmatrix} k_1 \\ k_2 \end{bmatrix} = \begin{bmatrix} 0.38956 \\ 0.22099 \end{bmatrix},$$

with solution

$$\mathbf{k}^T = [5.113 \quad 0.909].$$

In Examples 19.4.1 and 19.4.2 we were able to place the poles of the closed-loop system anywhere we desired. A natural question at this point is whether we can always do this. The answer to this question is no. To have complete control of the eigenvalues of the closed-loop system the *plant* state model must have the property of complete controllability. In Section 19.5 we first define complete controllability and then state a test for this property.

# 19.5 | CONTROLLABILITY

The reason that we were able to gain complete control of the dynamics of both the state models in Examples 19.4.1 and 19.4.2 has to do with the structure of the matrices that defined the systems. In both cases, the state models were "completely controllable."

In this section, we introduce the concept of controllability. This concept is crucial to developing what we will call the eigenvalue (pole) placement problem, which, in turn, leads to the design of regulators. Controllability is a concept that comes about rather naturally in the state space approach, but has applicability to the transfer function method as well.

## 19.5.1  Definitions

We provide here definitions of controllability for both continuous and discrete state models. The definitions are almost identical.

---

**Definition 19.5.1 (Controllability)**

The system

$$\dot{\mathbf{x}}(t) = \mathbf{A}\mathbf{x}(t) + \mathbf{B}\mathbf{u}(t),$$

where $\mathbf{A}$ is an $n \times n$ matrix of real constants, $\mathbf{B}$ is an $n \times p$ matrix of real constants, and $\mathbf{u}(t)$ is a $p \times 1$ vector of *scalar* functions is said to be completely state controllable if for any finite time $t_0$ there exits an *unconstrained* vector $\mathbf{u}(t)$ that will transfer the system from *any* given initial state $\mathbf{x}(t_0)$ to *any* given final state $\mathbf{x}(t_1)$ in a finite time interval $t_0 < t < t_1 < \infty$.

There are several important points about this definition worth noting. First, the input vector is *unconstrained*. That means that over time, some or all of the scalar time functions in **u** can be infinitely large in magnitude. Second, even though $t_1$ is finite, it can be arbitrarily large. Third, the systems we are most interested in, where $p = 1$ and the input is a scalar, are a subset of the systems covered by this theorem.

The definition of controllability for discrete time system parallels that for continuous systems.

---

**Definition 19.5.2 (Controllability)**

The system

$$\mathbf{x}(k+1) = \mathbf{F}\mathbf{x}(k) + \mathbf{g}u(k)$$

with **F** nonsingular, is said to be completely state controllable if there is a control sequence $\mathbf{u}(0), u(1), \ldots, u(N-1)$, with $N < \infty$, that will drive the system from the initial state $\mathbf{x}(0) = \mathbf{0}$ to *any* specified state $\mathbf{x}(N) \neq \mathbf{0}$.

---

As with the definition we gave for the continuous case, the control **u** can be arbitrarily large in magnitude at one or more points in time. Also although it would seem that $N$ can be arbitrarily large, we will see that it is never larger than the dimension $n$ of the state model.

Finally, just because a system is not completely state controllable does not mean we cannot find an adequate control. However, these definitions are important because there are related theorems that enable us to tell from the structure of the state model, that is from the matrix pair [**A**, **b**] or [**F**, **g**], whether the model is completely controllable. Controllability is important, because without it we will not be able to to use state feedback to arbitrarily choose all the eigenvalues of the closed-loop system.

## 19.5.2  Controllability Theorems

The two theorems we are about to state are analogous results for continuous and discrete state models. We will prove the theorem for the discrete case only. The theorems hold for the more general case where the input $\mathbf{u}(t)$ is is a $p \times 1$ vector of scalar functions and **B** is an $n \times p$ matrix of real constants.

---

**Theorem 19.5.1 (Controllability—Continuous State Model)**

The system

$$\dot{\mathbf{x}}(t) = \mathbf{A}\mathbf{x}(t) + \mathbf{B}\mathbf{u}(t),$$

is completely state controllable if and only if the matrix

$$\mathcal{C} = [\mathbf{B} \quad \mathbf{A}\mathbf{B} \quad \mathbf{A}^2\mathbf{B} \quad \ldots \quad \mathbf{A}^i\mathbf{B} \quad \ldots \quad \mathbf{A}^{n-1}\mathbf{B}]$$

is of *maximum* rank $n$.

---

We omit the proof of this theorem. We note that for $\mathbf{B}$, an $n \times p$ matrix, the controllability matrix $\mathcal{C}$ has $pn$ columns and $n$ rows. If $\mathbf{B}$ is $n \times 1$ then $\mathbf{B} \rightarrow \mathbf{b}$, an $n \times 1$ *vector*. In this case,

$$\mathcal{C} = [\mathbf{b} \quad \mathbf{Ab} \quad \mathbf{A}^2\mathbf{b} \quad \dots \quad \mathbf{A}^i\mathbf{b} \quad \dots \quad \mathbf{A}^{n-1}\mathbf{b}]$$

is an $n \times n$ square matrix. It is this latter matrix that will prove most useful.

We now state the corresponding result for discrete state models.

---

**Theorem 19.5.2 (Controllability—Discrete State Model)**

The system

$$\mathbf{x}(k+1) = \mathbf{Fx}(k) + \mathbf{Gu}(k),$$

with $\mathbf{F}$ an $n \times n$ matrix, $\mathbf{G}$ an $n \times p$ matrix, and $\mathbf{u}$ a $p \times 1$ vector of $p$ scalar inputs, is completely state controllable, if and only if the matrix

$$\mathcal{C} = [\mathbf{G} \quad \mathbf{FG} \quad \mathbf{F}^2\mathbf{G} \quad \dots \quad \mathbf{F}^{n-1}\mathbf{G}]$$

is of full rank $n$.

---

Luenberger (1979) offers an elegant proof of this theorem for the general case of multiple inputs and multiple outputs. The special case of a single input and single output is, however, the case of overriding importance, and all the control strategies developed in Chapter 20 are for this special case.

For the case of a single input and a single output, we can write

$$\mathbf{x}(1) = \mathbf{Fx}(0) + \mathbf{g}u(0),$$

$$\mathbf{x}(2) = \mathbf{Fx}(1) + \mathbf{g}u(1),$$

$$= \mathbf{F}[\mathbf{Fx}(0) + \mathbf{g}u(0)] + \mathbf{g}u(1)$$

$$= \mathbf{F}^2\mathbf{x}(0) + \mathbf{Fg}u(0) + \mathbf{g}u(1),$$

$$\mathbf{x}(3) = \mathbf{Fx}(2) + \mathbf{g}u(2)$$

$$= \mathbf{F}[\mathbf{F}^2\mathbf{x}(0) + \mathbf{Fg}u(0) + \mathbf{g}u(1)] + \mathbf{g}u(2)$$

$$= \mathbf{F}^3\mathbf{x}(0) + \mathbf{F}^2\mathbf{g}u(0) + \mathbf{Fg}u(1) + \mathbf{g}u(2)$$

$$\vdots$$

$$\mathbf{x}(n) = \mathbf{F}^n\mathbf{x}(0) + \mathbf{F}^{n-1}\mathbf{g}u(0) + \mathbf{F}^{n-2}\mathbf{g}u(1) + \cdots + \mathbf{Fg}u(n-2) + \mathbf{g}u(n-1).$$

Thus, we have

$$\mathbf{F}^{n-1}\mathbf{g}u(0) + \mathbf{F}^{n-2}\mathbf{g}u(1) + \cdots + \mathbf{Fg}u(n-2) + \mathbf{g}u(n-1) = \bar{\mathbf{x}}, \qquad \textbf{[19.12]}$$

where $\bar{\mathbf{x}} = \mathbf{x}(n) - \mathbf{F}^n\mathbf{x}(0)$.

Now, if our model has a single input and a single output, the controllability matrix is

$$\mathcal{C} = [\mathbf{g} \quad \mathbf{Fg} \quad \mathbf{F}^2\mathbf{g} \quad \cdots \quad \mathbf{F}^{n-1}\mathbf{g}],$$

an $n \times n$ *square* matrix. We see that the left-hand side of Eq. [19.12] is a linear combination of the columns of $\mathcal{C}$, where the scalar weighting coefficients are the controls $u(0), u(1), \ldots, u(n-1)$. If the columns of $\mathcal{C}$ are linearly independent then we certainly can find a set of scalar coefficients $u(0), u(1), \ldots, u(n-1)$ such that Eq. [19.12] is satisfied for *any* $\bar{\mathbf{x}}$. On the other hand, if we know that Eq. [19.12] is true for *any* $\bar{\mathbf{x}}$, then it follows that the columns of $\mathcal{C}$ are linearly independent and $\mathcal{C}$ is of maximum rank. Thus, if our state model has only a single input and a single output, it is easy to see that Theorem 19.5.2 is true.

Controllability has some interesting features that are easy to understand for the single-input, single-output case. First, note that we could have generalized Definition 19.5.2 somewhat because it is clear from Eq. [19.12] that for the single input, single output case we can find a control sequence even if $\mathbf{x}(0) \neq \mathbf{0}$. This is also true for the multiple input, multiple output case.

Next, suppose $\mathbf{x}(n) = \mathbf{0}$. Then Eq. [19.12] becomes

$$\mathbf{F}^{n-1}\mathbf{g}u(0) + \mathbf{F}^{n-2}\mathbf{g}u(1) + \cdots + \mathbf{Fg}u(n-2) + \mathbf{g}u(n-1) = -\mathbf{F}^n\mathbf{x}(0).$$

If $\mathbf{F}$ is singular, then so is $\mathbf{F}^n$. Hence, if $\mathbf{F}$ is singular, it may be that for *any* $\mathbf{x}(0)$, the vector $-\mathbf{F}^n\mathbf{x}(0)$ will always lie in a proper subspace of the $n$-dimensional vector space. In that case, it may not be necessary for $\mathcal{C}$ to be full rank to find a control that will take the output of the state model from an arbitrary starting point to the origin. All that would be required is that $\mathcal{C}$ have the necessary set of linearly independent columns to span the subspace that contains $-\mathbf{F}^n\mathbf{x}(0)$. For that reason, the property in Definition 19.5.2 is sometimes called reachability, rather than controllability, with the name controllability given to the weaker property of being able to drive the output from an arbitrary nonzero starting point to the origin.

If $\mathbf{F}$ is nonsingular, however, and $\mathbf{x}(n) = \mathbf{0}$, then we can write

$$\mathbf{F}^{-n}[\mathbf{g}u(n-1) + \mathbf{Fg}u(n-2) + \cdots + \mathbf{F}^{n-2}\mathbf{g}u(1) + \mathbf{F}^{n-1}\mathbf{g}u(0)] = -\mathbf{x}(0),$$

which leads to

$$\mathbf{F}^{-n}[\mathbf{g} \quad \mathbf{Fg} \quad \mathbf{F}^2\mathbf{g} \quad \cdots \quad \mathbf{F}^{n-1}\mathbf{g}] \begin{bmatrix} u(n-1) \\ u(n-2) \\ \vdots \\ u(0) \end{bmatrix} = -\mathbf{x}(0),$$

and finally

$$\mathbf{F}^{-n}\mathcal{C}\mathbf{u} = -\mathbf{x}(0), \qquad\qquad [19.13]$$

where

$$\mathbf{u} = \begin{bmatrix} u(n-1) \\ u(n-2) \\ \vdots \\ u(0) \end{bmatrix}$$

In this case $\mathcal{C}$ must be nonsingular. Thus, if $\mathbf{F}$ is nonsingular, then the concepts of reachability and controllability coincide. A more complete, and probably more lucid, discussion of these issues can be found in Kailath (1980).

Controllability is a much stronger condition than might be suspected from the definition. As we have just seen it requires at most $n$ control inputs to reach any destination in the state space. We illustrate this with Example 19.5.1.

**EXAMPLE 19.5.1**

Consider the system

$$\begin{bmatrix} x_1(k+1) \\ x_2(k+1) \end{bmatrix} = \begin{bmatrix} 1 & 2 \\ 0 & 1 \end{bmatrix} \begin{bmatrix} x_1(k) \\ x_2(k) \end{bmatrix} + \begin{bmatrix} 0 \\ 1 \end{bmatrix} u(k).$$

To check the controllability, we form the controllability matrix

$$\mathcal{C} = [\mathbf{g} \quad \mathbf{Fg}] = \begin{bmatrix} 0 & 2 \\ 1 & 1 \end{bmatrix}.$$

We next find a control sequence $u(0), u(1), \ldots, u(N)$, where $N$ is a finite integer, that will take the system from a known initial state

$$\begin{bmatrix} x_1(0) \\ x_2(0) \end{bmatrix}$$

to a specified final state

$$\begin{bmatrix} x_1(N) \\ x_2(N) \end{bmatrix}.$$

That is, we assume that $\mathbf{x}(0)$ and $\mathbf{x}(N)$ are known. The procedure is straightforward, and easily extended to systems of higher order, given a high tolerance for tedium.

We begin by finding

$$\begin{bmatrix} x_1(1) \\ x_2(1) \end{bmatrix} = \begin{bmatrix} 1 & 2 \\ 0 & 1 \end{bmatrix} \begin{bmatrix} x_1(0) \\ x_2(0) \end{bmatrix} + \begin{bmatrix} 0 \\ 1 \end{bmatrix} u(0)$$

$$= \begin{bmatrix} x_1(0) + 2x_2(0) \\ x_2(0) + u(0) \end{bmatrix}.$$

We next generate

$$\begin{bmatrix} x_1(2) \\ x_2(2) \end{bmatrix} = \begin{bmatrix} 1 & 2 \\ 0 & 1 \end{bmatrix} \begin{bmatrix} x_1(1) \\ x_2(1) \end{bmatrix} + \begin{bmatrix} 0 \\ 1 \end{bmatrix} u(0)$$

$$= \begin{bmatrix} x_1(1) + 2x_2(1) \\ x_2(1) + u(1) \end{bmatrix}$$

$$= \begin{bmatrix} x_1(0) + 2x_2(0) + 2[x_2(0) + u(0)] \\ x_2(0) + u(0) + u(1) \end{bmatrix}$$

$$= \begin{bmatrix} x_1(0) + 4x_2(0) \\ x_2(0) \end{bmatrix} + \begin{bmatrix} 2 & 0 \\ 1 & 1 \end{bmatrix} \begin{bmatrix} u(0) \\ u(1) \end{bmatrix}.$$

The right-hand side of this last equation is a matrix whose coefficients are *known* times a vector of controls. If we set the right-hand side equal to the desired final state, we have

$$\begin{bmatrix} x_1(N) \\ x_2(N) \end{bmatrix} = \begin{bmatrix} x_1(0) + 4x_2(0) \\ x_2(0) \end{bmatrix} + \begin{bmatrix} 2 & 0 \\ 1 & 1 \end{bmatrix} \begin{bmatrix} u(0) \\ u(1) \end{bmatrix}.$$

This equation can be rewritten as

$$\begin{bmatrix} u(0) \\ u(1) \end{bmatrix} = \begin{bmatrix} 2 & 0 \\ 1 & 1 \end{bmatrix}^{-1} \begin{bmatrix} x_1(N) - x_1(0) - 4x_2(0) \\ x_2(N) - x_2(0) \end{bmatrix}$$

$$= \begin{bmatrix} 0.5 & 0 \\ -0.5 & 1 \end{bmatrix} \begin{bmatrix} x_1(N) - x_1(0) - 4x_2(0) \\ x_2(N) - x_2(0) \end{bmatrix}.$$

Thus, we see that in two time steps, the system can be driven from an arbitrary initial state to an arbitrary final state.

---

With these two theorems in hand we are now in position to determine when we can arbitrarily choose all the eigenvalues of a system with full state feedback.

## 19.6 | CONTROLLABLE CANONICAL FORM

In this section we will develop a new canonical form for the state model. We will use the continuous state model to do so, but it will be clear from the development that the same transformation will work for the discrete model. In Chapter 18 we used the Jordan canonical form to reveal the basic stablity of the state model. The controllable canonical form has a different purpose, namely, to help us prove that if a system is completely controllable, then we can place the eigenvalues of the closed-loop system anywhere we wish, as long as we can measure all the states of the system.

The derivation of the canonical form is lengthy and tedious, but not conceptually difficult. Moreover, it is representative of the manipulations we need to learn to do to master state space analysis. Most of the intermediate steps are present to make the derivation easier to follow.

Given the system

$$\dot{\mathbf{x}}(t) = \mathbf{A}\mathbf{x}(t) + \mathbf{b}u(t), \qquad [19.14]$$

we are interested in establishing the conditions for which letting

$$u(t) = -\mathbf{k}^T\mathbf{x}(t)$$

enables us to assign any values we so choose to the eigenvalues of the resulting homogeneous system

$$\dot{\mathbf{x}}(t) = [\mathbf{A} - \mathbf{b}\mathbf{k}^T]\mathbf{x}(t).$$

Theorems 19.5.1 and 19.5.2 provide the conditions for achieving this. We will develop the result for the continuous state model, but we could just as well have used the discrete state model.

Suppose that the system of Eq. [19.14] is completely state controllable. Then the controllability matrix

$$\mathcal{C} = [\mathbf{b} \quad \mathbf{A}\mathbf{b} \quad \mathbf{A}^2\mathbf{b} \quad \dots \quad \mathbf{A}^i\mathbf{b} \quad \dots \quad \mathbf{A}^{n-1}\mathbf{b}]$$

is of full rank $n$, and hence invertible. Let

$$\mathcal{C}^{-1} = \begin{bmatrix} \mathbf{v}_1^T \\ \mathbf{v}_2^T \\ \vdots \\ \mathbf{v}_i^T \\ \vdots \\ \mathbf{v}_n^T \end{bmatrix},$$

where

$$\mathbf{v}_i^T,$$

$i = 1, 2, \dots, n$ represents the $i$th *row* of $\mathcal{C}^{-1}$.

We will use these two matrices to find a coordinate transformation that puts the system in a form that will make it easy to prove the result we are after. To that end consider

$$\mathbf{T} = \begin{bmatrix} \mathbf{v}_n^T \\ \mathbf{v}_n^T\mathbf{A} \\ \mathbf{v}_n^T\mathbf{A}^2 \\ \vdots \\ \mathbf{v}_n^T\mathbf{A}^i \\ \vdots \\ \mathbf{v}_n^T\mathbf{A}^{n-1} \end{bmatrix}.$$

To use $\mathbf{T}$ as a transformation to a new coordinate system we must now show that $\mathbf{T}$ is invertible. One way to do this is to show that the rows of $\mathbf{T}$ are linearly independent. That is, if

$$\alpha_0 \mathbf{v}_n^T + \alpha_1 \mathbf{v}_n^T \mathbf{A} + \alpha_2 \mathbf{v}_n^T \mathbf{A}^2 + \cdots + \alpha_i \mathbf{v}_n^T \mathbf{A}^i + \cdots + \alpha_{n-2} \mathbf{v}_n^T \mathbf{A}^{n-2} + \alpha_{n-1} \mathbf{v}_n^T \mathbf{A}^{n-1} = 0,$$

[19.15]

then

$$\alpha_0 = \alpha_1 = \cdots = \alpha_i = \cdots = \alpha_{n-1} = 0.$$

We can show this as follows. First, note that

$$\mathcal{C}^{-1}\mathcal{C} = \begin{bmatrix} \mathbf{v}_1^T \\ \mathbf{v}_2^T \\ \vdots \\ \mathbf{v}_i^T \\ \vdots \\ \mathbf{v}_n^T \end{bmatrix} [\mathbf{b} \quad \mathbf{Ab} \quad \mathbf{A}^2\mathbf{b} \quad \dots \quad \mathbf{A}^i\mathbf{b} \quad \dots \quad \mathbf{A}^{n-1}\mathbf{b}]$$

$$= \begin{bmatrix} \mathbf{v}_1^T \mathbf{b} & \mathbf{v}_1^T \mathbf{Ab} & \mathbf{v}_1^T \mathbf{A}^2\mathbf{b} & \dots & \mathbf{v}_1^T \mathbf{A}^i\mathbf{b} & \dots & \mathbf{v}_1^T \mathbf{A}^{n-1}\mathbf{b} \\ \mathbf{v}_2^T \mathbf{b} & \mathbf{v}_2^T \mathbf{Ab} & \mathbf{v}_2^T \mathbf{A}^2\mathbf{b} & \dots & \mathbf{v}_2^T \mathbf{A}^i\mathbf{b} & \dots & \mathbf{v}_2^T \mathbf{A}^{n-1}\mathbf{b} \\ \vdots & & & & & & \vdots \\ \mathbf{v}_i^T \mathbf{b} & \mathbf{v}_i^T \mathbf{Ab} & \mathbf{v}_i^T \mathbf{A}^2\mathbf{b} & \dots & \mathbf{v}_i^T \mathbf{A}^i\mathbf{b} & \dots & \mathbf{v}_i^T \mathbf{A}^{n-1}\mathbf{b} \\ \vdots & & & & & & \vdots \\ \mathbf{v}_n^T \mathbf{b} & \mathbf{v}_n^T \mathbf{Ab} & \mathbf{v}_n^T \mathbf{A}^2\mathbf{b} & \dots & \mathbf{v}_n^T \mathbf{A}^i\mathbf{b} & \dots & \mathbf{v}_n^T \mathbf{A}^{n-1}\mathbf{b} \end{bmatrix}.$$

It is important to note that we have written $\mathcal{C}^{-1}\mathcal{C}$ and not $\mathcal{C}\mathcal{C}^{-1}$, and that we have represented $\mathcal{C}^{-1}$ by *rows* and $\mathcal{C}$ by *columns*. Then each element in the product $\mathcal{C}^{-1}\mathcal{C}$ is the *inner* product of a row of $\mathcal{C}^{-1}$ with a *column* of $\mathcal{C}$.

Since

$$\mathcal{C}^{-1}\mathcal{C} = \mathbf{I},$$

we now have the important equation

$$\begin{bmatrix} \mathbf{v}_1^T \mathbf{b} & \mathbf{v}_1^T \mathbf{Ab} & \mathbf{v}_1^T \mathbf{A}^2\mathbf{b} & \dots & \mathbf{v}_1^T \mathbf{A}^i\mathbf{b} & \dots & \mathbf{v}_1^T \mathbf{A}^{n-1}\mathbf{b} \\ \mathbf{v}_2^T \mathbf{b} & \mathbf{v}_2^T \mathbf{Ab} & \mathbf{v}_2^T \mathbf{A}^2\mathbf{b} & \dots & \mathbf{v}_2^T \mathbf{A}^i\mathbf{b} & \dots & \mathbf{v}_2^T \mathbf{A}^{n-1}\mathbf{b} \\ \vdots & & & & & & \\ \mathbf{v}_i^T \mathbf{b} & \mathbf{v}_i^T \mathbf{Ab} & \mathbf{v}_i^T \mathbf{A}^2\mathbf{b} & \dots & \mathbf{v}_i^T \mathbf{A}^i\mathbf{b} & \dots & \mathbf{v}_i^T \mathbf{A}^{n-1}\mathbf{b} \\ \vdots & & & & & & \\ \mathbf{v}_n^T \mathbf{b} & \mathbf{v}_n^T \mathbf{Ab} & \mathbf{v}_n^T \mathbf{A}^2\mathbf{b} & \dots & \mathbf{v}_n^T \mathbf{A}^i\mathbf{b} & \dots & \mathbf{v}_n^T \mathbf{A}^{n-1}\mathbf{b} \end{bmatrix} \begin{bmatrix} 1 & 0 & \dots & 0 & \dots & 0 & 0 \\ 0 & 1 & 0 & \vdots & \dots & 0 & 0 \\ \vdots & 0 & \ddots & 0 & \dots & 0 & \vdots \\ 0 & \vdots & 0 & 1 & 0 & \dots & 0 \\ 0 & 0 & \vdots & 0 & \ddots & 0 & 0 \\ 0 & 0 & 0 & \vdots & 0 & 1 & 0 \\ 0 & 0 & 0 & 0 & \dots & 0 & 1 \end{bmatrix}$$

[19.16]

Of special importance is the last row on each side of the equation because it yields the following set of equations:

$$v_n^T b = 0,$$

$$v_n^T A b = 0,$$

$$v_n^T A^2 b = 0,$$

$$\vdots \quad \vdots$$

$$v_n^T A^i b = 0,$$

$$\vdots \quad \vdots$$

$$v_n^T A^{n-2} b = 0,$$

$$v_n^T A^{n-1} b = 1. \tag{19.17}$$

We are now ready to prove the linear independence of the rows of **T**. We first multiply Eq. [19.15] on the *right* by **b** to obtain

$$\alpha_0 v_n^T b + \alpha_1 v_n^T A b + \alpha_2 v_n^T A^2 b + \cdots + \alpha_i v_n^T A^i b + \cdots + \alpha_{n-2} v_n^T A^{n-2} b$$

$$+ \alpha_{n-1} v_n^T A^{n-1} b = 0. \tag{19.18}$$

Referring to Eq. [19.17], we see that the first $n - 1$ terms on the left-hand side of Eq. [19.18] are zero and the last term on the left is

$$\alpha_{n-1},$$

since, from Eq. [19.17],

$$v_n^T A^{n-1} b = 1.$$

Hence Eq. [19.18] reduces to

$$\alpha_{n-1} = 0.$$

We can now rewrite Eq. [19.15] as

$$\alpha_0 v_n^T + \alpha_1 v_n^T A + \alpha_2 v_n^T A^2 + \cdots + \alpha_i v_n^T A^i + \cdots + \alpha_{n-2} v_n^T A^{n-2} = 0. \tag{19.19}$$

We now repeat the process, but this time multiplying on the right by **Ab** to obtain

$$\alpha_0 v_n^T A b + \alpha_1 v_n^T A^2 b + \alpha_2 v_n^T A^3 b + \cdots + \alpha_i v_n^T A^{i+1} b + \cdots + \alpha_{n-2} v_n^T A^{n-1} b = 0. \tag{19.20}$$

Once again, the first $n - 2$ terms of the left-hand side are zero and the last term on the left is

$$\alpha_{n-2}.$$

Thus, Eq. [19.20] reduces to

$$\alpha_{n-2} = 0,$$

and Eq. [19.15] is further reduced to

$$\alpha_0 v_n^T + \alpha_1 v_n^T A + \alpha_2 v_n^T A^2 + \cdots + \alpha_i v_n^T A^i + \cdots + \alpha_{n-3} v_n^T A^{n-3} = 0. \tag{19.21}$$

If we now multiply Eq. [19.21] on the left by $\mathbf{A}^2\mathbf{b}$ and repeat our analysis, we can show that

$$\alpha_{n-3} = 0.$$

Continuing in this way for $n$ steps, we can show that all the $\alpha_i$ are equal to zero. Thus we have established that the $n$ rows of $\mathbf{T}$ are linearly independent and hence $\mathbf{T}$ is invertible.

We will use $\mathbf{T}$ as our transformation matrix to a new coordinate system. The transformation is

$$\mathbf{z} = \mathbf{Tx},$$

resulting in the system

$$\dot{\mathbf{z}}(t) = \mathbf{TAT}^{-1}\mathbf{z}(t) + \mathbf{T}b u(t).$$

We first form

$$\mathbf{TA} = \begin{bmatrix} \mathbf{v}_n^T \\ \mathbf{v}_n^T \mathbf{A} \\ \mathbf{v}_n^T \mathbf{A}^2 \\ \vdots \\ \mathbf{v}_n^T \mathbf{A}^i \\ \vdots \\ \mathbf{v}_n^T \mathbf{A}^{n-2} \\ \mathbf{v}_n^T \mathbf{A}^{n-1} \end{bmatrix} \mathbf{A} = \begin{bmatrix} \mathbf{v}_n^T \mathbf{A} \\ \mathbf{v}_n^T \mathbf{A}^2 \\ \mathbf{v}_n^T \mathbf{A}^3 \\ \vdots \\ \mathbf{v}_n^T \mathbf{A}^{i+1} \\ \vdots \\ \mathbf{v}_n^T \mathbf{A}^{n-1} \\ \mathbf{v}_n^T \mathbf{A}^n \end{bmatrix}.$$

We next form

$$\mathbf{TT}^{-1} = \begin{bmatrix} \mathbf{v}_n^T \\ \mathbf{v}_n^T \mathbf{A} \\ \mathbf{v}_n^T \mathbf{A}^2 \\ \vdots \\ \mathbf{v}_n^T \mathbf{A}^i \\ \vdots \\ \mathbf{v}_n^T \mathbf{A}^{n-1} \end{bmatrix} \begin{bmatrix} \mathbf{w}_1 & \mathbf{w}_2 & \cdots & \mathbf{w}_i & \cdots & \mathbf{w}_n \end{bmatrix}$$

$$= \begin{bmatrix} \mathbf{v}_n^T \mathbf{w}_1 & \mathbf{v}_n^T \mathbf{w}_2 & \cdots & \mathbf{v}_n^T \mathbf{w}_i & \cdots & \mathbf{v}_n^T \mathbf{w}_n \\ \mathbf{v}_n^T \mathbf{A}\mathbf{w}_1 & \mathbf{v}_n^T \mathbf{A}\mathbf{w}_2 & \cdots & \mathbf{v}_n^T \mathbf{A}\mathbf{w}_i & \cdots & \mathbf{v}_n^T \mathbf{A}\mathbf{w}_n \\ \vdots & & & \vdots & & \vdots \\ \mathbf{v}_n^T \mathbf{A}^i\mathbf{w}_1 & \mathbf{v}_n^T \mathbf{A}^i\mathbf{w}_2 & \cdots & \mathbf{v}_n^T \mathbf{A}^i\mathbf{w}_i & \cdots & \mathbf{v}_n^T \mathbf{A}^i\mathbf{w}_n \\ \vdots & & & \vdots & & \vdots \\ \mathbf{v}_n^T \mathbf{A}^{n-1}\mathbf{w}_1 & \mathbf{v}_n^T \mathbf{A}^{n-1}\mathbf{w}_2 & \cdots & \mathbf{v}_n^T \mathbf{A}^{n-1}\mathbf{w}_i & \cdots & \mathbf{v}_n^T \mathbf{A}^{n-1}\mathbf{w}_n \end{bmatrix}.$$

Then we have a second important result

$$
\begin{bmatrix}
\mathbf{v}_n^T \mathbf{w}_1 & \mathbf{v}_n^T \mathbf{w}_2 & \dots & \mathbf{v}_n^T \mathbf{w}_i & \dots & \mathbf{v}_n^T \mathbf{w}_n \\
\mathbf{v}_n^T \mathbf{A} \mathbf{w}_1 & \mathbf{v}_n^T \mathbf{A} \mathbf{w}_2 & \dots & \mathbf{v}_n^T \mathbf{A} \mathbf{w}_i & \dots & \mathbf{v}_n^T \mathbf{A} \mathbf{w}_n \\
\vdots & & & & & \\
\mathbf{v}_n^T \mathbf{A}^i \mathbf{w}_1 & \mathbf{v}_n^T \mathbf{A}^i \mathbf{w}_2 & \dots & \mathbf{v}_n^T \mathbf{A}^i \mathbf{w}_i & \dots & \mathbf{v}_n^T \mathbf{A}^i \mathbf{w}_n \\
\vdots & & & & & \\
\mathbf{v}_n^T \mathbf{A}^{n-2} \mathbf{w}_1 & \mathbf{v}_n^T \mathbf{A}^{n-2} \mathbf{w}_2 & \dots & \mathbf{v}_n^T \mathbf{A}^{n-2} \mathbf{w}_i & \dots & \mathbf{v}_n^T \mathbf{A}^{n-2} \mathbf{w}_n \\
\mathbf{v}_n^T \mathbf{A}^{n-1} \mathbf{w}_1 & \mathbf{v}_n^T \mathbf{A}^{n-1} \mathbf{w}_2 & \dots & \mathbf{v}_n^T \mathbf{A}^{n-1} \mathbf{w}_i & \dots & \mathbf{v}_n^T \mathbf{A}^{n-1} \mathbf{w}_n
\end{bmatrix}
=
\begin{bmatrix}
1 & 0 & \dots & 0 & \dots & 0 \\
0 & 1 & 0 & \vdots & \dots & 0 \\
\vdots & 0 & \ddots & 0 & \dots & 0 \\
0 & \vdots & 0 & 1 & 0 & \vdots \\
0 & 0 & \vdots & 0 & \ddots & 0 \\
0 & 0 & 0 & \dots & 0 & 1
\end{bmatrix}.
$$

$$[19.22]$$

We now form

$$
\mathbf{T}\mathbf{A}\mathbf{T}^{-1} =
\begin{bmatrix}
\mathbf{v}_n^T \mathbf{A} \\
\mathbf{v}_n^T \mathbf{A}^2 \\
\mathbf{v}_n^T \mathbf{A}^3 \\
\vdots \\
\mathbf{v}_n^T \mathbf{A}^{i+1} \\
\vdots \\
\mathbf{v}_n^T \mathbf{A}^{n-1} \\
\mathbf{v}_n^T \mathbf{A}^n
\end{bmatrix}
\begin{bmatrix} \mathbf{w}_1 & \mathbf{w}_2 & \dots & \mathbf{w}_i & \dots & \mathbf{w}_n \end{bmatrix}
$$

$$
=
\begin{bmatrix}
\mathbf{v}_n^T \mathbf{A} \mathbf{w}_1 & \mathbf{v}_n^T \mathbf{A} \mathbf{w}_2 & \dots & \mathbf{v}_n^T \mathbf{A} \mathbf{w}_i & \dots & \mathbf{v}_n^T \mathbf{A} \mathbf{w}_n \\
\mathbf{v}_n^T \mathbf{A}^2 \mathbf{w}_1 & \mathbf{v}_n^T \mathbf{A}^2 \mathbf{w}_2 & \dots & \mathbf{v}_n^T \mathbf{A}^2 \mathbf{w}_i & \dots & \mathbf{v}_n^T \mathbf{A}^2 \mathbf{w}_n \\
\vdots & & & & & \vdots \\
\mathbf{v}_n^T \mathbf{A}^{i+1} \mathbf{w}_1 & \mathbf{v}_n^T \mathbf{A}^{i+1} \mathbf{w}_2 & \dots & \mathbf{v}_n^T \mathbf{A}^{i+1} \mathbf{w}_i & \dots & \mathbf{v}_n^T \mathbf{A}^{i+1} \mathbf{w}_n \\
\vdots & & & & & \vdots \\
\mathbf{v}_n^T \mathbf{A}^{n-1} \mathbf{w}_1 & \mathbf{v}_n^T \mathbf{A}^{n-1} \mathbf{w}_2 & \dots & \mathbf{v}_n^T \mathbf{A}^{n-1} \mathbf{w}_i & \dots & \mathbf{v}_n^T \mathbf{A}^{n-1} \mathbf{w}_n \\
\mathbf{v}_n^T \mathbf{A}^n \mathbf{w}_1 & \mathbf{v}_n^T \mathbf{A}^n \mathbf{w}_2 & \dots & \mathbf{v}_n^T \mathbf{A}^n \mathbf{w}_i & \dots & \mathbf{v}_n^T \mathbf{A}^n \mathbf{w}_n
\end{bmatrix}.
\qquad [19.23]
$$

If we now compare Eq. [19.22] with Eq. [19.23], we see that the first $n-1$ rows of $\mathbf{T}\mathbf{A}\mathbf{T}^{-1}$ are identical to the last $n-1$ rows of the identity matrix. We do not have any information about the last row of $\mathbf{T}\mathbf{A}\mathbf{T}^{-1}$ so we simply assign symbols to these quantities. That is, we let

$$
\mathbf{v}_n^T \mathbf{A}^n \mathbf{w}_1 = -\alpha_0,
$$

$$
\mathbf{v}_n^T \mathbf{A}^n \mathbf{w}_2 = -\alpha_1,
$$

$$
\mathbf{v}_n^T \mathbf{A}^n \mathbf{w}_3 = -\alpha_2,
$$

$$
\vdots \quad \vdots
$$

$$\mathbf{v}_n^T \mathbf{A}^n \mathbf{w}_i = -\alpha_{i-1},$$

$$\vdots \quad \vdots$$

$$\mathbf{v}_n^T \mathbf{A}^n \mathbf{w}_n = -\alpha_{n-1}.$$

Thus,

$$
\mathbf{TAT}^{-1} \triangleq
\begin{bmatrix}
0 & 1 & 0 & 0 & \cdots & 0 & 0 \\
0 & 0 & 1 & 0 & \cdots & 0 & 0 \\
\vdots & \vdots & 0 & 1 & \cdots & \vdots & \vdots \\
0 & 0 & \vdots & \vdots & \ddots & 0 & 0 \\
0 & 0 & 0 & \cdots & 0 & 1 & 0 \\
0 & 0 & 0 & 0 & \cdots & 0 & 1 \\
-\alpha_0 & -\alpha_1 & -\alpha_3 & \cdots & -\alpha_{n-3} & -\alpha_{n-2} & -\alpha_{n-1}
\end{bmatrix}.
$$

Our last task is to determine $\bar{\mathbf{b}} = \mathbf{Tb}$.

$$
\mathbf{Tb} =
\begin{bmatrix}
\mathbf{v}_n^T \\
\mathbf{v}_n^T \mathbf{A} \\
\mathbf{v}_n^T \mathbf{A}^2 \\
\vdots \\
\mathbf{v}_n^T \mathbf{A}^i \\
\vdots \\
\mathbf{v}_n^T \mathbf{A}^{n-1}
\end{bmatrix}
\mathbf{b} =
\begin{bmatrix}
\mathbf{v}_n^T \mathbf{b} \\
\mathbf{v}_n^T \mathbf{A}\mathbf{b} \\
\mathbf{v}_n^T \mathbf{A}^2\mathbf{b} \\
\vdots \\
\mathbf{v}_n^T \mathbf{A}^i\mathbf{b} \\
\vdots \\
\mathbf{v}_n^T \mathbf{A}^{n-1}\mathbf{b}
\end{bmatrix}
=
\begin{bmatrix}
0 \\
0 \\
\vdots \\
0 \\
1
\end{bmatrix}.
$$

The last step follows from an inspection of Eq. [19.16], which reveals that the elements in $\bar{\mathbf{b}}$ are the elements in the last *row* of an $n \times n$ identity matrix.

We now have the original system in the controllable canonical form:

$$\dot{\mathbf{z}}(t) = \mathbf{\Lambda}\mathbf{z}(t) + \bar{\mathbf{b}}u(t), \qquad \text{[19.24]}$$

where

$$\mathbf{\Lambda} = \mathbf{TAT}^{-1} \quad \text{and} \quad \bar{\mathbf{b}} = \mathbf{Tb}.$$

We now let

$$u = -\bar{\mathbf{k}}^T \mathbf{z}.$$

Then Eq. [19.24] becomes

$$\dot{\mathbf{z}} = \mathbf{\Lambda}\mathbf{z}(t) - \bar{\mathbf{b}}\bar{\mathbf{k}}^T \mathbf{z}(t)$$

$$= [\mathbf{\Lambda} - \bar{\mathbf{b}}\bar{\mathbf{k}}^T]\mathbf{z}(t)$$

$$= \tilde{\mathbf{\Lambda}}\mathbf{z}(t),$$

where we have the obvious definition

$$[\mathbf{\Lambda} - \bar{\mathbf{b}}\bar{\mathbf{k}}^T] \triangleq \tilde{\mathbf{\Lambda}}.$$

We next investigate the properties of $\tilde{\mathbf{\Lambda}}$.

First we form

$$[\mathbf{\Lambda} - \bar{\mathbf{b}}\bar{\mathbf{k}}^T] = \begin{bmatrix} 0 & 1 & 0 & 0 & \cdots & 0 & 0 \\ 0 & 0 & 1 & 0 & \cdots & 0 & 0 \\ \vdots & \vdots & 0 & 1 & \cdots & \vdots & \vdots \\ 0 & 0 & \vdots & \vdots & \ddots & 0 & 0 \\ 0 & 0 & 0 & \cdots & 0 & 1 & 0 \\ 0 & 0 & 0 & 0 & \cdots & 0 & 1 \\ -\alpha_0 & -\alpha_1 & -\alpha_2 & \cdots & -\alpha_{n-3} & -\alpha_{n-2} & -\alpha_{n-1} \end{bmatrix}$$

$$- \begin{bmatrix} 0 \\ 0 \\ \vdots \\ 0 \\ 1 \end{bmatrix} [\bar{k}_0 \quad \bar{k}_1 \quad \cdots \quad \bar{k}_{n-2} \quad \bar{k}_{n-1}]$$

$$= \begin{bmatrix} 0 & 1 & 0 & 0 & \cdots & 0 \\ 0 & 0 & 1 & 0 & \cdots & 0 \\ \vdots & \vdots & 0 & 1 & \cdots & \vdots \\ 0 & 0 & \vdots & \vdots & \ddots & 0 \\ 0 & 0 & 0 & \cdots & 0 & 1 \\ -\alpha_0 & -\alpha_1 & -\alpha_2 & \cdots & -\alpha_{n-2} & -\alpha_{n-1} \end{bmatrix}$$

$$- \begin{bmatrix} 0 & 0 & 0 & \cdots & 0 & 0 \\ 0 & 0 & 0 & \cdots & 0 & 0 \\ \vdots & & & & & \vdots \\ 0 & 0 & 0 & 0 & 0 & 0 \\ \bar{k}_0 & \bar{k}_1 & \bar{k}_2 & \cdots & \bar{k}_{n-2} & \bar{k}_{n-1} \end{bmatrix}$$

$$= \begin{bmatrix} 0 & 1 & 0 & 0 & \cdots & 0 & 0 \\ 0 & 0 & 1 & 0 & \cdots & 0 & 0 \\ \vdots & \vdots & 0 & 1 & \cdots & \vdots & \vdots \\ 0 & 0 & \vdots & \vdots & \ddots & 0 & 0 \\ 0 & 0 & 0 & \cdots & 0 & 1 & 0 \\ 0 & 0 & 0 & 0 & \cdots & 0 & 1 \\ -(\alpha_0 + \bar{k}_0) & -(\alpha_1 + \bar{k}_1) & -(\alpha_2 + \bar{k}_2) & \cdots & -(\alpha_{n-3} + \bar{k}_{n-3}) & -(\alpha_{n-2} + \bar{k}_{n-2}) & -(\alpha_{n-1} + \bar{k}_{n-1}) \end{bmatrix}$$

We next find the eigenvalues of the controllable canonical system.

$$\text{Det}[\lambda I - \tilde{A}] = \text{Det}\begin{bmatrix} 0 & 1 & 0 & 0 & \cdots & 0 & 0 \\ 0 & 0 & 1 & 0 & \cdots & 0 & 0 \\ \vdots & \vdots & & 0 & 1 & \cdots & \vdots & \vdots \\ 0 & 0 & \vdots & \vdots & \ddots & 0 & 0 \\ 0 & 0 & 0 & \cdots & 0 & 1 & 0 \\ 0 & 0 & 0 & 0 & \cdots & 0 & 1 \\ (\alpha_0 + \bar{k}_0) & (\alpha_1 + \bar{k}_1) & (\alpha_2 + \bar{k}_2) & \cdots & (\alpha_{n-3} + \bar{k}_{n-3}) & (\alpha_{n-2} + \bar{k}_{n-2}) & (\lambda + \alpha_{n-1} + \bar{k}_{n-1}) \end{bmatrix}$$

$$= \lambda^n + (\alpha_{n-1} + \bar{k}_{n-1})\lambda^{n-1} + (\alpha_{n-2} + \bar{k}_{n-2})\lambda^{n-2}$$
$$+ \cdots + (\alpha_1 + \bar{k}_1)\lambda + (\alpha_0 + \bar{k}_0).$$

Thus we see that for the controllable canonical system we can place the eigenvalues anywhere we desire since by using $\bar{k}_0, \bar{k}_1, \ldots, \bar{k}_{n-1}$, we can control every coefficient in the characteristic equation.

The final question is what is $\mathbf{k}^T$ for the original system? To answer that question we compute

$$\text{Det}[\lambda I - (\Lambda - \bar{\mathbf{b}}\bar{\mathbf{k}}^T)] = \text{Det}[\lambda \mathbf{T}\mathbf{T}^{-1} - (\mathbf{T}A\mathbf{T}^{-1} - \mathbf{T}\mathbf{b}\bar{\mathbf{k}}^T\mathbf{T}\mathbf{T}^{-1})]$$
$$= \text{Det}\{\mathbf{T}[\lambda I - (A - \mathbf{b}\bar{\mathbf{k}}^T\mathbf{T})]\mathbf{T}^{-1}\}$$
$$= \text{Det}\ \mathbf{T} \times \text{Det}[\lambda I - (A - \mathbf{b}\bar{\mathbf{k}}^T\mathbf{T})] \times \text{Det}\ \mathbf{T}^{-1}.$$

We showed in Chapter 18 that if the matrix $\mathbf{T}$ is invertible, and

$$\text{Det}\ \mathbf{T} = \alpha,$$

then

$$\text{Det}\ \mathbf{T}^{-1} = \frac{1}{\alpha}.$$

This, in turn, means that we can write

$$\text{Det}[\lambda I - (\Lambda - \bar{\mathbf{b}}\bar{\mathbf{k}}^T)] = \text{Det}\ \mathbf{T} \times \text{Det}[\lambda I - (A - \mathbf{b}\bar{\mathbf{k}}^T\mathbf{T})] \times \text{Det}\ \mathbf{T}^{-1}$$
$$= \alpha \times \text{Det}[\lambda I - (A - \mathbf{b}\bar{\mathbf{k}}^T\mathbf{T}] \times \frac{1}{\alpha}$$
$$= \text{Det}[\lambda I - (A - \mathbf{b}\bar{\mathbf{k}}^T\mathbf{T})].$$

If we define

$$\bar{\mathbf{k}}^T\mathbf{T} \overset{\Delta}{=} \mathbf{k}^T,$$

then we have

$$\text{Det}[\lambda I - (\Lambda - \bar{\mathbf{b}}\bar{\mathbf{k}}^T)] = \text{Det}[\lambda I - (A - \mathbf{b}\mathbf{k}^T)]. \qquad \textbf{[19.25]}$$

Equation [19.25] says that if we use the control $u = \mathbf{k}^T\mathbf{x}$, where $\mathbf{k}^T = \bar{\mathbf{k}}^T\mathbf{T}$, in the original system we get exactly the same eigenvalues we obtained in the controllable canonical system using $u = -\bar{\mathbf{k}}^T\mathbf{z}$. Thus we have shown that if the original system is completely state controllable, then for a control $u = -\mathbf{k}^T\mathbf{x}$ the eigenvalues can be placed wherever we desire. It should be clear that this whole development could be repeated for the discrete state model by merely substituting $\mathbf{F}$ for $\mathbf{A}$ and $\mathbf{g}$ for $\mathbf{b}$.

# 19.7 | OBSERVABILITY

We conclude this chapter with a very closely related concept called observability. Controllability and observability can be thought of as duals of each other. We will need both concepts in the next chapter when we develop the controller observer. As before, there are corresponding definitions and theorems for the continuous and discrete cases. We will discuss both cases, but concentrate on the discrete case because control algorithms use the discrete model almost exclusively.

---

**Definition 19.7.1 (Observability—Continuous Model)**

The system

$$\dot{\mathbf{x}}(t) = \mathbf{A}\mathbf{x}(t),$$

$$\mathbf{Y}(t) = \mathbf{C}\mathbf{x}(t),$$

where $\mathbf{A}$ is an $n \times n$ matrix and $\mathbf{C}$ is a $p \times n$ matrix is said to be completely observable if for an arbitrary initial state $\mathbf{x}(0)$, there is a $0 < t_0 < \infty$ such that knowledge of $y(t)$ for $0 < t \leq t_0$ is sufficient to determine $\mathbf{x}(0)$.

---

The definition for the discrete case is essentially identical.

---

**Definition 19.7.2 (Observability—Discrete Model)**

The system

$$\mathbf{x}(k+1) = \mathbf{F}\mathbf{x}(k),$$

$$\mathbf{Y}(k) = \mathbf{H}\mathbf{x}(k),$$

where $\mathbf{F}$ is an $n \times n$ matrix and $\mathbf{H}$ is an $p \times n$ matrix is said to be completely observable if for an arbitrary initial state $\mathbf{x}(0)$, there is an $N < \infty$ such that knowledge of $\mathbf{Y}(0), \mathbf{Y}(1), \ldots, \mathbf{Y}(N)$ is sufficient to determine $\mathbf{x}(0)$.

---

Simply put, these definitions say that a system is observable, if by watching the system for some *finite* length of time, we can tell where it started from. We see that the definition for the discrete case is the same as that for the continuous case except that $t_0$ is replaced by a finite integer index $N$.

As was the case for controllability there are theorems relating the structure of the state model to its observability.

---

**Theorem 19.7.1 (Observability—Continuous Model)**

The system

$$\dot{\mathbf{x}}(t) = \mathbf{A}\mathbf{x}(t),$$

$$\mathbf{Y}(t) = \mathbf{C}\mathbf{x}(t),$$

where $\mathbf{A}$ is an $n \times n$ matrix and $\mathbf{C}$ is a $p \times n$ matrix is completely observable if and only if the $np \times n$ matrix

$$\mathcal{O} = \begin{bmatrix} \mathbf{C} \\ \mathbf{CF} \\ \mathbf{CF}^2 \\ \vdots \\ \mathbf{CF}^{n-1} \end{bmatrix}$$

is of maximum rank $n$.

---

The theorem for the discrete case is identical.

---

**Theorem 19.7.2 (Observability)**

The system

$$\mathbf{x}(k+1) = \mathbf{F}\mathbf{x}(k),$$

$$\mathbf{Y}(k) = \mathbf{H}\mathbf{x}(k),$$

where $\mathbf{F}$ is an $n \times n$ matrix and $\mathbf{H}$ is a $p \times n$ matrix is completely observable if and only if the $np \times n$ matrix

$$\mathcal{O} = \begin{bmatrix} \mathbf{H} \\ \mathbf{HF} \\ \mathbf{HF}^2 \\ \vdots \\ \mathbf{HF}^{n-1} \end{bmatrix}$$

matrix is of maximum rank $n$.

---

Again, Luenberger (1979) has a good proof for state models that have multiple inputs and multiple outputs. As was the case when we discussed controllability, the state model with a single input and single output is of of the greatest importance. For the single-input, single-output case the observability matrix is the *square* matrix

$$\mathcal{O} = \begin{bmatrix} \mathbf{h}^T \\ \mathbf{h}^T\mathbf{F} \\ \mathbf{h}^T\mathbf{F}^2 \\ \vdots \\ \mathbf{h}^T\mathbf{F}^{n-1} \end{bmatrix}.$$

Note that $\mathcal{O}$ is written in row format. That is, $\mathbf{h}^T, \mathbf{h}^T\mathbf{F}, \ldots, \mathbf{h}^T\mathbf{F}^{n-1}$ are *row* matrices. Now suppose, the system has a nonzero initial condition $\mathbf{x}(0)$, and we make the $n$ measurements,

$$y(0) = \mathbf{h}^T\mathbf{x}(0),$$

$$y(1) = \mathbf{h}^T\mathbf{F}\mathbf{x}(0),$$

$$y(2) = \mathbf{h}^T\mathbf{F}\mathbf{x}(1) = \mathbf{h}^T\mathbf{F}^2\mathbf{x}(0),$$

$$y(3) = \mathbf{h}^T\mathbf{F}\mathbf{x}(2) = \mathbf{h}^T\mathbf{F}^3\mathbf{x}(0),$$

$$\vdots$$

$$y(n-1) = \mathbf{h}^T\mathbf{F}\mathbf{x}(n-2) = \mathbf{h}^T\mathbf{F}^{n-1}\mathbf{x}(0),$$

If $\mathcal{O}$ is of maximum rank $n$. Then, after $n$ observations of the system, namely, $y(0), y(1), \ldots, y(n-1)$, we have enough information to find $\mathbf{x}(0)$ because we can write

$$\begin{bmatrix} \mathbf{h}^T \\ \mathbf{h}^T\mathbf{F} \\ \mathbf{h}^T\mathbf{F}^2 \\ \vdots \\ \mathbf{h}^T\mathbf{F}^{n-1} \end{bmatrix} \mathbf{x}(0) = \begin{bmatrix} y(0) \\ y(1) \\ y(2) \\ \vdots \\ y(n-1) \end{bmatrix}$$

That is,

$$\mathcal{O}\mathbf{x}(0) = \mathbf{y}, \qquad\qquad [19.26]$$

$$\mathbf{y} = \begin{bmatrix} y(0) \\ y(1) \\ y(2) \\ \vdots \\ y(n-1) \end{bmatrix}.$$

Since the right-hand side of Eq. [19.26] is known and since, by assumption, $\mathcal{O}$ is invertible, we can solve for $\mathbf{x}(0)$.

If, on the other hand, we know the state model is completely observable, after no more than $n$ measurements we will be able to identify the initial condition. The reason is that the matrix

$$\mathcal{O}_N = \begin{bmatrix} \mathbf{h}^T \\ \mathbf{h}^T\mathbf{F} \\ \mathbf{h}^T\mathbf{F}^2 \\ \vdots \\ \mathbf{h}^T\mathbf{F}^{N-1} \end{bmatrix},$$

where $N > n$ has the same rank as $\mathcal{O}$.

To see this, suppose, as suggested by Luenberger (1979), we think of forming $\mathcal{O}$ one row at a time. In other words, we form the series of matrices

$$\mathcal{O}_k = \begin{bmatrix} \mathbf{h}^T \\ \mathbf{h}^T \mathbf{F} \\ \mathbf{h}^T \mathbf{F}^2 \\ \vdots \\ \mathbf{h}^T \mathbf{F}^{k-1} \end{bmatrix},$$

$k = 1, 2, \ldots$, checking the rank every time we add a column. Suppose that for some $k$ adding the next row does not change the rank. That is,

$$\text{rank}\{\mathcal{O}_{k+1}\} = \text{rank}\{\mathcal{O}_k\}.$$

Thus, the last row added must be a linear combination of the previous rows, and we can write

$$\mathbf{h}^T \mathbf{F}^k = \alpha_0 \mathbf{h}^T + \alpha_1 \mathbf{h}^T \mathbf{F} + \alpha_2 \mathbf{h}^T \mathbf{F}^2 + \alpha_{k-1} \mathbf{h}^T \mathbf{F}^{k-1}. \qquad \textbf{[19.27]}$$

Now suppose we add the next row, namely, $\mathbf{h}^T \mathbf{F}^{k+1}$. Then the rank of $\mathcal{O}_{k+2}$ will be the same as that of $\mathcal{O}_{k+1}$ and $\mathcal{O}_k$. To see this we multiply Eq. [19.27] by $\mathbf{F}$ on the right to obtain

$$\mathbf{h}^T \mathbf{F}^{k+1} = \alpha_0 \mathbf{h}^T \mathbf{F} + \alpha_1 \mathbf{h}^T \mathbf{F}^2 + \alpha_2 \mathbf{h}^T \mathbf{F}^3 + \alpha_{k-1} \mathbf{h}^T \mathbf{F}^k, \qquad \textbf{[19.28]}$$

showing that the row $\mathbf{h}^T \mathbf{F}^{k+1}$ is also a linear combination of the previous rows.

From Eq. [19.28] we see that once the rank of $\mathcal{O}_k$ stops increasing it will never increase again. Thus, if we don't have $n$ linearly independent equations by the time we take $n$ measurements, we never will. This, in turn, shows that if the system is completely observable, then $\mathcal{O}$ must be of maximum rank. Thus, for the single-input, single-output state model it is relatively simple to establish Theorem 19.7.2. We now illustrate the ideas in this discussion with Example 19.7.1.

**EXAMPLE 19.7.1**

Consider the system

$$\begin{bmatrix} x_1(k+1) \\ x_2(k+1) \end{bmatrix} = \begin{bmatrix} 1 & -1 \\ 0 & -1 \end{bmatrix} \begin{bmatrix} x_1(k) \\ x_2(k) \end{bmatrix}$$

$$y(k) = \begin{bmatrix} 1 & 0 \end{bmatrix} \begin{bmatrix} x_1(k) \\ x_2(k) \end{bmatrix}.$$

We wish to show that the system is completely observable and then find the initial state if $y(0) = 1$ and $y(1) = 2$.

We check the observability of the system by first computing

$$\mathbf{h}^T \mathbf{F} = \begin{bmatrix} 1 & 0 \end{bmatrix} \begin{bmatrix} 1 & -1 \\ 0 & -1 \end{bmatrix}$$

$$= \begin{bmatrix} 1 & -1 \end{bmatrix},$$

and then

$$\mathcal{O} = \begin{bmatrix} \mathbf{h}^T \\ \mathbf{h}^T \mathbf{F} \end{bmatrix}$$

$$= \begin{bmatrix} 1 & 0 \\ 1 & -1 \end{bmatrix}.$$

Since $\mathcal{O}$ is of maximum rank 2, the system is observable.

The next task is to see if we can identify the initial state $\mathbf{x}(0)$ using the two observations of the output. From the first observation we have

$$y(0) = \begin{bmatrix} 1 & 0 \end{bmatrix} \begin{bmatrix} x_1(0) \\ x_2(0) \end{bmatrix}$$

$$= x_1(0).$$

Hence,

$$x_1(0) = y(0) = 1.$$

Next, from the state difference equation we can write

$$x_1(1) = x_1(0) - x_2(0),$$

$$x_2(1) = -x_2(0).$$

Then,

$$y(1) = x_1(1)$$

$$= x_1(0) - x_2(0).$$

We now have the system of equations

$$x_1(0) = y(0),$$

$$x_1(0) - x_2(0) = y(1),$$

which express the unknown initial conditions as a function of the *measured* outputs. In matrix form:

$$\begin{bmatrix} 1 & 0 \\ 1 & -1 \end{bmatrix} \begin{bmatrix} x_1(0) \\ x_2(0) \end{bmatrix} = \begin{bmatrix} y(0) \\ y(1) \end{bmatrix},$$

with solution

$$\begin{bmatrix} x_1(0) \\ x_2(0) \end{bmatrix} = \begin{bmatrix} 1 & 0 \\ 1 & -1 \end{bmatrix}^{-1} \begin{bmatrix} y(0) \\ y(1) \end{bmatrix}$$

$$= \begin{bmatrix} 1 & 0 \\ 1 & -1 \end{bmatrix} \begin{bmatrix} 1 \\ 2 \end{bmatrix}$$

$$= \begin{bmatrix} 1 \\ -1 \end{bmatrix}.$$

Thus, if the system is observable, recording $n$ outputs, where $n$ is the dimension of the system, is sufficient to determine the initial state. If the system is unobservable, we can watch it forever and never determine the initial state.

## 19.8 | OBSERVABLE CANONICAL FORM

Corresponding to the controllable canonical form we derived earlier is an observable canonical form. Actually there are other canonical forms for both controllability and observability that are explored in the problems. Here we merely outline the procedure for finding one of the observable canonical forms. Consider the discrete state model

$$\mathbf{x}(k+1) = \mathbf{F}\mathbf{x}(k),$$

$$y(k) = \mathbf{c}^T \mathbf{x}(k),$$

where we have specialized to the single output case. Suppose the system is completely observable, and let

$$\mathcal{O}^{-1} = [\mathbf{w}_1 \quad \mathbf{w}_2 \quad \dots \quad \mathbf{w}_i \quad \dots \quad \mathbf{w}_n].$$

First, we write

$$\mathcal{O}\mathcal{O}^{-1} = \begin{bmatrix} \mathbf{c}^T \\ \mathbf{c}^T \mathbf{F} \\ \vdots \\ \mathbf{c}^T \mathbf{F}^i \\ \vdots \\ \mathbf{c}^T \mathbf{F}^{n-1} \end{bmatrix} [\mathbf{w}_1 \quad \mathbf{w}_2 \quad \dots \quad \mathbf{w}_i \quad \dots \quad \mathbf{w}_n]$$

$$= \begin{bmatrix} \mathbf{c}^T \mathbf{w}_1 & \mathbf{c}^T \mathbf{w}_2 & \dots & \mathbf{c}^T \mathbf{w}_i & \dots & \mathbf{c}^T \mathbf{w}_n \\ \mathbf{c}^T \mathbf{F}\mathbf{w}_1 & \mathbf{c}^T \mathbf{F}\mathbf{w}_2 & \dots & \mathbf{c}^T \mathbf{F}\mathbf{w}_i & \dots & \mathbf{c}^T \mathbf{F}\mathbf{w}_n \\ \vdots & & & & & \vdots \\ \mathbf{c}^T \mathbf{F}^{i-1}\mathbf{w}_1 & \mathbf{c}^T \mathbf{F}^{i-1}\mathbf{w}_2 & \dots & \mathbf{c}^T \mathbf{F}^{i-1}\mathbf{w}_i & \dots & \mathbf{c}^T \mathbf{F}^{i-1}\mathbf{w}_n \\ \vdots & & & & & \vdots \\ \mathbf{c}^T \mathbf{F}^{n-1}\mathbf{w}_1 & \mathbf{c}^T \mathbf{F}^{n-1}\mathbf{w}_2 & \dots & \mathbf{c}^T \mathbf{F}^{n-1}\mathbf{w}_i & \dots & \mathbf{c}^T \mathbf{F}^{n-1}\mathbf{w}_n \end{bmatrix}.$$

It is important to note that we have written $\mathcal{O}\mathcal{O}^{-1}$ and not $\mathcal{O}^{-1}\mathcal{O}$, and that we have represented $\mathcal{O}^{-1}$ by *columns* and $\mathcal{O}$ by *rows*. Then each element in the product $\mathcal{O}\mathcal{O}^{-1}$ is the *inner* product of a row of $\mathcal{O}$ with a *column* of $\mathcal{O}^{-1}$.

If we now let use the transformation $\mathbf{z}(t) = \mathcal{O}\mathbf{x}(t)$, we can prove in a manner similar to that used to find the controllable canonical form that the model

$$\mathbf{x}(k+1) = \mathbf{F}\mathbf{x}(k) + \mathbf{g}u(k),$$

$$y(k) = \mathbf{c}^T \mathbf{x}(k),$$

can be transformed to the state model

$$\mathbf{z}(k + 1) = \mathbf{\Lambda}\mathbf{z}(k) + \bar{\mathbf{g}}u(k),$$

$$y(k) = \bar{\mathbf{c}}^T \mathbf{z}(k),$$

where

$$\mathbf{\Lambda} = \mathcal{O}\mathbf{F}\mathcal{O}^{-1} = \begin{bmatrix} 0 & 1 & 0 & 0 & \cdots & 0 & 0 \\ 0 & 0 & 1 & 0 & \cdots & 0 & 0 \\ \vdots & \vdots & 0 & 1 & \cdots & \vdots & \vdots \\ 0 & 0 & \vdots & \vdots & \ddots & 0 & 0 \\ 0 & 0 & 0 & \cdots & 0 & 1 & 0 \\ 0 & 0 & 0 & 0 & \cdots & 0 & 1 \\ -\alpha_0 & -\alpha_1 & -\alpha_2 & \cdots & -\alpha_{n-3} & -\alpha_{n-2} & -\alpha_{n-1} \end{bmatrix},$$

$$\bar{\mathbf{g}} = \mathcal{O}\mathbf{g} = \begin{bmatrix} \bar{g}_1 \\ \bar{g}_2 \\ \vdots \\ \bar{g}_i \\ \vdots \\ \bar{g}_n \end{bmatrix},$$

and

$$\bar{\mathbf{c}}^T = [1 \quad 0 \quad \cdots \quad 0 \quad \cdots \quad 0].$$

Problem 13 in Section 19.10.5 demonstrates the utility of the observable canonical form.

## 19.9 | REPRISE

In this chapter, we have worked our way to two very important results in state variable theory. The first of these results is that if the state model is completely state controllable, then by using a control of the form $u = -\mathbf{k}^T\mathbf{x}$, the eigenvalues can be placed wherever we desire. This result will be of great value for the development of the controller/observer equations in Chapter 20. The controller/observer equations arise because there are two glaring shortcomings to the results we have just obtained in this Chapter.

1.  The states of the system may not be physical states that can be measured by transducers.
2.  Even if the states can be measured, if they are large in number, then supplying all the transducers to measure and feed back all the states causes the resulting controller to be both expensive and probably physically large and cumbersome.

For these reasons full state feedback is seldom used. To circumvent these shortcomings, we will show in Chapter 20 that we we can use estimates (called observations) for most of the states, instead of actual measurements. Our ability to make these observations rests on the second important result discussed in these chapter, namely, observability. If a system is completely observable, then we will be able to find good estimates of the states we do not measure. Further, we will be able to use these estimates in place of the actual measurements in our control law. Thus, in the final chapter of this book we will be able to design controller/observers, where the control law will be exactly the same as those developed in this chapter, but the "states" we use in the control law will actually be estimates of the actual states, obtained from a recursive observer equation.

# 19.10 | PROBLEMS

## 19.10.1  Discrete State Model from Continuous State Model

Each pair of matrices $\mathbf{A}$ and $\mathbf{b}$ represent a state model

$$\dot{\mathbf{x}}(t) = \mathbf{A}\mathbf{x}(t) + \mathbf{b}u(t).$$

For each pair of matrices, find the discretized state model.

1. $\begin{bmatrix} 0 & 1 \\ 0 & -1 \end{bmatrix}, \begin{bmatrix} 0 \\ 1 \end{bmatrix}$
2. $\begin{bmatrix} 0 & 1 \\ -a^2 & -2a \end{bmatrix}, \begin{bmatrix} 0 \\ a^2 \end{bmatrix}$

3. $\begin{bmatrix} 0 & 1 \\ -6 & -5 \end{bmatrix}, \begin{bmatrix} 0 \\ 1 \end{bmatrix}$
4. $\begin{bmatrix} 0 & 1 \\ -1 & -1 \end{bmatrix}, \begin{bmatrix} 0 \\ 1 \end{bmatrix}$

5. $\begin{bmatrix} 0 & 2 \\ -1 & -1 \end{bmatrix}, \begin{bmatrix} 1 \\ 1 \end{bmatrix}$
6. $\begin{bmatrix} -2 & 1 \\ 0 & -1 \end{bmatrix}, \begin{bmatrix} 0 \\ 2 \end{bmatrix}$

7. $\begin{bmatrix} 0 & 1 \\ -2 & -3 \end{bmatrix}, \begin{bmatrix} 0 \\ 1 \end{bmatrix}$
8. $\begin{bmatrix} 0 & 1 \\ -4 & -3 \end{bmatrix}, \begin{bmatrix} 0 \\ 1 \end{bmatrix}$

9. $\begin{bmatrix} 0 & 1 \\ -0.6 & -0.5 \end{bmatrix}, \begin{bmatrix} 0 \\ 1 \end{bmatrix}$
10. $\begin{bmatrix} 0 & 1 \\ 0 & 0.75 \end{bmatrix}, \begin{bmatrix} 0 \\ 1 \end{bmatrix}$

11. $\begin{bmatrix} 0 & 1 \\ -2 & -3 \end{bmatrix}, \begin{bmatrix} 0 \\ 1 \end{bmatrix}$
12. $\begin{bmatrix} 0 & 1 \\ -2 & -3 \end{bmatrix}, \begin{bmatrix} 0 \\ 1 \end{bmatrix}$

13. $\begin{bmatrix} -1 & 1 \\ 0 & -2 \end{bmatrix}, \begin{bmatrix} 0 \\ 1 \end{bmatrix}$
14. $\begin{bmatrix} 0 & 2 \\ -1 & -1 \end{bmatrix}, \begin{bmatrix} 1 \\ 1 \end{bmatrix}$

## 19.10.2  Discrete State Model from Transfer Function

For each continuous transfer function, find the discrete state model in terms of the intersample period $T$.

1. $G(s) = \dfrac{1}{s^2}$
2. $G(s) = \dfrac{4}{s(s+3)}$

3.  $G(s) = \dfrac{ab}{(s+a)(s+b)}$          4.  $G(s) = \dfrac{a}{s(s+a)}$

5.  $G(s) = \dfrac{16}{s+8}$          6.  $G(s) = \dfrac{16}{(s+8)^2}$

7.  $G(s) = \dfrac{a^2}{(s+a)^2}$          8.  $G(s) = \dfrac{8}{(s+2)^2}$

### 19.10.3   Pole Placement

In each of the following problems the matrix pairs $[\mathbf{A}, \mathbf{b}]$ or $[\mathbf{F}, \mathbf{g}]$ represent the state models

$$\dot{\mathbf{x}}(t) = \mathbf{A}\mathbf{x} + \mathbf{b}u(t),$$

or

$$\mathbf{x}(k+1) = \mathbf{F}\mathbf{x}(k) + \mathbf{g}(k).$$

For $u = -\mathbf{k}^T\mathbf{x}$, find $\mathbf{k}^T$ that yields the desired eigenvalues. Check with MATLAB

1.  $\mathbf{A} = \begin{bmatrix} 0 & 1 \\ -4 & -2 \end{bmatrix}$, $\mathbf{b} = \begin{bmatrix} 0 \\ 1 \end{bmatrix}$, $\lambda_{1,2} = -3 \pm j2$

2.  $\mathbf{A} = \begin{bmatrix} -2 & 1 \\ 0 & -1 \end{bmatrix}$, $\mathbf{b} = \begin{bmatrix} 0 \\ 1 \end{bmatrix}$, $\lambda_1 = \lambda_2 = -5$

3.  $\mathbf{A} = \begin{bmatrix} -2 & 1 \\ 1 & -1 \end{bmatrix}$, $\mathbf{b} = \begin{bmatrix} 0 \\ 2 \end{bmatrix}$, $\lambda_{1,2} = -5 \pm j4$

4.  $\mathbf{A} = \begin{bmatrix} 2 & 1 \\ 4 & -2 \end{bmatrix}$, $\mathbf{b} = \begin{bmatrix} 0 \\ 1 \end{bmatrix}$, $\lambda_{1,2} = -4 \pm j4$

5.  $\mathbf{A} = \begin{bmatrix} 0 & 1 \\ 4 & -4 \end{bmatrix}$, $\mathbf{b} = \begin{bmatrix} 1 \\ 1 \end{bmatrix}$, $\lambda_1 = \lambda_2 = -6$

6.  $\mathbf{F} = \begin{bmatrix} 0 & 1 \\ 0 & 0.6 \end{bmatrix}$, $\mathbf{g} = \begin{bmatrix} 0 \\ 1 \end{bmatrix}$, $f_s = 5$ Hz, $\lambda_1 = \lambda_2$, with time constant 0.4 s

7.  $\mathbf{F} = \begin{bmatrix} -0.3 & 1 \\ 0 & -0.4 \end{bmatrix}$, $\mathbf{g} = \begin{bmatrix} 0 \\ 1 \end{bmatrix}$, $f_s = 10$ Hz, $\lambda_1 = \lambda_2$, with time constant 0.5 s

8.  $\mathbf{F} = \begin{bmatrix} 1 & 1 \\ 0 & -2 \end{bmatrix}$, $\mathbf{g} = \begin{bmatrix} 1 \\ 1 \end{bmatrix}$, $f_s = 20$ Hz, $\omega_n = 5$ rad/s, $\zeta = 0.8$

9.  $\mathbf{F} = \begin{bmatrix} 2 & 1 \\ 0 & 3 \end{bmatrix}$, $\mathbf{g} = \begin{bmatrix} 0 \\ 1 \end{bmatrix}$, $f_s = 50$ Hz, $\lambda_1 = \lambda_2$, with time constant of 0.1 s

10.  $\mathbf{F} = \begin{bmatrix} 1 & 1 \\ 0 & -2 \end{bmatrix}$, $\mathbf{g} = \begin{bmatrix} 1 \\ 1 \end{bmatrix}$, $f_s = 100$ Hz, $\omega_n = 10$ rad/s, $\zeta = 0.6$.

## 19.10.4 Controllabity and Observability—Part I

For each of the systems

$$\dot{x}(t) = \mathbf{A}x(t) + \mathbf{b}u(t),$$

$$y(t) = \mathbf{c}^T x(t),$$

or

$$x(k+1) = \mathbf{F}x(k) + \mathbf{b}u(k),$$

$$y(k) = \mathbf{h}^T x(k),$$

check the controllability and observability using MATLAB and draw an
implementation of the system.

1. $\mathbf{A} = \begin{bmatrix} -1 & 0 \\ 0 & -3 \end{bmatrix} \quad \mathbf{b} = \begin{bmatrix} 1 \\ 2 \end{bmatrix} \quad \mathbf{c}^T = [1 \quad 2]$

2. $\mathbf{A} = \begin{bmatrix} 0 & 1 \\ 0 & 0 \end{bmatrix} \quad \mathbf{b} = \begin{bmatrix} 0 \\ 1 \end{bmatrix} \quad \mathbf{c}^T = [1 \quad 0]$

3. $\mathbf{A} = \begin{bmatrix} 0 & 1 \\ 0 & 0 \end{bmatrix} \quad \mathbf{b} = \begin{bmatrix} 0 \\ 1 \end{bmatrix} \quad \mathbf{c}^T = [0 \quad 1]$

4. $\mathbf{A} = \begin{bmatrix} -1 & 1 & 0 \\ 0 & -1 & 0 \\ 0 & 0 & -1 \end{bmatrix} \quad \mathbf{b} = \begin{bmatrix} 0 \\ 0 \\ 1 \end{bmatrix} \quad \mathbf{c}^T = [1 \quad 0 \quad 0]$

5. $\mathbf{A} = \begin{bmatrix} -1 & 0 \\ 0 & -3 \end{bmatrix} \quad \mathbf{b} = \begin{bmatrix} 1 \\ 2 \end{bmatrix} \quad \mathbf{c}^T = [1 \quad 2]$

6. $\mathbf{A} = \begin{bmatrix} 0 & 1 \\ 0 & 0 \end{bmatrix} \quad \mathbf{b} = \begin{bmatrix} 0 \\ 1 \end{bmatrix} \quad \mathbf{c}^T = [1 \quad 0]$

7. $\mathbf{A} = \begin{bmatrix} 0 & 1 \\ 0 & 0 \end{bmatrix} \quad \mathbf{b} = \begin{bmatrix} 0 \\ 1 \end{bmatrix} \quad \mathbf{c}^T = [0 \quad 1]$

8. $\mathbf{A} = \begin{bmatrix} -1 & 1 & 0 \\ 0 & -1 & 0 \\ 0 & 0 & -1 \end{bmatrix} \quad \mathbf{b} = \begin{bmatrix} 0 \\ 0 \\ 1 \end{bmatrix} \quad \mathbf{c}^T = [1 \quad 0 \quad 0]$

9. $\mathbf{A} = \begin{bmatrix} -1 & 2 & 0 \\ 1 & -2 & 1 \\ 0 & 0 & -3 \end{bmatrix} \quad \mathbf{b} = \begin{bmatrix} 1 \\ 1 \\ 0 \end{bmatrix} \quad \mathbf{c}^T = [1 \quad 0 \quad 1]$

10. $\mathbf{F} = \begin{bmatrix} 0 & 2 & 0 \\ 0 & -0.5 & 1 \\ 0 & 0 & -1 \end{bmatrix} \quad \mathbf{g} = \begin{bmatrix} 1 \\ 0 \\ 0 \end{bmatrix} \quad \mathbf{h}^T = [1 \quad 0 \quad 0]$

11. $\mathbf{F} = \begin{bmatrix} -0.2 & 1 \\ 0 & -0.4 \end{bmatrix} \quad \mathbf{g} = \begin{bmatrix} 1 \\ 0 \end{bmatrix} \quad \mathbf{h}^T = [0 \quad 1]$

12. $\mathbf{F} = \begin{bmatrix} 0 & 1 \\ -1 & 0 \end{bmatrix}$   $\mathbf{g} = \begin{bmatrix} 1 \\ 0 \end{bmatrix}$   $\mathbf{h}^T = \begin{bmatrix} 1 & 0 \end{bmatrix}$

13. $\mathbf{F} = \begin{bmatrix} -0.5 & 0 & 1 \\ 0 & 0 & 1 \\ 0 & 0 & -1 \end{bmatrix}$   $\mathbf{g} = \begin{bmatrix} 0 \\ 1 \\ 0 \end{bmatrix}$   $\mathbf{h}^T = \begin{bmatrix} 1 & 0 & 0 \end{bmatrix}$

## 19.10.5   Controllability and Observability—Part II

1. Consider the system

$$\begin{bmatrix} x_1(k+1) \\ x_2(k+1) \end{bmatrix} = \begin{bmatrix} -\frac{1}{2} & 1 \\ 0 & -\frac{3}{4} \end{bmatrix} \begin{bmatrix} x_1(k) \\ x_2(k) \end{bmatrix} + \begin{bmatrix} 1 \\ 1 \end{bmatrix} u(k).$$

We desire to drive the output from $\mathbf{x}(0)$ to

$$\bar{\mathbf{x}} = \begin{bmatrix} 2 \\ 2 \end{bmatrix}$$

in one control step. Determine if there are any initial points $\mathbf{x}(0)$ for which this is possible.

2. Consider the system

$$\begin{bmatrix} x_1(k+1) \\ x_2(k+1) \end{bmatrix} = \begin{bmatrix} 0 & 1 \\ -0.5 & 1.5 \end{bmatrix} \begin{bmatrix} x_1(k) \\ x_2(k) \end{bmatrix} + \begin{bmatrix} 1 \\ 1 \end{bmatrix} u(k).$$

We desire to drive the output from $\mathbf{x}(0)$ to

$$\bar{\mathbf{x}} = \begin{bmatrix} 2 \\ 2 \end{bmatrix}$$

in one control step. Determine if there are any initial points $\mathbf{x}(0)$ for which this is possible.

3. Given

$$\dot{\mathbf{x}} = \mathbf{A}\mathbf{x} + \mathbf{b}u,$$

with

$$\mathbf{A} = \begin{bmatrix} -1 & 0 & 2 \\ 0 & -3 & 1 \\ 0 & 0 & -2 \end{bmatrix} \quad \text{and} \quad \mathbf{b} = \begin{bmatrix} 0 \\ 1 \\ 1 \end{bmatrix},$$

determine if the system is completely controllable.

4. Given

$$\dot{\mathbf{x}} = \mathbf{A}\mathbf{x} + \mathbf{b}u,$$

with

$$\mathbf{A} = \begin{bmatrix} -1 & 0 & 2 \\ 0 & -3 & 1 \\ 0 & 0 & -2 \end{bmatrix} \quad \text{and} \quad \mathbf{b} = \begin{bmatrix} 0 \\ 0 \\ 1 \end{bmatrix},$$

first, show the system is completely controllable, and then put the system in controllable canonical form and find $\mathbf{k}^T = [k_1 \ k_2 \ k_3]$ such that for $u = -\mathbf{k}^T x$, the system has eigenvalues

$$\lambda_1 = -4, \qquad \lambda_2 = -2 + j3, \qquad \lambda_3 = -2 - j3.$$

5.  Consider the system

$$\begin{bmatrix} x_1(k+1) \\ x_2(k+1) \end{bmatrix} = \begin{bmatrix} 0 & 1 \\ -\frac{1}{8} & -\frac{3}{4} \end{bmatrix} \begin{bmatrix} x_1(k) \\ x_2(k) \end{bmatrix},$$

$$y(k) = [1 \quad 0] \begin{bmatrix} x_1(k) \\ x_2(k) \end{bmatrix}.$$

If

$$y(0) = 1 \quad \text{and} \quad y(1) = 1,$$

what is $\mathbf{x}(0)$?

6.  Consider the system

$$\begin{bmatrix} x_1(k+1) \\ x_2(k+1) \end{bmatrix} = \begin{bmatrix} 0 & 1 \\ -\frac{1}{8} & -\frac{3}{4} \end{bmatrix} \begin{bmatrix} x_1(k) \\ x_2(k) \end{bmatrix},$$

$$y(k) = [1 \quad 0] \begin{bmatrix} x_1(k) \\ x_2(k) \end{bmatrix}.$$

If

$$y(1) = 1 \quad \text{and} \quad y(2) = 1,$$

what is $\mathbf{x}(0)$?

7.  Consider the system

$$\begin{bmatrix} x_1(k+1) \\ x_2(k+1) \end{bmatrix} = \begin{bmatrix} 0 & 1 \\ -0.16 & 1 \end{bmatrix} \begin{bmatrix} x_1(k) \\ x_2(k) \end{bmatrix},$$

$$y(k) = [1 \quad 0] \begin{bmatrix} x_1(k) \\ x_2(k) \end{bmatrix}.$$

If

$$y(0) = 1 \quad \text{and} \quad y(1) = 1,$$

what is $\mathbf{x}(0)$?

8.  Let

$$\dot{\mathbf{x}}(k+1) = \mathbf{F}\mathbf{x}(k),$$

$$y(k) = \mathbf{h}^T \mathbf{x}(k),$$

with

$$\mathbf{F} = \begin{bmatrix} 0 & 1 & 1 \\ 0 & 0 & 1 \\ 0 & 0 & 0 \end{bmatrix} \qquad \mathbf{c}^T = [1 \quad 0 \quad 0].$$

First determine if the system is completely observable. Now suppose we miss the first measurement $y(0)$. Can we still find $\mathbf{x}(0)$?

9. Let

$$\dot{\mathbf{x}}(k+1) = \mathbf{F}\mathbf{x}(k),$$
$$y(k) = \mathbf{h}^T\mathbf{x}(k),$$

with

$$\mathbf{F} = \begin{bmatrix} 0 & 1 \\ 0 & 0 \end{bmatrix} \mathbf{c}^T = [1 \quad 0].$$

First determine if the system is completely observable. Now suppose we miss the first measurement $y(0)$. Can we still find $\mathbf{x}(0)$?

10. $\mathbf{A} = \begin{bmatrix} -1 & \alpha_1 & 0 \\ 0 & -1 & \alpha_2 \\ 0 & 0 & -1 \end{bmatrix} \quad \mathbf{b} = \begin{bmatrix} 1 \\ 1 \\ 0 \end{bmatrix} \quad \mathbf{c}^T = [1 \quad 1 \quad 0],$

where $\alpha_1$ and $\alpha_2$ can be either zero or one. Determine what values $\alpha_1$ and $\alpha_2$ have to assume to make the system completely controllable. Is $\mathbf{b}$ really a factor in determining the controllability?

11. Let

$$\dot{\mathbf{x}} = \mathbf{A}\mathbf{x} + \mathbf{b}u.$$

And let the system be completely controllable. Let

$$\mathcal{C} = [\mathbf{b} \quad \mathbf{A}\mathbf{b} \quad \mathbf{A}^2\mathbf{b} \quad \ldots \quad \mathbf{A}^{n-1}\mathbf{b}].$$

Using the transformation

$$\mathbf{x} = \mathbf{S}\mathbf{z}, \qquad \mathbf{S} = \mathcal{C},$$

show that for the system

$$\dot{\mathbf{z}} = [\mathbf{S}^{-1}\mathbf{A}\mathbf{S}]\mathbf{z} + [\mathbf{S}^{-1}\mathbf{b}]u,$$

it has the form:

$$\mathbf{S}^{-1}\mathbf{A}\mathbf{S} = \begin{bmatrix} 0 & 0 & \ldots & 0 & \ldots & -\alpha_0 \\ 1 & 0 & \ldots & 0 & \ldots & -\alpha_1 \\ 0 & 1 & 0 & \ldots & 0 & -\alpha_3 \\ \vdots & 0 & \ddots & 0 & 0 & \vdots \\ 0 & \vdots & 0 & 1 & 0 & -\alpha_{n-2} \\ 0 & 0 & \ldots & 0 & 1 & -\alpha_{n-1} \end{bmatrix} \quad \mathbf{S}^{-1}\mathbf{b} = \begin{bmatrix} 1 \\ 0 \\ \vdots \\ 0 \end{bmatrix}.$$

12. Let

$$\dot{\mathbf{x}} = \mathbf{A}\mathbf{x} + \mathbf{b}u,$$
$$y = \mathbf{c}^T\mathbf{x}.$$

And let the system be completely observable.

$$
\text{Let } \mathcal{O} =
\begin{bmatrix}
\mathbf{c}^T \\
\mathbf{c}^T \mathbf{A} \\
\mathbf{c}^T \mathbf{A}^2 \\
\vdots \\
\mathbf{c}^T \mathbf{A}^i \\
\vdots \\
\mathbf{c}^T \mathbf{A}^{n-1}
\end{bmatrix}.
$$

Using the transformation

$$
\mathbf{z} = \mathcal{O}\mathbf{x},
$$

show that the system

$$
\dot{\mathbf{z}} = [\mathcal{O}\mathbf{A}\mathcal{O}^{-1}]\mathbf{z} + [\mathbf{Sb}]u,
$$

$$
y = \bar{\mathbf{c}}^T \mathbf{z}
$$

has the form:

$$
\mathcal{O}\mathbf{A}\mathcal{O}^{-1} =
\begin{bmatrix}
0 & 1 & 0 & 0 & \cdots & 0 & 0 \\
0 & 0 & 1 & 0 & \cdots & 0 & 0 \\
\vdots & \vdots & 0 & 1 & \cdots & \vdots & \vdots \\
0 & 0 & \vdots & \vdots & \ddots & 0 & 0 \\
0 & 0 & 0 & \cdots & 0 & 1 & 0 \\
0 & 0 & 0 & 0 & \cdots & 0 & 1 \\
-\alpha_0 & -\alpha_1 & -\alpha_3 & \cdots & -\alpha_{n-3} & -\alpha_{n-2} & -\alpha_{n-1}
\end{bmatrix},
$$

$$
\mathcal{O}\mathbf{b} =
\begin{bmatrix}
\bar{b}_1 \\
\bar{b}_2 \\
\vdots \\
\bar{b}_n
\end{bmatrix},
$$

$$
\bar{\mathbf{c}}^T = [1 \quad 0 \quad 0 \quad \cdots \quad 0].
$$

13. Let

$$
\begin{bmatrix}
x_1(k+1) \\
x_2(k+1) \\
x_3(k+1)
\end{bmatrix}
=
\begin{bmatrix}
0 & 1 & 0 \\
0 & 0 & 1 \\
-a_0 & -a_1 & -a_2
\end{bmatrix}
\begin{bmatrix}
x_1(k) \\
x_2(k) \\
x_3(k)
\end{bmatrix}
$$

$$
= \mathbf{c}^T = [1 \quad 0 \quad 0]
\begin{bmatrix}
x_1(k) \\
x_2(k) \\
x_3(k)
\end{bmatrix}.
$$

Given $y(0)$, $y(1)$, and $y(2)$, find $\mathbf{x}(0)$. Can you generalize to the $n$-dimensional case?

14. Consider the equations

$$\begin{bmatrix} x_1 \\ x_2 \\ x_3 \end{bmatrix} = \begin{bmatrix} 1 & 0 & 0 \\ 0 & 1 & 0 \\ 0 & 0 & 0 \end{bmatrix} \begin{bmatrix} y_1 \\ y_2 \\ y_3 \end{bmatrix}.$$

If **x** can be any point in three space, make a three-dimensional sketch of all values of **y** that solve these equations.

15. Consider the equations

$$\begin{bmatrix} x_1 \\ x_2 \\ x_3 \end{bmatrix} = \begin{bmatrix} 1 & 0 & 0 \\ 0 & 0 & 0 \\ 0 & 0 & 0 \end{bmatrix} \begin{bmatrix} y_1 \\ y_2 \\ y_3 \end{bmatrix}.$$

If **x** can be any point in three space, make a three-dimensional sketch of all values of **y** that solve these equations.

16. Consider the equations

$$\begin{bmatrix} x_1(k+1) \\ x_2(k+2) \\ x_3(k+3) \end{bmatrix} = \begin{bmatrix} -1 & 0 & 1 \\ 0 & -0.5 & 1 \\ 0 & 0 & -0.2 \end{bmatrix} \begin{bmatrix} x_1(k) \\ x_2(k) \\ x_3(k) \end{bmatrix} + \begin{bmatrix} 1 \\ 0 \\ 1 \end{bmatrix} u(k).$$

First check to see if the system in controllable. Then check to see of there are any points in the state space for which the system can be driven to the origin in one control step. Repeat for two control steps.

17. Consider the system

$$\begin{bmatrix} x_1(k+1) \\ x_2(k+1) \end{bmatrix} = \begin{bmatrix} 0 & 1 \\ -\frac{1}{8} & -\frac{3}{4} \end{bmatrix} \begin{bmatrix} x_1(k) \\ x_2(k) \end{bmatrix},$$

$$y(k) = [1 \quad 0] \begin{bmatrix} x_1(k) \\ x_2(k) \end{bmatrix}.$$

If

$$y(1) = 1 \quad \text{and} \quad y(2) = 1,$$

what is **x**(0)?

# FURTHER READINGS

Arnold, V. I. 1973. *Ordinary Differential Equations.* Cambridge, Mass.: MIT Press.

Brogan, William L. 1985. *Modern Control Theory,* 2nd ed. Englewood Cliffs, N.J.: Prentice-Hall.

D'Azzo, John J., and Constantine H. Houpis. 1988. *Linear Control System Design, Conventional and Modern.* New York: McGraw-Hill.

Kailath, Thomas. 1980. *Linear Systems,* Englewood Cliffs, N.J.: Prentice-Hall.

Luenberger, David G. 1979. *Introduction to Dynamics Systems: Theory, Models, Applications,* Vol. 1. New York: John Wiley & Sons.

Ogata, Katsuhiko. 1967. *State Space Analysis of Control Systems*. Englewood Cliffs, N.J.: Prentice-Hall.

Ogata, K. 1970. *Modern Control Engineering*. Englewood Cliffs, N.J.: Prentice-Hall.

Porter, William A. 1966. *Modern Foundations of Systems Engineering*. New York: Macmillan.

Saucedo, R., and E. E. Schiring. 1968. *Introduction to Continuous and Digital Control Systems*. New York: MacMillan.

Schultz, Donald G., and James L. Melsa. 1967. *State Functions and Linear Control Systems*. New York: McGraw-Hill.

# 20 Chapter

# The Controller/Observer

## 20.1 | INTRODUCTION

In this chapter we introduce the notion of an observer, a difference equation that produces an estimate of the actual state of the system at each time step. The reason for introducing the observer is that pole placement with full state feed back, as discussed in Chapter 19, is not very practical. First, for an $n$-dimensional system, it requires $n$ measurements, which, in turn, means $n$ transducers. Such a controller would be both expensive and bulky. Further, to be implementable all the states would have to be measurable. Even if such a state model formulation could be obtained, it might not be the preferred formulation. Therefore, the approach in this chapter will be to replace the actual state measurements in our control

$$u(k) = -\mathbf{k}^T \mathbf{x}(k),$$

with "observations" $\hat{\mathbf{x}}(k)$ of the states, making the control law

$$u(k) = -\mathbf{k}^T \hat{\mathbf{x}}(k).$$

It is natural to ask whether we can do this. The answer is yes, and this chapter is devoted to showing first, how, and then why we can substitute the observations for the actual measurements and still get a valid control.

Having solved the regulator problem using observations of the states rather than measurments of the states, we next turn our attention to the more interesting, and difficult, problem of making a sytem track a reference input signal. We will consider two approaches to the tracking problem. One will be a natural extension of our results for the regulator problem. The second approach will be radically different but will prove to be superior to the first approach in several ways.

## 20.2 | PREDICTION OBSERVER

The general idea of an observer is shown in Fig. 20.1 in block diagram form. The question, of course, is what we should put in the box labeled "observer." There are many answers to this question, some of which we will explore in this chapter.

**Figure 20.1** | Block diagram of a regulator with an observer.

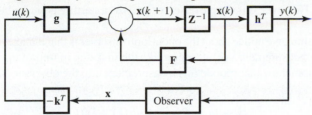

We begin answering the question by building the simplest possible observer, called an open-loop observer.

Suppose that we can model a given physical system with *perfect* accuracy by the difference equations

$$\mathbf{x}(k+1) = \mathbf{F}\mathbf{x}(k) + \mathbf{g}u(k),$$

$$y(k) = \mathbf{h}^T\mathbf{x}(k). \tag{20.1}$$

The assumption of perfect accuracy may seem unrealistic, but with a little reflection we see that we have made basically this same assumption throughout this book. We never know the model of the plant perfectly, but the control strategies we have developed in previous chapters were robust enough that, even though our plant model was not exact, the control we developed still worked well. The same is true in the present case.

Suppose further that we know $\mathbf{x}(0)$, the initial state of the system. Then, with these two assumptions we can simply write

$$\hat{\mathbf{x}}(k+1) = \mathbf{F}\hat{\mathbf{x}}(k) + \mathbf{g}u(k),$$

$$\hat{y}(k) = \mathbf{h}^T\hat{\mathbf{x}}(k). \tag{20.2}$$

Figure 20.2 provides a block diagram model of the system and the so-called "observer." Given that the assumptions we have made are true, then

$$\hat{y}(k) = y(k), \qquad k = 0, 1, 2, \ldots.$$

This open-loop observer is, of course, based on overly optimistic assumptions. We have already made the very strong assumption that the mathematical model represents

**Figure 20.2** | Open-loop observer.

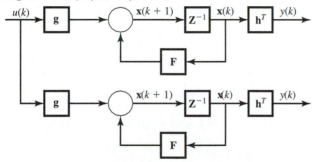

the system exactly. To add to that the assumption that the initial state is known exactly is unrealistic. However, this simple observer gives us a starting point for building better observers.

The first thing we notice about the open-loop observer is that it makes no use of our scalar output measurement $y(k)$. It seems like the first step in improving the observer should be to somehow incorporate this measurement into the observer. Therefore, we write

$$\hat{\mathbf{x}}(k + 1) = \mathbf{F}\hat{\mathbf{x}}(k) + \mathbf{g}u(k) + \mathbf{l}y(k), \qquad\qquad \textbf{[20.3]}$$

$$\hat{y}(k) = \mathbf{h}^T\hat{\mathbf{x}}(k).$$

We note that $\mathbf{l}$ must be an $n \times 1$ *column* vector since $y$ is a scalar function.

We now define

$$\mathbf{e}(k) \overset{\Delta}{=} \mathbf{x}(k) - \hat{\mathbf{x}}(x).$$

Then

$$\mathbf{e}(k + 1) = \mathbf{x}(k + 1) - \hat{\mathbf{x}}(k + 1)$$

$$= \mathbf{F}\mathbf{x}(k) + \mathbf{g}u(k) - [\mathbf{F}\hat{\mathbf{x}}(k) + \mathbf{g}u(k) + \mathbf{l}y(k)]$$

$$= \mathbf{F}[\mathbf{x}(k) - \hat{\mathbf{x}}(k)] - \mathbf{l}y(k)$$

$$= \mathbf{F}\,\mathbf{e}(k) - \mathbf{l}y(k).$$

We now have a state difference equation for $\mathbf{e}(k)$, but it is "forced" by the term $\mathbf{l}y(k)$. What we really need is an unforced or homogeneous error equation whose eigenvalues can be placed arbitrarily. We could then choose eigenvalues that would drive $\mathbf{e}(k)$ to zero quickly, thereby giving us accurate estimates of the states of the plant. To achieve this goal we note that

$$y(k) = \mathbf{h}^T\mathbf{x}(k).$$

If we substitute this last expression into the error equation we obtain

$$\mathbf{e}(k + 1) = \mathbf{F}\,\mathbf{e}(k) - \mathbf{l}[\mathbf{h}^T\mathbf{x}(k)].$$

This expression provides a clue as to how to get the desired homogenous equation. That is, we need to add another term to our observer equation, namely $\mathbf{l}\mathbf{h}^T\hat{\mathbf{x}}(k)$ that will enable us to write

$$\mathbf{l}\mathbf{h}^T\mathbf{x}(k) - \mathbf{l}\mathbf{h}^T\hat{\mathbf{x}}(k) = \mathbf{l}\mathbf{h}^T[\mathbf{x}(k) - \hat{\mathbf{x}}(k)]$$

$$= \mathbf{l}\mathbf{h}^T\mathbf{e}(k).$$

In other words, we go back to Eq. [20.3] and replace $y(k)$ by $y(k) - \mathbf{h}^T\hat{\mathbf{x}}(k)$. The error equation then becomes

$$\mathbf{e}(k + 1) = \mathbf{F}\,\mathbf{e}(k) - \mathbf{l}[y(k) - \mathbf{h}^T\hat{\mathbf{x}}(k)]$$

$$= \mathbf{F}\,\mathbf{e}(k) - \mathbf{l}[\mathbf{h}^T\mathbf{x}(k) - \mathbf{h}^T\hat{\mathbf{x}}(k)]$$

$$= \mathbf{F}\,\mathbf{e}(k) - \mathbf{l}\mathbf{h}^T[\mathbf{x}(k) - \hat{\mathbf{x}}(k)]$$

$$= [\mathbf{F} - \mathbf{l}\mathbf{h}^T]\mathbf{e}(k),$$

and we can now apply the pole placement technique that we proposed and validated in Chapter 19 to the homogeneous system

$$\mathbf{e}(k + 1) = [\mathbf{F} - \mathbf{lh}^T]\mathbf{e}(k) \qquad [20.4]$$

to ensure that $\mathbf{e}(k) \to \mathbf{0}$ as $k \to \infty$. The matrix $\mathbf{l}$ plays the same role $\mathbf{k}^T$ played in our development of pole placement in Chapter 19. That is, $\mathbf{l}$ provides $n$ design variables that we can use to place the eigenvalues of the error state model of Eq. [20.4] *wherever* we want them.

It is worth noting at that point that since

$$\mathbf{h}^T \hat{\mathbf{x}} = \hat{y}(k),$$

the observer equation could be written

$$\hat{\mathbf{x}}(k + 1) = \mathbf{F}\hat{\mathbf{x}}(k) + \mathbf{g}u(k) + \mathbf{l}[y(k) - \hat{y}(k)]. \qquad [20.5]$$

In other words, the prediction observer is simply the original plant, plus the term $\mathbf{l}[y(k) - \hat{y}(k)]$. This lends some plausibility to the observer equation since adding the difference between the actual output and the estimated output seems like a useful way to make use of the measurement of the output.

For computational purposes, we would like to reduce the observer equation to the simplest form. Thus, if in Eq. [20.3] we replace $y(k)$ by

$$y(k) - \mathbf{h}^T \hat{\mathbf{x}}(k),$$

and $u(k)$ by

$$-\mathbf{k}^T \hat{\mathbf{x}}(k),$$

we obtain

$$
\begin{aligned}
\hat{x}(k + 1) &= \mathbf{F}\hat{\mathbf{x}}(k) + \mathbf{g}u(k) + \mathbf{l}[y(k) - \mathbf{h}^T \hat{\mathbf{x}}(k)] \\
&= \mathbf{F}\hat{\mathbf{x}}(k) + \mathbf{g}[-\mathbf{k}^T \hat{\mathbf{x}}(k)] + \mathbf{l}[y(k) - \mathbf{h}^T \hat{\mathbf{x}}(k)] \\
&= [\mathbf{F} - \mathbf{gk}^T - \mathbf{lh}^T]\hat{\mathbf{x}}(k) + \mathbf{l}y(k).
\end{aligned}
$$

The pair of equations

$$\hat{\mathbf{x}}(k + 1) = [\mathbf{F} - \mathbf{gk}^T - \mathbf{lh}^T]\hat{\mathbf{x}}(k) + \mathbf{l}y(k), \qquad [20.6]$$

$$u(k) = -\mathbf{k}^T \hat{\mathbf{x}}(k), \qquad [20.7]$$

are called the "controller/observer" equations. These are the equations that would actually be implemented on a computer. The arguments in the second equation can be either $k + 1$ or $k$ as long as they are the same on *both* sides of the equation. The first equation (the observer equation) generates $\hat{\mathbf{x}}(k + 1)$, the observation used to generate the control applied at time $k + 1$. That is,

$$u(k + 1) = -\mathbf{k}^T \hat{\mathbf{x}}(k + 1).$$

The equations are normally written in the form of Eq. [20.6]. This convention may seem a little strange since what we are doing is using the observer equation to generate $u(k + 1)$ *based on measurements taken at* time $k$. That said, an example now seems appropriate.

**EXAMPLE 20.2.1**

Consider again the system of Example 19.2.1, namely,

$$G_p(s) = \frac{a}{s(s+a)},$$

for which we derived the discrete state model

$$\begin{bmatrix} x_1(k+1) \\ x_2(k+1) \end{bmatrix} = \begin{bmatrix} 1 & \frac{1}{a}(1 - e^{-aT}) \\ 0 & e^{-aT} \end{bmatrix} \begin{bmatrix} x_1(k) \\ x_2(k) \end{bmatrix} + \begin{bmatrix} \frac{aT+e^{-aT}-1}{a} \\ 1 - e^{-aT} \end{bmatrix} u(k),$$

$$y(k) = [1 \quad 0] \begin{bmatrix} x_1(k) \\ x_2(k) \end{bmatrix}.$$

We will first find a controller and then design an observer to go with the controller.

We want the control law to produce dominant complex poles (eigenvalues) with $\omega_n = 4$ rad/s and $\zeta = 0.8$. For $T = 0.1$ s and $a = 2$. The desired dominant poles in the $z$ plane are at

$$z = e^{(-3.2 \pm j2.4)(0.1)}$$

$$= e^{-0.32}[\cos(0.24) \pm j \sin(0.24)]$$

$$= 0.7503 \pm j0.1726$$

We then use the equations for finding $\mathbf{k}^T$ that we developed in Example 19.4.2, namely,

$$\begin{bmatrix} g_1 & g_2 \\ f_{22}g_1 - f_{12}g_2 & f_{11}g_2 - f_{21}g_1 \end{bmatrix} \begin{bmatrix} k_1 \\ k_2 \end{bmatrix} = \begin{bmatrix} \text{Trace}(\mathbf{F}) - 2a \\ \text{Det}(\mathbf{F}) - (a^2 + b^2) \end{bmatrix},$$

where $a = 0.7053$ and $b = 0.1726$.

For the system under study the equations are

$$\begin{bmatrix} 0.009365 & 0.1813 \\ -0.008762 & 0.1813 \end{bmatrix} \begin{bmatrix} k_1 \\ k_2 \end{bmatrix} \begin{bmatrix} 0.4081 \\ 0.2914 \end{bmatrix},$$

with solution

$$\mathbf{k}^T = [6.4335 \quad 1.9187].$$

We now wish to build an observer for this same system, so that we can apply the control law without measuring both states. That is, we will substitute the observation of the second state for the measurement of that state. Whether we can do this successfully is still an open question, at this juncture. We will give an affirmative answer to this question shortly.

For the moment, we concentrate on the error equation for a second-order system. Our goal is to work out a general solution symbolically for this system. The error equation is

$$\mathbf{e}(k+1) = [\mathbf{F} - \mathbf{l}\mathbf{h}^T]\mathbf{e}(k)$$

$$= \left[ \begin{bmatrix} f_{11} & f_{12} \\ f_{21} & f_{22} \end{bmatrix} - \begin{bmatrix} \ell_1 \\ \ell_2 \end{bmatrix} [h_1 \quad h_2] \right] \begin{bmatrix} e_1(k) \\ e_2(k) \end{bmatrix}$$

$$= \left[ \begin{bmatrix} f_{11} & f_{12} \\ f_{21} & f_{22} \end{bmatrix} - \begin{bmatrix} \ell_1 h_1 & \ell_1 h_2 \\ \ell_2 h_1 & \ell_2 h_2 \end{bmatrix} \right] \begin{bmatrix} e_1(k) \\ e_2(k) \end{bmatrix}$$

$$= \begin{bmatrix} f_{11} - \ell_1 h_1 & f_{12} - \ell_1 h_2 \\ f_{21} - \ell_2 h_1 & f_{22} - \ell_2 h_2 \end{bmatrix} \begin{bmatrix} e_1(k) \\ e_2(k) \end{bmatrix}.$$

Having gone through the manipulations in detail, we see that the subscript notation makes it possible to write this result down quite easily from memory.

We next compute the characteristic equation.

$$\text{Det}[z\mathbf{I} - [\mathbf{F} - \mathbf{l}\mathbf{h}^T]] = \text{Det} \left[ \begin{bmatrix} z & 0 \\ 0 & z \end{bmatrix} - \begin{bmatrix} f_{11} - \ell_1 h_1 & f_{12} - \ell_1 h_2 \\ f_{21} - \ell_2 h_1 & f_{22} - \ell_2 h_2 \end{bmatrix} \right]$$

$$= \text{Det} \begin{bmatrix} z - (f_{11} - \ell_1 h_1) & -(f_{12} - \ell_1 h_2) \\ -(f_{21} - \ell_2 h_1) & z - (f_{22} - \ell_2 h_2) \end{bmatrix}$$

$$= [z - (f_{11} - \ell_1 h_1)][z - (f_{22} - \ell_2 h_2)]$$

$$\quad - [(f_{21} - \ell_2 h_1)(f_{12} - \ell_1 h_2)]$$

$$= z^2 - (f_{11} + f_{22} - \ell_1 h_1 - \ell_2 h_2)z$$

$$\quad + [(f_{11} f_{22} - f_{11} \ell_2 h_2 - f_{22} \ell_1 h_1 + \ell_1 \ell_2 h_1 h_2)$$

$$\quad - (f_{12} f_{21} - f_{12} \ell_2 h_1 - f_{21} \ell_1 h_2 + \ell_1 \ell_2 h_1 h_2)]$$

$$= z^2 - (\text{Trace}\{\mathbf{F}\} - \ell_1 h_1 - \ell_2 h_2)z$$

$$\quad + [\text{Det}\{\mathbf{F}\} + (f_{21} h_2 - f_{22} h_1)\ell_1 + (f_{12} h_1 - f_{11} h_2)\ell_2].$$

Note that the equation is very similar to that in Example 19.4.2.

Then the characteristic equation of the closed-loop system is

$$z^2 - (\text{Trace}\{\mathbf{F}\} - \ell_1 h_1 - \ell_2 h_2)z$$

$$+ [\text{Det}\{\mathbf{F}\} + (f_{21} h_2 - f_{22} h_1)\ell_1 + (f_{12} h_1 - f_{11} h_2)\ell_2] = 0.$$

[20.8]

Remember that the $f_{ij}$ and $h_i$, $i, j = 1, 2$, are *known* constants. Thus, the only unknowns in this symbolic representation of the characteristic equation are $\ell_1$ and $\ell_2$. Note also that the cross terms involving $\ell_1 \ell_2$ drop out. This is the case for a system of any dimension. We know that they should based on our development of the controllable canonical form in Chapter 19.

Having achieved the symbolic representation of the characteristic equation for the error system, the next goal is to find the *desired* characteristic equation in terms of numbers that represent the poles of the error system. To that end, recall that the dominant poles of the closed system are

$$s = -3.2 \pm j2.4$$

in the $s$ plane. Because we want the observations to converge rapidly to the actual state values we choose a double pole at $s = -16$. This means that the time constant of the error system is one fifth that of the closed-loop system. The equivalent poles in the $z$ plane are at

$$z = e^{sT} = e^{(-16)(0.1)} = 0.2019.$$

Then the *desired* characteristic equation is

$$c(z) = (z - p_o)^2 = z^2 - 2p_o + p_o^2.$$

This produces an error system that is critically damped. For $p_o = 0.2019$, the characteristic equation becomes.

$$z^2 - 0.4038z + 0.0408 = 0. \tag{20.9}$$

Equating coefficients in Eqs. [20.8] and [20.9] yields

$$\text{Trace}\{\mathbf{F}\} - \ell_1 h_1 - \ell_2 h_2 = 2p_o,$$

$$\text{Det}\{\mathbf{F}\} + (f_{21}h_2 - f_{22}h_1)\ell_1 + (f_{12}h_1 - f_{11}h_2)\ell_2 = p_o^2.$$

These equations can be rearranged as

$$\begin{bmatrix} h_1 & h_2 \\ f_{22}h_1 - f_{21}h_2 & f_{11}h_2 - f_{12}h_1 \end{bmatrix} \begin{bmatrix} \ell_1 \\ \ell_2 \end{bmatrix} = \begin{bmatrix} \text{Trace}\{\mathbf{F}\} - 2p_o \\ \text{Det}\{\mathbf{F}\} - p_o^2 \end{bmatrix}. \tag{20.10}$$

For this particular example,

$$f_{21} = h_2 = 0 \quad \text{and} \quad h_1 = 1,$$

and the equations simplify to

$$\begin{bmatrix} 1 & 0 \\ f_{22} & -f_{12} \end{bmatrix} \begin{bmatrix} \ell_1 \\ \ell_2 \end{bmatrix} = \begin{bmatrix} \text{Trace}\{\mathbf{F}\} - 2p_o \\ \text{Det}\{\mathbf{F}\} - p_o^2 \end{bmatrix}.$$

The quantities on the right-hand side are all known. Then, the first equation yields

$$\ell_1 = 1 + e^{-0.2} - 2e^{-1.6} = 1.4149.$$

The second equation yields

$$\ell_2 = \frac{p_o^2 - f_{11}f_{22} + f_{22}\ell_1}{f_{12}} = \frac{(e^{-1.6})^2 - (1)(e^{-0.2}) + e^{-0.2}(1.4149)}{0.5(1 - e^{-0.2})} = 4.198.$$

Then for

$$\mathbf{l} = \begin{bmatrix} 1.4149 \\ 4.1980 \end{bmatrix},$$

the error system will have a double pole at $z = 0.2019$. The controller/observer is

$$\hat{\mathbf{x}}(k+1) = \mathbf{F}^O \hat{\mathbf{x}}(k) + \mathbf{l}y(k),$$

$$u(k) = -\mathbf{k}^T \hat{\mathbf{x}}(k),$$

where

$$\mathbf{F}^O = [\mathbf{F} - \mathbf{lh}^T - \mathbf{gk}^T].$$

Only the arithmetic details remain. We find that

$$[\mathbf{F} - \mathbf{lh}^T - \mathbf{gk}^T] = \begin{bmatrix} 1 & 0.09063 \\ 0 & 0.8187 \end{bmatrix} - \begin{bmatrix} 1.4149 \\ 4.1980 \end{bmatrix} [1 \quad 0]$$

$$- \begin{bmatrix} 0.009365 \\ 0.1812 \end{bmatrix} [6.4335 \quad 1.9187]$$

$$= \begin{bmatrix} -0.4752 & 0.07267 \\ -5.3642 & 0.4709 \end{bmatrix}.$$

We have included the details of the calculations for a couple of reasons. First, the numbers are quite small, and we need to ensure that the computations are done with sufficient precision to prevent round off errors. Second, it is clear that for higher-order systems, we need to write some simple programs in MATLAB or an equivalent language, so that these calculations can be done routinely without error.

The controller/ŏbserver equations that will be implemented on the microprocessor are

$$\hat{\mathbf{x}}(k+1) = \begin{bmatrix} -0.475190 & 0.072665 \\ -5.364205 & 0.470925 \end{bmatrix} \hat{\mathbf{x}}(k) + \begin{bmatrix} 1.4149 \\ 4.1980 \end{bmatrix} y(k),$$

$$u(k) = -[6.433532 \quad 1.918726] \begin{bmatrix} y(k-1) \\ \hat{x}_2(k) \end{bmatrix}.$$

Note that in the controller equation we use $y(k-1)$ in place of $\hat{x}_1(k)$. The reasoning for this is as follows. When we generate the control for time $k$ it will be based on the *measurement* of $y(k-1)$. From the observer we get both $\hat{x}_1 = \hat{y}$ and $\hat{x}_2$, but since, at time $k-1$, we *measured* the output, we use the measuement in preference to the observation $\hat{y}$. It may not seem right to have $y(k-1)$ paired with $x_2(k)$ on the right-hand side of the equation for $u$, but that is the correct thing to do. Remember, the measurement to produce the control at time $k$ is made at time $k-1$. As we remarked earlier the conventional way of writing the controller/observer equations can be confusing.

Since the computation of $\hat{\mathbf{x}}(k)$ is based on $y(k-1)$, given the speed of modern microprocessors the observation $\hat{\mathbf{x}}(k)$ and the control $u(k)$ will be available almost immediately after time $k-1$. The control $u(k)$ will then be held in memory until time $k$, at which time it is output to the D/A converter. This raises the following question. Since we will again measure $y(k)$ at time $k$, why not make the control

$$u(k) = -[6.433532 \quad 1.918726] \begin{bmatrix} y(k) \\ \hat{x}_2(k) \end{bmatrix},$$

and take advantage of the more recent information? Doing so results in a slight asynchronization since we cannot instantaneously measure $y(k)$ and then put out the control, but the delay is so slight that it has no significant effect on the control. Further,

**Figure 20.3 |** System response using prediction observer.

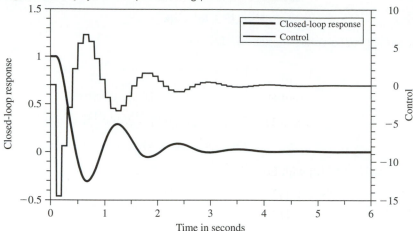

the control will be asynchronous anyway, because the time it takes the computer program to contact the D/A converter and download an output is never exactly the same. The idea of substituting $y(k)$ for $y(k-1)$ is leading us toward what is called a *current* observer, which will be discussed in Section 20.4.

The response of the system for

$$\begin{bmatrix} x_1(0) \\ x_2(0) \end{bmatrix} = \begin{bmatrix} 1 \\ 0 \end{bmatrix}$$

and using $y(k-1)$ in the control is shown in Fig. 20.3. The response is a little oscillatory, but certainly stable.

## 20.3 | SEPARATION THEOREM

Having developed what is called a prediction observer, and substituted the observations for actual measurements in the control law, we now consider the validity of this control law. More specifically, is it reasonable to replace measurements of the state with estimates of the state in the controller? To answer that question, consider letting

$$u(k) = -\mathbf{k}^T \hat{\mathbf{x}}(k).$$

Substituting this control into the original plant equation, and combining with the error equation yields

$$\mathbf{x}(k+1) = \mathbf{F}\mathbf{x}(k) - \mathbf{g}\mathbf{k}^T \hat{\mathbf{x}}(k),$$
$$\mathbf{e}(k+1) = [\mathbf{F} - \mathbf{l}\mathbf{h}^T]\mathbf{e}(k). \qquad \textbf{[20.11]}$$

Now

$$\mathbf{e}(k) = \mathbf{x}(k) - \hat{\mathbf{x}}(k),$$

which we can rewrite as

$$\hat{\mathbf{x}}(k) = \mathbf{x}(k) - \mathbf{e}(k).$$

Substituting this latter expression in the first of Eqs. [20.11] yields

$$\mathbf{x}(k + 1) = \mathbf{F}\mathbf{x}(k) - \mathbf{g}\mathbf{k}^T[\mathbf{x}(k) - \mathbf{e}(k)]$$

$$= [\mathbf{F} - \mathbf{g}\mathbf{k}^T]\mathbf{x}(k) + \mathbf{g}\mathbf{k}^T\mathbf{e}(k). \qquad \text{[20.12]}$$

Combining Eq. [20.12] with Eq. [20.11] yields

$$\begin{bmatrix} \mathbf{x}(k + 1) \\ \mathbf{e}(k + 1) \end{bmatrix} = \begin{bmatrix} \mathbf{F} - \mathbf{g}\mathbf{k}^T & \mathbf{g}\mathbf{k}^T \\ \mathbf{0} & \mathbf{F} - \mathbf{l}\mathbf{h}^T \end{bmatrix} \begin{bmatrix} \mathbf{x}(k) \\ \mathbf{e}(k) \end{bmatrix}. \qquad \text{[20.13]}$$

Equation [20.13] is a $2n \times 2n$ homogeneous system in the state vector

$$\tilde{\mathbf{x}}(k) = \begin{bmatrix} \mathbf{x}(k) \\ \mathbf{e}(k) \end{bmatrix}.$$

The characteristic polynomial is

$$\text{Det} \begin{bmatrix} [z\mathbf{I} - (\mathbf{F} - \mathbf{g}\mathbf{k}^T)] & -\mathbf{g}\mathbf{k}^T \\ \mathbf{0} & [z\mathbf{I} - (\mathbf{F} - \mathbf{l}\mathbf{h}^T)] \end{bmatrix}$$

$$= \text{Det}[z\mathbf{I} - (\mathbf{F} - \mathbf{g}\mathbf{k}^T)] \times \text{Det}[z\mathbf{I} - (\mathbf{F} - \mathbf{l}\mathbf{h}^T)].$$

Thus, the characteristic equation is

$$\text{Det}[z\mathbf{I} - (\mathbf{F} - \mathbf{g}\mathbf{k}^T)] \times \text{Det}[z\mathbf{I} - (\mathbf{F} - \mathbf{l}\mathbf{h}^T)] = 0. \qquad \text{[20.14]}$$

Equation [20.14] is a most remarkable result. It says that we can substitute the observations for perfect measurements without changing the eigenvalues of the closed-loop system or the eigenvalues of the error system. Thus, we can:

1.  Design the controller $\mathbf{k}^T$ as if we had perfect measurements.
2.  Place the eigenvalues of the error system where we want them using $\mathbf{l}$.
3.  Put the observations in place of the measurements in the controller.

This is a straightforward three-step process that has to be done only once. Rather remarkable.

## 20.4 | CURRENT OBSERVER

The prediction observer developed in the previous section has the advantage that the control at time $k + 1$ is calculated using information available at time $k$. Thus, the entire intersample period $T$ is available to compute the control. Typically, the sampling rate $f_{sample}$ is between 10 and 1000 Hz.

Given the current speed of microprocessors, A/D converters, and D/A converters, the control can be computed and output to the plant in microseconds. Thus, the control to be applied at time $k + 1$ is available very shortly after time $k$. Most of the intersample period is spent waiting for time $k + 1$ to arrive so the control signal can be output. For that reason, it seems reasonable to consider an observer based on more current information.

As it stands now, for the *prediction* observer

$$u(k) = -[6.4335 \quad 1.9187] \begin{bmatrix} y(k-1) \\ \hat{x}_2(k) \end{bmatrix}.$$

As discussed previously $\hat{x}_2(k)$ is based on the measurement $y(k-1)$. It would seem that we could improve the control if we could base the estimate of $\hat{x}_2(k)$ on $y(k)$. Such an observer is called a "current" observer. Our next goal is to design a current observer that yields a homogeneous error equation.

Perhaps the most intuitive place to start is simply to replace $y(k)$ and $\hat{y}(k)$ in Eq. [20.5] by $y(k + 1)$ and $\hat{y}(k + 1)$. That is,

$$\hat{\mathbf{x}}(k+1) = \mathbf{F}\hat{\mathbf{x}}(k) + \mathbf{g}u(k) + \mathbf{l}[y(k+1) - \hat{y}(k+1)]. \qquad \textbf{[20.15]}$$

As before, the goal is to achieve a homogeneous error equation. We first rewrite Eq. [20.15] as

$$
\begin{aligned}
\hat{\mathbf{x}}(k+1) &= \mathbf{F}\hat{\mathbf{x}}(k) + \mathbf{g}u(k) + \mathbf{l}[y(k+1) - \hat{y}(k+1)] \\
&= \mathbf{F}\hat{\mathbf{x}}(k) + \mathbf{g}u(k) + \mathbf{l}[y(k+1) - \mathbf{h}^T[\mathbf{F}\hat{\mathbf{x}}(k) + \mathbf{g}u(k)]] \\
&= [\mathbf{F} - \mathbf{l}\mathbf{h}^T\mathbf{F}]\hat{\mathbf{x}}(k) + \mathbf{l}y(k+1) + [\mathbf{I} - \mathbf{l}\mathbf{h}^T]\mathbf{g}u(k).
\end{aligned}
$$

Then repeating our error system analysis, we have

$$
\begin{aligned}
\mathbf{e}(k+1) &= \mathbf{x}(k+1) - \hat{\mathbf{x}}(k+1) \\
&= \mathbf{F}\mathbf{x}(k) + \mathbf{g}u(k) - \{[\mathbf{F} - \mathbf{l}\mathbf{h}^T\mathbf{F}]\hat{\mathbf{x}}(k) + \mathbf{l}y(k+1) + [\mathbf{I} - \mathbf{l}\mathbf{h}^T]\mathbf{g}u(k)\} \\
&= \mathbf{F}\mathbf{x}(k) + \mathbf{g}u(k) - [\mathbf{F} - \mathbf{l}\mathbf{h}^T\mathbf{F}]\hat{\mathbf{x}}(k) \\
&\quad - \mathbf{l}[\mathbf{h}^T[\mathbf{F}\mathbf{x}(k) + \mathbf{g}u(k)]] - [\mathbf{I} - \mathbf{l}\mathbf{h}^T]\mathbf{g}u(k) \\
&= [\mathbf{F} - \mathbf{l}\mathbf{h}^T\mathbf{F}][\mathbf{x}(k) - \hat{\mathbf{x}}(k)] + \mathbf{g}u(k) - \mathbf{l}\mathbf{h}^T\mathbf{g}u(k) - [\mathbf{I} - \mathbf{l}\mathbf{h}^T]\mathbf{g}u(k) \\
&= [\mathbf{F} - \mathbf{l}\mathbf{h}^T\mathbf{F}]\mathbf{e}(k) + [\mathbf{I} - \mathbf{l}\mathbf{h}^T]\mathbf{g}u(k) - [\mathbf{I} - \mathbf{l}\mathbf{h}^T]\mathbf{g}u(k) \\
&= [\mathbf{F} - \mathbf{l}\mathbf{h}^T\mathbf{F}]\mathbf{e}(k).
\end{aligned}
$$

Thus, the current observer of Eq. [20.15] results in a homogeneous error equation

$$\mathbf{e}(k+1) = [\mathbf{F} - \mathbf{l}\mathbf{h}^T\mathbf{F}]\mathbf{e}(k), \qquad \textbf{[20.16]}$$

to which we can apply the pole placement theorem, to ensure that $\mathbf{e}(k) \to \mathbf{0}$ as $k \to \infty$.

Going back to the observer equation and making the substitution

$$u(k) = -\mathbf{k}^T\hat{\mathbf{x}}(k),$$

yields

$$
\begin{aligned}
\hat{\mathbf{x}}(k+1) &= [\mathbf{F} - \mathbf{lh}^T\mathbf{F}]\hat{\mathbf{x}}(k) + [\mathbf{I} - \mathbf{lh}^T]\mathbf{g}u(k) + \mathbf{l}y(k+1) \\
&= [\mathbf{F} - \mathbf{lh}^T\mathbf{F}]\hat{\mathbf{x}}(k) - [\mathbf{I} - \mathbf{lh}^T]\mathbf{g}\mathbf{k}^T\hat{\mathbf{x}}(k) + \mathbf{l}y(k+1) \\
&= [\mathbf{F} - [\mathbf{I} - \mathbf{lh}^T]\mathbf{g}\mathbf{k}^T - \mathbf{lh}^T\mathbf{F}]\hat{\mathbf{x}}(k) + \mathbf{l}y(k+1).
\end{aligned}
$$

Finally, the controller/observer equations are

$$\hat{\mathbf{x}}(k+1) = [\mathbf{F} - [\mathbf{I} - \mathbf{lh}^T]\mathbf{g}\mathbf{k}^T - \mathbf{lh}^T\mathbf{F}]\hat{\mathbf{x}}(k) + \mathbf{l}y(k+1), \qquad \textbf{[20.17]}$$

$$u(k) = -\mathbf{k}^T\hat{\mathbf{x}}(k). \qquad \textbf{[20.18]}$$

Note that the observer plant matrix is a modified form of that for the prediction observer. In the case of the prediction observers,

$$\mathbf{F}^O = \mathbf{F} - \mathbf{g}\mathbf{k}^T - \mathbf{lh}^T,$$

while for the current observer

$$\mathbf{F}^O = \mathbf{F} - [\mathbf{I} - \mathbf{lh}^T]\mathbf{g}\mathbf{k}^T - \mathbf{lh}^T\mathbf{F}.$$

Thus, in the current observer $\mathbf{g}\mathbf{k}^T$ is multiplied on the left by $[\mathbf{I} - \mathbf{lh}^T]$ and $\mathbf{lh}^T$ is multiplied on the right by $\mathbf{F}$.

---

**EXAMPLE 20.4.1**

Consider again the system of Examples 19.2.1 and 20.2.1, with

$$G_p(s) = \frac{a}{s(s+a)},$$

with $a = 2$. We use the same control law as in Example 20.2.1 so for $T = 0.1$ s, the discrete state model is again

$$
\begin{bmatrix} x_1(k+1) \\ x_2(k+1) \end{bmatrix} = \begin{bmatrix} 1 & 0.09063 \\ 0 & 0.81873 \end{bmatrix} \begin{bmatrix} x_1(k) \\ x_2(k) \end{bmatrix} + \begin{bmatrix} 0.009365 \\ 0.181269 \end{bmatrix} u(k),
$$

and the controller

$$\mathbf{k}^T = [6.4335 \quad 1.9187].$$

We now turn our attention to the observer equation. For the prediction observer, the error equation is

$$\mathbf{e}(k+1) = [\mathbf{F} - \mathbf{lh}^T\mathbf{F}]\mathbf{e}(k).$$

A useful intermediate step is to let

$$\bar{\mathbf{h}}^T = \mathbf{h}^T \mathbf{F}$$

$$= [h_1 \quad h_2] \begin{bmatrix} f_{11} & f_{12} \\ f_{21} & f_{22} \end{bmatrix}$$

$$= [h_1 f_{11} + h_2 f_{21} \quad h_1 f_{12} + h_2 f_{22}]$$

$$= [\bar{h}_1 \quad \bar{h}_2].$$

Having computed $\bar{\mathbf{h}}^T$, the equations developed for the prediction observer can now be used with $\bar{\mathbf{h}}^T$ substituted for $\mathbf{h}^T$. That is,

$$\begin{bmatrix} \bar{h}_1 & \bar{h}_2 \\ f_{22}\bar{h}_1 - f_{21}\bar{h}_2 & f_{11}\bar{h}_2 - f_{12}\bar{h}_1 \end{bmatrix} \begin{bmatrix} \ell_1 \\ \ell_2 \end{bmatrix} = \begin{bmatrix} \text{Trace}\{\mathbf{F}\} - 2p_o \\ \text{Det}\{\mathbf{F}\} - p_o^2 \end{bmatrix}. \qquad \textbf{[20.19]}$$

There is another, more subtle reason for computing $\bar{\mathbf{h}}^T$. If the pair $(\mathbf{F}, \bar{\mathbf{h}}^T)$ is not completely observable, then we cannot build the observer. It is *not enough* for the pair $(\mathbf{F}, \mathbf{h}^T)$ to be observable, we must have $(\mathbf{F}, \bar{\mathbf{h}}^T)$ observable.

For the system being studied in this example,

$$\bar{\mathbf{h}}^T = [f_{11} \quad f_{12}] = [1 \quad 0.09063].$$

Note that

$$\bar{\mathcal{O}} = \begin{bmatrix} \bar{\mathbf{h}}^T \\ \bar{\mathbf{h}}^T \mathbf{F} \end{bmatrix} = \begin{bmatrix} 1 & 0.09063 \\ 1 & 0.16484 \end{bmatrix}$$

is of full rank. Thus, we will be able to build the observer.

As before, the dominant poles of the closed system in the $s$ plane are

$$s = -3.2 \pm j2.4.$$

Because we want the observations to converge rapidly to the actual state values we again choose a double pole at $s = -16$. Making this choice enables a comparison with Example 20.2.1. Thus, the equivalent poles in the $z$ plane are, again, at

$$z = e^{sT} e^{(-16)(0.1)} = 0.2019,$$

and, as before for the prediction observer, the *desired* characteristic equation is

$$z^2 - 0.4038z + 0.04076 = 0, \qquad \textbf{[20.20]}$$

so that

$$2p_o = 0.4038 \quad \text{and} \quad p_o^2 = 0.04076.$$

Substituting into Eq. [20.19], yields

$$\begin{bmatrix} 1 & 0.09063 \\ 0.8187 & 0 \end{bmatrix} \begin{bmatrix} \ell_1 \\ \ell_2 \end{bmatrix} = \begin{bmatrix} 1.8187 - 0.4038 \\ 0.81873 - 0.04076 \end{bmatrix}.$$

The solution of these equations is

$$\mathbf{l} = \begin{bmatrix} 0.9502 \\ 5.1275 \end{bmatrix},$$

yielding an error system with a double pole at $z = 0.2019$.

As can be seen the matrix $\mathbf{l}$ for the current observer is similar to the matrix $\mathbf{l}$ found earlier for the prediction observer. This makes sense because $\bar{\mathbf{h}}^T$ is very similar to $\mathbf{h}^T$.

The controller/observer is then

$$\hat{\mathbf{x}}(k+1) = [\mathbf{F} - [\mathbf{I} - \mathbf{lh}^T]\mathbf{gk}^T - \mathbf{lh}^T\mathbf{F}]\hat{\mathbf{x}}(k) + \mathbf{l}y(k+1),$$

$$u(k) = -\mathbf{k}^T\hat{\mathbf{x}}(k).$$

The arithmetic details are

$$[\mathbf{I} - \mathbf{lh}^T]\mathbf{gk}^T = \left\{ \begin{bmatrix} 1 & 0 \\ 0 & 1 \end{bmatrix} - \begin{bmatrix} 0.9502 \\ 5.1275 \end{bmatrix} [1 \quad 0] \right\}$$

$$\times \begin{bmatrix} 0.009365 \\ 0.181269 \end{bmatrix} [6.4335 \quad 1.9187]$$

$$= \begin{bmatrix} 0.002300 & 0.000895 \\ 0.8573 & 0.2557 \end{bmatrix},$$

and

$$\mathbf{lh}^T\mathbf{F} = \begin{bmatrix} 0.9502 \\ 5.1275 \end{bmatrix} [1 \quad 0] \begin{bmatrix} 1 & 0.09064 \\ 0 & 0.8187 \end{bmatrix}$$

$$= \begin{bmatrix} 0.9502 & 0.08612 \\ 5.1275 & 0.4647 \end{bmatrix}.$$

Then,

$$[\mathbf{F} - [\mathbf{I} - \mathbf{lh}^T]\mathbf{gk}^T - \mathbf{lh}^T\mathbf{F}] = \begin{bmatrix} 0.04679 & 0.003618 \\ -5.3642 & 0.09834 \end{bmatrix}.$$

Finally, the controller/observer equations are

$$\hat{\mathbf{x}}(k+1) = \begin{bmatrix} 0.04679 & 0.003618 \\ -5.9847 & 0.09834 \end{bmatrix} \hat{\mathbf{x}}(k) + \begin{bmatrix} 0.9502 \\ 5.1275 \end{bmatrix} y(k+1),$$

$$u(k) = -[6.4335 \quad 1.9187] \begin{bmatrix} y(k) \\ \hat{x}_2(k) \end{bmatrix}.$$

Note, again, that in the controller equation we use $y(k)$ in place of $\hat{x}_1(k)$, since there is no sense in using an observation when we have the measurement. In the current observer, however, $\hat{x}_2(k)$ is based on $y(k)$ rather than $y(k-1)$.

The response for an initial condition of

$$\begin{bmatrix} x_1(0) \\ x_2(0) \end{bmatrix} = \begin{bmatrix} 1 \\ 0 \end{bmatrix}$$

is shown in Fig. 20.4. As we can see, the response with the current observer is better than that for the prediction observer.

**Figure 20.4** | System response with current observer.

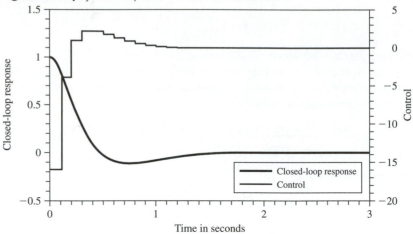

### 20.5 | EQUIVALENT TRANSFER FUNCTION

For the single-input, single-output (SISO) case it is possible to represent the controller observer as a feedback compensator. The development here is for the prediction observer, but it could just as well have been done for the current observer.

The prediction controller/observer equations, repeated here for convenience, are

$$\hat{\mathbf{x}}(k+1) = [\mathbf{F} - \mathbf{g}\mathbf{k}^T - \mathbf{l}\mathbf{h}^T]\hat{\mathbf{x}}(k) + \mathbf{l}y(k), \qquad \textbf{[20.21]}$$

$$u(k) = -\mathbf{k}^T\hat{\mathbf{x}}(k). \qquad \textbf{[20.22]}$$

Applying the $\mathcal{Z}$ transform to these equations, assuming zero initial conditions, yields

$$z\hat{\mathbf{x}}(z) = [\mathbf{F} - \mathbf{g}\mathbf{k}^T - \mathbf{l}\mathbf{h}^T]\hat{\mathbf{x}}(z) + \mathbf{l}y(z) \qquad \textbf{[20.23]}$$

$$u(z) = -\mathbf{k}^T\hat{\mathbf{x}}(z). \qquad \textbf{[20.24]}$$

Solving the first of these transformed equations for $\hat{\mathbf{x}}(z)$ gives

$$\hat{\mathbf{x}}(z) = [z\mathbf{I} - (\mathbf{F} - \mathbf{g}\mathbf{k}^T - \mathbf{l}\mathbf{h}^T)]^{-1}\mathbf{l}y(z).$$

Substituting this expression for $\hat{\mathbf{x}}(z)$ into the expression for $u(z)$ results in

$$u(z) = -\mathbf{k}^T[z\mathbf{I} - (\mathbf{F} - \mathbf{g}\mathbf{k}^T - \mathbf{l}\mathbf{h}^T)]^{-1}\mathbf{l}y(z),$$

or

$$\frac{u(z)}{y(z)} = -\mathbf{k}^T[z\mathbf{I} - (\mathbf{F} - \mathbf{g}\mathbf{k}^T - \mathbf{l}\mathbf{h}^T)]^{-1}\mathbf{l}. \qquad \textbf{[20.25]}$$

The right-hand side of Eq. [20.25] is the transfer function between the output and the input. That is, we have the system shown in Fig. 20.5 with

$$H(z) = -\mathbf{k}^T[z\mathbf{I} - (\mathbf{F} - \mathbf{g}\mathbf{k}^T - \mathbf{l}\mathbf{h}^T)]^{-1}\mathbf{l}.$$

**Figure 20.5 |** Equivalent block diagram for prediction controller/observer.

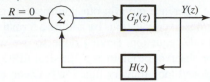

**EXAMPLE 20.5.1**

Consider the prediction controller observer of Example 20.2.1. For this example,

$$[\mathbf{F} - \mathbf{lh}^T - \mathbf{gk}^T] = \begin{bmatrix} -0.47519 & 0.072665 \\ -5.364205 & 0.470925 \end{bmatrix}.$$

Then,

$$\text{Adj}[z\mathbf{I} - [\mathbf{F} - \mathbf{lh}^T - \mathbf{gk}^T]] = \begin{bmatrix} z - 0.470925 & -0.072665 \\ 5.364205 & z + 0.47519 \end{bmatrix},$$

and

$$\text{Det}\{z\mathbf{I} - [\mathbf{F} - \mathbf{lh}^T - \mathbf{gk}^T]\} = (z + 0.47519)(z - 0.470925)$$

$$+ (5.364205)(0.072665)$$

$$= z^2 + 0.0042654z + 0.16601.$$

We next form

$$\mathbf{k}^T \text{Adj}[z\mathbf{I} - [\mathbf{F} - \mathbf{lh}^T - \mathbf{gk}^T]]\mathbf{l} = 17.16(z - 0.7722).$$

Then, finally,

$$H(z) = -\frac{\mathbf{k}^T \text{Adj}\{z\mathbf{I} - (\mathbf{F} - \mathbf{lh}^T - \mathbf{gk}^T)\}}{\text{Det}\{z\mathbf{I} - (\mathbf{F} - \mathbf{lh}^T - \mathbf{gk}^T)\}}$$

$$= -\frac{17.16(z - 0.7722)}{(z + 0.00213 - j0.4074)(z + 0.00213 + j0.4074)}.$$

## 20.6 | REFERENCE INPUT

In this section we add a reference input to our system. The analysis so far has been for what is called the regulator problem, where the goal of the control is to bring the system back to steady state.

We will investigate two approaches. The first approach will be a natural extension of our development for the regulator problem. This first approach will work, but as we will see, it is difficult to implement for systems of large dimension. The second approach is very different but proves to be superior, in most respects, to the first approach.

## 20.7 | EQUIVALENT $T_c(z)$

One way to include the reference input in our control strategy is simply to modify the *regulator* controller/observer equations by adding a term to the observer equation and a term to the controller equation. Having done so, we will then show that we can recast the controller observer problem as a classical SISO problem. We do so by finding an equivalent closed-loop transfer function between the reference input and the output. We then determine the coefficients of both the numerator and denominator of this equivalent closed-loop transfer function to obtain the desired performance. We will use the prediction observer in the following discussion.

For the prediction observer, our equations become

$$\hat{\mathbf{x}}(k+1) = [\mathbf{F} - \mathbf{g}\mathbf{k}^T - \mathbf{l}\mathbf{h}^T]\hat{\mathbf{x}}(k) + \mathbf{l}y(k) + \mathbf{m}r(k),$$

$$u(k) = -\mathbf{k}^T\hat{\mathbf{x}}(k) + dr(k),$$

where $\mathbf{m}$ is an $n \times 1$ column matrix and $d$ is a scalar. A block diagram of this system is shown in Fig. 20.6.

We begin our analysis by simplifying the notation somewhat. Let

$$\mathbf{F}^{\mathcal{O}} \triangleq \mathbf{F} - \mathbf{g}\mathbf{k}^T - \mathbf{l}\mathbf{h}^T.$$

Then, the controller/observer equations can be written

$$\hat{\mathbf{x}}(k+1) = \mathbf{F}^{\mathcal{O}}\hat{\mathbf{x}}(k) + \mathbf{l}y(k) + \mathbf{m}r(k),$$

$$u(k) = -\mathbf{k}^T\hat{\mathbf{x}}(k) + dr(k). \qquad \textbf{[20.26]}$$

We next take the $\mathcal{Z}$ transform of the original plant equations:

$$\mathbf{x}(k+1) = \mathbf{F}\mathbf{x}(k) + \mathbf{g}u(k),$$

$$y(k) = \mathbf{h}^T\mathbf{x}(k),$$

to obtain

$$z\mathbf{x}(z) = \mathbf{F}\mathbf{x}(z) + \mathbf{g}u(z),$$

$$y(z) = \mathbf{h}^T\mathbf{x}(z).$$

We use zero initial conditions, as is the normal case in deriving transfer functions.

**Figure 20.6 |** Feedback control with reference input.

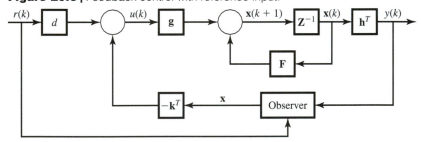

The first equation yields

$$\mathbf{x}(z) = [z\mathbf{I} - \mathbf{F}]^{-1}\mathbf{g}u(z),$$

which can then be substituted into the second equation to give

$$y(z) = \mathbf{h}^T\mathbf{x}(z) = \mathbf{h}^T[z\mathbf{I} - \mathbf{F}]^{-1}\mathbf{g}u(z).$$

This, in turn, leads to

$$\frac{y(z)}{u(z)} = \mathbf{h}^T[z\mathbf{I} - \mathbf{F}]^{-1}\mathbf{g}.$$

This is the transfer function of the plant, that is, $G_p'(z)$. The reader should be certain that he understands why the right-hand side is a transfer function. Recall that

$$[z\mathbf{I} - \mathbf{F}]^{-1} = \frac{\text{Adj}\{z\mathbf{I} - \mathbf{F}\}}{\text{Det}\{z\mathbf{I} - \mathbf{F}\}}.$$

Now $\text{Adj}\{z\mathbf{I} - \mathbf{F}\}$ is an $n \times n$ matrix, each of whose *elements* is a polynomial in $z$ with real coefficients. Since $\mathbf{h}^T$ is a $1 \times n$ row matrix and $\mathbf{g}$ an $n \times 1$ column matrix, then

$$\alpha(z) = \mathbf{h}^T\text{Adj}\{z\mathbf{I} - \mathbf{F}\}\mathbf{g}$$

is a $1 \times 1$ *scalar* polynomial in $z$. Similarly,

$$\beta(z) = \text{Det}[z\mathbf{I} - \mathbf{F}]$$

is also a polynomial in $z$. Thus

$$\frac{y(z)}{u(z)} = \frac{\mathbf{h}^T\text{Adj}\{z\mathbf{I} - \mathbf{F}\}\mathbf{g}}{\text{Det}\{z\mathbf{I} - \mathbf{F}\}} = \frac{\alpha(z)}{\beta(z)}$$

is a ratio of polynomials in $z$.

We next apply the $\mathcal{Z}$ transform to the controller/observer equations. Since we assumed $\mathbf{x}(0) = \mathbf{0}$, we will also assume $\hat{\mathbf{x}}(0) = \mathbf{0}$. Then,

$$z\hat{\mathbf{x}}(z) = \mathbf{F}^{\mathcal{O}}\hat{\mathbf{x}}(z) + \mathbf{l}y(z) + \mathbf{m}r(z),$$

$$u(z) = -\mathbf{k}^T\hat{\mathbf{x}}(z) + dr(z).$$

The first of these equations can be solved for $\hat{\mathbf{x}}(x)$, yielding

$$\hat{\mathbf{x}}(z) = [z\mathbf{I} - \mathbf{F}^{\mathcal{O}}]^{-1}\mathbf{l}y(z) + [z\mathbf{I} - \mathbf{F}^{\mathcal{O}}]^{-1}\mathbf{m}r(z).$$

Substituting this expression into the controller equation yields

$$u(z) = -\{\mathbf{k}^T[z\mathbf{I} - \mathbf{F}^{\mathcal{O}}]^{-1}\mathbf{l}\}y(z) - \{\mathbf{k}^T[z\mathbf{I} - \mathbf{F}^{\mathcal{O}}]^{-1}\mathbf{m}\}r(z) + dr(z).$$

As before, we can simplify the notation by letting

$$\mathbf{k}^T[z\mathbf{I} - \mathbf{F}^{\mathcal{O}}]^{-1}\mathbf{m} = \frac{\mathbf{k}^T\text{Adj}[z\mathbf{I} - \mathbf{F}^{\mathcal{O}}]\mathbf{m}}{\text{Det}[z\mathbf{I} - \mathbf{F}^{\mathcal{O}}]} = \frac{\gamma(z)}{\eta(z)},$$

$$\mathbf{k}^T[z\mathbf{I} - \mathbf{F}^{\mathcal{O}}]^{-1}\mathbf{l} = \frac{\mathbf{k}^T\text{Adj}[z\mathbf{I} - \mathbf{F}^{\mathcal{O}}]\mathbf{l}}{\text{Det}[z\mathbf{I} - \mathbf{F}^{\mathcal{O}}]} = \frac{\phi(z)}{\eta(z)},$$

where

$$\beta(z) = \text{Det}[z\mathbf{I} - \mathbf{F}] \quad \text{and} \quad \eta(z) = \text{Det}[z\mathbf{I} - \mathbf{F}^O].$$

Then

$$u(z) = -\frac{\phi(z)}{\eta(z)} y(z) - \frac{\gamma(z)}{\eta(z)} r(z) + dr(z). \qquad \text{[20.27]}$$

We next substitute Eq. [20.27] into our expression for $\mathbf{x}(z)$ to obtain

$$\mathbf{x}(z) = [z\mathbf{I} - \mathbf{F}]^{-1} \mathbf{g} u(z)$$

$$= [z\mathbf{I} - \mathbf{F}]^{-1} \mathbf{g} \left[ -\frac{\phi(z)}{\eta(z)} y(z) - \frac{\gamma(z)}{\eta(z)} r(z) + dr(z) \right].$$

Then,

$$y(z) = \mathbf{h}^T \mathbf{x}(z)$$

$$= \mathbf{h}^T [z\mathbf{I} - \mathbf{F}]^{-1} \mathbf{g} \left[ -\frac{\phi(z)}{\eta(z)} y(z) - \frac{\gamma(z)}{\eta(z)} r(z) + dr(z) \right]$$

$$= \frac{\alpha(z)}{\beta(z)} \left[ -\frac{\phi(z)}{\eta(z)} y(z) - \frac{\gamma(z)}{\eta(z)} r(z) + dr(z) \right].$$

This last expression can be rearranged as

$$y(z) + \frac{\alpha(z)}{\beta(z)} \frac{\phi(z)}{\eta(z)} y(z) = \frac{\alpha(z)}{\beta(z)} \left[ d - \frac{\gamma(z)}{\eta(z)} \right] r(z),$$

or

$$\frac{y(z)}{r(z)} = \frac{[d - \gamma(z)/\eta(z)][\alpha(z)/\beta(z)]}{1 + [\alpha(z)/\beta(z)][\phi(z)/\eta(z)]}, \qquad \text{[20.28]}$$

or finally

$$\frac{y(z)}{r(z)} = \frac{d[\eta(z) - \gamma(z)/d]\alpha(z)}{\beta(z)\eta(z) + \alpha(z)\phi(z)}. \qquad \text{[20.29]}$$

Thus, the scalar $d$ that we introduced ends up as the gain of the equivalent transfer function. Further,

$$\eta(z) - \frac{\gamma(z)}{d} = \text{Det}\{[z\mathbf{I} - \mathbf{F}^O]\} - \mathbf{k}^T \text{Adj}[z\mathbf{I} - \mathbf{F}^O]\bar{\mathbf{m}},$$

where $\bar{\mathbf{m}} = \mathbf{m}/d$. This means the two new terms we introduced, $\mathbf{m}r(z)$ and $dr(z)$ affect only the *numerator* of the equivalent transfer function.

In addition,

$$\beta(z)\eta(z) + \alpha(z)\phi(z) = \alpha_c(z)\alpha_e(z),$$

where

$$\alpha_c(z) = \text{Det}[z\mathbf{I} - (\mathbf{F} - \mathbf{g}\mathbf{k}^T)] \quad \text{and} \quad \alpha_e(z) = \text{Det}[z\mathbf{I} - (\mathbf{F} - \mathbf{l}\mathbf{h}^T)].$$

This last statement may not seem very obvious, but we can prove it in an indirect way by finding $y(k)$ for the regulator problem. That is, we consider the $\mathcal{Z}$ transform of Eqs. [20.6], namely,

$$z\hat{\mathbf{x}}(z) - z\hat{\mathbf{x}}(0) = [\mathbf{F} - \mathbf{g}\mathbf{k}^T - \mathbf{l}\mathbf{h}^T]\hat{\mathbf{x}}(z) + \mathbf{l}y(z)$$

$$= \mathbf{F}^O\hat{\mathbf{x}}(z) + \mathbf{l}y(z),$$

$$u(z) = -\mathbf{k}^T\hat{\mathbf{x}}(z).$$

We include the initial condition here because in the regulator problem, there is no reference input, just a nonzero initial condition that causes the system to exhibit its dynamics. Thus, all we can obtain is an expression for $y(k)$. However, we know from our previous development of the separation theorem for the prediction observer that the denominator of the expression we obtain for $Y(z)$ will be

$$\mathrm{Det}\{z\mathbf{I} - [\mathbf{F} - \mathbf{g}\mathbf{k}^T]\} \times \mathrm{Det}\{z\mathbf{I} - [\mathbf{F} - \mathbf{l}\mathbf{h}^T]\}.$$

Continuing our development of an expression for $Y(z)$, we see that the first of the two preceding equations can be solved for $\hat{\mathbf{x}}(z)$, yielding

$$\hat{\mathbf{x}}(z) = z[z\mathbf{I} - \mathbf{F}^O]^{-1}\hat{\mathbf{x}}(0) + [z\mathbf{I} - \mathbf{F}^O]^{-1}\mathbf{l}y(z).$$

Substituting this last equation in the equation for $u(z)$ yields

$$u(z) = -\mathbf{k}^T\{z[z\mathbf{I} - \mathbf{F}^O]^{-1}\hat{\mathbf{x}}(0) + [z\mathbf{I} - \mathbf{F}^O]^{-1}\mathbf{l}y(z)\}.$$

Then applying the $\mathcal{Z}$ transform to

$$\mathbf{x}(k+1) = \mathbf{F}\mathbf{x}(k) + \mathbf{g}u(k)$$

yields

$$z\mathbf{x}(z) - z\mathbf{x}(0) = \mathbf{F}\mathbf{x}(z) + \mathbf{g}u(z),$$

which when solved for $\mathbf{x}(z)$, yields

$$\mathbf{x}(z) = z[z\mathbf{I} - \mathbf{F}]^{-1}\mathbf{x}(0) + [z\mathbf{I} - \mathbf{F}]^{-1}\mathbf{g}u(z),$$

and we can then write

$$y(z) = \mathbf{h}^T\mathbf{x}(z)$$

$$= \mathbf{h}^T\{z[z\mathbf{I} - \mathbf{F}]^{-1}\mathbf{x}(0) + [z\mathbf{I} - \mathbf{F}]^{-1}\mathbf{g}u(z)\}$$

$$= \mathbf{h}^T[z[z\mathbf{I} - \mathbf{F}]^{-1}\mathbf{x}(0)]$$

$$\quad + [\mathbf{h}^T[z\mathbf{I} - \mathbf{F}]^{-1}\mathbf{g}][-\mathbf{k}^T z[z\mathbf{I} - \mathbf{F}^O]^{-1}\hat{\mathbf{x}}(0) - \mathbf{k}^T[z\mathbf{I} - \mathbf{F}^O]^{-1}\mathbf{l}y(z)]$$

$$= \{\mathbf{h}^T z[z\mathbf{I} - \mathbf{F}]^{-1}\mathbf{x}(0)\} - \{\mathbf{h}^T[z\mathbf{I} - \mathbf{F}]^{-1}\mathbf{g}\}\{\mathbf{k}^T z[z\mathbf{I} - \mathbf{F}^O]^{-1}\hat{\mathbf{x}}(0)\}$$

$$\quad - \{\mathbf{h}^T[z\mathbf{I} - \mathbf{F}]^{-1}\mathbf{g}\}\{\mathbf{k}^T[z\mathbf{I} - \mathbf{F}^O]^{-1}\mathbf{l}y(z)\}.$$

Thus,

$$y(z) = \frac{\{\mathbf{h}^T z[z\mathbf{I} - \mathbf{F}]^{-1}\mathbf{x}(0)\} - \{\mathbf{h}^T[z\mathbf{I} - \mathbf{F}]^{-1}\mathbf{g}\}\{\mathbf{k}^T z[z\mathbf{I} - \mathbf{F}^O]^{-1}\hat{\mathbf{x}}(0)\}}{1 + \{\mathbf{h}^T[z\mathbf{I} - \mathbf{F}]^{-1}\mathbf{g}\}\{\mathbf{k}^T[z\mathbf{I} - \mathbf{F}^O]^{-1}\mathbf{l}\}},$$

or

$$y(z) = \frac{\{\mathbf{h}^T z[z\mathbf{I} - \mathbf{F}]^{-1}\mathbf{x}(0)\} - \{\mathbf{h}^T [z\mathbf{I} - \mathbf{F}]^{-1}\mathbf{g}\}\{\mathbf{k}^T z[z\mathbf{I} - \mathbf{F}^{\mathcal{O}}]^{-1}\hat{\mathbf{x}}(0)\}}{1 + \alpha(z)\phi(z)/\beta(z)\eta(z)}.$$

The denominator of the right-hand side of this last equation is *identical* to the denominator of the equivalent transfer function for the reference input case. Thus, once we clear fractions, the characteristic polynomial for the case of a reference input will be the same as the characteristic polynomial for the *regulator* problem, and we know from the analysis leading to the separation theorem that the characteristic polynomial for the regulator case is

$$p(z) = \alpha_c(z)\alpha_e(z),$$

where

$$\alpha_c z = \mathrm{Det}\{z\mathbf{I} - [\mathbf{F} - \mathbf{g}\mathbf{k}^T]\} \quad \text{and} \quad \alpha_e(z) = \mathrm{Det}\{z\mathbf{I} - [\mathbf{F} - \mathbf{l}\mathbf{h}^T]\}.$$

Remarkably, when we add the reference input, we do *not* change the eigenvalues of the system, but merely gain the ability to adjust the *zeros* of the equivalent transfer function. This means that the design of a controller/observer with a reference input is very similar to the direct design methods developed in Chapter 15, and we can use some of the results from that developemnt to design a closed-loop transfer function that meets certain criteria such as time to peak, percent overshoot, and steady state error.

As preparation for such a design, we work out symbolically in Example 20.7.1 the form of the closed-loop transfer function for a system of dimension two.

**EXAMPLE 20.7.1**

Consider the system

$$\mathbf{x}(k + 1) = \mathbf{F}\mathbf{x}(k) + \mathbf{g}u(k),$$

$$y(k) = \mathbf{h}^T\mathbf{x}(k),$$

with

$$\mathbf{F} = \begin{bmatrix} f_{11} & f_{12} \\ f_{21} & f_{22} \end{bmatrix} \qquad \mathbf{g} = \begin{bmatrix} g_1 \\ g_2 \end{bmatrix} \qquad \mathbf{h}^T = [h_1 \quad h_2].$$

Then,

$$F^{\mathcal{O}} \triangleq [\mathbf{F} - \mathbf{g}\mathbf{k}^T - \mathbf{l}\mathbf{h}^T]$$

$$= \begin{bmatrix} f_{11} & f_{12} \\ f_{21} & f_{22} \end{bmatrix} - \begin{bmatrix} g_1 \\ g_2 \end{bmatrix} [k_1 \quad k_2] - \begin{bmatrix} \ell_1 \\ \ell_2 \end{bmatrix} [h_1 \quad h_2]$$

$$= \begin{bmatrix} f_{11} & f_{12} \\ f_{21} & f_{22} \end{bmatrix} - \begin{bmatrix} g_1 k_1 & g_1 k_2 \\ g_2 k_1 & g_2 k_2 \end{bmatrix} - \begin{bmatrix} \ell_1 h_1 & \ell_1 h_2 \\ \ell_2 h_1 & \ell_2 h_2 \end{bmatrix}$$

$$= \begin{bmatrix} f_{11}^{\mathcal{O}} & f_{12}^{\mathcal{O}} \\ f_{21}^{\mathcal{O}} & f_{22}^{\mathcal{O}} \end{bmatrix},$$

where

$$f_{11}^O = f_{11} - g_1 k_1 - \ell_1 h_1, \qquad f_{12}^O = f_{12} - g_1 k_2 - \ell_1 h_2,$$
$$f_{21}^O = f_{21} - g_2 k_1 - \ell_2 h_1, \qquad f_{22}^O = f_{22} - g_2 k_2 - \ell_2 h_2.$$

Then,

$$\eta(z) = \text{Det}[z\mathbf{I} - \mathbf{F}^O]$$

$$= \text{Det}\begin{bmatrix} z - f_{11}^O & - f_{12}^O \\ - f_{21}^O & z - f_{22}^O \end{bmatrix}$$

$$= z^2 - \left(f_{11}^O + f_{22}^O\right)z + \left(f_{11}^O f_{22}^O - f_{12}^O f_{21}^O\right),$$

and

$$\gamma(z) = \mathbf{k}^T \text{Adj}\,[z\mathbf{I} - \mathbf{F}^O]\mathbf{m}$$

$$= [k_1 \quad k_2]\begin{bmatrix} z - f_{22}^O & f_{12}^O \\ f_{21}^O & z - f_{11}^O \end{bmatrix}\begin{bmatrix} m_1 \\ m_2 \end{bmatrix}$$

$$= [k_1 \quad k_2]\begin{bmatrix} m_1 z - m_1 f_{22}^O + m_2 f_{12}^O \\ m_1 f_{21}^O + m_2 z - m_2 f_{11}^O \end{bmatrix}$$

$$= (k_1 m_1 + k_2 m_2)z + \left(k_1 m_2 f_{12}^O + k_2 m_1 f_{21}^O - k_1 m_1 f_{22}^O - k_2 m_2 f_{11}^O\right).$$

We also find

$$\alpha(z) = \mathbf{h}^T \text{Adj}[z\mathbf{I} - \mathbf{F}]\mathbf{g}$$

$$= (h_1 g_1 + h_2 g_2)z + (h_1 g_2 f_{12} + h_2 g_1 f_{21} - h_1 g_1 f_{22} - h_2 g_2 f_{11})$$

We include this formula even though in most cases we will not need it. That is because $\alpha(z)$ is simply the numerator of $G_p'(z)$, and there are other ways to find this, such as using a table of $\mathcal{Z}$ transforms. Since we already know that the denominator factors into $\alpha_c(z)\alpha_e(z)$, we need to find only $\gamma(z)$ and $\eta(z)$.

We next construct

$$\frac{\gamma(z)}{d} = \frac{(k_1 m_1 + k_2 m_2)z + \left(k_1 m_2 f_{12}^O + k_2 m_1 f_{21}^O - k_1 m_1 f_{22}^O - k_2 m_2 f_{11}^O\right)}{d}$$

$$= (k_1 \bar{m}_1 + k_2 \bar{m}_2)z + \left(k_1 \bar{m}_2 f_{12}^O + k_2 \bar{m}_1 f_{21}^O - k_1 \bar{m}_1 f_{22}^O - k_2 \bar{m}_2 f_{11}^O\right),$$

where

$$\bar{m}_i = \frac{m_i}{d}, \qquad i = 1, 2.$$

We are now in a position to construct the equivalent transfer function

$$\frac{y(z)}{r(z)} = \frac{d[\eta(z) - \gamma(z)/d]\alpha(z)}{\beta(z)\eta(z) + \alpha(z)\phi(z)}.$$

Then,

$$
\begin{aligned}
\eta(z) - \frac{\gamma(z)}{d} &= \left[ z^2 - \left( f_{11}^O + f_{22}^O \right) z + f_{11}^O f_{22}^O - f_{12}^O f_{21}^O - (k_1 \bar{m}_1 + k_2 \bar{m}_2) z \right] \\
&\quad - \left( k_1 \bar{m}_2 f_{12}^O + k_2 \bar{m}_1 f_{21}^O - k_1 \bar{m}_1 f_{22}^O - k_2 \bar{m}_2 f_{11}^O \right) \\
&= z^2 - [k_1 \bar{m}_1 + k_2 \bar{m}_2 + \text{Trace}(\mathbf{F}^O)] z \\
&\quad + \left[ \left( k_1 f_{22}^O - k_2 f_{21}^O \right) \bar{m}_1 \right. \\
&\quad + \left. \left( k_2 f_{11}^O - k_1 f_{12}^O \right) \bar{m}_2 + \text{Det}(\mathbf{F}^O) \right].
\end{aligned}
$$

[20.30]

This looks like a formidable expression, but, in fact, it reduces to the same problem we have solved twice before. That is suppose we *choose* the zeros to be $z_0$ and $z_1$, then the *desired* polynomial is

$$
\begin{aligned}
\eta(z) - \frac{\gamma(z)}{d} &= (z - z_0)(z - z_1) \\
&= z^2 - (z_0 + z_1) z + z_0 z_1.
\end{aligned}
$$

Then equating coefficients leads to

$$
\begin{bmatrix} -k_1 & -k_2 \\ k_2 f_{21}^O - k_1 f_{22}^O & k_1 f_{12}^O - k_2 f_{11}^O \end{bmatrix} \begin{bmatrix} \bar{m}_1 \\ \bar{m}_2 \end{bmatrix} = \begin{bmatrix} \text{Trace}\{\mathbf{F}^O\} - (z_0 + z_1) \\ \text{Det}\{\mathbf{F}^O\} - z_0 z_1 \end{bmatrix}.
$$

[20.31]

Equation [20.31] is similar to the equations developed earlier for finding $\mathbf{k}^T$ and **l**. Note carefully, however, the minus sign in front of $k_1$ and $k_2$ on the left-hand side of the equation.

We now have all the mathematical tools we need to carry out a design, which we do next in Example 20.7.2

## EXAMPLE 20.7.2

Consider the system of Example 20.2.1. For $a = 2$ rad/s and $T = 0.1$ s, the discrete state model was

$$
\begin{bmatrix} x_1(k+1) \\ x_2(k+1) \end{bmatrix} = \begin{bmatrix} 1 & 0.09064 \\ 0 & 0.81873 \end{bmatrix} \begin{bmatrix} x_1(k) \\ x_2(k) \end{bmatrix} + \begin{bmatrix} 0.009365 \\ 0.181269 \end{bmatrix} u(k).
$$

The controller turned out to be

$$
\mathbf{k}^T = [6.4335 \quad 1.9187],
$$

and the prediction observer matrix was

$$
\mathbf{l} = \begin{bmatrix} 1.4149 \\ 4.1980 \end{bmatrix}.
$$

Using these results, we now design a closed-loop transfer function that has zero steady state error to both step and ramp inputs.

We know that the equivalent closed-loop transfer function is

$$T_c(z) = \frac{d[\eta(z) - \gamma(z)/d]\alpha(z)}{\alpha_c(z)\alpha_e(z)}$$

$$= \frac{d[\eta(z) - \gamma(z)/d]\alpha(z)}{(z - 0.7053 - j0.1726)(z - 0.7053 + j0.1726)(z - 0.2019)^2}.$$

It is worth noting that $\alpha(z)$, the numerator of $G'_p(z)$, contains a gain factor.

Now recall that when we discussed direct design techniques in Chapter 15, we chose

$$T_c(z) = \frac{K(z - c)}{(z - a - jb)(z - a + jb)}$$

as the simplest form of $T_c(z)$ that would enable us to set the steady state error to both step and ramp inputs. We used the location of the zero to obtain zero steady state error to a ramp input. Once the zero was determined, we used $K$ to ensure zero steady state error to a step input. This analysis was easy to do, and, in fact, we were able to establish a formula for computing the zero location.

In the present case, $T_c(z)$ has four poles and two zeros. Since we have an extra zero, we elect to *cancel* one of the poles of the observer error system. That is, we elect to have

$$\eta(z) - \frac{\gamma(z)}{d} = (z - \delta)(z - 0.2019).$$

If we do this, then

$$T_c(z) = \frac{d(z - \delta)(z - 0.2019)\alpha(z)}{(z - 0.7053 - j0.1726)(z - 0.7053 + j0.1726)(z - 0.2019)^2}$$

$$= \frac{d(z - \delta)\alpha(z)}{(z - 0.7053 - j0.1726)(z - 0.7053 + j0.1726)(z - 0.2019)}.$$

By cancelling one of the poles of the observer error system, we simplify our subsequent calculations and the closed-loop transfer function.

The expression for the steady state error to a ramp is not as simple at that we derived in Chapter 15, because we have three poles and two zeros rather than two poles and one zero. Nonetheless, the cancellation does simplify the arithmetic. The formula for steady state error to a ramp input is

$$e_{ss} = \frac{1}{K_v T} = \left[ \sum_{i=1}^{n} \frac{1}{z - p_i} - \sum_{i=1}^{m} \frac{1}{z - z_i} \right]. \qquad [20.32]$$

To apply the formula to the problem under consideration, we first need to find $\alpha(z)$, the numerator of the plant transfer function. Since

$$G_p(s) = \frac{a}{s(s + a)},$$

we have

$$G'_p(z) = \frac{(aT - 1 + e^{-aT})z + (1 - e^{-aT} - aTe^{-aT})}{a(z - 1)(z - e^{-aT})}.$$

For $T = 0.1$ s and $a = 2$,

$$G'_p(z) = \frac{0.009366(z + 0.9355)}{(z - 1)(z - 0.8187)}.$$

For the present problem the desired closed-loop transfer function has poles

$$a \pm jb = 0.7053 \pm j0.1726 \quad \text{and} \quad c = 0.2019,$$

and zeros

$$\delta \quad \text{and} \quad \kappa = -0.9355.$$

We elect to solve for the unknown $\delta$ symbolically. Applying Eq. [20.32] we obtain

$$\left( \frac{1}{1 - a - jb} + \frac{1}{1 - a + jb} + \frac{1}{1 - c} \right) - \left( \frac{1}{1 - \delta} + \frac{1}{1 - \kappa} \right) = \frac{1}{K_v T}.$$

Rearranging we have

$$\frac{1}{1 - \delta} = \frac{2(1 - a)}{(1 - a)^2 + b^2} + \frac{1}{1 - c} - \frac{1}{1 - \kappa} - \frac{1}{K_v T},$$

or finally,

$$\delta = 1 - \frac{1}{\dfrac{2(1 - a)}{(1 - a)^2 + b^2} + \dfrac{1}{1 - c} - \dfrac{1}{1 - \kappa} - \dfrac{1}{K_v T}}.$$

The right-hand side contains the two complex poles of the closed-loop design based on $\mathbf{k}^T$, the remaining pole of the error system determined by $\mathbf{l}$, and the zero of the plant. Using the same $\mathbf{k}^T$ and $\mathbf{l}$ from our previous examples, the same dominant closed-loop poles, and requiring zero steady state error to a ramp input we obtain

$$\delta = 1 - \frac{1}{\dfrac{2(1 - 0.7053)}{(1 - 0.7053)^2 + 0.1726^2} + \dfrac{1}{1 - 0.2019} - \dfrac{1}{1 + 0.9355} - \dfrac{1}{\infty T}}$$

$$= 1 - \frac{1}{5.0532 + 1.25298 - 0.51664}$$

$$= 0.8273.$$

We can now write out the desired numerator of the equivalent closed-loop system, namely,

$$\left[ \eta(z) - \frac{\gamma(z)}{d} \right] \alpha(z) = (z - 0.8273)(z - 0.2019)(z + 0.9355).$$

All that is left is to compute the entries in $\mathbf{F}^O$ and apply Eq. [20.31]. To that end

$$f_{11}^O = f_{11} - g_1 k_1 - \ell_1 h_1$$

$$= 1 - (0.009365)(6.4335) - (1.4149)(1)$$

$$= -0.47519,$$

$$f_{12}^O = f_{12} - g_1 k_2 - \ell_1 h_1$$

$$= 0.090635 - (0.009365)(1.9187) - (1.4149)(0)$$

$$= 0.072665,$$

$$f_{21}^O = f_{21} - g_2 k_1 - \ell_2 h_1$$

$$= 0 - (0.1813)(6.4335) - (4.1980)(1)$$

$$= -5.3642,$$

$$f_{22}^O = f_{22} - g_2 k_2 - \ell_2 h_2$$

$$= 0.8187 - (0.1813)(1.9187) - (4.1980)(0)$$

$$= 0.470925.$$

Then Eq. [20.31] becomes

$$\begin{bmatrix} 6.43353 & 1.91873 \\ 13.3222 & -1.37925 \end{bmatrix} \begin{bmatrix} \bar{m}_1 \\ \bar{m}_2 \end{bmatrix} = \begin{bmatrix} 1.033442 \\ 0.001014 \end{bmatrix}.$$

The solution of these equations is

$$\bar{\mathbf{m}} = \begin{bmatrix} 0.04145 \\ 0.39963 \end{bmatrix}.$$

Next, we determine $d$ using the fact that the steady state error to a step input should be zero. To ensure this, we must have

$$\lim_{z \to 1} T_c(z) = 1.$$

Thus,

$$\lim_{z \to 1} \frac{0.0093655 d(z - 0.8273)(z + 0.9355)}{(z - 0.7053 - j0.1726)(z - 0.7053 + j0.1726)(z - 0.2019)} = 0.0336494 d.$$

Then,

$$d = \frac{1}{0.0336494} = 29.72.$$

Having found $d$ we can now find

$$\mathbf{m} = d\bar{\mathbf{m}} = 29.72 \begin{bmatrix} 0.041445 \\ 0.399626 \end{bmatrix} = \begin{bmatrix} 1.23222 \\ 11.88009 \end{bmatrix}.$$

Then the controller observer is

$$\begin{bmatrix} \hat{x}_1(k+1) \\ \hat{x}_2(k+1) \end{bmatrix} = \begin{bmatrix} -0.4752 & 0.07267 \\ -5.3642 & 0.4709 \end{bmatrix} \begin{bmatrix} y(k) \\ \hat{x}_2(k) \end{bmatrix} + \begin{bmatrix} 1.4149 \\ 4.1980 \end{bmatrix} y(k)$$

$$+ \begin{bmatrix} 1.2322 \\ 11.8801 \end{bmatrix} r(k),$$

$$u(k) = -[6.4335 \quad 1.9187] \begin{bmatrix} y(k) \\ \hat{x}_2(k) \end{bmatrix} + 29.73 r(k).$$

The time response and the control for a unit step input are shown in Fig. 20.7. The overshoot is quite large and probably could be reduced by increasing the sampling

**Figure 20.7 |** Step response and control reference input.

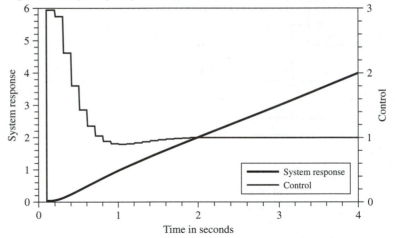

**Figure 20.8 |** Ramp response and control reference input.

rate. The response to a ramp input is shown in Fig. 20.8. As we can see, the steady state tracking error is zero.

## 20.7.1   Model Following Control

The system shown in Fig. 20.9(a) represents a radically different approach to the reference input (tracking) problem. A desired output response is generated and subtracted from an observation of the state to create a vector error signal that is multiplied by a controller and added to a control signal $u_m$ created by passing the output of the desired closed-loop system through the inverse of the plant. The resulting control $u$

**Figure 20.9 |** Generation of $Y_m$ for model following controller/observer.

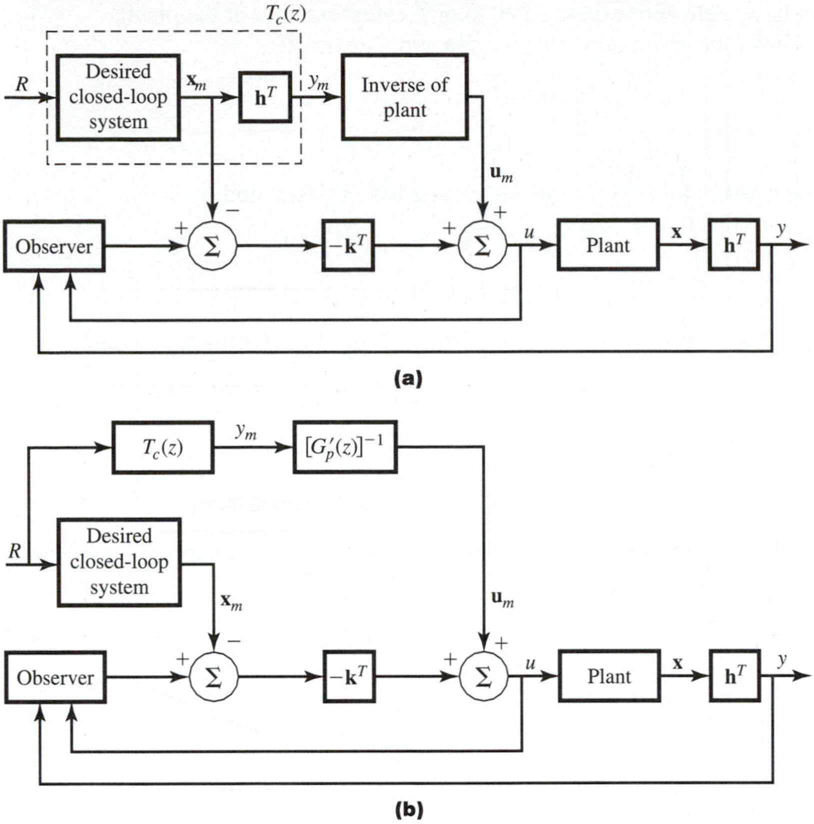

(a)

(b)

is then applied to the actual plant.

There are various ways to obtain the desired closed-loop system, a subject we have touched on in the past. There is a good deal more that could be said about specifying the desired closed-loop response, but we won't do that here.

The output of the desired closed-loop response goes to both the output of the observer and to the inverse of the plant model. We note that the inverse of the plant model may be noncausal. Figure 20.9(b) shows the desired closed-loop system $T_c(z)$ and the inverse of the plant $[G'_p(z)]^{-1}$ as transfer functions. The key question is whether the product

$$T_c(z)[G'_p(z)]^{-1}$$

is causal. If the product is not causal, then one alternative is to add poles to the inverse of the plant to make it causal. Note that as far as implementation is concerned all we need is the *product*

$$T_c(z)[G'_p(z)]^{-1}$$

to be causal. It is not necessary for the plant inverse to be causal as long as the desired plant has a pole-zero excess equal to or greater than that of the plant.

Under the assumption that we can generate $u_m$, let

$$\mathbf{x}_m(k+1) = \mathbf{F}_m \mathbf{x}_m(k) + \mathbf{g}_m u(k),$$

$$y_m(k) = \mathbf{h}_m^T \mathbf{x}_m(k),$$

be the *known* model of the desired closed-loop system, and

$$\mathbf{x}(k+1) = \mathbf{F}\mathbf{x}(k) + \mathbf{g}u(k),$$

$$y(k) = \mathbf{h}^T \mathbf{x}(k),$$

be the model of the plant dynamics. Then, using Fig. 20.9(b), let the observer be

$$\hat{\mathbf{x}}(k+1) = \mathbf{F}\hat{\mathbf{x}}(k) + \mathbf{g}u(k) + \mathbf{l}[y(k) - \mathbf{h}^T \hat{\mathbf{x}}(k)].$$

The controller is

$$u(k) = -\mathbf{k}^T [\hat{\mathbf{x}}(k) - \mathbf{x}_m(k)] + u_m(k).$$

It is now a straightforward matter to show that the separation theorem holds and that the error system is homogeneous. Let

$$\mathbf{e}(k) \overset{\Delta}{=} \mathbf{x}(k) - \hat{\mathbf{x}}(k).$$

Then

$$\begin{aligned}
\mathbf{e}(k+1) &= [\mathbf{F}\mathbf{x}(k) + \mathbf{g}u(k)] \\
&\quad - [\mathbf{F}\hat{\mathbf{x}}(k) + \mathbf{g}u(k) + \mathbf{l}(y(k) - \mathbf{h}^T \hat{\mathbf{x}}(k))] \\
&= \mathbf{F}[\mathbf{x}(k) - \hat{\mathbf{x}}(k)] - \mathbf{l}[y(k) - \mathbf{h}^T \hat{\mathbf{x}}(k)] \\
&= \mathbf{F}[\mathbf{x}(k) - \hat{\mathbf{x}}(k)] - \mathbf{l}[\mathbf{h}^T \mathbf{x}(k) - \mathbf{h}^T \hat{\mathbf{x}}(k)] \\
&= [\mathbf{F} - \mathbf{l}\mathbf{h}^T]\mathbf{e}(k).
\end{aligned}$$

This shows the error system is homogeneous. Although we used the prediction observer, we could have used the current observer and still achieved a homogeneous error equation.

To show that the separation theorem holds, first substitute

$$-\mathbf{k}^T [\hat{\mathbf{x}}(k) - \mathbf{x}_m(k)] + u_m(k)$$

for $u(k)$ in the plant equation to obtain

$$\begin{aligned}
\mathbf{x}(k+1) &= \mathbf{F}\mathbf{x}(k) + \mathbf{g}[-\mathbf{k}^T [\hat{\mathbf{x}}(k) - \mathbf{x}_m(k)] + u_m(k)] \\
&= \mathbf{F}\mathbf{x}(k) - \mathbf{g}\mathbf{k}^T \hat{\mathbf{x}}(k) + \mathbf{g}\mathbf{k}^T \mathbf{x}_m(k) + \mathbf{g}u_m(k).
\end{aligned}$$

If we now add and subtract $\mathbf{g}\mathbf{k}^T \mathbf{x}(k)$ from this last expression we obtain

$$\mathbf{x}(k+1) = \mathbf{F}\mathbf{x}(k) + \mathbf{g}\mathbf{k}^T [\mathbf{x}(k) - \hat{\mathbf{x}}(k)] + \mathbf{g}\mathbf{k}^T \mathbf{x}_m(k) + \mathbf{g}u_m(k) - \mathbf{g}\mathbf{k}^T \mathbf{x}(k),$$

which, after some rearrangement, becomes

$$\mathbf{x}(k+1) = [\mathbf{F} - \mathbf{g}\mathbf{k}^T]\mathbf{x}(k) + \mathbf{g}\mathbf{k}^T\mathbf{e}(k) + \mathbf{g}[\mathbf{k}^T\mathbf{x}_m(k) + u_m(k)]. \qquad [20.33]$$

Combining Eq. [20.33] with the homogeneous error equation, yields

$$\begin{bmatrix} \mathbf{x}(k+1) \\ \mathbf{e}(k+1) \end{bmatrix} = \begin{bmatrix} [\mathbf{F} - \mathbf{g}\mathbf{k}^T] & \mathbf{g}\mathbf{k}^T \\ \mathbf{0} & [\mathbf{F} - \mathbf{l}\mathbf{h}^T] \end{bmatrix} \begin{bmatrix} \mathbf{x}(k) \\ \mathbf{e}(k) \end{bmatrix} + \begin{bmatrix} \mathbf{g} \\ \mathbf{0} \end{bmatrix} \bar{u}(k),$$

where

$$\bar{u}(k) = \mathbf{k}^T\mathbf{x}_m(k) + u_m(k).$$

From our previous analysis, it is clear that the characteristic polynomial of this combined system is

$$\alpha(z) = \text{Det}[z\mathbf{I} - (\mathbf{F} - \mathbf{g}\mathbf{k}^T)] \times \text{Det}[z\mathbf{I} - (\mathbf{F} - \mathbf{l}\mathbf{h}^T)].$$

Example 20.7.3 helps to illustrate how model following is implemented.

---

**EXAMPLE 20.7.3**

In Example 19.2.1, we found the discrete state model for the system

$$G_p(s) = \frac{a}{s(s+a)},$$

for $a = 2$. That model was

$$\begin{bmatrix} x_1(k+1) \\ x_2(k+1) \end{bmatrix} = \begin{bmatrix} 1 & \frac{1}{a}(1 - e^{-aT}) \\ 0 & e^{-aT} \end{bmatrix} + \begin{bmatrix} \frac{aT + e^{-aT} - 1}{a} \\ 1 - e^{-aT} \end{bmatrix} u(k),$$

$$y(k) = \begin{bmatrix} 1 & 0 \end{bmatrix} \begin{bmatrix} x_1(k) \\ x_2(k) \end{bmatrix}$$

For $T = 0.1$ s and $a = 2$, we have

$$\mathbf{F} = \begin{bmatrix} 1 & 0.0906346 \\ 0 & 0.8187308 \end{bmatrix} \qquad \mathbf{g} = \begin{bmatrix} 0.0093654 \\ 0.181269 \end{bmatrix}.$$

In this case, we decide to critically damp the system, that is, let $\omega_n = 4$ and $\zeta = 1.0$. For this choice, the controller is

$$\mathbf{k}^T = \begin{bmatrix} 5.996 & 2.3277 \end{bmatrix}.$$

Choosing the error system to have two poles at $s = -16$, or $z = 0.2019$, yields

$$\mathbf{l}_p = \begin{bmatrix} 1.4149 \\ 4.19800 \end{bmatrix}.$$

The resulting *prediction* controller/observer observer equations were

$$\hat{\mathbf{x}}(k+1) = \mathbf{F}^O\hat{\mathbf{x}}(k) + \mathbf{l}y(k),$$

$$u(k) = -\mathbf{k}^T\hat{\mathbf{x}}(k),$$

where

$$\mathbf{F}^O = [\mathbf{F} - \mathbf{l}\mathbf{h}^T - \mathbf{g}\mathbf{k}^T].$$

For $T = 0.1$ s and $a = 2$, and the $\mathbf{k}^T$ and $\mathbf{l}_p$ given here, we get

$$\hat{\mathbf{x}}(k+1) = \begin{bmatrix} -0.47109 & 0.06884 \\ -5.9264 & 0.39679 \end{bmatrix}\hat{\mathbf{x}}(k) + \begin{bmatrix} 1.4149 \\ 4.19800 \end{bmatrix} y(k),$$

$$u(k) = -[5.996 \quad 2.3277]\begin{bmatrix} y(k) \\ \hat{x}_2(k) \end{bmatrix}.$$

For this same choice of $a$, $T$, and error system poles at $z = 0.2019$, we get

$$\mathbf{l}_c = \begin{bmatrix} 0.950213 \\ 5.127453 \end{bmatrix}.$$

Recalling that the *current* controller/observer equations are

$$\hat{\mathbf{x}}(k+1) = [\mathbf{F} - [\mathbf{I} - \mathbf{l}\mathbf{h}^T]\mathbf{g}\mathbf{k}^T - \mathbf{l}\mathbf{h}^T\mathbf{F}]\hat{\mathbf{x}}(k) + \mathbf{l}y(k+1),$$

$$u(k) = -\mathbf{k}^T\hat{\mathbf{x}}(k),$$

we have for $T = 0.1$ s and $a = 2$,

$$\begin{bmatrix} x_1(k+1) \\ x_2(k+1) \end{bmatrix} = \begin{bmatrix} 0.046991 & 0.003427 \\ -5.2849 & 0.043846 \end{bmatrix} + \begin{bmatrix} 0.950213 \\ 5.127453 \end{bmatrix} y(k+1),$$

$$u(k) = -[5.996 \quad 2.3277]\begin{bmatrix} y(k) \\ \hat{x}_2(k) \end{bmatrix}.$$

It is important to note that the matrices $\mathbf{k}^T$ and $\mathbf{l}$ that we will use in the model following control are *exactly* the matrices that we calculated for the *regulator* problem, and that the analysis leading to the homogeneous error equation goes through the same way whether we use the current observer or the prediction observer. All that remains is to choose $T_c(z)$.

To that end, we choose the continuous, desired, *closed-loop* transfer function to be

$$T_c(s) = \frac{a^2}{(s+a)^2}.$$

The continuous system exhibits zero steady state error to a step input. Then, the step-invariant transform of $T_c(s)$ is

$$T_c(z) = \frac{A[z + (B/A)]}{(z - e^{-aT})^2},$$

with

$$A = 1 - e^{-aT} - aTe^{-aT} \quad \text{and} \quad B = e^{-2aT} - e^{-aT} + aTe^{-aT}.$$

The state model for this continuous transfer function is then

$$\begin{bmatrix} x_1(k+1) \\ x_2(k+1) \end{bmatrix} = \begin{bmatrix} aTe^{-aT} + e^{-aT} & te^{-aT} \\ -a^2Te^{-aT} & -aTe^{-aT} + e^{-aT} \end{bmatrix} \begin{bmatrix} x_1(k) \\ x_2(k) \end{bmatrix}$$

$$+ \begin{bmatrix} 1 - e^{-aT} - aTe^{-aT} \\ a^2Te^{-aT} \end{bmatrix} u(k),$$

$$y(k) = \begin{bmatrix} 1 & 0 \end{bmatrix} \begin{bmatrix} x_1(k) \\ x_2(k) \end{bmatrix}.$$

Choosing $a = -4$, and then for $T = 0.1$ s we have

$$T_c(z) = \frac{0.06155(z + 0.7658)}{(z - 0.6703)^2}.$$

For these same values the state model is

$$\begin{bmatrix} x_1(k+1) \\ x_2(k+1) \end{bmatrix} = \begin{bmatrix} 0.93845 & 0.06703 \\ -1.07251 & 0.402192 \end{bmatrix} \begin{bmatrix} x_1(k) \\ x_2(k) \end{bmatrix} + \begin{bmatrix} 0.061552 \\ 1.07251 \end{bmatrix} u(k),$$

$$y(k) = \begin{bmatrix} 1 & 0 \end{bmatrix} \begin{bmatrix} x_1(k) \\ x_2(k) \end{bmatrix}.$$

The final piece of the puzzle is to find

$$T_c(z)[G'_p(z)]^{-1} = \begin{bmatrix} \frac{0.06155(z + 0.7658)}{(z - 0.6703)^2} \end{bmatrix} \begin{bmatrix} \frac{(z - 1)(z - 0.8187)}{0.009365(z + 0.9355)} \end{bmatrix}$$

$$= \frac{6.5723(z + 0.7658)(z - 1)(z - 0.8187)}{(z - 0.6703)^2(z + 0.9355)}.$$

The simulated step response and control are shown in Fig. 20.10.

**Figure 20.10 |** Step response and control for model following control.

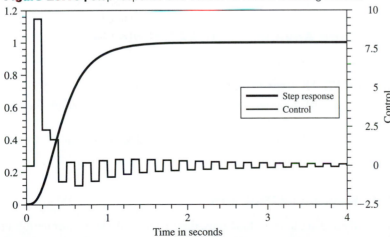

Time in seconds

## 20.8 | REPRISE

In this chapter, we have developed the idea of an observer and then combined it with a control law to obtain a so-called controller/observer. Crucial to this design strategy is a separation theorem that enables us to design the control $\mathbf{k}^T$ as if we had perfect measurements of all the system states, and then replace the perfect measurements of the states with observations of the states in the control law.

We used these results to investigate both the regulator problem and the reference input problem. Both prediction and current observers were developed. Of the two approaches to the tracking problem, the model-following technique is clearly easier to implment.

## 20.9 | PROBLEMS

### 20.9.1 Simple MATLAB Projects

These exercises are relatively easy and prove extremely helpful in solving later problems. In each case, write a short MATLAB program to find $\mathbf{k}^T$, $\mathbf{l}$, and the controller/observer equations for both the prediction and current observers for a particular plant transfer function. These programs build on the MATLAB exercises from Chapter 19.

1.  $G_p(s) = \dfrac{1}{s^2}$

2.  $G_p(s) = \dfrac{a}{s+a}$

3.  $G_p(s) = \dfrac{a}{s(s+a)}$

4.  $G_p(s) = \dfrac{a^2}{(s+a)^2}$

5.  $G_p(s) = \dfrac{a^2+b^2}{(s+a)^2+b^2}$

### 20.9.2 More Advanced MATLAB Projects

The following problems are reasonably challenging.

1.  Write a MATLAB program for the regulator problem.
2.  Write a MATLAB program for the tracking problem for the equivalent $T_c(z)$ method.
3.  Write a MATLAB program for the tracking problem for the model-following method.

### 20.9.3 Regulator Problem

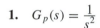

For each of these plant transfer functions, design the requested controller/observer to meet the stated specifications. Then find the step response of the compensated system using a MATLAB simulation program you have written.

1. Prediction controller/observer:
   a. Dominant closed-loop poles with $\omega_n = 4$ rad/s and $\zeta = 0.8$.
   b. Error system critically damped. Poles of error system have time constant one-fourth that of dominant closed-loop poles.
   c. $f_s = 20$ Hz.
   d. $G_p(s) = \dfrac{1}{s(s+1)}$.

2. Prediction controller/observer:
   a. Dominant closed-loop poles with $\omega_n = 6$ rad/s and $\zeta = 0.8$.
   b. Error system critically damped. Poles of error system have time constant one-fourth that of dominant closed-loop poles.
   c. $f_s = 20$ Hz.
   d. $G_p(s) = \dfrac{1}{s(s+1)}$.

3. Prediction controller/observer:
   a. Dominant closed-loop poles with $\omega_n = 6$ rad/s and $\zeta = 0.8$.
   b. Error system critically damped. Poles of error system have time constant one-fourth that of dominant closed-loop poles.
   c. $f_s = 20$ Hz.
   d. $G_p(s) = \dfrac{1}{s(s+1)}$.

4. Prediction controller/observer:
   a. Dominant closed-loop poles critically damped with a time constant of 0.2 s.
   b. Error system critically damped. Poles of error system have time constant one-third that of dominant closed-loop poles.
   c. $f_s = 25$ Hz.
   d. $G_p(s) = \dfrac{4}{s^2}$.

5. Current controller/observer:
   a. Dominant closed-loop poles with $\omega_n = 5$ rad/s and $\zeta = 0.6$.
   b. Error system critically damped. Poles of error system have time constant one-fourth that of dominant closed-loop poles.
   c. $f_s = 10$ Hz.
   d. $G_p(s) = \dfrac{4}{s^2}$.

6. Prediction controller/observer:
   a. Dominant closed-loop poles with $\omega_n = 5$ rad/s and $\zeta = 0.8$.
   b. Error system critically damped. Poles of error system have time constant one-fourth that of dominant closed-loop poles.
   c. $f_s = 10$ Hz.
   d. $G_p(s) = \dfrac{4}{s+2}$.

7. Current controller/observer:
   a. Dominant closed-loop poles with $\omega_n = 5$ rad/s and $\zeta = 0.8$.
   b. Error system critically damped. Poles of error system have time constant one-fourth that of dominant closed-loop poles.

   c.  $f_s = 10$ Hz.

   d.  $G_p(s) = \dfrac{4}{s(s+10)}$.

**8.** Prediction controller/observer:

   a.  Dominant closed-loop poles with $\omega_n = 5$ rad/s and $\zeta = 0.8$.

   b.  Error system critically damped. Poles of error system have time constant one-fourth that of dominant closed-loop poles.

   c.  $f_s = 10$ Hz.

   d.  $G_p(s) = \dfrac{4}{s(s+2)}$.

**9.** Current controller/observer:

   a.  Dominant closed-loop poles with $\omega_n = 5$ rad/s and $\zeta = 0.8$.

   b.  Error system critically damped. Poles of error system have time constant one-fourth that of dominant closed-loop poles.

   c.  $f_s = 10$ Hz.

   d.  $G_p(s) = \dfrac{4}{s(s+2)}$.

**10.** Prediction controller/observer:

   a.  Dominant closed-loop poles with $\omega_n = 5$ rad/s and $\zeta = 1/\sqrt{2}$.

   b.  Error system critically damped. Poles of error system have time constant one-fourth that of dominant closed-loop poles.

   c.  $f_s = 10$ Hz.

   d.  $G_p(s) = \dfrac{10}{s(s+10)}$.

**11.** Current controller/observer:

   a.  Dominant closed-loop poles with $\omega_n = 5$ rad/s and $\zeta = 1/\sqrt{2}$.

   b.  Error system critically damped. Poles of error system have time constant one-fourth that of dominant closed-loop poles.

   c.  $f_s = 10$ Hz.

   d.  $G_p(s) = \dfrac{10}{s(s+10)}$.

**12.** Prediction controller/observer:

   a.  Dominant closed-loop poles with $\omega_n = 5$ rad/s and $\zeta = 1/\sqrt{2}$.

   b.  Error system critically damped. Poles of error system have time constant one-third that of dominant closed-loop poles.

   c.  $f_s = 20$ Hz.

   d.  $G_p(s) = \dfrac{16}{(s+4)^2}$.

**13.** Current controller/observer:

   a.  Dominant closed-loop poles with $\omega_n = 5$ rad/s and $\zeta = 1/\sqrt{2}$.

   b.  Error system critically damped. Poles of error system have time constant one-third that of dominant closed-loop poles.

   c.  $f_s = 20$ Hz.

   d.  $G_p(s) = \dfrac{101}{(s+1)^2 + 10^2}$.

**14.** Current controller/observer:

   a.  Dominant closed-loop poles with $\omega_n = 5$ rad/s and $\zeta = 1/\sqrt{2}$.

b. Error system critically damped. Poles of error system have time constant one-third that of dominant closed-loop poles.

c. $f_s = 20$ Hz.

d. $G_p(s) = \dfrac{101}{(s+1)^2 + 10^2}$.

## 20.9.4 Tracking Problem—Equivalent $T_c(s)$ Method

For each of these plant transfer functions, design the requested controller/observer equations to meet the stated specifications, using either the equivalent transfer function method or the model-following method. Then find the step response of the compensated system using a MATLAB simulation program you have written.

1. Prediction controller/observer:
   a. Dominant closed-loop poles with $\omega_n = 5$ rad/s and $\zeta = 0.6$.
   b. Error system critically damped. Poles of error system have time constant one-fourth that of dominant closed-loop poles.
   c. Zero steady state error to both step and ramp inputs.
   d. $f_s = 20$ Hz.
   e. $G_p(s) = \dfrac{4}{s^2}$.

2. Prediction controller/observer:
   a. Dominant closed-loop poles with $\omega_n = 5$ rad/s and $\zeta = 0.8$.
   b. Error system critically damped. Poles of error system have time constant one-fourth that of dominant closed-loop poles.
   c. Zero steady state error to a step input, 10% error to a ramp input.
   d. $f_s = 25$ Hz.
   e. $G_p(s) = \dfrac{4}{s(s+4)}$.

3. Prediction controller/observer:
   a. Dominant closed-loop poles with $\omega_n = 5$ rad/s and $\zeta = 0.8$.
   b. Error system critically damped. Poles of error system have time constant one-fourth that of dominant closed-loop poles.
   e. Zero steady state error to both step and ramp inputs.
   d. $f_s = 40$ Hz.
   e. $G_p(s) = \dfrac{4}{s^2(s+2)}$.

4. Prediction controller/observer:
   a. Dominant closed-loop poles with $\omega_n = 5$ rad/s and $\zeta = 1/\sqrt{2}$.
   b. Error system critically damped. Poles of error system have time constant one-fourth that of dominant closed-loop poles.
   c. Zero steady state error to both step and ramp inputs.
   d. $f_s = 10$ Hz.
   e. $G_p(s) = \dfrac{10}{s(s+10)}$.

5. Current controller/observer:
   a. Dominant closed-loop poles with $\omega_n = 5$ rad/s and $\zeta = 1/\sqrt{2}$.

   b.   Error system critically damped. Poles of error system have time constant one-fourth that of dominant closed-loop poles.
   c.   Zero steady state error to both step and ramp inputs.
   d.   $f_s = 20$ Hz.
   e.   $G_p(s) = \dfrac{10}{s(s + 10)}$.

6.   Prediction controller/observer:
   a.   Dominant closed-loop poles with $\omega_n = 5$ rad/s and $\zeta = 1/\sqrt{2}$.
   b.   Error system critically damped. Poles of error system have time constant one-third that of dominant closed-loop poles.
   c.   Zero steady state error to both step and ramp inputs.
   d.   $f_s = 20$ Hz.
   e.   $G_p(s) = \dfrac{101}{(s + 1)^2 + 10^2}$.

7.   Current controller/observer:
   a.   Dominant closed-loop poles with $\omega_n = 5$ rad/s and $\zeta = 1/\sqrt{2}$.
   b.   Error system critically damped. Poles of error system have time constant one-third that of dominant closed-loop poles.
   c.   Zero steady state error to both step and ramp inputs.
   d.   $f_s = 20$ Hz.
   e.   $G_p(s) = \dfrac{101}{(s + 1)^2 + 10^2}$.

## 20.9.5   Tracking Problems—Model Following

These problems are based on Example 20.7.3. Let the desired closed-loop transfer function be

$$X(s) = \frac{\omega_n^2}{s^2 + 2\zeta\omega_n s + \omega_n^2}.$$

1.   Prediction controller/observer:
   a.   Dominant closed-loop poles with $\omega_n = 5$ rad/s and $\zeta = 0.6$.
   b.   Error system critically damped. Poles of error system have time constant one-fourth that of dominant closed-loop poles.
   c.   $f_s = 20$ Hz.
   d.   $G_p(s) = \dfrac{4}{s(s + 0.1)}$.

2.   Prediction controller/observer:
   a.   Dominant closed-loop poles with $\omega_n = 5$ rad/s $\zeta = 0.8$.
   b.   Error system critically damped. Poles of error system have time constant one-fourth that of dominant closed-loop poles.
   c.   $f_s = 25$ Hz.
   d.   $G_p(s) = \dfrac{4}{s(s + 8)}$.

3.   Prediction controller/observer:
   a.   Dominant closed-loop poles with $\omega_n = 5$ rad/s and $\zeta = 0.8$.

   b.  Error system critically damped. Poles of error system have time constant one-fourth that of dominant closed-loop poles.

   c.  $f_s = 40$ Hz.

   d.  $G_p(s) = \dfrac{4}{s(s+2)}$.

**4.** Prediction controller/observer:

   a.  Dominant closed-loop poles with $\omega_n = 5$ rad/s and $\zeta = 1/\sqrt{2}$.

   b.  Error system critically damped. Poles of error system have time constant one-fourth that of dominant closed-loop poles.

   c.  $f_s = 10$ Hz.

   d.  $G_p(s) = \dfrac{10}{s(s+10)}$.

**5.** Current controller/observer:

   a.  Dominant closed-loop poles with $\omega_n = 5$ rad/s and $\zeta = 1/\sqrt{2}$.

   b.  Error system critically damped. Poles of error system have time constant one-fourth that of dominant closed-loop poles.

   c.  $f_s = 20$ Hz.

   d.  $G_p(s) = \dfrac{10}{s(s+10)}$.

**6.** Prediction controller/observer:

   a.  Dominant closed-loop poles with $\omega_n = 5$ rad/s and $\zeta = 1/\sqrt{2}$.

   b.  Error system critically damped. Poles of error system have time constant one-third that of dominant closed-loop poles.

   c.  $f_s = 20$ Hz.

   d.  $G_p(s) = \dfrac{101}{(s+1)^2 + 10^2}$.

**7.** Current controller/observer:

   a.  Dominant closed-loop poles with $\omega_n = 5$ rad/s and $\zeta = 1/\sqrt{2}$.

   b.  Error system critically damped. Poles of error system have time constant one-third that of dominant closed-loop poles.

   c.  $f_s = 20$ Hz.

   d.  $G_p(s) = \dfrac{101}{(s+1)^2 + 10^2}$.

# FURTHER READINGS

Astrom, Karl J., and Bjorn Wittenmark. 1997. *Computer Controlled Systems—Theory and Design*, 3rd ed., Saddle River, N.J., N.J.: Prentice Hall.

Cadzow, James A. 1973. *Discrete Time Systems—An Introduction with Interdisciplinary Applications*, Englewood Cliffs, N.J.: Prentice Hall.

Franklin, Gene F., J. David Powell, and Michael L. Workman. 1998. *Digital Control of Dynamic Systems*, 3rd ed., Menlo Park, CA.: Addison-Wesley.

Houpis, Constance H., and Gary B. Lamont. 1992. *Digital Control Systems—Theory, Hardware, Software*, 2nd ed., New York: McGraw-Hill.

Luenberger, David G. 1979. *Introduction to Dynamic Systems—Theory, Models, and Applications*. New York: John Wiley and Sons.

Saucedo, Roberto, and Earl E. Schiring. 1968. *Introduction to Continuous and Digital Control Systems*. New York: MacMillan.

# INDEX